GENETICS

GENETICS

IRWIN H. HERSKOWITZ

Saint Louis University

Little, Brown and Company

BOSTON   TORONTO

PREFACE

INTEREST in the study of genes has increased greatly in the past few decades and grows at an ever-increasing pace. This is due both to the rapid advances in our understanding of the gene and to the important applications made of this knowledge. Even more significant has been the recognition of the fundamental importance of genetic knowledge for the future advancement of numerous other areas of scientific investigation and for the preservation and improvement of the well-being of mankind in general.

The amount of instruction in genetics given in junior and senior high school classes of biology and general science is increasing, and many of the institutes sponsored by the U.S. National Science Foundation for high school teachers of biology give concentrated instruction in genetics. There is also an increasing amount of genetics taught in introductory courses of biology, botany, and zoology at the college level and a separate course in genetics has become a requirement in many colleges for students majoring in biology or agriculture. It is now generally recognized that genetics has become a core discipline, knowledge of which is essential for an understanding of modern and future biology.

The impact of the gene is being felt, moreover, not only by the professional teacher and research worker in biology, but also by students of a number of other related, and seemingly unrelated, disciplines. Medical and dental schools are increasingly interested in the genetic training of their students both before and after they start their professional preparation. More and more students whose major interest is in biochemistry, chemistry, psychology, biophysics, physics, statistics, or mathematics find that the study of genes offers new and challenging opportunities in these various fields. Finally, the importance of genetics for life in our atomic and interplanetary age has been recognized by scholars in the humanities and arts as well as by the informed general public.

This mounting interest in the gene has led or will doubtless soon lead to considerable modification in the teaching of genetics at the college level. Because the fund of knowledge regarding the nature and consequences of genes is growing so rapidly, usually more than one single semester course is required to cover the material that is considered essential knowledge for the professional biologist. One solution has been to have two courses in genetics, of which one is general and the other advanced. Many smaller colleges are now initiating a course in general genetics for the first time. Because of the interest of the nonprofessional biologist, the general genetics course already given is being modified in numerous colleges so that it can be taken in the earlier rather than the later years of college study.

The question is, what should be the content and aim of an introductory course in genetics? There is general agreement on one score, namely, that a first course should provide an understanding of the nature of the gene, for this knowledge is prerequisite for its fruitful application to the solution of problems in biology and all the other fields mentioned. There are a number of textbooks on genetics which help satisfy this requirement. However, it is my personal conviction that there are several other desiderata for such a course, toward whose realization an appropriate textbook can make significant contributions. I shall take this opportunity to mention several qualities a general genetics text should have and how the present text attempts to meet these criteria.

The text should be so organized that the principles dealing with the nature of the gene are separated as much as possible from the applications or uses of these principles. Too often students finish an elementary course without a clear understanding of the basic principles regarding genes, on the one hand, and the consequences of these principles, on the other. In the table of contents all the Chapters containing either basic concepts of the gene or information necessary for the comprehension of basic concepts are indicated by an asterisk, while Chapters concerned entirely with the applications or consequences of these basic principles are not so marked. The marked Chapters dealing with the nature of the gene include all those which define, or delimit, the genetic material operationally in terms of its recombinational, mutational, functional, chemical, and replicational properties, while the other Chapters are concerned primarily with the utilization of genetic principles for the elucidation of problems in morphology (traits), in development and physiology of individuals, in populations, and in evolution. While it would seem essential at one time or another during the course to study many or all the Chapters dealing with the nature of the genetic material, any or all of the Chapters concerning applications may be omitted at the discretion of the instructor.

A text should be used as a supplement to, and not a substitute for, the teacher. It has become impossible, as well as undesirable, to include in one text how each principle of genetics has been proven in the case of every plant and animal studied. It is even less possible to give examples of the application of each of these principles to all the different kinds of organisms. Accordingly, in the present text only one or a few experimentally favorable or historically important organisms are usually employed to establish a principle or to illustrate an application. Additional proofs, applications, or examples are left to the instructor who, depending upon his and his students' training and interest, can supply other illustrations by means of lectures and laboratory sessions or by means of assignments to detailed accounts in other texts and in the original literature. A text, therefore, should be used to present the fundamentals, while the instructor should serve to clarify, amplify, coordinate, and integrate them. There is little value in having the student attend lectures in which all the time is spent listening to the same material that was discussed in the text.

Since the study of the gene is an experimental rather than a descriptive procedure, the text should, whenever feasible, derive the principles from the results of experiments. The plan has been to build a solid structure of genetic theory upon evidences and reasoning presented earlier or concurrently. Sentences, paragraphs, section or chapter headings, which state conclusions to be arrived at sometime later in the text have been avoided. In general the attempt has been made to adhere as much as possible to the following method of presentation: to recognize a problem, offer evidence related to it, analyze all reasonable explanations, and draw whatever conclusions are warranted on the basis of the information presented. Digressions from the main purposes are avoided, so, for example, a history of pregenetic thought is not presented.

Not the least value of a concise text is the challenge the student may be given to utilize the books and journals in the library. The reading of genetic works in the original by uninformed students is relatively unfruitful for the effort expended, but may be a very rewarding experience if done after reading appropriate sections of the text. Accordingly references requiring different degrees of sophistication are given at the ends of Chapters.

Part of a letter by G. Mendel and the Nobel Prize Lectures presented by geneticists are included in the book as Supplements. These Supplements should be completely understandable, or nearly so, if the appropriate Chapters preceding them have been read, and can serve as a review and overview of genetic principles and their applications. The Supplements can also function to bridge the gap between the textbook and the research worker, giving the reader some idea of the history of the subject and the personalities of the people involved.

In certain cases it has been considered desirable in the present work to combine the results, obtained by different people at different times using different organisms and methods, into a single organized body of information, rather than to try to prove a principle or illustrate an application using a patchwork of evidences in which each worker is given his due priority. Since the later Chapters deal with recent advances in genetics, whose discussion may be absent from already published textbooks, additional information can be gained from reading the original scientific literature. Accordingly, more references are given to particular workers in the later than in the earlier Chapters. The citations to the literature included in the Nobel Prize talks should prove especially valuable to those who wish to do additional reading on key topics.

It is hoped that the student will benefit, whatever his future course of study, from the numerous opportunities this text provides for him to think scientifically — to study the design of experiments, to analyze the information these provide, and to reach valid conclusions. Because a genetics course is elected more and more frequently by students who do not wish to specialize in biology and because it should be no longer a course only for upper classmen, I have tried to use simple biological examples and terminology whenever possible, and have explained in some detail certain biological phenomena generally understood by students specializing in biology. Because many students in a first course in genetics are deficient in training in chemistry and physics I have also explained certain aspects of these sciences, important for understanding genes and their behavior, in somewhat more detail than is found in the usual text. On the other hand, since elaborate statistical analysis is needed usually only to demonstrate certain complex applications of genetic principles, the mathematics of genetics has been de-emphasized here, leaving it to the individual instructor to elaborate upon, as he sees fit, in the lecture and laboratory periods.

Questions and problems are presented after each Chapter. Instructors or students who would like to have additional discussion and examination questions covering much of the material in this book as well as reading assignments in other basic textbooks can find these in the *Study Guide and Workbook for Genetics* (McGraw-Hill Book Co., Inc., 1960) which I prepared.

Finally, it should be emphasized that because this textbook of genetics has been prepared by a fellow human being it therefore has certain limitations. This book or any other text is subject to a very personal factor in that the author has selected certain information for presentation and rejected other material considered less essential. Moreover, while each author does the best he can with the knowledge available, what is accepted by him one day is quickly subject to improvement or rejection by him consequent to the discoveries of the next day. To foster these impressions the present work is written, as much as possible, as a personal discussion between you and me; it is aimed to help you think critically, to challenge the experimental evidence I have presented, the reasoning I have used in its evaluation, and the conclusions I have arrived at. You are cordially invited to play this thinking game with me. But since reasoning reigns supreme here do not look for a superfluity of visual material, whose presence sometimes substitutes looking for thinking. I suggest that you keep pencil and paper handy so you can make your own visual aids and provide yourself with experience in using the knowledge contained here. Readers who already have some ideas about genes should note that certain concepts of the gene change during the course of this book. At some earlier point in the book the view of the gene may be quite different from the one commonly held and/or different from the one presented later. Retain an open mind. Be alert to those occasions on which I shall draw incorrect conclusions, or what at one point may seem like a valid conclusion but which later, either in this book or in tomorrow's discoveries, proves to be only partially true or even wrong.

Suggestions for Use of the Book

This book can be used several ways. It contains more information than can be covered in the usual one-semester introductory course for undergraduates.

A *one-semester course* (meeting about 31–45 hours) can be based upon (1) the 31 Chapters marked with asterisks, or (2) the first 35 Chapters, omitting at will certain unstarred Chapters before Chapter 35, or (3) the following 24 Chapters: 1–4, 6, 31–49, supplemented as needed with several lectures on material in unread Chapters.

A *two-semester course* (meeting a total of about 60–90 hours) can be based upon the first 30 Chapters the first semester and the last 19 Chapters the second semester. Or, the 31 Chapters with asterisks can be used the first semester and the remaining 18 unstarred Chapters the second.

Making use of the Supplements and reference lists, for additional reading and discussion, the book can be used also in upper class and graduate introductory genetics courses.

Acknowledgments

Those figures for which credit is not otherwise given were prepared by William J. Briggs. I wish to thank my wife, Reida Postrel Herskowitz, for preparing the typescript. I am especially indebted to my present and former students for numerous suggestions.

IRWIN H. HERSKOWITZ

CONTENTS

*1	Genetic Material	1
*2	Gene Segregation	8
*3	Mitosis	16
*4	Meiosis	23
*5	Segregation in Man — Multiple Allelism	32
*6	Independent Segregation	39
7	Gene Interaction and Phenotypic Expression	49 ±
8	Gene Interaction and Continuous Traits	56 ✓
9	Multiple Alleles and Lethals	62
10	Pleiotropism, Penetrance and Expressivity	68
11	Studies of Human Twins	74
*12	Sex-Linkage	81
13	Sex Determination (I)	94
14	Sex Determination (II)	100
*15	Intergenic Linkage	111
*16	Crossing Over and Chiasma	116
*17	Gene Arrangement and Chiasmata	128
*18	Changes Involving Whole Genomes and Single Whole Chromosomes	137
*19	Structural Changes within Chromosomes	150
20	Cytogenetics of Oenothera	162
21	Natural and Induced Chromosomal Changes	173
22	Position Effect and Allelism in Drosophila	185
*23	Gene and Point Mutations	197
24	Point Mutants — Their Detection and Effects in Individuals	204
*25	The Genetic Control of Mutability	213
26	The Gene Pool in Cross-Fertilizing Populations	224

ix

27 Mutation and Selection — Nonrandom Mating and Heterosis *229*

*28 Mutational Loads and Their Consequences to Populations *239*

29 Races and the Origin of Species *252*

30 Developmental Genetics *262*

*31 Biochemical Genetics (I) *271*

*32 Biochemical Genetics (II) *281*

*33 Chemical Nature of Genes *293*

*34 Organization, Replication, and Types of DNA *in Vivo* *306*

*35 Replication of DNA *in Vitro*...................................... *320*

*36 Bacteria: Clones and Mutation *329*

*37 Bacteria: Recombination (I. *Transformation and Chain Recombination* in Vitro) *340*

*38 Bacteria: Recombination (II. *Conjugation*) *349*

*39 Bacteria: Recombination (III. *The Episome F*) *356*

*40 Bacteria: Recombination (IV. *Episomes and Nucleotide-Sharing*) *366*

*41 Bacteria: Recombination (V. *Transduction*) *374*

*42 Viruses: Recombination in Bacteriophage (I) *382*

*43 Viruses: Recombination in Bacteriophage (II) *390*

*44 Viruses: Bacterial, Animal, and Plant *400*

45 Extranuclear Genes and Their Interrelations with Nuclear Genes *409*

*46 Gene Action and Operons *421*

*47 Gene Action and Amino Acid Coding *427*

48 The Biochemical Evolution of Genetic Material *439*

*49 Genes — Nature and Consequence *444*

Author Index, *453*   **Subject Index,** *457*

Supplements:

  I *Part of a Letter (1867) from Gregor Mendel to C. Nägeli*

 II *Nobel Prize Lecture (1934) of Thomas Hunt Morgan*

III *Nobel Prize Lecture (1946) of Hermann Joseph Muller*

IV *Nobel Prize Lecture (1958) of George Wells Beadle*

 V *Nobel Prize Lecture (1958) of Edward Lawrie Tatum*

VI *Nobel Prize Lecture (1959) of Arthur Kornberg*

VII *Nobel Prize Lecture (1958) of Joshua Lederberg*

The essential feature of the operational viewpoint is that an object or phenomenon under experimental investigation cannot usefully be defined in terms of assumed properties beyond experimental determination but rather must be defined in terms of the actual operations that may be applied in dealing with it. . . .

What is a gene in operational terms?

L. J. STADLER, "The Gene,"
Science, 120: 811–819, 1954

Must we geneticists become bacteriologists, physiological chemists and physicists, simultaneously with being zoologists and botanists? Let us hope so.

H. J. MULLER, "Variation Due to Change in the Individual Gene,"
American Naturalist, 56: 32–50, 1922

Chapter *1

GENETIC MATERIAL

SINCE human beings are curious, you surely have already noticed certain things about yourself. In the first place, you recognize yourself as being the same kind of creature as your parents. Your parents gave rise to you, another human — not to a cereal, a fish, or a bird. This is so even though the raw materials from which you were initially constructed and from which you subsequently grew were originally nonhuman. Let us, therefore, start by assuming the existence of some intrinsic factor which determines that humans shall beget humans. We can call this inborn factor for the genesis of like from like the *genetic factor*. Since each kind or species of living thing, be it plant or animal, produces offspring of its own kind we can generalize and hypothesize that each species of organism has such a built-in genetic factor. But we must now also admit that the genetic factors for dog, for apple tree, and for man must all differ in some way in order to produce such different organisms as end products.

You must have also noticed that, in respect to certain details, you are similar to and different from your parents. What is the basis for this? You have already observed from common experience that the environment in which parents and children live can sometimes be the cause of similarities and differences between them. Thus, if the caloric content of the diets of parents and children is similar they will weigh more nearly alike than if their caloric intake is different. Are all similarities and differences among human

beings produced by environment? Or, does the intrinsic genetic factor we have invented to be responsible for like begetting like play a role in the production of the detailed similarities and differences which we see upon comparing children with parents?

This question may be answered after considering the results of studying certain bean plants.[1] The particular kind of bean plant referred to reproduces as we do, sexually, a difference being that a single plant performs the functions both of male and of female parent. Assume, for the present, that the genetic factor is transmitted from the parent to the offspring, and that the transmitted factor must be the same type as that of the parent. Let us also assume that the genetic factor has a natural rather than a supernatural or spiritual basis. If the genetic factor has a natural basis it ought to have a material basis and have chemical and/or physical properties as have other material things. We are led, therefore, to postulate the existence of *genetic material*. Let us now consider a particular bean seed. When the plant grown from this seed produces offspring bean seeds (Figure 1–1A), we find that the offspring bean seeds vary from each other in size, some being very small, some small, and some medium. On our hypotheses these seeds must all have the same type of genetic material, genetic constitution, or *genotype*. The simplest explanation we can offer for the size differences between them is that this variation was caused by environmental differences which occurred during seed formation. This idea can be tested by growing each of these seeds and scoring the size of seeds that they produce. When this is done it is found that each seed also produces offspring bean seeds of very small, small, and medium sizes, regardless of the size of the parent seed itself. And this test can be made generation after generation with the same result. We can term such a line of descent,

[1] Based upon W. Johannsen's experiments.

1

whose members carry the same genotype, a *pure line*. The expression of the genotype in traits or characters (bean size in our example) is called the *phenotype*. So environmental differences have caused the same genotype to produce a variety of phenotypes, and we conclude that the differences between the seeds of a pure line are environmentally produced and are not due to any differences in genotype.

But consider next another particular bean seed, of this same species of bean, that gives rise to offspring beans (Figure 1–1B) which are very large, large, and medium sized. Since each of these produces offspring beans which again show the same range of phenotypes we are clearly dealing with another and different pure line, within which phenotypic variability is attributable to environmental fluctuation.

How can we explain the differences between these two different pure lines, one of which can produce very small and small bean seeds while the other can produce very large and large ones? All the beans were grown under the same environmental conditions, so these phenotypic differences cannot be due to environmental differences; instead they must be due to genotypic differences. So we must conclude that the genetic material in these two pure lines is different.

How can we explain the fact that some of the seeds in both of these genotypically different pure lines are similar — medium sized? In this case different genotypes have produced the same phenotype through the action of the environment.

What is the consequence of the fact already mentioned that under similar environmental conditions the average size of the beans produced within a pure line remains the same regardless of the size of the specific beans planted? Thus in the pure line first described the offspring bean seeds have the same average size whether the very small or the medium seed is used as parent. Similarly the average size of seed produced in the second pure line is the same when either the medium or the very large seed is the parent. In other words selection for bean size within pure lines is futile, as would be expected on our hypothesis that all members of a pure line are genetically identical.

Throughout the bean experiments described, effort was made to keep the environment the same. This does not mean that the environment did not vary, but that it varied approximately in the same directions and to the same degree for all individuals in the study. In this particular work it happened that phenotypic variability due to the fluctuations of environment was not so great as to completely mask the phenotypic effect of a genetic difference. In any randomly chosen case, however, one cannot predict to what degree any particular phenotype will be influenced by the genotype and by the environment. So theoretically both phenotypic similarities and phenotypic differences between two individuals of the same species could result from each one of the following four combinations:

1. Identical genotypes in near-identical environments.
2. Different genotypes in near-identical environments.
3. Identical genotypes in different environments.
4. Different genotypes in different environments.

Following are specific examples of how each combination can result in either phenotypic difference or phenotypic similarity:

1. Identical genotypes in near-identical environments:
   Phenotypic difference — one small and one medium sized bean from the same pure line.
   Phenotypic similarity — two small sized beans from the same pure line.

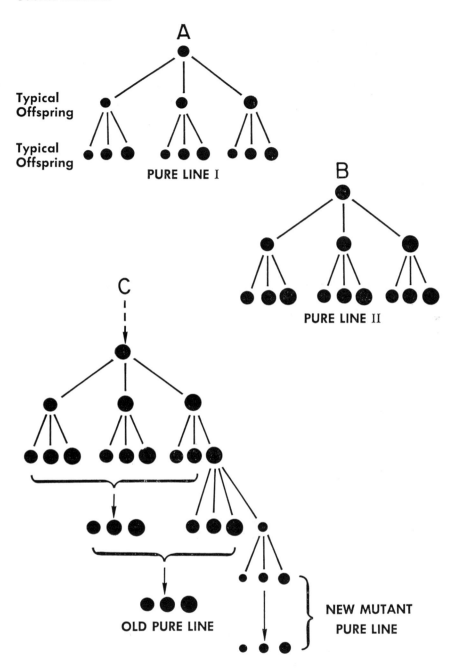

FIGURE 1–1. *Relative sizes of seeds obtained from self-fertilized bean plants.*

2. Different genotypes in near-identical environments:

   Phenotypic difference — one small and one large bean from genetically different pure lines.

   Phenotypic similarity — two medium sized beans from genetically different pure lines.

3. Identical genotypes in different environments:

   Phenotypic difference — one bean plant grown in the light is green while another grown in the dark is white, though both are from the same pure line.

   Phenotypic similarity — if two rabbits come from a certain pure line (genetically black rabbits), both will have black coats even though one individual grew at high and the other individual grew at low temperatures.

4. Different genotypes in different environments:

   Phenotypic difference — a rabbit from a genetically black line, grown in a cold climate, has black fur, while a rabbit from a Himalayan line, grown under temperate conditions, is Himalayan, i.e., white except for the extremities (paws, tail, snout, and ears) which are black (see Figure 1–2).

   Phenotypic similarity — a rabbit from a genetically black line grown at a moderate temperature and a rabbit from a genetically Himalayan line grown at a cold temperature are both black furred.

The case of coat color in rabbits is instructive in another respect. The rabbit that is genetically black will always produce a black coat no matter what the temperature, so long as it is not lethal. For this genotype there seems to be no range of phenotypic expression with respect to temperature variations. In the Himalayan strain, however, the situation is different, as already described in part. If grown at very high temperatures such rabbits would have coats that are entirely white. In this case the *phenotypic range of reaction*, or *norm of reaction*,

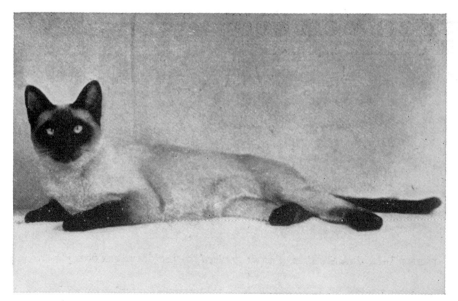

FIGURE 1–2. *Male Siamese cat, grown under temperate conditions, showing the same pigmentation pattern as the Himalayan rabbit. (After C. E. Keeler and V. Cobb.)*

of the genotype is relatively great, varying with increasing temperature from completely black through the Himalayan pattern to completely white.

We are now in a position to answer the question concerned with the basis of similarities and differences between children or between them and their parents. Extending the principles just described for beans and rabbits to all other kinds of organisms, including man, we conclude that not only is the genetic material in different species of organisms different, but it can differ from one organism to another in the same species. Phenotypic similarities between individuals may occur when they are carrying the same or different genotypes, and phenotypic differences between individuals may or may not be accompanied by genotypic differences.

Having agreed that genetic variation exists within as well as between species, we may ask: how does genetic variation arise? If you breed a pure line of large beans for many generations you will find on rare occasions a very small bean which will give rise to offspring beans ranging from tiny to small, and which clearly make up a new, different, pure line (Figure 1–1C). What apparently has happened is that the genetic material in the pure line of large beans has somehow changed to another transmissible form which henceforth causes the production on the average of very small beans. Such a change in the genotype that is transmitted to progeny may be said to be produced by the process of *mutation*, while the new type of individual may be called a *mutant*.

Just as it is easy to ascribe differences between dogs and cats to genetic differences, so it is often simple to tell that certain differences between lines of the same species have a genetic basis. There are many strains or breeds of pigeons, dogs, cattle, and of other domesticated animals each of which differs from the other in phenotype. That many of these differences are due to genetic

differences has been established by the retention of these phenotypic differences even after the different breeds are grown generation after generation in essentially identical environments. Revealed in this way, the genotypes within a species are of immense variety. We should keep this already present genetic variation in mind in seeking to learn something more about the nature of the genetic material.

In order to learn more about the genetic material we should examine more closely the material things comprising organisms, particularly those materials which are transmitted from parent to offspring. Most types of organisms are composed of usually microscopic building blocks called *cells* plus substances which have been manufactured by cells. These organisms start life either as a single cell, or by the fusion of two cells into one, or as a group of nonfusing cells derived from their parents. In those cases where the new individual starts life as one or a group of nonfusing cells derived from a single parent, *reproduction is said to be asexual*, while in cases where two parents contribute cells, reproduction is said to be *sexual*. In sexual reproduction two cells, called *gametes*, fuse in the process of fertilization into one cell, called the *zygote*, which is the start of a new individual. In higher animals these gametes are called *egg* (female) and *sperm* (male), and the zygote the *fertilized egg*. In the bean plant, male and female gametes are produced in the same individual which, as already mentioned, serves as both parents, and self-fertilization normally occurs; in human beings the two kinds of gametes are produced in separate individuals of different *sex*, so that cross-fertilization always occurs.

When is this hypothetical inborn genetic material transferred? Is it transferred simultaneously with the very inception of the new individual or is it transferred sometime after? Is the transfer accomplished only once, several, many times, or continuously? We may get some answer by considering certain organisms, composed of but a single cell, which reproduce asexually by dividing into two cells. In this process the parent becomes extinct, so to speak, its individuality being replaced by two daughter cells of the same kind. Once formed, the two daughters often separate, never to meet again. In such a case, at least, the genetic material, whatever it is, must have been transmitted before the completion of cell division. Accordingly, we should examine this process of cell division in some detail for clues concerning the physical basis of the genetic factor.

The preceding reasoning has led us to postulate the existence of genetic material, which is transmissible and mutable (capable of mutation), and which together with the environment determines phenotypes. But before we examine cell division for additional evidence of some physical basis for the genetic material, let us consider some work which may provide us with more information with regard to the transmissive properties of the genetic material.

SUMMARY AND CONCLUSIONS

Organisms are assumed to contain an intrinsic genetic factor which is responsible for like reproducing like. This genetic factor is presumed to have a material basis.

Accordingly, the genetic material must be different in different species of organisms and may be different in different lines or breeds of the same species. Variations in phenotype may be due to either or both genetic and environmental differences. The contribution of one of these two factors to phenotypic variability may be detected by avoiding variability in the other of these two factors.

Genotypic differences arise by the process of mutation. The genetic material is presumably transmitted from parents to offspring by means of the cellular bridge between generations.

REFERENCES

Johannsen, W., 1909. *Elemente der exakten Erblichkeitslehre.* Jena. See also a translation of the summary and conclusions of his 1903 paper, "Heredity in Populations and Pure Lines," in *Classic Papers in Genetics*, Peters, J. A. (Ed.), Englewood Cliffs, N.J., Prentice-Hall, 1959, pp. 20–26.

WILHELM LUDWIG JOHANNSEN *(1861–1926). (By permission of Genetics, Inc., vol. 8, p. 1, 1923.)*

Phenotypic variation among associates in the Department of Zoology, Columbia University, 1954. Phenotypic similarity is reflected in the interest of numbered individuals in genetical-cytological matters.

1. John A. Moore
2. Arthur W. Pollister
3. Howard Levene
4. Francis J. Ryan
5. Franz Schrader
6. Leslie C. Dunn
7. Theodosius Dobzhanksy

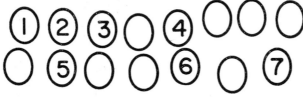

QUESTIONS FOR DISCUSSION

1.1. Has the phenotype of one generation any effect upon the genotype of the next? Explain.

1.2. What do you think of the thesis that the genotype is more important to organisms than is the environment?

1.3. Is the environment for two organisms ever identical? Explain.

1.4. What is meant by an operational definition?

1.5. Define the genetic factor. Have you given an operational or a nonoperational definition? Explain.

1.6. When the same similarities or differences in phenotype can be produced by either the environment or the genotype, can one ever be sure which is the determining factor? Explain.

1.7. What evidence can you give to support the view that the genetic material is transmitted from parent to offspring? Do you think this evidence constitutes conclusive proof of transmission? Explain.

1.8. What conclusions can you come to regarding the genetic factor in Himalayan rabbits and in Siamese cats?

1.9. Assume the genetic factor has a supernatural basis. Could we learn anything about it from the use of the scientific method of investigation? Explain.

1.10. Do you think human beings provide good material for the study of the genetic factor? Explain.

1.11. What size limitations can you give to the genetic material?

1.12. Is the existence of genetic material presumed or proven? Explain.

Chapter *2

GENE SEGREGATION

W E HAVE been led to postulate the existence of genetic material from observations regarding the similarities and the differences in phenotypes which occur among offspring and between them and their parents. Hypothetically, this material is transmitted from generation to generation, and we can hope to learn more about it by studying the occurrence of traits in lines of descent. Perhaps this procedure will reveal additional transmission properties of the genetic material. We shall, therefore, continue to study what we may call transmission genetics.

There is a choice to be made at this point. We could investigate the genetic material either in lines reproducing asexually or in lines, like the beans already discussed, which reproduce sexually by self-fertilization. In both cases we would be dealing with pure lines. However, instead of taking either of those paths of investigation let us turn our attention to the study of the genetic material in organisms reproducing sexually by cross-fertilization. In the experimental work described henceforth, it can be assumed, unless stated to the contrary, that appropriate precaution has been taken to assure that *the phenotypic similarities and differences described are genotypic in origin* and are not the result of varying environmental conditions.

It is possible to obtain different strains of a cross-fertilizing animal or plant which show phenotypic differences with respect to a given trait. For example, for the trait height one

line might be short, the other tall; or for the trait color one line might be red and the other white. The question raised now is what will happen phenotypically in the offspring if two lines showing different alternatives for the same trait are crossed? Can we, by studying the results of the first and subsequent generations, learn anything regarding the genetic material?

Let us consider some specific experiments like this which can be performed with the garden pea,[1] first with respect to what should be done and why it should be done. Then we can examine the results obtained and discuss what they reveal regarding the genetic material.

The garden pea plant is a favorable organism for these studies because it is simple and inexpensive to raise and the length of a generation is short enough to permit the study of a number of generations in succession. Although garden peas are normally self-fertilizing, it is possible also to cross-fertilize them; in fact the experimenter can control all mating by simple and appropriate techniques. Moreover there exist a number of strains differing phenotypically with regard to different traits. It is necessary, of course, to breed these strains by self-fertilization for several generations and to observe the phenotypes, to make sure that pure lines have indeed been obtained.

Which pure lines should we cross together? Since we do not know what phenotype to expect in the offspring it would be unwise to use as parents two lines whose flowers differ, say, in shades of pink or whose seeds differ only in average size. For such traits might be subject to variation due to the action of the environment which could cause the phenotypes in the two parental strains to overlap. This would confuse our deciding from the phenotypes what genotypes were present. So we should first select for use only strains which show a sharp, nonoverlapping, easily

[1] Based upon G. Mendel's experiments.

8

detected, difference. Second, to avoid unnecessary complexity in following the results of the matings, we should use only strains having a single major difference.

Third, we should use only lines which can be successfully cross-fertilized in both directions; that is, where matings can be made reciprocally — the line furnishing the male gamete in some crosses with a second line also provides the female gametes in other crosses with this second line. This is a desirable step whose purpose is to determine whether it makes any difference upon which parental line the offspring start their development (as pea seeds formed on the maternal parent).

Fourth, all crosses should be fully fertile; that is, the parental lines should be hardy plants growing vigorously and producing full sets of seed capable of growing to maturity, not only when self-fertilized but when crossed to each other reciprocally. If this precaution is not taken it is possible that insufficient numbers of offspring will be obtained or, more important, that the offspring observed will be an incomplete sample of those whose development started. Deaths that occur between the time of fertilization and the time that we make our observations regarding the phenotype of the offspring may lead to serious bias. Differential viability for different genotypes could cause us to miss, or underestimate the frequency of, certain phenotypes; this would give us misleading results with regard to genotypes, especially on the view that the genetic material is transmitted at the time the new organism starts its existence, i.e., at the time of fertilization.

Two strains of garden pea, one producing colored flowers and the other colorless flowers, satisfy the prerequisites discussed. The breeding procedure followed and the observations made are now described, accurate records of parental and offspring phenotypes having been kept, of course.

Cross-fertilizations were made reciprocally between pure line colored flowers and pure line colorless flowers, these individuals serving as the *parents of the first generation* (P_1). The offspring seeds were planted and the color of their flowers scored. All these offspring, which comprise what we may call the *first filial generation* (F_1), were phenotypically uniform, having colored flowers just like one of the P_1. The F_1 results were the same for the reciprocal matings. In the discussion which follows in this Chapter and subsequent ones, it will be correct to assume that *all crosses were made reciprocally and produced identical results, unless a statement to the contrary is made.*

What can we conclude about the genetic material from these results? Let us use symbols as a shorthand method of representing the genetic material — *C* for the genetic material whose effect produces colored flowers, present in all members of the colored flowered pure line, and *c* for the genetic material producing colorless flowers, present in all the colorless flowered pure line individuals. All F_1 individuals must contain *C* since they produce colored flowers. What has happened to *c*? Has it failed to be transmitted?

We may learn more by permitting the F_1 colored to serve as P_2 (second parental generation) and reproduce by self-fertilization to yield F_2 progeny. When this is done, and large enough numbers of F_2 are obtained from each P_2 plant, it is found that among the offspring of every P_2 some are colored and some are white. In terms of genetic material, then, these F_2 must carry, respectively, *C* or *c*. It is no surprise that some F_2 contain *C*, but where did the *c* come from which is necessary for colorless F_2? One could at first suppose that in these cases *c* either arose spontaneously from some nongenetic origin or that *C* mutated to *c*. We can bypass the first possible explanation by *assuming that genetic material can arise only from pre-existing genetic material and that this material is self-reproducing (self-replicating).*

The second explanation can be eliminated by the fact that in the pure line containing C, mutations to c are found to be thousands of times more rare than the occurrence of c among the F_2. So, if the P_2 (F_1) were genotypically like pure line C individuals, as we have assumed, mutation could not be the explanation for the difference in breeding behavior between P_1 C and P_2 C.

In the absence of a simpler explanation, we are faced with the necessity of postulating that the *genetic material is not always composed of a single indivisible unit.* The appearance of c in F_2 can be explained by making the more complex assumption that each P_2 (F_1) contains not only C but c as well; in other words, that in some individuals the genetic material contains two units. Let us use the word *gene* to refer to *a unit or restricted portion of the genetic material.* But, if we assume that there is a pair of genes in the P_2, we shall have to apply this rule to all other individuals in our experiment. For, in science, we obey *the law of parsimony (Occam's rule)* which states that we must not multiply hypotheses or assumptions needlessly. So, instead of having some individuals with paired genes and others with these singly, we shall require all to have a pair of genes in their genetic material. Accordingly, the two pure lines and the P_1 must have been CC and cc, and all F_1 must have been Cc. Those F_2 which are colorless must be cc.

Now your attention is called to the individuals in F_2 that are cc. These have colorless flowers that are phenotypically identical with those of the original pure line of colorless used in the P_1. And, in fact, crosses of F_2 colorless individuals either with themselves or with any other colorless individual (F_2, or pure line) produce all colorless progeny. In other words, F_2 cc individuals are genotypically just as pure with respect to the trait under consideration as are pure line individuals. This is true despite the fact that both c's in the F_2 had been carried in F_1 individuals

where C was the other member of the pair of genes. We conclude, therefore, that when c is transmitted to the F_2 it is uncontaminated, or untainted, by having been in the presence of C in the F_1 even though it had not been expressed in any noticeable way in the phenotype of those individuals. We can generalize this conclusion and state that *the nature and transmission of any gene is uninfluenced by whatever its partner gene* (allele) *may be.*

Since each P_2 produced colored and white F_2 offspring, each P_2 had the genotype Cc composed necessarily of C from the CC P_1 and c from the cc P_1. This specifies that one and only one member of a pair of genes in a parent is transmitted to each individual offspring, so that *in the transmission process the members of a parental pair of genes must become separated, or segregated, from each other.* The paired, or *diploid*, condition of the genes, then, becomes an unpaired, single, or *haploid* (*monoploid*) one during transmission, but diploidy is restored in the offspring because a haploid genotype is contributed to it by each parent.

Accepting the hypothesis that paired genes are segregated at the time they are transmitted to progeny, are the two alleles in a parent equally likely to be transmitted to offspring? We already know, from the F_2 produced by self-fertilization of F_1 Cc, that both genes of a given individual are transmissible. Let us test the hypothesis that both members of a pair of alleles are equally transmissible. If so, then, the male parent (or part) would contribute C half the time and c half the time; similarly 50% of the time C and 50% of the time c would be contributed by the female parent (or part). Finally, assume diploidy is restored at random; that is, the haploid gene from one parent enters an offspring without regard to the haploid gene contributed by the other parent. Accordingly, an offspring which receives C from the female (50% of offspring) will have an equal chance of receiving C or c from the male, so that of all offspring 25% will be *CC* and 25% *Cc*. Those offspring receiving *c* from the female (50% of offspring) will have an equal chance of receiving *C* or *c* from the male, so that the contribution to all the offspring genotypes will be 25% *Cc* and 25% *cc* from this source. On this basis the F_2 would be predicted to contain 25% of individuals that are *CC*, 50% that are *Cc*, and 25% *cc*. This expectation can be expressed as relative frequencies in several ways: ¼ *CC* : ½ *Cc* : ¼ *cc*, or 1 *CC* : 2 *Cc* : 1 *cc*, or .25 *CC* : .50 *Cc* : .25 *cc*. As already reasoned *CC* and *Cc* are phenotypically indistinguishable, having colored flowers, so that phenotypically 75% of the F_2 would be colored and 25% would be colorless. What is their relative frequency in the F_2 actually observed?

Although a penny has in theory a 50% chance of falling head up and a 50% chance of falling tail up, you realize that a sufficiently large number of tosses is required to actually obtain approximately 50% heads, 50% tails. So, in the present case, an accurate test of the theoretical expectation of 75% colored and 25% colorless will be obtained only if a sufficiently large sample of offspring is scored. Accordingly, instead of scoring just the offspring of one P_2 we shall total the results for the offspring of all P_2. And when this is done, it turns out that the actual results (among 929 plants, 75.9% were colored and 24.1% colorless) are very close to expectation.

It should be emphasized that obtaining or not obtaining the phenotypic ratio ¾ colored to ¼ colorless is a critical test neither for genes being paired, nor of their untaintability, nor of their segregation — these properties of genes having been previously established on other grounds. The ratio merely tests the ideas that segregation of paired uncontaminable genes results in an equal chance for offspring to receive either haploid product of segregation from a parent and that the haploid products from different parents come together at random to restore the diploid condition.

If all the assumptions so far made are correct, the 75% of F_2 which are colored should be of two genotypes, ⅓ *CC*, breeding like pure line *CC* individuals, and ⅔ breeding like the F_1 *Cc* individuals. Accordingly, each F_2 colored plant is permitted to self-fertilize and, in fact, very nearly ⅓ produce only colored F_3 whereas ⅔ produce F_3 of both colored and colorless types. The theoretical genotypic ratio expected in the F_2, ¼ *CC* : ½ *Cc* : ¼ *cc*, is, in this way, fully confirmed in experience. The gene model we have proposed to explain these phenotypic results is summarized in Figure 2–1. It is convenient to introduce two additional terms at this time. A *homozygote* is an individual that is pure with respect to the genes in question, like *CC* or *cc*, while a *heterozygote*, or hybrid, is impure in this respect, like *Cc*.

An independent test of all the hypotheses presented in this Chapter can be made in the following way. F_1 colored plants are crossed to colorless plants, this cross being symbolized genetically: F_1 *Cc* × *cc*. As the result of segregation half of the offspring should receive *C* and half *c* from the *Cc* parent, and all should receive a *c* from the *cc* parent. So, the genotypes of the offspring from this cross should be, theoretally, *Cc* 50% of the time and *cc* 50% of the time, and the expected phenotypic ratio should be, then, ½ colored : ½ colorless. This expectation is actually observed (85 colored : 81 colorless).

The next question we may ask is, are the principles we have established generally applicable? Thus far they apply strictly only to the genic determination of flower color in garden peas. Now it is possible to test all these ideas six additional times, using six other traits each of which occurs in two clear-cut alternatives and fulfills the prerequisites for suitability already described. In each case, when two appropriate pure lines were crossed the F_1 hybrids produced

FIGURE 2–1. *Genotypic model proposed to explain the phenotypic results of certain crosses involving colored and colorless flowered pea plants.*

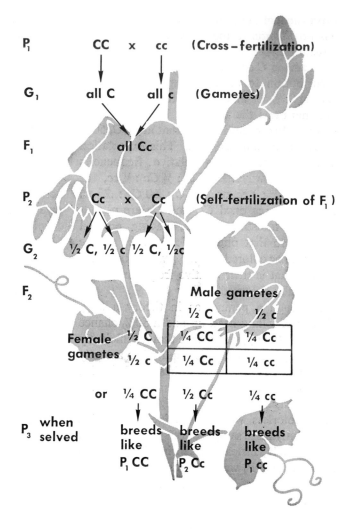

were phenotypically uniform, as before. Moreover, self-fertilization of the F_1 gave F_2 which were proven to occur in the expected 1 : 2 : 1 genotypic ratio.

Recall that the *Cc* phenotype is indistinguishable from *CC*. In *Cc* individuals the phenotypic expression of *c* is masked by the expression of *C*. The ability of a gene to express itself phenotypically in the presence of a different allele is described in terms of *dominance*. In the present case *C* is said to be the *dominant* gene when present with *c*, which is called, accordingly, *recessive*. It

should also be noted particularly that the concept of the gene so far developed has no dependency upon the occurrence or non-occurrence of dominance. Indeed, testing our postulates has been made more complicated by the fact that *C* is, for all intents and purposes, completely dominant to *c*, since our F_1 *Cc* showed only the expression of *C* and the presence of *c* was detected only upon breeding F_1 individuals. Also, only upon further breeding of colored F_2 were we able to determine that ⅓ were *CC* and ⅔ *Cc*. Dominance, then, refers to the phenotypic expression of genes in diploid condition and has no relation to their mechanism of transmission.

It turned out, for the six other traits used to test the general applicability of our gene concept, that in each case one allele was dominant to the other alternative one in the hybrid. From this, one might be led to conclude that dominance is a universal phenomenon since it was found in each of seven different studies on the occurrence and transmission of traits based on genes in the garden pea. However, before making this decision examine the results of breeding certain chickens. Here black × white produces blue-gray F_1. Mating two blue-gray F_1 produces in F_2 ¼ black, ½ blue-gray, and ¼ white. You see in this case that dominance does not occur at all, so that dominance is not a rule for the phenotypic expression of alleles in heterozygotes. Note that when dominance is absent, genotypes can be written with certainty from a knowledge of phenotypes.

It should be realized that it was cross-fertilization that made it possible to show that genes occur as pairs, which after segregation become unpaired, then recombine to form pairs in the offspring. In other words, the view that the genetic material contains separable paired units is based upon the recombination which these units undergo in cross-fertilization. At this point we ought to consider the meaning of the term *genetic recombination*. You will agree that the genetic units themselves are not required to undergo novel changes (mutations) when undergoing recombination. That is, the types of genes present in a genetically recombinant individual had already existed before recombination. Given an individual whose gene pair is AA', segregation followed by self-fertilization may produce AA' again. But, this genotype is not considered a genetic recombination, but rather a *reconstitution* of the original arrangement of the units. However, the self-fertilization under discussion may also produce AA or $A'A'$. These represent two new genetic combinations, and are considered to be genetic recombinations. Accordingly, when events lead to the production of "old" combinations and "new" combinations of genes, it is only the latter type of grouping which is called genetic recombination. This usage is reasonable in view of the importance that new combinations have in our understanding of genetic material (we were able to derive the principle of segregation only because new combinations of genes were produced by sexuality). Accordingly, genetic recombination should be identified with the reassortment or regrouping of genes as a consequence of which new arrangements of them are produced. Any process that has the potential of producing new arrangements of genetic units is, therefore, a mechanism for genetic recombination.

The phenotypic results of the experiments discussed in this and the preceding Chapter have led us to hypothesize the existence of genetic material which is self-replicating, mutable, and transmissible. The pea plant experiments reveal that the genetic material can be partitioned into a pair of units by means of the operation or technique of genetic recombination. There may be techniques or operations other than recombination which may be employed to study the nature of the genetic material. Should these different operations reveal that the total genetic material is divisible into smaller units, this would not necessarily imply an equivalence among the units. Thus, to use a nongenetic analogy, a book (equivalent to the total genetic material) can be partitioned operationally in terms of chapters, pages, paragraphs, words, letters, illustrations, and so forth. Each operation reveals something about the book, but the different units by which it is described are necessarily neither identical nor mutually inclusive.

The present Chapter has revealed that the genetic material contains a pair of genes.

But you should recognize that the properties of these genes must be expressed in terms of recombination, the operation by which they were detected. It is conceivable that other operations will also partition the genetic material into units, whose characteristics will have to be expressed in terms of the operations employed for their detection. However, until it is found that the different units revealed by different operations are not equivalent, we shall use the term *gene* to refer to any unit of the genetic material, regardless of the operation by which the unit was discovered. In most of the genetic literature to be referred to subsequently, as well as in the greater portion of this book, it is usually simple for the reader to determine from the context of the discussion which operations are involved when the term *gene* is used.

The possibility exists that the genetic material may be shown, via the study of genetic recombination, to contain more than two genes, in which case the maximum size of a gene would be reduced. Henceforth, we will be interested in any attempts to learn to what extent the genetic material can be partitioned into genes, for such work leads us to a better understanding of the nature of the genetic material in terms of its recombinational properties. Remember that near the beginning of this Chapter we chose to investigate the genetic material from its recombinational properties, and have postponed the study of the nature and consequence of the genetic material as revealed by other, nonrecombinational, techniques or operations.

SUMMARY AND CONCLUSIONS

Genetic material is assumed to be self-replicating and to arise only from pre-existing genetic material. The term *gene* is used to refer to a unit or restricted portion of the total genetic material as discovered via any operational procedure. The genes discovered in the present Chapter were revealed by recombination.

Genes occur in pairs. When they are transmitted in sexual reproduction the members of a pair segregate so that any offspring receives only one member of a pair from each parent. The gene is uncontaminated by the type of gene that is its allele prior to segregation, and enters the new individual uninfluenced by the type of gene being contributed from the other parent.

REFERENCES

Mendel, G., 1866. "Experiments in Plant Hybridization," translated in Sinnott, E. W., L. C. Dunn, and Th. Dobzhansky, *Principles of Genetics*, 5th Ed., New York, McGraw-Hill, 1958, pp. 419–443; also in Dodson, E. O., *Genetics, the Modern Science of Heredity*, Philadelphia, Saunders, 1956, pp. 285–311; also in *Classic Papers in Genetics*, Peters, J. A. (Ed.), Englewood Cliffs, N.J., Prentice-Hall, 1959, pp. 1–20.

The Birth of Genetics, Supplement to Genetics, 35, No. 5, Part 2, 1950, 47 pp. Contains English translation of G. Mendel's letters to C. Nägeli (1866–1873), and papers by H. De Vries, by C. Correns, and by E. Tschermak published in 1900.

QUESTIONS FOR DISCUSSION

2.1. How would you recognize that a line of garden peas had become genotypically pure for a given trait?

2.2. Criticize the assumption that genes come only from pre-existing genes and do not arise *de novo*.

2.3. Does a parent lose its genetic material when it is transmitted to progeny? Defend your answer.

2.4. Is it necessary to assume that genes are able to reproduce themselves? Explain.

2.5. List all the assumptions required to explain a 3 : 1 ratio in F_2 on a genetic basis.

2.6. A black and a white guinea pig are mated and produce all black offspring. Two such offspring when mated produce mostly black but some white progeny. Explain these results genetically.

2.7. A cross of two pink flowered plants produces offspring whose flowers are either red, pink, or white. Defining your genetic symbols, give all the different kinds of genotypes involved and the phenotypes they represent.

2.8. What operation was employed in studying the gene in the present Chapter? Define a gene in terms of size.

2.9. Discuss the role of dominance in the study of genes.

2.10. Do organisms that reproduce asexually have genes?

2.11. What relation has a gene to the phenotypic effect with which it is associated?

2.12. Do you agree with the statement on p. 10 that a cross between two colorless pea plants results in "all colorless progeny"? Why?

2.13. Throughout this book the use of the word "heredity" and its derivatives has been avoided. Why do you think this is, or is not, justified?

Chapter *3

MITOSIS

I N LOOKING for the biological basis for the transmission of genetic material from parents to progeny your attention has been called (p. 5) to the cellular bridge between generations. Remember that it is only via this bridge that genic transmission may take place, at least in single-celled organisms for whom cell division is equivalent to reproduction. Moreover, all cellular organisms are remarkably similar in the way that they accomplish cell division. To initiate our present search for the material basis of genes let us examine briefly certain general features of cell structure and the appearance of cells undergoing division, as seen under the microscope.

There are two major parts of the cell, a peripheral portion called the *cytosome*, containing substances making up *cytoplasm*, and a more central portion called the *nucleus*, containing *nucleoplasm*. In the final stages of cell division in higher plants, the cytoplasm is divided by the formation of a cell plate, which starts internally and proceeds toward the periphery until the separation into two daughter cells is complete. In the case of animal cells, a furrow starts peripherally and proceeds inward, until the parent cell is cleaved into two. The degree to which the two daughter cells are identical with respect to cytoplasmic components depends upon the position of the cell plate or furrow in the parent cell. In some cases these occur in the middle of the cell, but in many other cases they are located off-center, so that the two daughter cells contain very different

16

amounts of cytoplasm. Although cytoplasmic components often may be distributed unequally between daughter cells, this is not true for the nuclear contents. Nuclear division usually directly precedes cytosomal division. But the nucleus does not simply separate into two parts by forming a furrow or cell plate. Instead of simply and directly separating into two parts, the nucleus undergoes a remarkable series of preparatory activities before it divides; this process of indirect nuclear division is called *mitosis*.

Even though a nucleus shows no visible evidence that it is going to undergo mitosis, it is known to be very active chemically. In appearance (Figure 3–1A), it is bounded by a *nuclear membrane* and is filled by a more or less homogeneous-appearing ground substance in which one or more small bodies called *nucleoli* are located.

The first indication that the nucleus is going to divide is the appearance in its ground substance of a mass of separate fibers (Figure 3–1B), some of which seem to be associated with the nucleoli. These fibers are called *chromosomes*. This appearance marks the start of the first phase of mitosis, or *prophase*. Careful cytological observation reveals that each chromosome is in turn composed of two delicate threads irregularly coiled about each other. Each of the paired threads within a chromosome is called a *chromatid*. As prophase continues the chromatids within each chromosome become shorter and thicker and untwist from each other (Figure 3–1C). The nucleoli become smaller and it is believed that some of the material incorporated to thicken the chromatids is derived from the nucleoli. By the end of prophase (Figure 3–1D) the nucleoli and nuclear membrane have disappeared and the chromatids have formed thick rods which begin to move actively for the first time. Active motility is not the property of the entire chromosome, but is restricted to a particular region of it called the *centromere*.

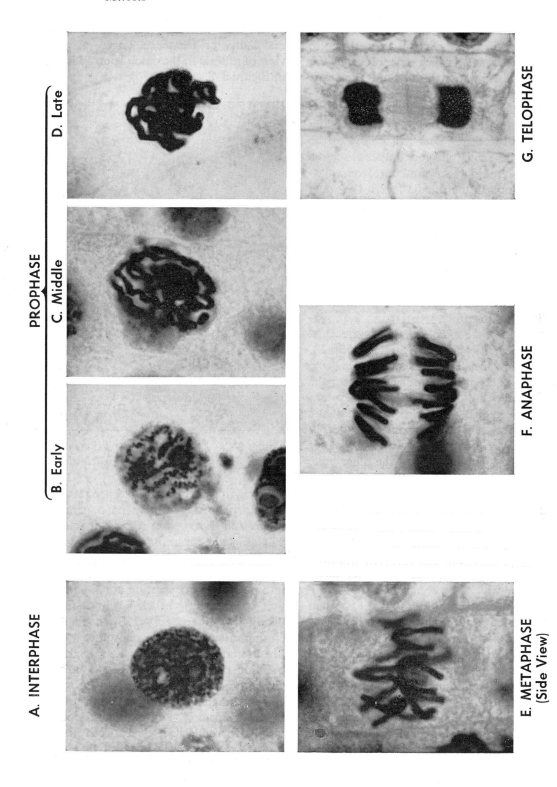

PROPHASE

B. Early   C. Middle   D. Late

A. INTERPHASE

E. METAPHASE
(Side View)

F. ANAPHASE

G. TELOPHASE

FIGURE 3–1. *Mitosis in the onion root tip. (Courtesy of R. E. Cleland.) (By permission of McGraw-Hill Book Co., Inc., from Study Guide and Workbook for Genetics, by I. H. Herskowitz, copyright 1960.)*

This movement of centromeres occurs in a particular direction relative to a structure called the *spindle* which has been in the process of formation throughout prophase. When completed, the spindle has an appearance similar to what you will see upon spreading your fingers and touching corresponding fingertips together. Your wrists serve as the poles of the spindle and your fingers as spindle fibers. The chromosomes migrate from whatever position in the spindle region they may have, so that their centromeres come to lie in a single plane perpendicular to the axis between the poles, that is, at the equator of the spindle, which is represented by the plane formed where your fingertips touch. Now the rest of the chromosome, being passive, can be in any plane in the spindle. Once all the centromeres have arrived at the equatorial plane of the spindle, mitosis has reached the middle phase, or *metaphase* (Figure 3–1E).

Until now the chromatids of a chromosome are still attached to each other at or near the centromere, although elsewhere they are largely free. They next also separate at the centromeres, the two centromeres suddenly moving apart, one going toward one pole of the spindle, the other toward the other pole, with the rest of each chromatid, now called a chromosome, being passively dragged along. This stage, in which the chromatids separate, move toward and arrive at the poles as chromosomes, is called *anaphase* (Figure 3–1F).

Once the chromosomes are at the poles, the last stage, or *telophase* (Figure 3–1G), occurs, in which the events that follow appear to be the reverse of those that happened in prophase. Specifically, the spindle disintegrates, a new nuclear membrane is formed around the chromosomes, and nucleoli reappear containing material probably drained away from the chromosomes. The chromosomes become thinner and longer and then can be seen to consist of two delicate threads (chromatids) wound one about the other. Finally, as the chromosomes lose their visible

identity the nucleus enters the *intermitotic, interphase*, or *metabolic* stage. A general view of mitosis in the onion root tip is shown in Figure 3–2.

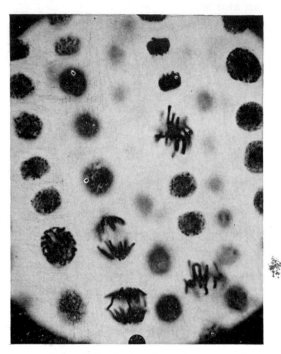

FIGURE 3–2. *Mitosis in the onion root tip — general view.* (*Courtesy of R. E. Cleland.*)

In reading this generalized account of the mitotic phases, you may have gained the impression that, in one respect, it was either incomplete or misleading. For it was stated that the prophase chromosome is composed of two chromatids, that metaphase puts these into position for separation at anaphase, and that once separated their newly attained individuality is recognized by calling them chromosomes. But chromosomes were defined as containing two visible threads! The question rightly asked is, does the anaphase chromosome contain the two threads or chromatids that are seen at telophase? This would be true if each chromatid somehow visibly reproduced itself between the time it was seen relatively uncoiled at prophase and the next time it was seen relatively uncoiled, at telophase. Note that we have been discussing the replication of chromatids as detected by microscopic observation. We can also study chromosome and chromatid replication using other operations. Accordingly, let us consider some evidence regarding chromosome replication at the chemical level, in the hope that this will help us understand its replication at the visible level.

Chromosomes ("colored bodies") are unique in the cell since they are the only objects which stain purple by a procedure called the Feulgen-Rossenbeck technique. It is possible to measure the amount of chromosomal material by the amount of purple stain taken up by the chromosomes. It is found that the amount of chromosomal material does not change between prophase and telophase, but doubles over a period of hours during the intermitotic stage. At the start of prophase, therefore, each chromosome has already replicated chemically. At the visible level, however, this is not yet apparent, so that each of the two visible chromatids in a chromosome also contains the chemical materials for an identical chromatid which is still invisible under the microscope. This new material is submicroscopic either because it has not yet assumed a proper chromatid form or has done so but is so tightly paired with its sister chromatid that together they appear as one strand. However, before the next occasion when unwound threads can be seen, that is, at the telophase of the same mitosis, this replication at the visible level has already been accomplished. So, the submicroscopic chemical reproduction which takes place in a given interphase stage is not visible in chromatid form until the next telophase.

What are the consequences of mitosis? Speaking in terms of visible structures, the chromosomal content of the parent nucleus has become repeated in each daughter nucleus, so that the subsequent division of the cytoplasm produces daughter cells whose chromosomal composition is identical to each other and to the parent cell from which they were derived. The cells of different species are different in that either they have different numbers of chromosomes per nucleus or the chromosomes differ in appearance, or both. Different chromosomes may differ from each other in their size, their stainability with various dyes, and in the location of their centromeres. Almost all chromosomes have a subterminal centromere which separates the chromosome into two parts (*arms*); all chromosomes are linearly arranged and unbranched. When very careful analyses are made, any two species can be shown to differ in their chromosome complements.

Examination at metaphase of the kinds of chromosomes within the nucleus of sexually reproducing organisms typically shows that for each chromosome which arrives at the equatorial plane there is another chromosome very similar or identical to it in appearance which also takes a position independently in this plane. Chromosomes thus occur as pairs, and the members of a pair are called *homologous chromosomes*, or *homologs*, whereas chromosomes of different pairs are *nonhomologous*, or *non homologs*. It should be repeated that the members of a pair of homologs assume their position at mitotic metaphase independently of each other.

The number of chromosomes seen in typical mitosis of the garden pea is 14 (2N, or the diploid number of chromosomes) or 7 pairs; in Indian corn (maize) there are 10 pairs, in human beings 23. Whatever number of chromosomes is present in the zygote, then, other things being equal, the same number of chromosomes will be found in every cell of a multicellular organism descended from the zygote by cell divisions in which mitosis has occurred.

From the information presented, we are now in a position to hypothesize what may be the material basis for genes. While it is possible that we may find other kinds of genes, using other criteria or operations, the kind that we have identified by recombination possesses certain specific properties including a very regular mode of transmission (Chapter 2). One regular cellular component transmitted by all cells to daughter cells is the chromosomes. These have several properties of interest with respect to genes: chromosomes reproduce themselves and are transmitted equally to the daughter cells so that these are identical, in this respect, to each other and to their parent cell.

We shall make the reasonable assumptions that genes arise only by a process which involves the replication of pre-existing genes, and also that different alleles arise only from each other by mutation, that is, by a gene changing to an alternative form of that gene which in turn is involved in reproducing the alternative form until it mutates. It is found that chromosomes may occasionally become visibly altered in certain ways. In these cases all chromosomes mitotically derived from such a modified chromosome have exactly the same alteration. Therefore, both genes and chromosomes are capable of mutation and are subsequently involved in replicating their new form.

Another property of the gene is the retention of its individuality regardless of the nature of its allelic gene. One indirect evidence has already been cited for believing this is true also for the chromosomes. This is the independent way that each chromosome arrives at metaphase. It might be thought, when the chromosomes "disappear" during interphase, that their individuality is lost and even that their contents are dispersed. Evidence that the nuclear material is not dispersed into the cytoplasm between mitoses already has been presented in the retention of the full amount of chromosomal material within the nucleus during interphase, insofar as revealed by the Feulgen-Rossenbeck

chromosome-staining procedure. Nevertheless, it is possible that those components of chromosomes which remain intranuclear may become scrambled during interphase and later resynthesize their proper form during the next prophase. Four lines of evidence can be mentioned bearing on this question. The first three come from studying the appearance of successive mitoses. It is possible to observe the positions of chromosomes at late anaphase or telophase and again observe the position of the chromosomes as they enter the next prophase. When this is done it is found that the chromosomes have held the same relative positions, as expected had they retained their integrity during interphase. Second, since the nucleolar material does not disperse during interphase, those parts of the chromosomes with which the nucleolus is associated probably remain associated during that interval. Third, it sometimes happens that two originally identical homologs are modified by mutation so that one is changed in one respect and the other is changed in a different respect. The finding that, mitosis after mitosis, these two homologs retain their separate differences is evidence that each homolog, like each allele, has retained its individuality cell generation after cell generation. Finally, there is more direct evidence on the retention of chromosomal individuality during interphase from cells of the larval salivary glands of certain fruit flies. For these cells have interphase nuclei, and it is possible, because of their giant size, to squash them open and show that they contain the correct number of relatively uncoiled chromosomes linearly identical to the chromosomes seen during mitosis.

You may already be impressed with the points of similarity between genes and chromosomes. However, your attention is called to what is an apparent disparity in behavior between the two. If all nuclei divide by mitosis, then a gamete should contain the same number of chromosomes as the other cells derived from the original zygote, and since the zygote of any generation combines two gametes, the number of chromosomes should increase in the zygotes of successive generations. Yet we know that paired genes in one generation remain paired genes in the next sexual generation, so that their diploid condition is maintained generation after generation via segregation and fertilization. We are led to assume, therefore, that something paralleling segregation of genes must take place for chromosomes. This is reasonable in view of the statement already made that all individuals of a species have a characteristic chromosomal composition. In actual fact, as expected, the gametes do not contain the paired, diploid, chromosome number. Instead each contains a complete, unpaired, haploid, set of chromosomes. The zygote therefore has the diploid chromosome constitution restored because each gamete furnishes a haploid set of chromosomes, one set contributed by the sperm from the father, and another set by the egg from the mother. In this way chromosomes remain as pairs, sexual generation after sexual generation, and the number of chromosomes remains unchanged. Clearly, then, the cell divisions preceding gamete formation cannot be invariably mitotic, but must involve at some point a special mechanism for reducing chromosome number. The nature of this special kind of nuclear behavior is investigated in the next Chapter.

SUMMARY AND CONCLUSIONS

Studies of cell division in which nuclei divide mitotically reveal that, of all cellular components, the chromosomes are the structures most likely to serve as the material basis for genes. This hypothesis receives support from several of the properties of chromosomes which parallel established or assumed properties of genes. Chromosomes come only from pre-existing chromosomes; chromosomes can mutate on occasion, the mutant chromosome then replicating the mutant form; different species have different chromosomal compositions; the chromosome content is identical both quantitatively and qualitatively in each cell of a line produced by asexual reproduction; chromosomes are unpaired in gametes and paired in zygotes; each chromosome retains its individuality, mitotic cell generation after mitotic cell generation, regardless of the nature of its homologous chromosome.

REFERENCES

Flemming, W., 1879. "Contributions to the Knowledge of the Cell and its Life Phenomena," as abridged and translated in *Great Experiments in Biology*, Gabriel, M. L., and S. Fogel (Eds.), Englewood Cliffs, N.J., Prentice-Hall, 1955, pp. 240–245.

Schrader, F., *Mitosis: the Movement of Chromosomes in Cell Division*, New York, Columbia University, 1953.

Scientific American, Sept. 1961, Vol. 205, No. 3, "The Living Cell," articles by J. Brachet and by D. Mazia.

Swanson, C. P., *Cytology and Cytogenetics*, Englewood Cliffs, N.J., Prentice-Hall, 1957.

QUESTIONS FOR DISCUSSION

3.1. What are the consequences of mitosis?

3.2. Including those properties of chromosomes listed in the Summary and Conclusions, state the corresponding gene property and whether it is one which is proved or assumed. Give evidence or reasons for accepting or rejecting these as genic properties.

3.3. If the chromosomes serve as the material basis for genes, each cell of the body derived by mitosis should carry the same genotype. Using a multicellular plant, describe how you would test this idea.

3.4. What are the advantages or disadvantages of chromosome coiling?

3.5. Can you imagine a spindle which is too small for normal cell division? Explain.

3.6. Suppose certain nuclei normally do not divide with the aid of a spindle. In what respect would this affect your ideas about genes?

3.7. Is it scientifically correct to assume at this point that; (1) all genes recombine, (2) chromosomes are equal to genes? Explain.

3.8. Discuss the statement that all cell divisions are normally mitotic.

3.9. Differentiate between replication of chromatids and of chromosomal material.

3.10. List the events that must take place before a given telophase chromosome can give rise to a chromosome made entirely of chromosomal material not yet synthesized.

Chapter *4

MEIOSIS

By what kind of process do both male and female gametes come to contain only one set of chromosomes, composed of one member of each pair of chromosomes found in the nucleus of an ordinary body, or *somatic*, cell? Gametes cannot be produced by regular mitotic division or they would be diploid. The reduction from two sets to one has been found to be brought about by another type of indirect nuclear process, called *meiosis*, which actually requires two successive nuclear divisions to accomplish this result.

Since the diploid number of chromosomes is maintained generation after generation in sexually reproducing forms, it is not surprising that meiosis always occurs at some time in the life cycle of each sexually reproducing individual. In most animals meiosis comprises the last two nuclear divisions before the mature sperm or egg is produced. Meiosis occurs at different times in the life history of different plants, but almost never immediately before the formation of gametes. There are minor variations in different species in the details with which meiosis is carried out; what is presented here is a generalized account of its main features.

In order that the cytological description of the meiotic process may be more meaningful to you, several assumptions will be made. Suppose that the processes which direct the nucleus to divide act especially early in the case of meiosis, before the chromosomes have attained the degree of coiling first seen in mitotic prophase. Suppose further that a

relatively more uncoiled state of the chromosome is, under these conditions, associated with an especially strong attraction of like chromosome parts for like parts and that this attractive force extends over considerable, though still microscopic, distances. Then, with one additional novelty which will be described later, the meiotic process will occur in a predictable way when the chromosomes undergo in sucession two divisions of a mitotic nature.

In prophase of the first meiotic division, just as in the case of mitotic prophase, each chromosome would contain two chromatids plus an equal amount of chromosomal material not yet visible as chromatids (Chapter 3). But, now, because of the early onset of nuclear division, homologous chromosomes would pair point for corresponding point (making a bundle of four chromatids plus an equal amount of future chromatid material). Once paired, the chromosomes would proceed as pairs to the equator of the spindle for the metaphase. (Recall that in mitosis, on the other hand, each chromosome of the two sets present behaves independently of its homologous chromosome in going to the spindle's equator.) At anaphase the members of a pair would separate and go to opposite poles (note each anaphase chromosome would still contain two chromatids plus an equivalent amount of future chromatid material). In the interphase which follows the first telophase, no synthesis of future chromatid material would take place since what was made in the previous interphase had not been used to make visible chromatids in the first meiotic division. So, the second meiotic division could now take place at any time and proceed as a typical mitosis. In the second meiotic prophase each chromosome would contain two chromatids and two future chromatids. Each chromosome would proceed to metaphase independently; at anaphase the two chromatids would separate and go to opposite poles of the spindle (once separated the chromatids may be called chromosomes, as mentioned in the previous Chapter). By telophase the future chromatid would become visible so that each telophase chromosome contains two chromatids.

While mitosis always involves chromosome duplication and separation alternately, in meiosis one duplication is followed by two separations. The result is the maintenance of the diploid chromosome condition in mitosis, but a reduction from the diploid to the haploid (monoploid) condition when meiosis is completed.

Let us now examine the actual meiotic process in some detail (Figure 4–1), after which a more complete discussion will be made of specific cytological phenomena and their genetic implications. Prophase of the first meiotic division (*prophase I*) is of long duration, as compared to mitotic prophase, and is divided into several substages each of which has its own distinguishing characteristics.

1. As they emerge from the intermitotic phase the chromosomes are long and thin, more so than in the earliest prophase of mitosis. This is the *leptonema* (thin thread) stage of prophase I.

2. Next the thin threads pair with each other in a process called *synapsis*. This pairing is very exact, being not merely between homologous chromosomes, but between exactly corresponding individual points of the homologs. Synapsis proceeds zipperwise until the two homologs are completely apposed. This is the *zygonema* (joining thread) stage.

3. The apposition of homologs becomes so tight that it is difficult to identify two separate chromosomes (*pachynema*, thick thread, stage) (Figure 4–2A).

4. Following this, the tight pairing of the pachynema is relaxed and then it can be clearly seen that each pair of synapsed chromosomes contains four threads, two visible chromatids for each chromosome (Figure

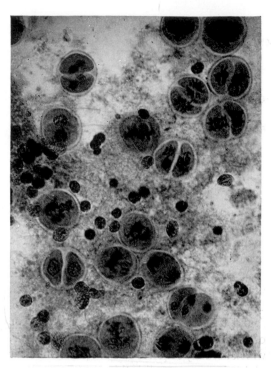

FIGURE 4–1. *Meiosis in the lily — general view.* (*Courtesy of R. E. Cleland.*)

4–2B, C). A pair of synapsed chromosomes is called a *bivalent* when referring to chromosomes, but is called *tetrad* when referring to chromatids. Although the chromatids separate from each other in pairs here and there, they are still all in close contact with each other at other places along their length. Each place where the four chromatids are still held together is called a *chiasma* (cross; the plural is *chiasmata*) (Figure 4–3A). A chiasma is characterized by the fact that the two chromatids which synapse to make a pair on one side of the point of contact separate at the point of contact and synapse with other partners

FIGURE 4–2. (*Opposite*). *Meiosis in the lily. The leptonema and zygonema stages of prophase I have been omitted.* (*Courtesy of R. E. Cleland.*) (*By permission of McGraw-Hill Book Co., Inc., from* Study Guide and Workbook for Genetics, *by I. H. Herskowitz, copyright 1960.*)

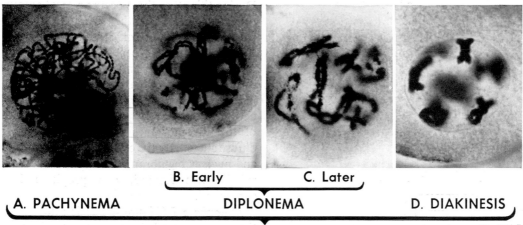

B. Early   C. Later

A. PACHYNEMA   DIPLONEMA   D. DIAKINESIS

PROPHASE I

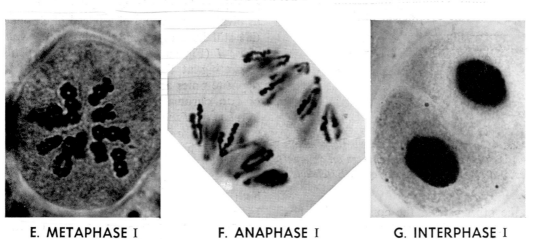

E. METAPHASE I   F. ANAPHASE I   G. INTERPHASE I
(Equatorial View)   (Side View)

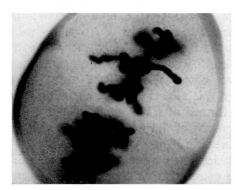 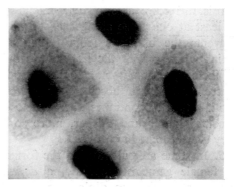

H. METAPHASE II   I. TELOPHASE II
(Side View)

A

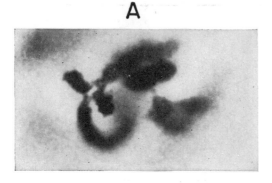

B

FIGURE 4–3. *Lily diplonema showing chromatids (1–4) with different synaptic partners on different sides of a chiasma.* (*Courtesy of R. E. Cleland.*)

on the other side of the contact point, i.e., the partners making up two synapsed pairs of chromatids are different on the two sides of the place of contact (Figure 4–3B).

It is, therefore, the occurrence of chiasmata at least at one place along each tetrad that prevents the bivalents from falling apart. Chiasmata comprise the last feature unique to meiosis, which is not found in mitosis where tetrads are absent. As *diplonema* (double thread) continues, the chromosomes become shorter and thicker, more so than they ever become in mitosis.

5. In some animals, during the formation of female gametes especially, a *diffuse* or *growth stage* follows diplonema, in which the chromosomes and nucleus revert to the appearance found in a nondividing cell.

During this stage there occurs a great amount of cytoplasmic growth. In human beings this stage may last for decades, after which the rest of meiosis occurs and mature eggs ready for ovulation are produced.

6. *Diakinesis* (Figure 4–2D) is characterized by the maximal contraction of diplonema chromosomes, or by maximal recontraction of the chromosomes which had entered a diffuse stage. By the end of this stage nucleoli and nuclear membrane have disappeared, the spindle has formed, and prophase I is completed.

Metaphase I (Figure 4–2E) is attained by the movement of chromosomes to the mid-spindle, as in mitosis, except that they move as bivalents, made up of a tetrad of chromatids still held together by chiasmata. *Anaphase I* (Figure 4–2F) shows the bivalents separating at their centromeres, moving to opposite poles as univalents, each composed of two chromatids (making now a *dyad*). In *telophase I* the daughter nuclei are formed, and *interphase I* (Figure 4–2G) follows. The length of interphase I varies in different organisms.

The second meiotic division proceeds in both daughter nuclei as expected from mitosis. In *prophase II*, the univalents containing dyads (each equal to a chromosome with its two chromatids) contract; at *metaphase II* (Figure 4–2H) each univalent lines up at the equator of the spindle independently; at *anaphase II* the members of a dyad separate and go to opposite poles as *monads* (each equivalent to a single chromosome containing its two chromatids). Since two nuclei undergo this second division, there are four nuclei formed at *telophase II* (Figure 4–2I). Photographs of the meiotic process in corn can be seen in Figure 4–4 (pp. 28–29).

Consider now the consequences of meiosis. At the completion of meiosis each nucleus contains one representative of each pair of chromosomes that was present in the nucleus at the start of meiosis. Meiosis, then, could provide the physical basis for the segregation of paired genes. What relationship exists at the completion of meiosis between the two haploid sets of chromosomes, one of which was previously contributed by each parent to the zygote? Is it a fact that the maternally-derived and the paternally-derived members of a chromosome pair segregate so that only one or the other is present in a given gamete? Is the haploid set of chromosomes in a gamete composed of all maternally-derived or of all paternally-derived chromosomes?

For typical meiosis, the answers to these two questions depend upon two events. The first of these is the manner in which the centromeres of the bivalents become arranged at the equator of the spindle at metaphase I. Relative to the poles of the spindle, each bivalent arranges itself at the equator independently of other bivalents, so that it is purely a matter of chance whether the maternal chromosome will go to one specified pole and the paternal chromosome to the other, or vice versa. Consider the distribution of two bivalents only, for example. Of the many cells undergoing meiosis at metaphase I, approximately half will have the two paternal univalents going to one pole and the two maternal univalents going to the other pole at anaphase I, and approximately half will have one maternal and one paternal going to one pole and one paternal and one maternal to the other. As a result, the chromosomal content of all haploid nuclei produced at the completion of meiosis will be 25% paternal, paternal; 25% maternal, maternal; 25% paternal, maternal; 25% maternal, paternal. Because the centromeres of each bivalent line up at metaphase I with an equal frequency in the one direction to that in the other and because each bivalent does so independently of all other bivalents, we see that the segregation which follows occurs independently for different pairs of chromosomes. Note also that, when we were considering the fate of two bivalents,

50% of haploid products had the same combinations of nonhomologous chromosomes as entered the individual in the parental gametes, therefore retaining the old or parental combinations, whereas 50% of haploid products carried new, nonparental combinations or recombinations. Let us defer considering the genetic implications of this until we have discussed the second factor in meiosis which bears upon the maternal-paternal chromosome content of gametes. This second factor will modify in some respects the conclusions just reached.

Recall the chiasmata which are seen at prophase I during diplonema. On the basis of certain evidence, it may be considered that each chiasma represents a place where one maternal chromatid of one univalent and one paternal chromatid of the other have "broken" at exactly corresponding positions and cross-united. If such an exchange had taken place, the continued close pairing between paternal chromatid segments and between maternal chromatid segments would produce the chiasma configuration seen. Accordingly, a tetrad containing one chiasma would have the paternal (p) and maternal (m) linear constitution, as shown in Figure 4–5 where the centromere is represented by C. From this Figure you can see that, following one chiasma, one chromatid remains entirely maternal, one remains entirely paternal, but the other two are composed of segments of both paternal and maternal origin. Note again that in any one chiasma only two of the four chromatids exchange parts. However, since a tetrad normally contains several chiasmata, usually each of the four chromatids has exchanged at one place or another with a chromatid derived from the other parent and consequently has a biparental composition along its length.

We can now return to our questions regarding the maternal-paternal chromosome content of the haploid products of meiosis. Since the centromeres of the bivalents sepa-

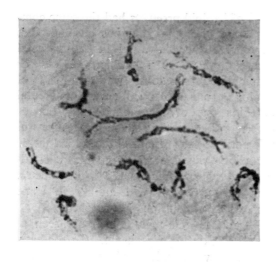

DIPLONEMA

ANAPHASE I (Middle)

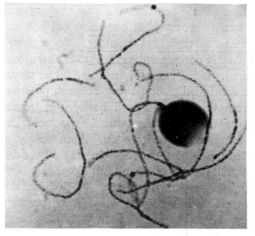

PACHYNEMA

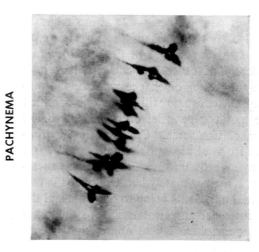

METAPHASE I

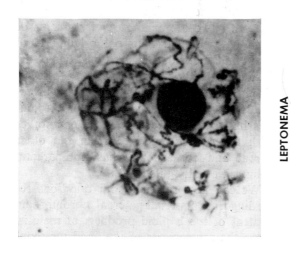

LEPTONEMA

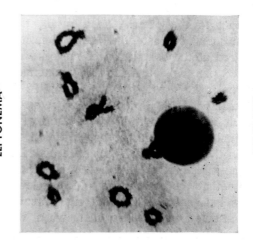

DIAKINESIS

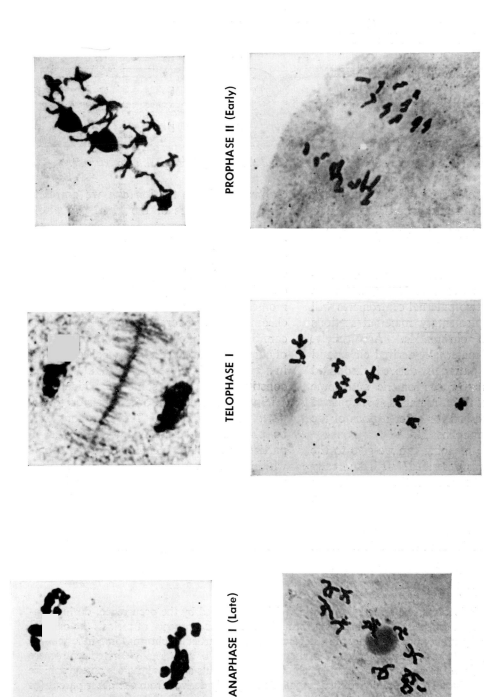

PROPHASE II (Early)

TELOPHASE I

ANAPHASE I (Late)

ANAPHASE II

METAPHASE II

PROPHASE II (Late)

FIGURE 4–4. *Meiosis in corn. The zygonema stage is omitted. Anaphase I (middle) shows one bivalent whose univalents are delayed in separation because they are still held together by a chiasma. Prophase II and later stages show the events taking place in one of the two nuclei produced by the first meiotic division. (Courtesy of M. M. Rhoades.)*

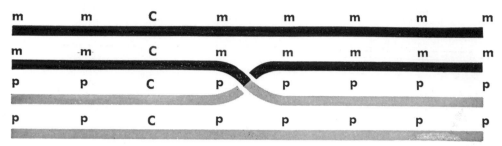

FIGURE 4–5.   *Chiasma showing paternal (p) and maternal (m) composition of strands.*

rate at anaphase I, segregation of maternal from paternal centromeres occurs at the first meiotic division. Then, depending upon the location and number of chiasmata at diplonema, the dyad having the maternal centromeres will contain different paternal segments along its two chromatids, while the dyad with the two paternal centromeres will have the complementary maternal sections along its two chromatids. Accordingly, segregation of maternally-derived chromatid material from paternally-derived chromatid material occurs for centromeric and some other regions of the chromatids at anaphase I and is accomplished for other regions of the chromatids at anaphase II.

What genetic meaning can we give to the meiotic processes described? It has already been established that when the members of a pair of genes segregate they do so cleanly, entering the gametes of an individual just the same as they were when they originally entered that individual at fertilization. What chromosomal constitution can we correlate with the properties of the gene? A whole haploid set of chromosomes (a *genome*) cannot be the physical basis of a gene since, though the gametes produced by an individual contain a single genome, this is usually constituted (ignoring chiasmata, for the moment) of some maternal and some paternal chromosomes. Moreover, a pair of genes cannot be identified even with an entire pair of chromosomes, since a haploid chromosome in a gamete is, because of chiasmata, typically constituted of parts some of which were originally maternal and other parts originally paternal in derivation. The gene may only be physically associated, therefore, with a particular small segment of a chromosome within which a chiasma cannot be formed with a corresponding segment on a homologous chromosome. Such a segment would always retain its pure maternal or pure paternal constitution after segregation; its maximal size would equal the gene's maximal size.

SUMMARY AND CONCLUSIONS

Meiosis involves two essentially mitotic divisions modified by the occurrence, during prophase I, of synapsis and of chiasmata formation. As a consequence of meiosis the original pair of genomes becomes single in the gametes. Any particular chromosome in a genome of a gamete has an equal chance of having a maternally- or a paternally-derived centromere (because of the random manner in which different bivalents align themselves on the spindle at metaphase I) and usually contains segments originally derived from the other parent (as a consequence of chiasmata).

The hypothesis that the gene has a physical basis in chromosomal material may now be made more specific — a gene is physically associated with a short segment of a chromosome within which a chiasma cannot be formed.

REFERENCES

DeRobertis, E. D. P., Nowinski, W. W., and Saez, F. A., *General Cytology*, 3rd Ed., Philadelphia, Saunders, 1960.

Rhoades, M. M., "Meiosis" in *The Cell: Biochemistry, Physiology, Morphology*, Brachet, J., and A. E. Mirsky (Eds.), Vol. 3, *Chromosomes, Mitosis, and Meiosis*, pp. 1–75, New York, Academic Press, 1961.

Sutton, W. S., 1903. "The Chromosomes in Heredity," Biol. Bull., 4:231–251. Reprinted in *Great Experiments in Biology*, Gabriel, M. L., and S. Fogel (Eds.), Englewood Cliffs, N.J., Prentice-Hall, 1955, pp. 248–254; also in *Classic Papers in Genetics*, Peters, J. A. (Ed.), Englewood Cliffs, N.J., Prentice-Hall, 1959, pp. 27–41.

Swanson, C. P., *Cytology and Cytogenetics*, Englewood Cliffs, N.J., Prentice-Hall, 1957.

Van Beneden, E., 1883. "Researches on the Maturation of the Egg and Fertilization," translated in *Great Experiments in Biology*, Gabriel, M. L., and S. Fogel (Eds.), Englewood Cliffs, N.J., Prentice-Hall, 1955, pp.245–248.

Wilson, E. B., *The Cell in Development and Heredity*, 3rd Ed., New York, Macmillan, 1937.

EDMUND B. WILSON *(1856–1939), American cytologist. (By permission of Genetics, Inc., vol. 34, p. 1, 1949.)*

QUESTIONS FOR DISCUSSION

4.1. Can sexually reproducing organisms reproduce asexually? Is the reverse true? Explain.

4.2. What are the similarities and differences between mitosis and meiosis?

4.3. Suppose the meiotic process had never evolved. What do you think would have been the consequence?

4.4. Certain unusual chromosomes are rings rather than rods. Could a ring chromosome have any difficulty during meiosis that a rod chromosome could not have? Explain.

4.5. How many bivalents are present at metaphase I in man, corn, the garden pea?

4.6. Discuss the statement: During meiosis, each segment of a chromosome segregates independently of its homologous segment and of all other chromosome segments.

4.7. Argue against the hypothesis that the physical basis of genes lies in the chromosomes.

4.8. What do you suppose happens during meiosis in individuals possessing an odd number of chromosomes?

4.9. Suppose an animal has a diploid chromosome number of six. What proportion of all its gametes would receive all the centromeres originally derived from the father? from the mother? from either the father or mother? from both the father and mother?

4.10. If you could see under a microscope only a single dead cell at metaphase, how could you tell whether the cell was undergoing mitosis, metaphase I, or metaphase II?

4.11. What are the similarities and differences between the segregation of genes and of chromosomes?

Chapter *5

SEGREGATION IN MAN
— MULTIPLE ALLELISM

In this Chapter we shall discuss how segregation of genes may be studied in human beings and also examine some traits found in mankind which may be based upon the presence of a single pair of genes. Although we choose to discuss genes in humans, because of the great interest we naturally have in ourselves, it should be remembered that the genetic principles applied here would be expected to hold equally well for any other sexually reproducing species.

The study of human genetics is complicated by the fact that, unlike other species of plants and animals, our species is not bred experimentally. Because of this we shall have to make use of special methods of study. There are several approaches to the study of human genetics which may prove fruitful; these include the *pedigree*, *family*, *population*, and *twin* methods. The present discussion deals primarily with studies utilizing the first two methods.

The pedigree method uses phenotypic records of families (family trees) extending over several generations. In recording pedigrees certain conventional symbols are used (Figure 5–1). In such pedigree charts a square or ♂ represents a male, a circle or ♀ represents a female; filled-in symbols represent persons affected by the anomaly under discussion. The family method utilizes the phenotypes only of parents and their offspring; that is, uses data from a single generation.

Albinism, lack of melanin pigment, is a rare

disease, which occurs approximately in one birth per 20,000. Studies of families, and of pedigrees like the one in Figure 5–2, yield the following facts, each of which is discussed relative to the hypothesis that albinism occurs in homozygotes for a recessive gene "*a*":

1. Both parents of albinos may be non-albino, i.e., normally pigmented. This may be explained by the occurrence of a homozygous child (*aa*) from the marriage of two heterozygotes (*Aa* × *Aa*).

2. The trait appears most frequently in progeny which share a common ancestor. This is readily demonstrable, for example, in Sweden and Japan where the per cent of cousin marriages is less than 5% in the general population but is 20–50% among parents of albino children. Since albinos are rare, so also is the *a* gene. The chance of obtaining homozygous, *aa*, individuals will be small indeed if the parents are unrelated, since even if the first parent is *Aa* or *aa* the second parent will most likely be *AA*. On the other hand, if again the first parent is *Aa* or *aa*, marriage with a related individual makes it much more likely that the second parent will carry an *a*, received from the ancestor held in common with the first parent.

3. In families of two children, in which albinism appears though both parents are non-albino, it is observed that the nonalbino and albino children are in the relative proportion of 3 : 4. On the hypothesis under consideration, the parents must be *Aa* × *Aa*. The chances from such marriages that a given child is nonalbino is ¾ and that it is albino ¼. Each child produced from such a marriage has these same chances for nonalbinism and albinism, chances which are independent of the genotypes (or phenotypes) of the children preceding or following it in the family. Accordingly, of all two-child families whose parents are *Aa*, ¾ will have the first child nonalbino, and of these ¾ will also have the second child nonalbino. Thus, 9⁄16 of all two-child families from heterozygous parents will

FIGURE 5–1. *Symbols used in human pedigrees.*

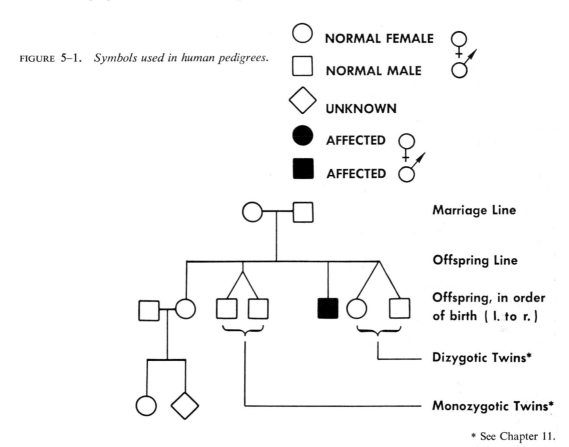

NORMAL FEMALE

NORMAL MALE

UNKNOWN

AFFECTED

AFFECTED

Marriage Line

Offspring Line

Offspring, in order
of birth (l. to r.)

Dizygotic Twins*

Monozygotic Twins*

* See Chapter 11.

have been excluded from our sample, since both children will be normally pigmented. Our sample will include the following, however: all those families whose first child is normal ($\frac{3}{4}$) and second child is albino ($\frac{1}{4}$), making up $\frac{3}{16}$ ($\frac{1}{4}$ of $\frac{3}{4}$) of all families; those families where the reverse is true ($\frac{3}{4}$ of $\frac{1}{4}$), comprising another $\frac{3}{16}$ of all families; and those families in which both children are albino ($\frac{1}{4}$ of $\frac{1}{4}$), which make up $\frac{1}{16}$ of all families. So every seven albino-containing families scored will give, on the average, 6 normal children (three from each of the two kinds of families containing one albino) and 8 albinos (three from each of the two kinds of families containing one albino and two from each family containing two albinos), so that the ratio expected is 3 : 4 as nonalbino : albino.

It may be noted that the observed proportions of nonalbino and albino children in families of three, or of four, or of more children from normal parents also fit the expected proportions calculated in a similar manner.

4. Marriages between two albinos produce only albino children, as expected genetically from *aa* $\times$ *aa*.

5. Twins arising from the same zygote (monozygotic or identical twins) are either both albino or nonalbino. Since such twins are genetically identical they would be expected to be both normal, *AA* or *Aa*, or both albino, *aa*.

These evidences offer clear proof that human albinism is usually the result of a single pair of genes.

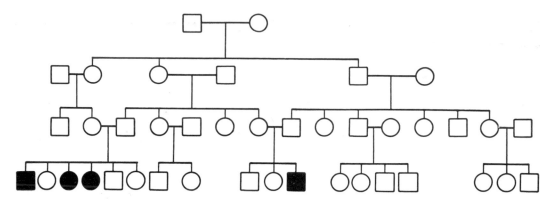

FIGURE 5-2. *A pedigree of albinism in man.*

The anomaly of *woolly hair* is a rare trait in Norwegians and can be attributed, after a study of pedigrees, to the presence of a rare dominant gene, call it *W*. For, when woolly-haired individuals (*Ww*) marry normal-haired individuals (*ww*), it is predicted and found that approximately 50% of children have woolly and 50% normal hair. Note that the affected parent is represented as a heterozygote, the trait being so rare that the homozygote *WW* is probably nonexistent, since, barring mutation, an individual with this genotype would have to have parents both of whom had woolly hair.

A study of pedigrees was instrumental in clarifying the nature of certain *ataxias*, which involve a lack of neuromuscular coordination, found in certain families in Sweden. In some families, affected people had parents who were apparently unrelated, whereas other affected people had parents who were first cousins. From the rarity of this disease it was suggested that the ataxia was being caused by the presence of a dominant gene in heterozygous condition in those cases where the parents were unrelated, and by the presence of a recessive gene in homozygous condition in those cases where the parents were related. When careful clinical tests were made by a neurologist it was found that, indeed, there were differences in symptoms in the cases where the parents were and were not related. In this way a combination of pedigree and medical studies established the genetic basis and nature of two kinds of ataxia.

Numerous family studies have been made regarding *blood type*. However, before discussing their genetic meaning, we shall need to know just what is meant by a blood type or blood group.

Human blood contains red blood corpuscles (cells) carried in a fluid medium, the plasma. The corpuscles carry on their surfaces substances called *antigens*, while the plasma contains, or may form, substances called *antibodies*. An antibody is a very specific kind of molecule, which is capable of reacting with and binding a specific antigen. This reaction may be visualized as a lock (antibody) which holds or binds a particular key (antigen). If a rabbit is injected with a suitable antigenic material, in the form of foreign red blood cells to which it has never before been exposed, certain antibody-producing cells of the rabbit will manufacture an abundance of antibodies which will appear in its plasma, some of which will be used to react specifically with the antigenic component of the foreign red blood cells. If, on some later occasion, the same antigen is injected into the rabbit's blood stream there will be, now, already present, specific antibodies to bind the antigen. The antigen-antibody complex then formed often causes the blood to clump or agglutinate. It is simple to arrange the procedure so that this reaction may be observed in a test tube or on a glass slide.

What is done [1] is to inject red blood corpuscles from different people into different rabbits, with the result that the rabbits form antibodies against the antigens introduced. The rabbit's blood, devoid of cells, can then serve as an antiserum, containing antibodies, which will clump any red blood cells added to it carrying the original types of antigens. It is found that two very distinct antisera are formed by these rabbits, and that any person's blood cells tested with these two antisera can react in one of three ways: the red blood cells are agglutinated or clumped either in one antiserum (arbitrarily called anti-M), or in the other (called anti-N), or in both of these antisera. So all people can be classified by their blood cell antigens as belonging to either M, or N, or MN blood group, respectively.

When parents and their offspring are tested for "*MN*" *blood type* such family studies give the results shown in Figure 5-3. Parents of type 6 give offspring which are in the proportion of 1 : 2 : 1 for M : MN : N blood types. This suggests these blood types are the phenotypic consequence of the presence of a pair of segregating genes. If we let *M* = the gene for blood group antigen M, *M′* = the allelic gene which produces the N blood group antigen, mating 6 must be, genetically, $MM′ \times MM′$ and the offspring $1MM : 2MM′ : 1M′M′$. Note that these alleles show no dominance of one over the other phenotypically, *MM′* individuals showing both M and N blood group phenotype. All the other family results also are consistent with the genetic explanation proposed for MN blood groups.

PARENTS		CHILDREN		
		M	MN	N
1	M x M	ALL	—	—
2	N x N	—	—	ALL
3	M x N	—	ALL	—
4	MN x N	—	½	½
5	MN x M	½	½	—
6	MN x MN	¼	½	¼

FIGURE 5-3. *Distribution of MN blood group phenotypes in different human families.*

Still two other antisera, called anti-A and anti-B, can be prepared.[2] When blood from different people is tested using these antisera it is found to be of one of four types: clumped in anti-A (blood type A), clumped in anti-B (blood type B), clumped in both (type AB), and clumped in neither (O).

Family studies of "*ABO*" *blood types* give the phenotypic results shown in Figure 5-4. Note there that two kinds of results are obtained from A × O and also from B × O parents. In each case one result (marriage types 9 and 11) may be explained by assuming that the non-O parent is a heterozygote in which the gene for O is recessive. Let *i* be the gene for O blood group type and I^A the gene for A blood, the latter being dominant. Then the parents are: in marriage type 9 $I^A i \times ii$, in type 10 $I^A I^A \times ii$, and in 13 $ii \times ii$. In order to explain 11 and 12 we shall have to assume the presence of a gene I^B for B blood group, which is also a dominant allele of *i* and from which it segregates. Then mating 11 is $I^B i \times ii$ and 12 is $I^B I^B \times ii$. Note that we have made a new supposition with regard to genes. In the former case the alternative

---

[1] Based upon K. Landsteiner's work.

[2] Based upon work of K. Landsteiner and P. Levine.

PARENTS		CHILDREN			
		A	AB	B	O
7	AB x AB	¼	½	¼	—
8	AB x O	½	—	½	—
9*	*IₐIo* A x O	½	—	—	½
10*	A x O	ALL	—	—	—
11*	B x O	—	—	½	½
12*	B x O	—	—	ALL	—
13	O x O	—	—	—	ALL

* In some families.

FIGURE 5–4. *Distribution of ABO blood group phenotypes in different human families.*

allelic form of *i* is I^A while in the latter case it is I^B. This means that we are making the additional assumption that *the gene can exist in more than one alternative condition*, so that a gene can have multiple, different, alleles. Of course, while any individual has only one pair of genes, these may be of the same or of different types. Since the heterozygote $I^A I^B$ shows no dominance, and appears as AB blood type, all the results indicated in the table are explained. (Some readers may have suspected that multiple allelism was possible from the fact that three different genes were involved in the presence and absence of the ataxias already described.)

There are a number of other ways to type blood. One of these involves the presence or absence of what is called the *Rhesus* or *Rh factor*. Red blood cells from Rhesus monkeys may be injected into rabbits; if a second injection of Rhesus blood is given some time later, it will be clumped. This is explained by the presence of an antigen carried by Rhesus red blood cells against which the rabbit had manufactured antibodies before its second exposure to Rhesus blood. The antigen involved here is called Rh. Instead of injecting Rhesus red blood cells into a rabbit which has anti-Rh antibodies in its serum, suppose human blood is injected. In this event it turns out that 85% of people have blood which is clumped, these people having what is called the Rhesus-positive (or Rh-positive) blood type, whereas 15% of people have blood which is not clumped, and have the Rhesus-negative (or Rh-negative) blood type. Accordingly, 85% of humans have the same Rh antigen as have Rhesus monkeys, while 15% do not. A combination of family and pedigree studies shows that presence of Rh antigen in human beings is controlled by a dominant gene, call it *R*, and its absence to a recessive allele, say *r*, their distribution following the principle of segregation.

Finally, let us consider the genetic basis for certain kinds of *anemia*. Among Italians who live in Italy or who have emigrated, there may be an anemia of two special kinds. One type, severe and usually fatal in childhood, is called Cooley's anemia or thalassemia major;

the other type, a more moderate anemia, is called microcytemia, or thalassemia minor. Pedigree and family studies all support the hypothesis that t. major children are homozygotes (*tt*) for a pair of genes. Both their parents have t. minor and are heterozygotes (*Tt*) for this gene. Analysis on a population level has resulted in the classification of more than 100,000 people in Italy as *TT*, *Tt*, or *tt*. Notice that in the case of thalassemia, neither *T* nor *t* is completely dominant (nor recessive).

You have seen, therefore, that some morphological and some chemical characteristics of man are based upon segregating genes. While the relation between the alleles in the heterozygote with respect to their phenotypic expression may involve complete, partial, or no dominance, in no case does this have an effect either on the genes themselves or upon their segregation and recombination.

Another important point to remember is that initially someone had to collect the phenotypic data in pedigree and family studies, and then apply the principles known about genes to explain these data genetically, using the simplest suitable explanations in much the same way as was illustrated here for albinism and for MN and ABO blood types. Sometimes the data are insufficient and the investigator is left with several equally probable genetic explanations.

SUMMARY AND CONCLUSIONS

Data furnished in pedigree and family studies provide evidence that there are a number of human traits whose occurrence is based upon the effect of a pair of genes. These traits are of a morphological as well as of a chemical nature, the alleles sometimes showing complete, partial, or no phenotypic dominance in the heterozygote.

It was necessary to postulate that a gene can exist in any one of more than two alternative states.

REFERENCES

Mohr, O. L., "Woolly Hair a Dominant Mutant Character in Man," J. Hered., 23 : 345–352, 1932.

Neel, J. V., and Schull, W. J., *Human Heredity*, University of Chicago, 1954, pp. 83–86, 89–91, 240–241.

Stern, C., *Principles of Human Genetics*, San Francisco, Freeman, 1961.

QUESTIONS FOR DISCUSSION

5.1. What is the difference between the pedigree and family methods of investigation?

5.2. What evidence is there that pigmentation (albinism vs. nonalbinism) is due to genes that are segregating?

5.3. Two nonalbinos marry and have an albino child. What is the chance that the next child is albino? nonalbino? that of the next two children, both are albinos? nonalbinos? one is albino and one nonalbino?

5.4. What proportion of three-child families, whose parents are both heterozygous for albinism, have (a) no albino children? (b) all albino children? (c) at least one albino child?

5.5. Would you conclude that the gene for woolly hair is completely dominant to nonwoolly hair? Explain.

5.6. Discuss the occurrence of dominance with respect to blood group types.

5.7. Why was it necessary to assume that a gene may have more than two allelic forms?

5.8. A baby has blood type AB. What can you tell about the genotypes of its parents? What would you predict about the blood types of children it will later produce?

5.9. If one parent is A. blood type and the other is B, give their respective genotypes if they produced a large number of children whose blood types were:

a. All AB.
b. Half AB, half B.
c. Half AB, half A.
d. ¼ AB, ¼ A, ¼ B, ¼ O.

5.10. Give examples in man of complete, partial, and no dominance.

5.11. Is the occurrence of complete dominance helpful in determining the genic basis of alternatives for a given trait? Explain.

5.12. What do you suppose is meant by multiple allelism?

5.13. Have you learned anything new about genic properties from this Chapter? Justify your answer.

Chapter *6

INDEPENDENT SEGREGATION

IN THE preceding Chapters we have discussed the transmission genetics of alternative genes for a single trait and have found that a single pair of genes could explain the data in each case. The question asked now is, what will be the genetic unit of transmission when two or more different traits are followed simultaneously in breeding experiments?

The answer to this may lie in the results of some additional experiments performed with the garden pea.[1] Previous studies had already shown that, like the flower color trait described in Chapter 2, seed shape and seed color were each due to a single pair of genes. That is, a P_1 of pure line round $\times$ pure line wrinkled seeds gave round F_1, round being dominant. Self-fertilizing the F_1 round gave F_2 which were in the proportion of 3 round : 1 wrinkled. Similarly, a P_1 of pure line yellow $\times$ pure line green seeds gave yellow F_1, yellow being dominant, and self-fertilization of the yellow F_1 gave 3 yellow : 1 green in F_2.

The question presented above may be asked relative to the seed traits of shape and color. What will happen when individuals are crossed that simultaneously differ with regard to both of these traits? Suppose in P_1 a round yellow strain is crossed with a wrinkled green strain, these strains being available as pure lines. In F_1 only round yellow seeds are obtained (Figure 6–1). This result is what would be expected had we been studying shape and color of seeds separately. We find in this case, therefore, that there is

[1] Based upon experiments of G. Mendel.

39

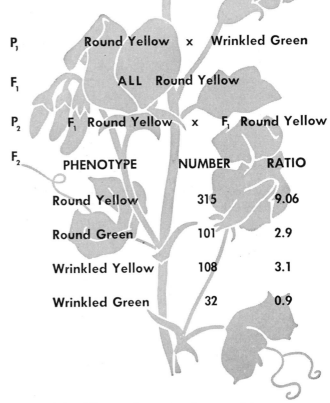

P_1	Round Yellow $\quad$ x $\quad$ Wrinkled Green	
F_1	ALL Round Yellow	
P_2	F_1 Round Yellow $\quad$ x $\quad$ F_1 Round Yellow	
F_2		

PHENOTYPE	NUMBER	RATIO
Round Yellow	315	9.06
Round Green	101	2.9
Wrinkled Yellow	108	3.1
Wrinkled Green	32	0.9

FIGURE 6–1. *Phenotypic results from studying two traits simultaneously.*

no phenotypic effect of the dominance of one trait upon the phenotypic expression of the other trait.

Self-fertilization of the round yellow F_1 gives offspring which, when counted in sufficiently large numbers, occur in the relative frequencies of 9 round yellow : 3 round green : 3 wrinkled yellow : 1 wrinkled green. Notice that segregation and recombination have occurred for each trait, as revealed in F_2 by 12 round : 4 wrinkled and by 12 yellow : 4 green. So, in this case there is also no effect of one trait upon the segregation-recombination behavior of the genetic material for a different trait.

From these results what else can we decide regarding the gene? Until now, we have been able to explain all the experimental data presented by supposing that each sexually reproducing individual contains only a single pair of genes. Accordingly, we shall still consider that each P_1 individual carries but a single pair of genes, but require each gene to have two simultaneous effects, one on seed shape and the other on seed color. The results obtained are consistent with this expectation in the following respect: the F_1 are round yellow, and the F_2 give a 3 : 1 ratio for yellow vs. green and also for round vs. wrinkled. But, on this hypothesis, the F_2 would be of only two types — 3 round yellow : 1 wrinkled green! The facts are that in F_2 not only these grandparental (P_1) combinations are found but two new, recombinational classes of offspring appear, namely, round green and wrinkled yellow! *Apparently, then, what is genetically transmitted is not composed of a single pair of indivisible units, but is composed of separable pairs of units, each pair capable of undergoing segregation and recombination.*

Let us assume, therefore, that each sexually reproducing organism contains more than one pair of genes. In the present case, let R (round) and r (wrinkled) be the alleles of one pair of genes while Y (yellow) and y (green) are the alleles of the second pair. The P_1, then, would be $RR\ YY$ (round yellow) and $rr\ yy$ (wrinkled green). Each pair of genes would undergo segregation so that a gamete would contain only one member of each pair. In this manner the former parent would produce only RY gametes and the latter one only ry, and all F_1 would be $Rr\ Yy$ (round yellow) as observed.

On the current hypothesis, the gametes formed by the F_1 would contain either R or r, and, moreover, would contain either Y or y. Since R and Y do not always go together into a gamete, nor do r and y, there must be four genotypes possible in gametes,

RY, Ry, rY, ry. Since these possible haploid genotypes will be found both in male and in female gametes, it is expected that the F_2 would contain the diploid genotypes and their corresponding phenotypes indicated in Figure 6–2. Note that nine different genotypes are possible in F_2, four giving the round yellow phenotype, two giving round green, two giving wrinkled yellow, and one wrinkled green. This is consistent with the fact that four phenotypes were actually found in F_2, substantiating our hypothesis that the genetic material transmitted in a gamete is composed of subunits, each of which has the properties of a gene.

How can we account for the fact that the observed F_2 phenotypes occurred in the relative proportions of 9 : 3 : 3 : 1, respectively? This can be done by making the simple assumption that *the segregation of the members of one pair of genes occurs independently of the segregation of the members of another pair of genes.* As a result of this (see Figure 6–3) half of all gametes receive R, of which half will carry Y and half y; the other half of all gametes receive r, of which half will carry Y and half y. Thus the male gamete population in the P_2 will be 25% RY, 25% Ry, 25% rY, and 25% ry. The P_2 also produce female gametes of the same four genotypes in the same relative frequencies. Since fertilization has already been assumed to occur at random the F_2 expected are shown in Figure 6–4.

The branching track in Figure 6–4 can be read beginning at the top: ¼ of female gametes are RY and are fertilized ¼ of the time by RY male gametes (producing $\frac{1}{16}$ of all offspring as $RR\ YY$), ¼ of the time fertilization is by Ry male gametes (so that $\frac{1}{16}$ of all offspring are $RR\ Yy$ from this origin), etc. By summing up like classes, the kinds and relative numbers of genotypes and of phenotypes are obtained as shown in the chart.

The branching track may be used to obtain the 9 : 3 : 3 : 1 phenotypic ratio more simply.

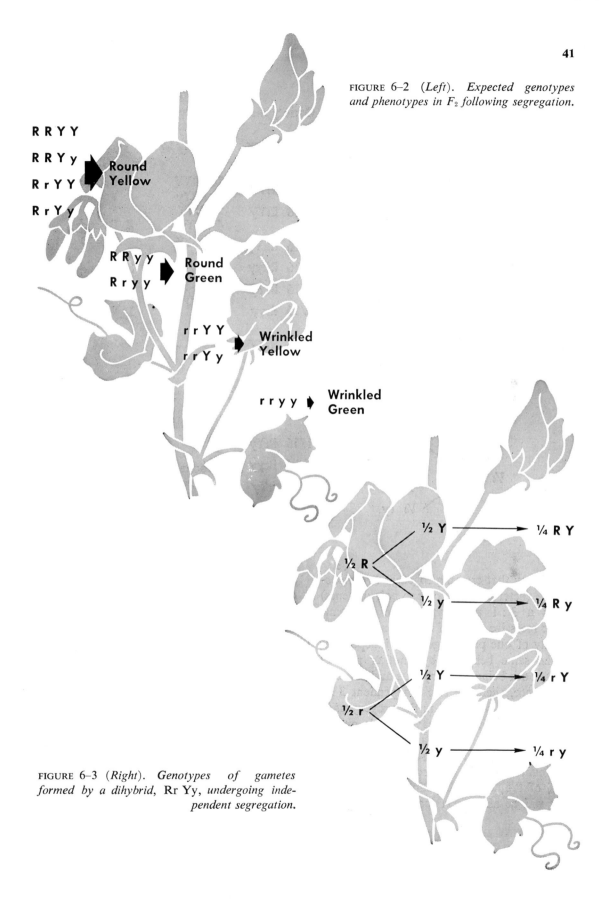

R R Y Y

R R Y y

R r Y Y → **Round Yellow**

R r Y y

R R y y
R r y y → **Round Green**

r r Y Y
r r Y y → **Wrinkled Yellow**

r r y y → **Wrinkled Green**

½ R ──┬── ½ Y ───→ ¼ R Y
      └── ½ y ───→ ¼ R y

½ r ──┬── ½ Y ───→ ¼ r Y
      └── ½ y ───→ ¼ r y

FIGURE 6–2 (*Left*). *Expected genotypes and phenotypes in F₂ following segregation.*

FIGURE 6–3 (*Right*). *Genotypes of gametes formed by a dihybrid,* Rr Yy, *undergoing independent segregation.*

TYPES AND RELATIVE FREQUENCY OF GAMETES

OFFSPRING

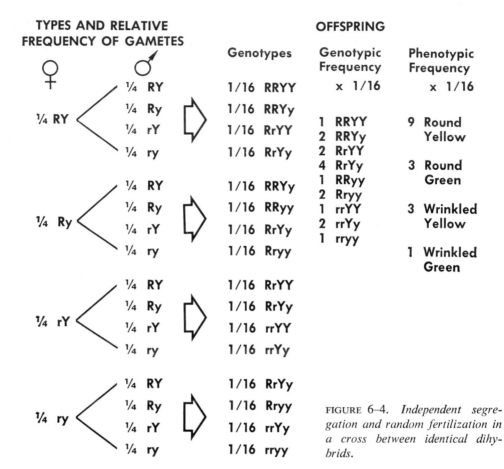

Genotypes	Genotypic Frequency	Phenotypic Frequency
	x 1/16	x 1/16

1/16 RRYY

1/16 RRYy

1/16 RrYY

1/16 RrYy

1/16 RRYy

1/16 RRyy

1/16 RrYy

1/16 Rryy

1/16 RrYY

1/16 RrYy

1/16 rrYY

1/16 rrYy

1/16 RrYy

1/16 Rryy

1/16 rrYy

1/16 rryy

Genotypic Frequency:
1 RRYY
2 RRYy
2 RrYY
4 RrYy
1 RRyy
2 Rryy
1 rrYY
2 rrYy
1 rryy

Phenotypic Frequency:
9 Round Yellow
3 Round Green
3 Wrinkled Yellow
1 Wrinkled Green

FIGURE 6–4. *Independent segregation and random fertilization in a cross between identical dihybrids.*

You know that crossing together two *monohybrids* (heterozygotes for one pair of genes) yields a 3 : 1 phenotypic ratio of dominant : recessive trait. If the recombinational activity of one pair of genes is independent of the same behavior by another pair of genes, both being heterozygous and showing dominance, then the two independent 3 : 1 ratios may be combined in the progeny as in Figure 6–5. That chart may be read: among the offspring, the ¾ which are round (because of segregation, random fertilization, and the dominance of R in the cross $Rr \times Rr$) will be ¾ of the time also yellow and ¼ of the time will be also green (because of segrega-

tion, random fertilization, and the dominance of Y in the cross $Yy \times Yy$); so, of all progeny ⁹⁄₁₆ will be round yellow and ³⁄₁₆ round green, etc.

You see, then, that independent segregation by two different pairs of genes results in the formation of gametes whose gene combinations, new and old, are in equal frequency. In the present case, the *dihybrid* (heterozygote for two pairs of genes) received both R and Y from one parent and both r and y from the other, its gametic recombinations being Ry and rY. Had the dihybrid received Ry from one parent and rY from the other, the gametic recombinations would have been

RY and *ry*, and the old combinations *Ry* and *rY*. So, regardless of how the genes enter the individual, the dihybrid forms four, equally frequent, genetically different gametes.

The types and frequencies of gametes formed by the *Rr Yy* dihybrid can be determined more easily after mating it with a *double recessive* individual, i.e., an individual homozygous recessive for both pairs of genes concerned. In the cross of *Rr Yy* × *rr yy*, the double recessive parent produces only *ry* gametes while the dihybrid produces four different and equally frequent types, *RY*, *Ry*, *rY*, *ry*. Accordingly, the finding that among the offspring of this cross (Figure 6–6) very nearly 25% are round yellow (55 offspring), 25% round green (51 offspring), 25% wrinkled yellow (49 offspring), and 25% wrinkled green (52 offspring) is a direct confirmation

both of segregation by the members of a single pair of genes and of independent segregation by different pairs of genes.

Whenever one is dealing with complete dominance, a cross to an individual recessive for the pairs of genes involved will always serve to identify the genotype of the other parent, since the phenotypic types and frequencies of the offspring will correspond to the genotypic types and frequencies occurring in the gametes of the latter. This kind of cross is therefore called a *test cross*, and is also called a *backcross* if one of the parents in the series of crosses had been homozygous recessive for the genes under study.

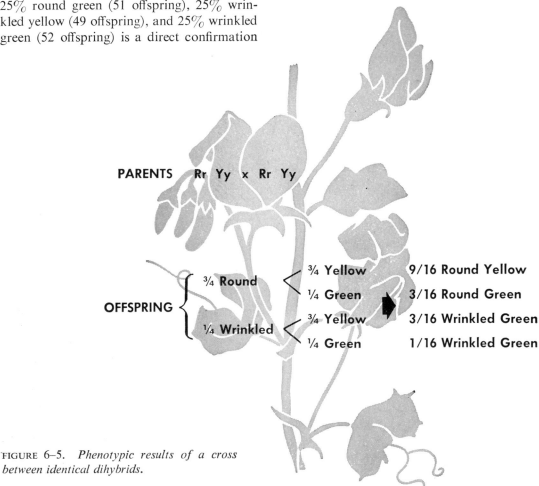

PARENTS   Rr Yy x Rr Yy

OFFSPRING

¾ Round   ¾ Yellow   9/16 Round Yellow
  ¼ Green   3/16 Round Green
¼ Wrinkled   ¾ Yellow   3/16 Wrinkled Green
  ¼ Green   1/16 Wrinkled Green

FIGURE 6–5. *Phenotypic results of a cross between identical dihybrids.*

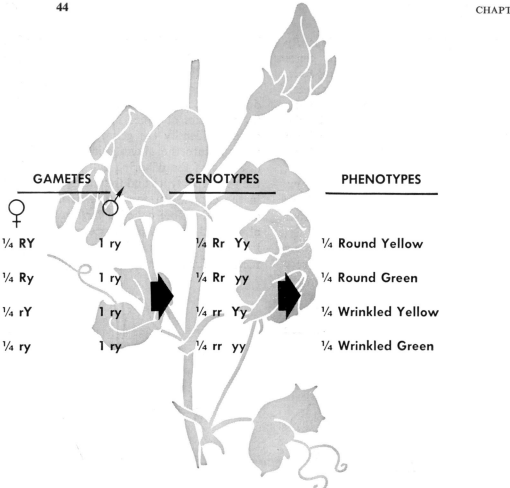

GAMETES		GENOTYPES	PHENOTYPES
♀	♂		
¼ RY	1 ry	¼ Rr Yy	¼ Round Yellow
¼ Ry	1 ry	¼ Rr yy	¼ Round Green
¼ rY	1 ry	¼ rr Yy	¼ Wrinkled Yellow
¼ ry	1 ry	¼ rr yy	¼ Wrinkled Green

FIGURE 6–6. *Test cross or backcross of the F_1 dihybrid* (Rr Yy) *with the double recessive individual* (rr yy).

We are now in a position to return to a consideration of the material basis for genes. If one gene pair is to be physically associated with the corresponding short regions on a pair of homologous chromosomes within which a chiasma cannot occur, the question is, where in relation to one pair of genes is a second pair located? Two possibilities occur — either both pairs are on the same chromosome pair or they are on different, nonhomologous chromosome pairs. Let us examine the assumption that different pairs of genes are located on different pairs of chro-

mosomes. If this is true, then there are several different arrangements that the parts of different pairs of chromosomes may take relative to each other at metaphase I of meiosis (Figure 6–7).

It has been established that different pairs of chromosomes line up at metaphase I independently of each other. Moreover, it is entirely reasonable that the way centromeres in a tetrad orient toward the poles at metaphase I would be uninfluenced by the presence or absence of chiasmata in that tetrad. If, then, as in Case A, there is no chiasma between the centromere and gene pair *Aa* nor between the centromere and gene pair *Bb*, alignments I and II, being equally frequent, will result in four different,

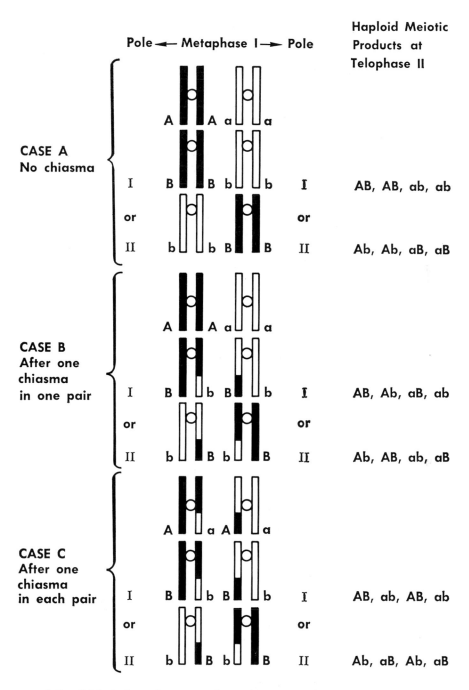

FIGURE 6–7. *Meiotic fate of gene pairs located in nonhomologous chromosomes.*

equally frequent types of gametes at the end of meiosis. The same result is also obtained either when there is a chiasma between the centromere and the gene in question in one tetrad but not the other (Case B), or when a chiasma occurs in each of the tetrads (Case C). Therefore, independent segregation of different pairs of chromosomes can serve as the physical basis for independent segregation of different pairs of genes, regardless of chiasma formation.

Let us examine, now, the consequences of assuming that *A* and *B* are on one and the same chromosome while *a* and *b* are on the homologous chromosome of the pair (Figure 6–8). When there is no chiasma, Case A, only the old (maternal and paternal) combinations are found in the gametes. When there is a chiasma between the two different pairs of genes, Case B, then all four classes occur with equal frequency (two old and two new combinational types). But, unless every tetrad has a chiasma in the region between linked genes, the number of old gene combinations found among the gametes will exceed the new combinations. Although a tetrad usually contains one or more chiasma, there are numerous points along the chromosome where a chiasma can arise. It would necessitate an additional hypothesis to require that each tetrad have a chiasma within a given interval. Moreover, we have no knowledge as to the genic interval, that is, the distance between genes presumed to be on the same chromosome. Accordingly, we shall neglect, for the time being, the possibility that genes on the same chromosome pair could form old and new combinations with equal frequency — that is, we shall assume that two pairs of genes which do so, and are therefore segregating independently of each other, must be located on different pairs of chromosomes. Evidence that is at least consistent with this presumption is obtained from studies with

FIGURE 6–8. *Meiotic fate of gene pairs located in the same pair of chromosomes.*

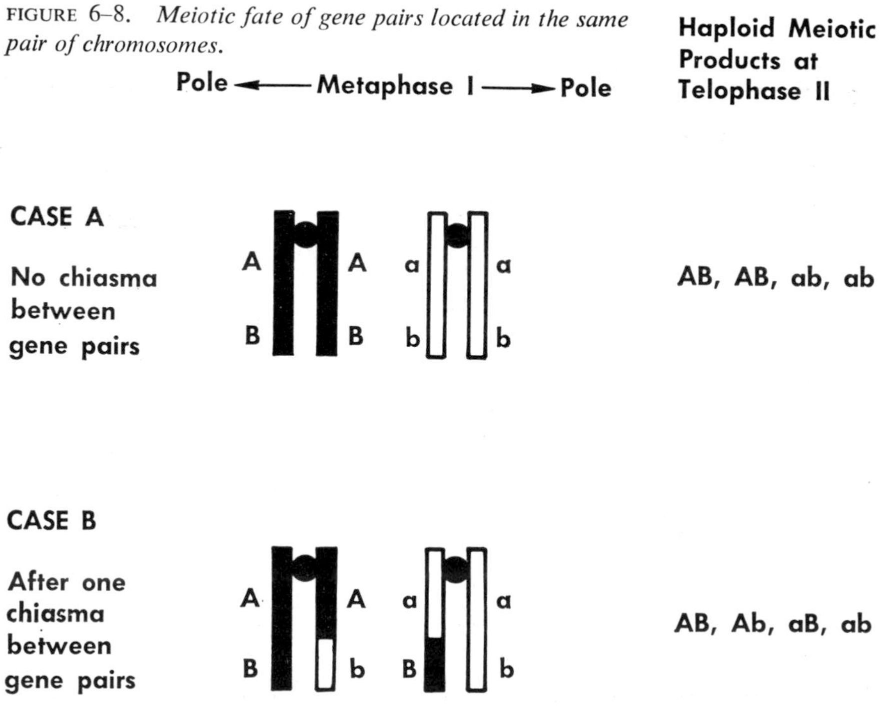

Haploid Meiotic Products at Telophase II

Pole ←——— Metaphase I ———→ Pole

CASE A

No chiasma between gene pairs

AB, AB, ab, ab

CASE B

After one chiasma between gene pairs

AB, Ab, aB, ab

garden peas. From the breeding behavior of hybrids it is possible to establish the existence of seven different pairs of genes (each happening to show dominance in the hybrid condition), each pair segregating independently of all the others. Cytological observation shows that the garden pea possesses a diploid number of seven pairs of chromosomes, so that the number of chromosome pairs is large enough for each pair of genes to be located on a different pair of chromosomes.

SUMMARY AND CONCLUSIONS

When two different traits were studied separately, in each case the phenotypic alternatives were found to be due to the presence of a single pair of genes. Studies were then made of the distribution of phenotypes in successive generations when these two pairs of traits were followed simultaneously in the same individuals.

The data obtained showed that each trait is due to the presence of a different pair of genes, proving that the genetic material is made not of a single indivisible pair of genes but of a number of pairs. The results, moreover, are best explained on the principle that the segregation of one pair of genes is at random with respect to the segregation of all other pairs tested. The simplest hypothesis for the physical basis of independent segregation is that different pairs of genes reside in different pairs of chromosomes.

REFERENCES

Mendel, G. See references at the end of Chapter 2.

Supplement I (at the end of this book).

QUESTIONS FOR DISCUSSION

6.1. Make genetic diagrams for the crosses and progeny discussed in the second paragraph on p. 39. Be sure to define your symbols.

6.2. Is a test cross or backcross used to determine genotypes from phenotypes in cases of no dominance? Explain.

6.3. What types and frequencies of gametes are formed by the following genotypes, all gene pairs segregating independently?

    a. *Aa Bb CC*
    b. *AA BB Cc DD*
    c. *Aa Bb Cc*
    d. *Mm Nn Oo Pp*

6.4. How many different genotypes are possible in offspring from crosses in which both parents are undergoing independent segregation for the following numbers of pairs of heterozygous genes — 1, 2, 3, 4, n?

6.5. What conclusions could you reach about the parents if the offspring had phenotypes in the following proportions?

    a. 3 : 1
    b. 1 : 1
    c. 9 : 3 : 3 : 1
    d. 1 : 1 : 1 : 1

6.6. Would you be justified in concluding that a pair of chromosomes can contain but a single pair of genes? Explain.

6.7. A father of blood group types M and O has a child of MN and B blood types. What genotypes are possible for the mother?

6.8. What proportion of the offspring of the following crosses, involving independent segregation, will be completely homozygous?

a. *Aa Bb* $\times$ *Aa Bb*
b. *AA BB CC* $\times$ *AA bb cc*
c. *Aa BB Cc* $\times$ *AA Bb cc*
d. *AA'* $\times$ *A''A'''*

6.9. Why, following independent segregation, would you expect that gametes fertilize at random with respect to their genotypes?

6.10. Discuss the particulate nature of the genetic material.

6.11. Does the discovery of independent segregation affect your concept of gene size? Explain.

6.12. Discuss your current understanding of the term "genetic recombination."

Chapter 7

GENE INTERACTION
AND PHENOTYPIC EXPRESSION

Y OU ARE already familiar with some of the phenotypic consequences of gene interaction, in that the phenotype of a heterozygote may show the effects of only one allele, or some of the effects of both alleles, or the complete effects of both alleles. These phenotypic consequences have already been called complete, partial, and no dominance, respectively. In the garden pea hybrids already discussed, complete dominance was responsible for the 3:1 phenotypic ratio obtained from crossing two monohybrids. This necessitated the extra labor of testing the offspring possessing the dominant phenotype in order to identify the 1:2:1 genotypic ratio predicted from such crosses. Had no dominance obtained the phenotypic ratio would have been the same as the genotypic one. Nevertheless, in all cases genes were segregating, and the specific ratios observed depended only upon the dominance relation within the gene pair, that is, the relation between the expression of one allele and that of its partner.

You have seen also that complete dominance had no influence upon the independence of the segregation of different pairs of genes within a given individual. The genotypic ratio expected from crossing two particular dihybrids has already been derived (Chapter 6). Let us rederive this ratio, employing more general symbols for genes, for reasons soon to be apparent, using the branching track method in a still slightly

different way. Let A and A' be one pair of alleles and B and B' another. Mating $AA'BB'$ by $AA'BB'$ will give the genotypic ratio shown in Figure 7–1.

Note that among every 16 offspring, on the average, there would be 9 different genotypes: 1 with all unprimed gene symbols, 1 with all primed gene symbols, and 7 others having 3 primed or 3 unprimed or 2 primed gene symbols. Let us re-examine how this genotypic ratio gave rise to the 9:3:3:1 phenotypic ratio in crosses between dihybrid garden peas. Two factors were responsible. One was the occurrence of dominance within each pair of alleles, the other was the fact that the trait determined by one pair of genes was unassociated with the trait determined by the other pair of genes. In what way does the phenotypic ratio expected from crosses between dihybrids for unrelated traits depend upon whether dominance obtains for neither, one, or both pairs of genes? This can be answered with the aid of the left side of Figure 7–2.

In any column in Figure 7–2, boxes filled with the same symbol have identical phenotypes. Note that in DI the genotypic and phenotypic ratios are identical, and that the other D columns have two or more genotypes represented by a single phenotype. DI could be exemplified by the phenotypic expectation from matings between two people both having AB and MN blood types (see Chapter 4). DII could be exemplified by the phenotypic expectation from matings between two people both of MN blood type and heterozygous for albinism (see Chapter 4). We have already discussed DIII in Chapter 6.

It should be recalled that the genes for round-wrinkled and the genes for yellow-green though affecting the same part of a pea plant, the seed, act on different traits — texture and color, there being no obvious relationship between the two. So in this and the other cases under D a particular part

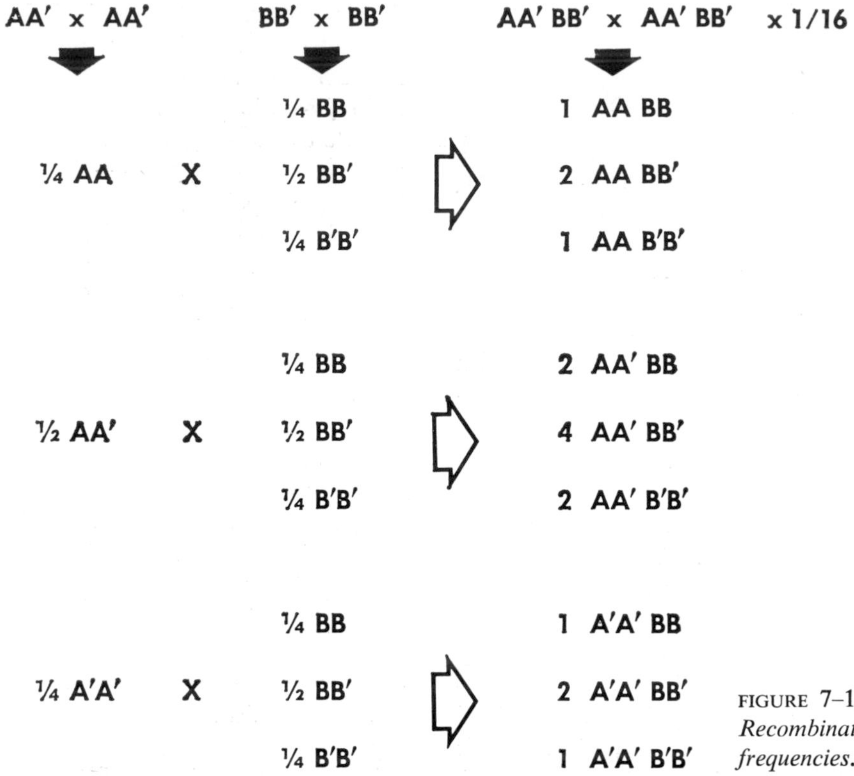

AA′ × AA′   BB′ × BB′   AA′ BB′ × AA′ BB′   × 1/16

⬇   ⬇   ⬇

                ¼ BB   1 AA BB

¼ AA   ×   ½ BB′   ⟹   2 AA BB′

                ¼ B′B′   1 AA B′B′

                ¼ BB   2 AA′ BB

½ AA′   ×   ½ BB′   ⟹   4 AA′ BB′

                ¼ B′B′   2 AA′ B′B′

                ¼ BB   1 A′A′ BB

¼ A′A′   ×   ½ BB′   ⟹   2 A′A′ BB′

                ¼ B′B′   1 A′A′ B′B′

FIGURE 7–1.
*Recombination
frequencies.*

of an organism is capable of showing the presence of any phenotype due to one pair of genes at the same time as it shows any phenotype of another pair. Under D, then, the two pairs of genes produce effects which are independently distinguishable because they do not impose upon each other's expression, i.e., they do not *superpose.*

What phenotypic ratios are expected when the two different pairs of genes affect the same trait in the same direction (Figure 7–2, S)? The ratio in SI would follow if any unprimed gene contributed an equal and cumulative effect on the phenotype, say by forming melanin pigment, the primed genes contributing none of this effect. SII would follow for cumulative effects when *AA*, *AA′*, and *BB′* each produces equal phenotypic effect, say on height, *BB* produces twice this effect,

and *A′A′* and *B′B′* produces none of this effect. SIII would follow if either *A* or *B* gives the full phenotypic effect, say on flower color, only *A′A′ B′B′* producing none of this effect.

In each of the examples under S the ratios obtained were simplifications of the corresponding ratios found under D, due to the fact that different combinations of alleles from two different pairs of genes acting in the same direction gave the same phenotypic effect. In these cases, then, different pairs of genes have a common phenotypic background on which their effects superpose, the effect of one gene interfering with the detection of the effect of the other pair.

What may the phenotypic ratios from crosses between identical dihybrids become, when both pairs of genes show dominance

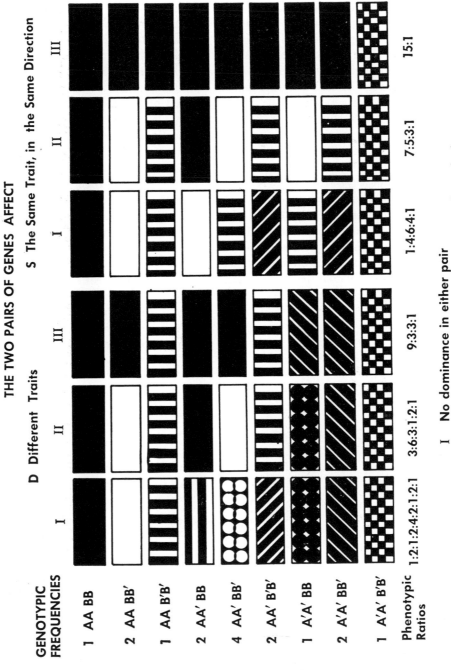

FIGURE 7–2. *Some of the ratios obtainable following crosses between identical dihybrids.*

but act, not in the same direction, but in different, opposite, or antagonistic ways? Suppose, now, both pairs of genes affect the same trait but the effect of one gene pair is completely antagonistic to the detection of the effect of another gene pair. An example of such a unilateral opposition to phenotypic expression occurs in the fruit fly, *Drosophila* (Figure 7–3).[1] A' is a recessive allele which reduces the wing to a stump while B' is a recessive allele which causes the wing to be curled, the dominant allele A making for normal length of wing and the dominant allele B for straightness of the wing. A cross between two identical dihybrids does not produce the customary 9:3:3:1 ratio. In the present case, the ratio becomes 9 flies with long, straight wings : 3 with long, curled wings : 4 flies whose wings are mere stumps (of which one quarter would have had curled wings had the full wing formed). Here, then,

a genotype of one gene pair suppresses the detection of the phenotypes from another gene pair.

In other cases the two pairs of genes may show mutual opposition to phenotypic expression. Suppose the dominant alleles A and B each independently contribute something different but essential for the production of red pigment, whereas their corresponding recessive alleles A' and B' fail to make the respective independent contributions to red pigment production. Then crosses between two identical dihybrids will produce 9 red : 7 nonred (composed of 3 homozygotes for A', 3 homozygotes for B', and 1 homozygote for both A' and B'). Depending upon how you look at it, examples of unilateral opposition to phenotypic expression may also be thought to involve unilateral cooperation, and cases of mutual opposition to involve mutual cooperation.

In all cases where two pairs of genes affect the same trait, whether they interact phenotypically by superposition or by antagonism,

---

[1] References to the genetics of *Drosophila* are given at the end of this Chapter.

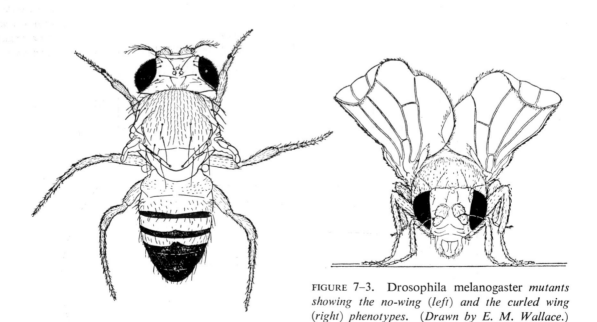

FIGURE 7–3. Drosophila melanogaster *mutants showing the no-wing (left) and the curled wing (right) phenotypes. (Drawn by E. M. Wallace.)*

one pair of genes has had an effect upon distinguishing the effects of the other. The general term *epistasis* may be used in these cases to describe the interference with, suppression or masking of, the phenotypic expression of one pair of genes by the members of a different pair of genes. Genes whose detection is hampered by nonallelic genes are said to be hypostatic, i.e., to exhibit *hypostasis*. As dominance implies recessiveness, so epistasis implies hypostasis. (The term *dominance* is properly used only to describe the masking by one allele of the phenotypic expression of its partner, when this is a different allele.) There need be no relationship between the dominance of a gene to its allele and the ability of the gene to be epistatic to nonallelic genes. So, in theory, epistatic action may depend upon the presence of A, or A', or AA'; moreover, hypostatic reactions may depend upon the presence of B, or B', or BB'. In view of this, it should be noted that in crosses between identical dihybrids, epistasis-hypostasis can produce phenotypic ratios that are still different from those already described.

Consider yet another example of a dihybrid in which both pairs of genes show dominance but no epistasis. Specifically, as found in *Drosophila*, the dull red eye color of flies caught in nature is due to the presence of both brown and red pigments. Let A be the allele which produces the red pigment and A' its recessive allele which produces no red pigment; let B be another gene producing the brown pigment whose allele B' fails to make brown pigment. A mating between two dull red dihybrid flies (from a cross of pure brown by pure red) will produce offspring which are in the proportion 9 dull red (containing AB) : 3 red (containing $AB'B'$) : 3 brown (containing $A'A'B$) : 1 white (containing $A'A'B'B'$). The latter phenotypic class is new to the cross, resulting, so to speak, from the additive subtraction of both eye pigments. This case illustrates that not only may non-allelic genes act upon different traits, or upon the same trait in the same or a different manner, but that their interaction may result in *apparently novel phenotypes*. The latter interactions do not change the number of phenotypes obtained, but change their nature.

A slightly more complex illustration of apparently novel phenotypes comes from crossing certain fowl (Figure 7–4). An individual, from a pure line of "rose" combs is mated with another individual from a pure line of "pea" combs. All the F_1 show "walnut" combs. Crosses of two F_1 "walnut" type individuals provides F_2 which occur in the ratio 9 "walnut" (AB) : 3 "rose" ($AB'B'$) : 3 "pea" ($A'A'B$) : 1 "single" ($A'A'B'B'$). The newly appearing single proves to be the double recessive; pea is homozygous recessive for one pair of genes but not the other; rose is the recessive type reciprocal to pea; while walnut is homozygous recessive for neither pair of genes.

In view of the present discussion, it seems that any given phenotypic trait may be the result of the cooperative or opposing interaction of several gene pairs acting directly, and of all other gene pairs acting indirectly. We are led to suppose, therefore, that the total phenotype is the product of the total genotype acting together with the environment. Two other generalizations may be made. First, dominance and epistasis cause phenotypic ratios to deviate from genotypic ratios. The occurrence of the one and/or the other results in a reduction in number of phenotypic classes. It should not be implied that modifications of ratios result from direct effects of one gene upon another, but rather that the changed ratios result from conflicting gene effects at the physiological or biochemical level. Something of the nature of such conflicts can be predicted in a general way from the kind of modified ratio obtained. Second, in no case does a modified phenotypic ratio serve to disprove the validity of either segregation or independent segregation, since

ROSE COMB

PEA COMB

WALNUT COMB

SINGLE COMB

FIGURE 7–4. *Comb types in chickens.*

phenotypic expression, and not genotypic recombination, is tested by phenotypes. In fact it is true that segregation and independent segregation were first proven despite the misleading phenotypic simplifications wrought by the occurrence of dominance, and that the principle of independent segregation could also have been first proven from crosses involving epistasis or apparently novel phenotypes.

SUMMARY AND CONCLUSIONS

The phenotypic expression of genes depends upon their alleles, insofar as dominance is involved, and upon nonalleles, insofar as epistasis (including superposition and antagonism) and the production of apparently novel phenotypes are involved. The absence both of dominance and epistasis will always produce phenotypic ratios which directly represent genotypic ratios, whereas the occurrence of one, the other, or both reduces the number of phenotypic classes. In any case, segregation and independent segregation, being genic properties, are totally uninfluenced by the manner whereby genes do or do not come to phenotypic expression.

REFERENCES

Bateson, W., *Mendel's Principles of Heredity*, Cambridge, England, Cambridge University Press, 1909.

Bibliography on the Genetics of Drosophila: Part I by H. J. Muller (Edinburgh, Oliver and Boyd, 1939, 132 pp.). Parts II and III by I. H. Herskowitz (Oxford, Alden Press, 1953, 212 pp., and Bloomington, Indiana University Press, 1958, 296 pp., respectively).

WILLIAM BATESON (*1861–1926*).
(*By permission of Genetics, Inc., vol. 12, p. 1, 1927.*)

QUESTIONS FOR DISCUSSION

7.1. Does this Chapter present any new information about genetic recombination? Explain.

7.2. What is the maximum number of genotypes possible in the progeny if the parents are monohybrids?

7.3. Two green corn plants when crossed produce offspring of which approximately $\frac{9}{16}$ are green and $\frac{7}{16}$ are white. How can you explain these results?

7.4. Does genic interaction occur only when identical monohybrids (or identical dihybrids) are crossed? Explain.

7.5. Three walnut-combed chickens were crossed to single-combed individuals. In one case the progeny were all walnut-combed. In another case one of the progeny was single-combed. In the third case the progeny were either walnut- or pea-combed. Give the genotypes of all parents and offspring mentioned.

7.6. Would you expect to find epistasis in man in marriages involving genetic alternatives:

        a. For woolly hair and for baldness?
        b. For brown eyes and for albinism?
        c. For baldness and for brown eyes?
        d. For ABO blood type and for MN blood type?

7.7. When two plants are crossed it is found that $\frac{63}{64}$ of the progeny are phenotypically like the parents, while $\frac{1}{64}$ of the progeny are different from either parent but resemble each other. Give a genetic explanation for this.

7.8. Suppose two unrelated albinos married and had eight children, four albino and four nonalbino. How could you explain these results?

Chapter **8**

GENE INTERACTION
AND CONTINUOUS TRAITS

THUS FAR we have been utilizing _discontinuous_ traits to study genes. Such traits occur in clear-cut, qualitatively different alternatives, like flower color in garden peas, albinism vs. pigmentation, or blood types in human beings. In each case an individual belongs clearly to one phenotypic alternative or another. This is the consequence of several factors. First, although the interaction of many or all genes may ultimately be required for a given phenotype to appear, the major contributions to the particular phenotypic alternatives previously considered have been the effect of only one or two pairs of genes. Second, in each case the effect of normal environmental fluctuations resulted either in no effect or in a much smaller effect than had the one or the two pairs of genes with major effects for this trait.

For practical or for theoretical reasons we are also interested in the genetic basis for certain _continuous_ traits, like height of corn, or intelligence in man, in which individuals are not sharply separable into types or classes. Such traits are also called _quantitative_ traits because a continuous range of phenotypes is observed which requires that an individual be measured in order to be scored. Are quantitative traits also determined genically? Let us make the simplest assumption that they differ from qualitative traits only in degree, in that they are _multi-genic_ (_multiple factor, multi-factorial, polygenic_) — that is, that the alternatives involved are due not to

56

a few pairs of genes with large effects, but to many gene pairs, the effect of any single one being difficult to distinguish. Accordingly, since each pair of genes would contribute only slightly toward the expression of the quantitative trait, we would expect that the effect of environment might be relatively larger than that of any single gene. As examples of environmental influence in such cases, the effect of fertilizer upon corn ear size and of diet upon height in human beings can be mentioned.

It may be illuminating to realize that the same trait may be determined in certain respects qualitatively and in other respects quantitatively. Thus, in garden peas one pair of genes may decide whether the plant shall be normal or dwarf, while the actual size of the normal plant will be the result of multi-genic interaction, with the environment playing a significant role. Similarly, a single pair of genes can determine which of these discontinuous alternatives — serious mental deficiency or normality — a human being has, but individuals who are normal have degrees of mental ability which vary in a continuous way.

If our hypothesis is correct, that quantitative traits are determined multi-genically, it ought to be possible to derive other characteristics of the transmission genetics of quantitative characters, consistent with actual observations, by considering the same trait, first as if determined by one or two or three gene pairs (i.e., as a qualitative trait) and, then, as if determined by 10 or more pairs (i.e., as a quantitative trait). Let the trait be color, and the alternatives in P_1 black and white. In all cases let us assume there is no dominance. Then, whether 1, 2, 3, 10, or 20 gene pairs are involved, the F_1 will be uniform and phenotypically intermediate (medium gray) between the two P_1. Examine the results of matings between F_1 (by cross- or self-fertilization) in each case (Figure 8–1). Note that as the number of gene pairs increases the number of classes of F_2 offspring increases. When the number of classes becomes large, environmental action may cause individuals to fall out of their phenotypic class, so to speak, into the space between classes or into an adjacent phenotypic class. In this way classes become numerous, then indiscrete, resulting finally in a continuous range of phenotypes.

Note also that as the number of gene pairs determining the trait increases, the fraction of all F_2 resembling either P_1 becomes smaller. Thus, with one pair of genes ½ of F_2 are either black or white, with two pairs ⅛, with three pairs ¹⁄₃₂, etc. As a consequence of this, as the number of genes increases from 10 to 20, etc., the continuous distribution of phenotypic types forms an F_2 curve which becomes more and more narrow in shape. In other words, the chance of recovering in F_2 any phenotype, a given distance off the mean, decreases as gene pair number increases. While it may be possible to identify whether 1, 2, or 3 gene pairs cause a given character, it is almost impossible to know exactly how many are involved whenever more than 3 are concerned. Nevertheless,

a measure of how the population varies relative to the average phenotype can give information as to the approximate number of genes involved and can be of predictive value also.

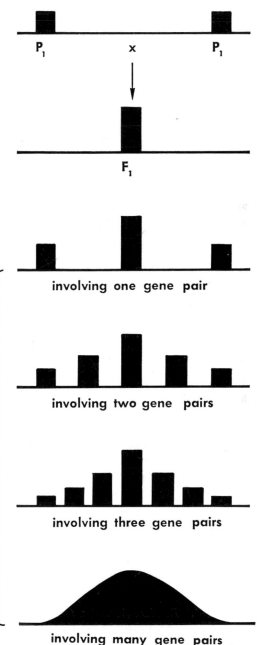

FIGURE 8–1. *Dependence of number of phenotypic classes upon number of gene pairs. Horizontal axis shows classes, vertical axis indicates relative frequencies.*

Measurement of the variability of a trait can be made statistically as follows: the *mean*, *m* (the simple arithmetic average), is found. The *variance*, *v* (the measure of variability), is determined for a group of measurements by determining the difference between each measurement and the mean, squaring this difference in each case, adding all the values obtained, and dividing the total by 1 less than the number of measurements involved. (The square root of *v* is called the *standard deviation*.) With a given sample size, other things being equal, the greater the variance the smaller the number of gene pairs involved. Detailed statistical procedures for utilizing variance may be found in any standard text on elementary statistical methods.

Let us next consider the effect of dominance upon the expression of quantitative traits, as revealed partly by considering its effect on qualitative traits. When a qualitative trait is determined by 1, 2, or 3 pairs of genes not showing dominance, there are, as in Figure 8–1, 3, 5, or 7 possible phenotypic classes, respectively. However, as a result of dominance the number of classes is reduced, as you will recall from the discussion in Chapter 7 and Figure 7–2. Since our estimate of the number of gene pairs responsible for a phenotype is directly connected with the number of phenotypic classes, the number of gene pairs involved in a quantitative trait will be underestimated where there is dominance. This is important since many genes show complete or partial dominance.

In fact, one can construct a hypothetical case where two pairs of genes with dominance can give much the same phenotypic result as one pair with no dominance. Suppose gene *A* (as *AA* or *Aa*) adds 2 units of effect while its recessive allele *a* (as *aa*) adds only 1 unit; suppose *B* (as *BB* or *Bb*) subtracts 1 unit of effect while its recessive allele *b* (as *bb*) has no effect at all. Then a 2-unit individual (*AA bb*) mated with a 0-unit one (*aa BB*) will give all intermediate 1-unit F_1 (*Aa Bb*). The F_2 from the mating of the F_1 can be derived by a branching track shown in Figure 8–2. The phenotypic ratio obtained in F_2 of 3 : 10 : 3 might be, in practice, difficult to distinguish from the 1 : 2 : 1 ratio obtained from crossing monohybrids showing no dominance.

There is a second effect of dominance upon inheritance of quantitative traits which can be illustrated by means of two crosses involving the genes just described. In the first, two 0-unit individuals are crossed, *aa Bb* × *aa Bb*, yielding ¾ *aa B–* (0 unit) and ¼ *aa bb* (1 unit). Here the parents, being at one extreme (0 units), produce offspring which are, on the average, less extreme (0.25 unit). In the second case, two 2-unit individuals are crossed, *Aa bb* × *Aa bb* yielding ¾ *A– bb* (2 units) and ¼ *aa bb* (1 unit). Here the parents are at the other extreme (2 units) but produce offspring which, on the average, are less

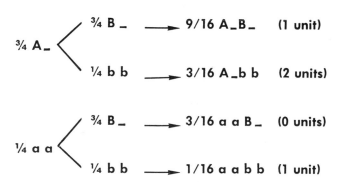

FIGURE 8–2. *Results of crossing together the dihybrids described in the text.*

extreme (1.75 units). These results typify an effect of dominance called *regression,* as a consequence of which an individual phenotypically extreme in either direction will have progeny less extreme.

Figure 8–3 illustrates the principle of regression. Had no dominance obtained the average offspring from parents at A, B, and C would have been at the corresponding points A′, B′, C′, respectively, in the offspring curve. (The environment would have been the cause of some phenotypic fluctuation around these mean points in the offspring curve.) In the case of dominance, however, the offspring of A would be, on the average, to the right of A, as shown by arrows, while the offspring of C would be, on the average, to the left of C. The loss of extreme individuals generation after generation would not make the entire population more and more homogeneous phenotypically, however, since there would be an exactly counterbalancing tendency from the average, C, members of the population to produce offspring more extreme than themselves in either direction. The result, as in cases of no dominance, is that the distribution curve for the offspring would be the same as for the parent population.

Now, suppose a population of individuals showed a quantitative character and we wanted to obtain a line of them which was, on the average, say, larger. We would use the largest individuals as parents (Figure 8–4). Had the genes involved shown no dominance then the very first offspring generation would have the same mean as the group selected as parents. But since dominance usually obtains, regression will occur, and the mean size of the first generation of offspring will be somewhat less than that of the selected parents but somewhat more than the original mean. By continuing to select the largest individuals to serve as parents over a number of generations, the offspring of succeeding generations will approach closer and closer the size of the selected parents.

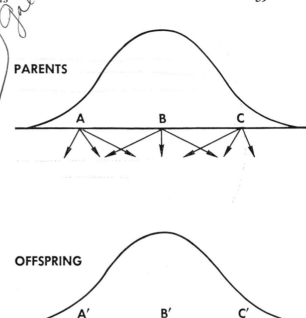

FIGURE 8–3 (*Above*). *The principle of regression.*

FIGURE 8–4 (*Below*). *Selection for a quantitative character.*

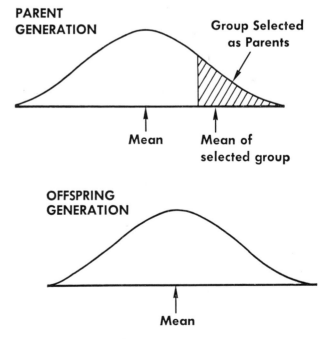

SUMMARY AND CONCLUSIONS

Genes are the basis for both continuous and discontinuous traits. Continuous traits are usually based upon many gene pairs each of which has a phenotypic effect that is small and often matched or exceeded by the action of the environment.

The variability of a quantitative trait is such that the larger the number of genes determining it, the narrower is the distribution curve and the smaller the chance of recovering either of the extreme phenotypes in the offspring. Dominance has the effect of reducing the number of phenotypic classes and of placing proportionally more offspring in extreme classes. Consequently, dominance usually causes the underestimation of the number of genes determining a quantitative trait. Dominance also causes regression, so that only when selection of parents is continued over a number of generations will offspring eventually be obtained which are phenotypically like the parents selected.

REFERENCES

Falconer, D. S., *Introduction to Quantitative Genetics*, New York, Ronald Press, 1961.

Kempthorne, O., *An Introduction to Genetic Statistics*. New York, Wiley, 1957.

Levene, H., "Statistical Inferences in Genetics," in *Principles of Genetics*, 5th Ed., E. W. Sinnott, L. C. Dunn, and Th. Dobzhansky, New York, McGraw-Hill, 1958, Chap. 29, pp. 388–418.

QUESTIONS FOR DISCUSSION

8.1. Do the genes for quantitative traits show epistasis? Explain.

8.2. Does the environment have a more important role in determining the phenotype in cases of quantitative than in cases of qualitative traits? Explain.

8.3. Under what circumstances are only seven phenotypes possible when three pairs of genes determine a quantitative trait?

8.4. Discuss the statement: No new principles of genetics have originated from the study of polygenic traits.

8.5. Suppose each gene with a capital letter causes a plant to grow an additional inch in height, *aa bb cc dd ee* plants being 12 inches tall. Assume independent segregation and parents of the following genotypes: *Aa BB cc Dd EE* × *aa bb CC Dd Ee*.

    a. How tall are the parents?
    b. How tall will the tallest F_1 be?
    c. How tall will the shortest F_1 be?
    d. What proportion of all F_1 will be the shortest?
    e. Is dominance and/or epistasis involved in this system? Explain.

8.6. Assume, in man, that the difference in skin color is due primarily to two pairs of genes which segregate independently: *BB CC* is black, *bb cc* is white, any three genes for black produce dark skin, any two medium skin, and any one produces light skin color. Give the genotypes of parents who are:

    a. Both medium, but have one black and one white child.
    b. Both black but have an albino child.
    c. Both medium and can have only medium children.
    d. Medium and light and have a large number of children:
        ⅜ medium, ⅜ light, ⅛ dark, ⅛ white.

8.7. In selecting for a quantitative trait, is the desired phenotype established in a pure line more easily when dominance does or does not occur? Explain.

8.8. Measure the length of ten lima beans to the nearest millimeter. Calculate the variance of this sample. To what can you attribute this variance?

8.9. Is it of any advantage to an organism to have a trait determined quantitatively, that is, by many gene pairs, rather than qualitatively, that is, by the action principally of one or a few gene pairs? Why?

Chapter 9

MULTIPLE ALLELES AND LETHALS

IN ORDER to explain the transmission genetics of ABO blood group type it was necessary to postulate (Chapter 5) that a gene can exist in any one of several different allelic forms. Many cases are known where the gene may be one of a whole series of different alleles, so that each of these genes forms a *multiple allelic series*.

ABO Blood Group

Human beings can be classified into A, B, AB, and O blood types based upon a series of three alleles, I^A, I^B, i (Chapter 5). Of course, any person carries only any two of these alleles. South American Indians are almost all *ii*. Certain Indian tribes in North America have predominantly A or O blood type. All other populations contain not only these types, but B and AB also. It has been shown that A blood type is really comprised of three different subtypes resulting from slightly different forms of I^A which can be called I^{A1}, I^{A2}, I^{A3}. Three different alternatives are known also for I^B, producing three subtypes within the B blood group. Only one type O is known. (Recently, *i* has been found to produce a unique type of antigen.)

Does it seem confusing that we first said there are three alleles for ABO blood type, and then later stated that there are seven? The number of alleles discovered will depend, of course, upon how carefully or in how much detail one wishes to study phenotypes. Let us imagine that the multiple allelic series under consideration produces pigmentation instead of blood antigens. Let I^{A1}, I^{A2},

I^{A3} produce light, medium, and dark blue pigment, respectively, and I^{B1}, I^{B2}, I^{B3} produce light, medium, and dark green pigment, respectively, all showing no dominance with respect to each other, but all dominant to *i*, which produces no pigment at all. For some purposes we may be perfectly willing to classify individuals with respect to their carrying an allele capable of producing blue, green, or no pigment. In this event we would need to recognize only three alleles. But if we wanted to study more detailed genetic relationships among individuals, or the detailed basis for phenotypes, we would need to recognize all seven alleles. So, for many practical purposes, people are classified just as if the ABO blood group had only three alleles.

It should be recalled that the I^A and I^B alleles produce qualitatively different antigenic effects.

Eye Color in Drosophila

One of the series of multiple alleles which occurs in the fruit fly, *Drosophila*, involves eye color. In this case the different alleles can be arranged in a series that shows a gradation effect on eye color, ranging from dull red to white: *dull red* (w^+), *blood* (w^{bl}), *coral* (w^{co}), *apricot* (w^a), *buff* (w^{bf}), and *white* (w). The w^+ allele is dominant to the others listed, and is the allele commonly found in flies living in nature. (Note that a slightly different system of symbolizing genes is being used here. This and other conventions for the use of symbols are described on p. 111.) You can think of the different alleles as all producing the same kind of phenotypic effect, but less of it in proceeding from w^+ to w, the *white* allele being completely inefficient in this respect.

Coat Color in Rabbits

The multiple allelic series for coat color in rabbits combines properties of both of the allelic series already discussed. On the one hand, there is a gradation effect from full pigmentation to white — *agouti* (*C*), *chinchilla* (*c^{ch}*) and *albino* (*c*). On the other hand, another allele, *c^h*, does not produce a simple dilution in color, but under normal temperature conditions results in a change in coat color pattern to one called Himalayan (already discussed in Chapter 1). The *C* allele is completely dominant to all the others listed, *c^h* is completely dominant to *c*, while *c^{ch}* is only partly dominant to *c^h* or *c*.

Self-sterility in Nicotiana

Among sexually reproducing plants it is not uncommon to find that self-fertilization does not occur even though the male and female gametes are produced at the same time on a given plant. The reason for this has been studied in tobacco, *Nicotiana*, where it was found that if pollen grains (which will furnish the male gametes) fall on the stigma of the same plant, they fail to grow down the style. The inability of pollen to grow will mean that the male gametes will fail to reach the ovary (which furnishes the female gametes), so that self-fertilization is prevented, and self-sterility ensues. The clue to the explanation for this phenomenon comes from the observation that different percentages of pollen from a completely self-sterile plant may grow down the style of other plants.

The results of certain crosses are shown in Figure 9–1. Genetically identical pistils were exposed to pollen from the same plant (A), from a second plant (B), and from a third one (C). No pollen, approximately half, and

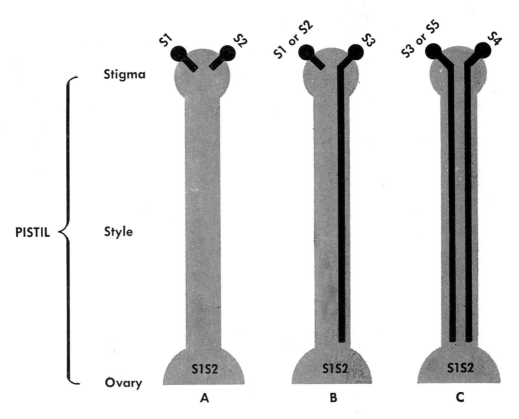

FIGURE 9–1. *Multiple alleles for cross- or self-sterility.*

approximately all, respectively, were able to grow down the style of the host. Note, in B, that although all the pollen used came from one diploid individual, half of it could and half of it could not grow on its host. It is known that the stigma and style are diploid tissues, while pollen grains are haploid. These results suggest that what is important in determining whether or not a pollen grain can grow down a style is not the diploid genotype of its parent, but the haploid genotype contained in itself.

Let us assume that self- or cross-sterility is due to a single pair of genes. Call $s3$ the allele contained in the pollen which permits pollen to grow in case B. The pollen grains from the host plant furnishing the pistil cannot contain $s3$ or the pollen would be able to grow on their own parent, and they cannot (case A). So, host pistil tissue in this experiment cannot contain $s3$, and one of its alleles can be called $s1$. Then, half of the pollen from the host individual will carry $s1$ (case A); but since these failed to grow, we must assume that any pollen grain carrying an s allele also present in the host pistil will fail to grow. Ignoring mutation, the other allele in the host pistil cannot be $s1$, too, since one $s1$ would have had to be received from a paternal pollen grain growing down a maternal style that carried $s1$ as one of its two alleles. Since the second allele in the pistils illustrated cannot be either $s1$ or $s3$, let us call it $s2$. So, the other half of pollen from the pistil parent will contain $s2$, and also fail to grow in self-pollination (case A). In B the pollen grains which fail to grow are either $s1$ or $s2$, employing the law of parsimony, but which they are cannot be determined without additional tests. In C, since all the pollen grew, one pollen allele must be a different one, call it $s4$; the other pollen allele may be $s3$ or a still different one, $s5$, and a decision on this requires additional tests.

In these cases the phenotypic alternatives

for pollen are to grow or not to grow. Whenever the pollen grains from any one plant are placed on a given stigma and both alternatives occur, the phenotypes form a 1 : 1 ratio. All these results and others are consistent with the assumptions made, that self- or cross-sterility is regulated by a single pair of genes which form a multiple allelic series. Some species have fifty or more multiple alleles forming a series responsible for self-sterility, or group sterility, or group incompatibility.

Wing Venation in Drosophila

In different wild populations of *Drosophila*, which we may designate as 1, 2, and 3, the venation on the wings is complete and identical, and when all possible hybrids are made between these populations, the venation remains unchanged. This result would suggest that all three populations are genotypically identical in this respect. On the other hand, there is a mutant strain in which the venation is incomplete, the cubitus vein being interrupted (*ci = cubitus interruptus*) in homozygotes (Figure 9–2). Hybrids, formed by crosses between *ci* and wild populations 1 or 2, are found to have complete venation, so that the gene for normal venation, ci^+, in

FIGURE 9–2. *Normal (a) and cubitus interruptus (b) wings of* Drosophila melanogaster. *(Courtesy of C. Stern; by permission of Genetics, Inc., vol. 28, p. 443, 1943.)*

these populations is completely dominant to *ci*. But the hybrid of *ci* with wild flies from population 3, $ci^{+3} ci$, shows the cubitus vein interrupted! Moreover, the lack of dominance of ci^{+3} over *ci* can be shown to be an effect of this gene pair rather than a modifying effect of some other gene pair. Apparently, then, the ci^+ allele in population 3 is different from the one in populations 1 and 2. Thus, alleles which at first seem alike may prove to be different when tested further. Such alleles are said to be *isoalleles*. Some other techniques which may be employed to detect isoalleles include the response of the tested alleles to the presence of nonallelic genes, to environmental changes as of temperature and humidity, and to agents which modify mutation rates. The number of alleles that can be proven isoallelic will depend upon how many different phenotypic criteria you employ to compare alleles, and how small a phenotypic difference you are able to recognize. The more delicate the tests and the larger their number, the greater is the chance for demonstrating isoallelism.

Although we have described isoalleles among the genes normally expressed in individuals living in the wild (wild type isoalleles), there are also isoalleles for mutant genes (mutant isoalleles). For instance, it has been proven that the mutant gene *w*, producing white eye in different strains of *Drosophila*, actually comprises a series of multiple isoalleles (w^1, w^2, w^3, etc.).

Lethals

In the snapdragon (*Antirrhinum*) one can find two kinds of full grown plants, those which are green and those which are a paler green called auria. Green crossed by green produces only green, but auria by auria produces seedlings of which 25% are green (AA), 50% auria (Aa), and 25% white (aa). The latter die, after exhausting the food in the seed from which they grew, because they lack chlorophyll and cannot synthesize food. So,

among the grown plants, the phenotypic ratio observed is ⅓ green : ⅔ auria. In this case, then, lack of dominance gives a 1 : 2 : 1 ratio among seedlings, characteristic of a cross between monohybrids, which because of lethality becomes a 2 : 1 ratio among the older survivors.

These ratios were discovered in the reverse order in a case in mice. In this case, in which genetic lethality was first demonstrated, crosses between two yellow mice never gave all yellow progeny, but always gave 2 yellow : 1 nonyellow. It was then shown that from such matings ¼ of the fertilized eggs which should have completed development failed to do so and aborted early. Those dying were clearly the homozygotes of one type, with nonyellows being the other homozygous type, since crosses between nonyellows produced only nonyellows. Note that the gene symbols usually employed will not be satisfactory here. For now we have two effects to describe for each gene — one effect on color and one on viability. Moreover, the allele which is dominant for the one effect is recessive for the other, and vice versa. This problem is solved by using base letters with superscripts for each gene (Figure 9–3), where the base letter refers to one trait and the superscript refers to the other trait. Let the superscript *l* be the recessive lethal effect of the gene dominant for yellow, *Y*, and *L* be the superscript for the dominant normal viability of the allele recessive for nonyellow, *y*. Then the F_1 from crossing two yellow mice ($Y^l y^L \times Y^l y^L$) are 1 $Y^l Y^l$ (dies) : 2 $Y^l y^L$ (yellow) : 1 $y^L y^L$ (nonyellow).

In both the snapdragon and mouse cases described, death resulted from the presence of an allele in homozygous condition. Those alleles which kill the individual before it can reproduce are called *lethal genes* or *lethals* — those producing this effect only when homozygous are *recessive lethals*, while those acting this way when heterozygous are *dominant lethals*.

P_1 **yellow**   **x**   **yellow**

         $Y^I \, y^L$ $Y^I \, y^L$

G_1 $\frac{1}{2}Y^I \, , \, \frac{1}{2}y^L$ $\frac{1}{2}Y^I \, , \, \frac{1}{2}y^L$

F_1 $\left[\begin{array}{c} \frac{1}{4}Y^IY^I \\ \textbf{dies} \end{array}\right]$ $\begin{array}{c} \frac{1}{2}Y^Iy^L \\ \textbf{yellow} \end{array}$ $\begin{array}{c} \frac{1}{4}y^L\,y^L \\ \textbf{nonyellow} \end{array}$ FIGURE 9–3. *Results of matings between yellow mice.*

From the biological standpoint, lethality is characterized not by the absence of an individual or a class of offspring, but by its inability to reproduce. So, for example, a genotype which causes complete sterility is genically lethal, even should its possessor live forever. Lethals which actually kill the organism may act very early or very late in development, or at any stage in between. Sometimes a lethal effect is produced not by one gene or a pair, but by the combined effect of several nonallelic genes. In this case, some of the nonalleles are contributed by each parent, and the offspring dies because the nonalleles, viable when separate, are lethal when present together.

Different alleles, recessive or dominant, have been shown to affect viability to different degrees. These effects cover the entire spectrum — ranging from those which are lethal, to those which are greatly or slightly detrimental, to those which are apparently neutral or even beneficial (Figure 9–4). When there is differential viability for different nonalleles or alleles, phenotypic ratios may be significantly modified from those expected. The importance of the precautions to be taken, relative to the viability and fertility of the individuals bred in experiments designed to establish principles of transmission genetics, has been discussed in Chapter 2, and is by now obvious.

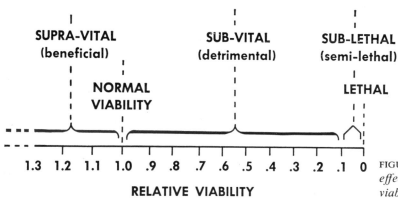

FIGURE 9–4. *Classification of effects that mutants have on viability.*

SUMMARY AND CONCLUSIONS

The different alternative states which a gene may assume in a multiple allelic series may produce different degrees of effect upon a quantitative phenotypic result, or may involve apparently different qualitative effects, or both. Dominance is absent when the alleles in the hybrid produce qualitatively different effects, and may or may not obtain when purely quantitative effects are involved.

The establishment of isoallelism in any given case is largely a matter of the precision and variety of the testing procedures employed. Different alleles may produce detectable differences upon viability by acting at any stage in the life history of individuals, and may modify the expected phenotypic ratio so that certain classes of offspring are in excess, or in reduced frequency, or are absent. The effect mentioned last is produced by dominant and (homozygous) recessive lethal genes.

REFERENCES

Hadorn, E., *Developmental Genetics and Lethal Factors*, New York, Wiley, 1961.

Race, R. R., and Sanger, R., *Blood Groups in Man*, 3rd Ed., Springfield, Ill., C. C. Thomas, 1959.

Wiener, A. S., and Wexler, I. B., *Heredity of the Blood Groups*, New York, Grune & Stratton, 1958.

QUESTIONS FOR DISCUSSION

9.1. How would you prove that you were dealing with multiple alleles, rather than multiple pairs of genes?

9.2. How many different genotypes are possible when there are four different alleles of a single gene?

9.3. Does the discussion in the text imply that: (a) there is an infinite variety of isoalleles? (b) no two genes are ever identical? Explain.

9.4. Describe how you would proceed to test whether the genes for white eye in two different populations of *Drosophila* were alleles, isoalleles, or nonalleles.

9.5. An agouti rabbit crossed to a chinchilla rabbit produced an agouti offspring. What genotypic and phenotypic results would you expect from crossing the F_1 agouti with an albino?

9.6. For each of the following matings involving *Nicotiana* give the percentage of aborted pollen tubes and the genotypes of the offspring.

$$\begin{array}{ccc} & \male & \female \\ \text{a.} & s1\ s2 & \times\ s1\ s3 \\ \text{b.} & s1\ s3 & \times\ s2\ s4 \\ \text{c.} & s1\ s4 & \times\ s1\ s4 \\ \text{d.} & s3\ s4 & \times\ s2\ s3 \end{array}$$

9.7. Two curly-winged stubble-bristled *Drosophila* are mated. Among a large number of adult progeny scored there are 4 curly stubble : 2 curly only : 2 stubble only : 1 neither curly nor stubble (which were therefore normal, wild-type). Explain these results genetically.

9.8. Could you prove the existence of multiple allelism in an organism that reproduces asexually only? Explain.

9.9. Discuss the factors which can modify the expected phenotypic ratio.

Chapter 10

PLEIOTROPISM,
PENETRANCE AND EXPRESSIVITY

Pleiotropism

HOW MANY phenotypic effects does a gene have? In comparing the phenotypes of two genetically different lines of rabbits, one chinchilla ($c^{ch}c^{ch}$) and one white (cc) there is only one apparent phenotypic difference — the presence vs. the absence of coat pigment. Saying that the c^{ch} gene has many effects — to produce pigment on the ears, on the trunk, on the limbs, on the tail, and to produce no pigment in the intestine, none in the pancreas, etc., complicates the description without adding any more meaning. In the case of Himalayan rabbits ($c^{h}c^{h}$), the coat itself is usually variegated, being black at the extremities and white elsewhere (Chapters 1 and 9). Does that mean this allele has a different kind of action in different parts of the coat? No. For the pigment differences are attributed rather to the effect of temperature upon the action (at less than 34° C) or inaction (at more than 34° C) of an enzyme, produced by this genotype, which transforms nonpigmented into pigmented material. Thus, where the body temperature is less than 34° C, as it is at the extremities, pigment is produced, while on the warm parts of the body no pigment is formed because of heat inactivation of this enzyme. The Himalayan pattern is attributed, then, to an allele whose single effect is modified by differences in the environment.

In discussing the MN blood groups (Chapter 5), it was stated that M produces M antigen while M' produces N antigen. In this case

it might be thought first that the gene has two effects, since one allele produces M but not N antigen and the other produces N but not M antigen. But, again, the lack of an effect cannot be counted as an effect, and it is simpler to think of this gene as having the ability to produce a single antigen whose specific nature depends upon the particular allele that is present. This, then, is a case in which one trait may be affected in different qualitative ways. In Chapter 9 we discussed a multiple allelic series for eye color in *Drosophila*. There also we were dealing with one trait, in that case eye color pigment, different alleles affecting it in an apparently quantitative manner. In the last Chapter we also considered a case of inheritance in the snapdragon. But there again we were dealing not with two different effects of a gene, one on pigmentation and the other on viability, but rather on the single activity, chlorophyll production, which had lethality as the consequence of its failure.

The question posed refers then to whether or not a gene has effects upon two or more traits which are apparently independent of, or unrelated to, each other in their origin. Such effects of a gene we can call *multiple, manifold, or pleiotropic effects*.

None of the examples just mentioned dealt with such multiple effects. However, we have already discussed a case which seems to fulfill these requirements. This is the case of the yellow mouse. The allele which produces yellow coat color as a dominant effect also has a recessive lethal effect. On the presumption that homozygotes for this allele would have had yellow body color had they survived, and on the basis that there is no obvious relation between coat color and viability, it could be concluded that this is a case where the gene shows pleiotropism.

Studies have been made to test the idea that, in general, genes are pleiotropic. The procedure in one of these studies [1] was as

[1] Based upon Th. Dobzhansky's work.

68

follows: two strains of *Drosophila* were obtained that were practically identical genetically (isogenic) except that one was pure for the gene for *dull red eye color* (w⁺) and the other was pure for its allele *white* (w). Then some other trait was chosen for examination in these two strains, a trait which is apparently unconnected with that for color of eyes. The trait selected was the shape of an organ, located internally, called a spermatheca, which is found in females and is used to store the sperm that they receive. The ratio of the diameter to the height of this organ was determined for the two strains. This index of shape was found to be significantly different in the dull red as compared to the white strain. From this result it can be concluded that the eye color gene studied is pleiotropic. The results of other studies have shown that many different genes are morphologically pleiotropic.

Another example [2] may be taken from *Drosophila*. There is a recessive lethal gene

[2] Based upon E. Hadorn's work.

called *lethal-translucida* which causes pupae to become translucent and die. Using suitable techniques, it is possible to compare the kinds and amounts of chemical substances in the blood fluid of normal larvae and pupae, with those found in the recessive lethal homozygotes (Figure 10–1). When this is done, some substances are found to be equal in amount in both genotypes (peptide III), others are more abundant in the lethal than in the normal individual (peptide I, peptide II, and proline), still others are less abundant (glutamine) or absent (cystine) in the lethal. This case illustrates that pleiotropism can occur at the biochemical level.

One of the most instructive studies of pleiotropism involves the genetic disease in man called sickle cell anemia. Homozygotes for a certain allele show the following different effects, either singly or in any combination: anemia, enlarged spleen, heart trouble, paralysis from brain damage, kidney trouble, and skin lesions. As a consequence, homozygotes for the gene for sickling usually die

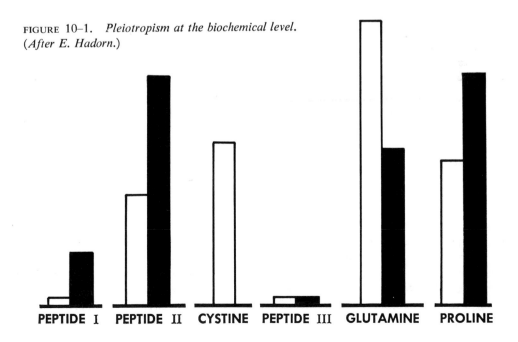

FIGURE 10–1. *Pleiotropism at the biochemical level.* (*After E. Hadorn.*)

PEPTIDE I   PEPTIDE II   CYSTINE   PEPTIDE III   GLUTAMINE   PROLINE

as adolescents or young adults; this allele, therefore, almost always functions as a recessive lethal.

It is found that the red blood cells of these homozygotes may become sickle-shaped instead of being disc-shaped (Figure 10–2). Sickle-shaped cells may clump and clog blood vessels in various parts of the body leading to the malfunctions of all the organs already mentioned; in addition, since these corpuscles are defective, they are destroyed by the body, which as a consequence becomes anemic.

We see, then, that the wide variety of apparently unrelated phenotypic effects of the gene for sickling are but consequences of the sickling of red blood cells. Moreover, studies at the biochemical level show that the sickling behavior itself is the result of the presence of an abnormal type of hemoglobin which sickle cell homozygotes carry in their red blood cells. There is, then, a *pedigree of causes* for the multiple effects of the gene for sickling. The first cause is the gene, the second is the abnormal hemoglobin it produces, the third is the sickling that follows, the fourth is the subsequent red cell clumping and destruction which produce gross organic defects and anemia.

In this case all the multiple effects of the gene are attributed to a *single or unitary effect which is of a biochemical, perhaps enzymatic, nature*. This single effect then affects many varied chemical reactions which are involved in the production of different, at first apparently unrelated, traits. We may even hypothesize that most, if not all, genes have a single primary phenotypic effect. It may yet be found that the pleiotropic effects described in the mouse and *Drosophila* are tertiary or even further removed effects in a pedigree of causes, whose primary cause is genic and whose single secondary cause is still undetermined. Replying to the question with which this section started, the simplest hypothesis is that most, if not all, genes have *one primary phenotypic effect* following which a *pedigree of causes* ends in *pleiotropism*.

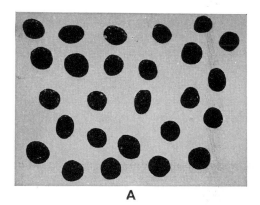

A

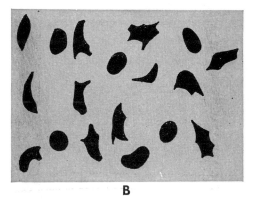

B

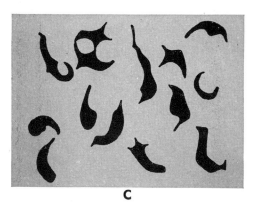

C

FIGURE 10–2. *Silhouettes showing various types of human red blood cells: normal, in normal homozygote (A), sickle cell trait, in mutant heterozygote (B), sickle cell disease, in mutant homozygote (C).*

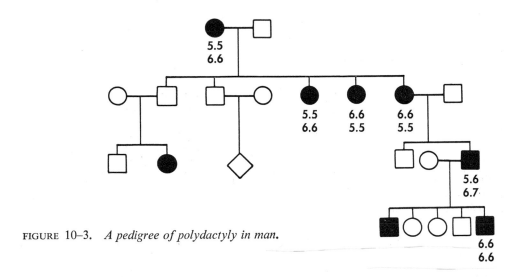

FIGURE 10–3. *A pedigree of polydactyly in man.*

Penetrance and Expressivity

One of the reasons for the ease with which the principles of transmission genetics were established is the fact that each of the genotypes used expressed itself repeatedly in approximately the same way, despite the normal fluctuations of the environment. We shall refer to the ability of a genotype or of its parts to be expressed phenotypically in one way or another as *penetrance*. Most genes studied up to now are fully penetrant.

Consider a pedigree for *polydactyly* (Figure 10–3), a rare condition in human beings in which individuals may have more than five digits on a limb. The topmost female was affected, having five fingers on each hand, but six toes on each foot. Her husband was normal with respect to this trait. This couple had five children, of whom three were affected. This result suggests that polydactyly is due to a single dominant gene, *P*, so that the parents would be, then, mother *Pp*, father *pp*. Consistent with this hypothesis is the result of the marriage of one of their affected daughters to a normal man which produced two sons, one of whom was affected, and this affected son, in turn, had five children including some affected and some unaffected.

But examine now the left side of this pedigree. Shown here is the first-born son who was unaffected, yet had an affected daughter. How may this be explained? It might be supposed that this son was genotypically *pp* and that his daughter was a mutant individual, *Pp*, derived from an egg or a sperm in which the *p* gene underwent mutation to the *P* allele. The following reasoning argues against this interpretation, however. It was noted already that polydactyly is rare, so that mutations from *p* to *P* must be still more rare. Therefore, the chance that such a mutation will occur in a sex cell of one of two normal parents in this pedigree is very small. Examination of other pedigrees for polydactyly also reveals other cases in which two normal individuals have an affected child. It is extremely improbable, then, that such a rare mutation, if it occurs at random among normal individuals, would occur so often among the normal ones in polydactyly pedigrees.

A different explanation is that the first-born son was in fact *Pp* but that the *P* was not penetrant in him, though it was in his daughter. This interpretation is supported by the kind of expression the *P* gene produced in the affected individuals in this pedigree. These individuals may have the normal number of fingers but have extra toes, or they may have the reverse; they may have different numbers of toes on the two feet, or they may have extra fingers on one hand and the normal number on the other. The expression of polydactyly, so far as the number of extra digits is concerned, is clearly quite variable. Accordingly, since it is possible to have no expression on one limb of an individual known to be *Pp* it must also occur that, on occasion, expression fails on all four limbs of an individual with this genotype.

The *P* gene, therefore, has a penetrance of less than 100%, sometimes failing to produce any detectable phenotypic effect when present. So, while a polydactylous person is certain to carry *P*, a normal phenotype can represent either the *Pp* or *pp* genotype. Since polydactyly is rare it is usually quite safe to score as *pp* the genotype of a normal individual who marries into a line of descent containing *P*.

It has already been mentioned that the way that *P* is expressed in an individual is quite variable with respect to the number and position of extra digits. Further variability of expression is demonstrated by the different degrees of development which the extra digits show. The term *expressivity* is used to refer to the kind of effect produced by a genotype when it is penetrant. So, in individuals where *P* is nonpenetrant there is no expressivity, and when *P* is penetrant its expressivity is variable.

What factors are involved in the production of variable penetrance, or, in cases of penetrance, of variable expressivity? A study of a genetically uniform line of guinea pigs showed that polydactyly occurred more frequently in the litters from younger than from older mothers. In this case the physiological changes accompanying age modified penetrance. In another case, a genetically uniform line of *Drosophila* flies showed a greater

per cent of penetrance of an abnormal abdomen phenotype when moisture content during development was high than when it was low. These are both examples of how variations in penetrance can be produced by variations in the environment of different individuals of essentially identical genotype.

You are already familar with the effect of variations in genotype upon penetrance, under essentially constant environmental conditions. Remember that the penetrance of an allele may depend upon the nature of its partner allele in cases of complete or partial dominance, and that the penetrance of one or a pair of alleles may be modified by its epistatic-hypostatic relations to nonallelic genes (Chapter 7). Similarly, it can be shown that variable expressivity may be the consequence of differences in either or both the environment and the genotype.

Several additional points should be made. The terms *penetrance* and *expressivity* were used to compare the phenotypic events which occur in different individuals. That is, once any phenotypic expression occurred within an individual, the genotype was said to be penetrant, and all other phenotypic comparisons between penetrant individuals were considered matters of expressivity. In fact, however, one can also correctly speak about penetrance within an individual in those cases where the particular genotype has two or more occasions to express itself. Thus, for example, the gene for polydactyly has two apparently equal chances to be penetrant in the case of the hands, and two apparently equal chances to be penetrant in the case of the feet. So the genotype may be penetrant in one hand (six fingers) and not in the other (five fingers), it may be penetrant in the feet (6.6) and not in the hands (5.5). When differences in penetrance (or expressivity) are shown by essentially duplicate parts of the same individual (one hand having seven and the other six digits, or one hand having one large extra digit and the other, one small extra one), you can be reasonably certain that these differences have an environmental and not a genetic basis. However, when different individuals are compared with respect to penetrance or expressivity, it is often impossible to attribute, with assurance, similarities or differences among them to genotype or to environment, if both of these factors are varying in uncontrolled ways (as already discussed in Chapter 1).

SUMMARY AND CONCLUSIONS

A gene usually produces effects upon a wide variety of morphological and biochemical traits. These pleiotropic effects are the consequence of a pedigree of causes traceable, in some cases, to a single effect on the part of the gene. It is hypothesized that most, if not all, genes have a single primary phenotypic effect of a biochemical nature.

Penetrance and expressivity depend upon both the genotype and the environment. The most practicable traits for the study of transmission genetics are those whose penetrance is 100% and whose expressivity is uniform when subjected to the normal variations of environment.

REFERENCES

Dobzhansky, Th., and Holtz, A. M., "A Re-examination of Manifold Effects of Genes in *Drosophila melanogaster*," Genetics, 28:295–303, 1943.

Hadorn, E., "Patterns of Development and Biochemical Pleiotropy," Cold Spring Harbor Symp. on Quant. Biol., 21:363–374, 1956.

Goldschmidt, R. B., *Theoretical Genetics*, Berkeley and Los Angeles, University of California, 1955.

QUESTIONS FOR DISCUSSION

10.1. In what respects are the terms penetrance and dominance similar and in what respects are they different?

10.2. Is it the gene for dull red eye color which is pleiotropic in *Drosophila*, or is it the allele for white eye color? Explain.

10.3. Most of the genes studied in *Drosophila* affect the exoskeleton of the fly. Do you suppose these genes also have effects on the internal organs? Why?

10.4. Would you expect to find individuals that are homozygous for polydactyly? Explain. What phenotype would you expect them to have? Why?

10.5. Why are genes whose penetrance is 100% and expressivity is uniform particularly valuable in a study of gene properties?

10.6. Two normal people marry and have a single child who is polydactylous on one hand only. How can you explain this?

10.7. A certain type of baldness is due to a gene which is dominant in men and recessive in women. A nonbald man marries a bald woman and they have a bald son. Give the genotypes of all individuals and discuss the penetrance of the genes involved.

10.8. A man has one brown eye and one blue eye. Explain.

10.9. How could you distinguish whether a given phenotype was due to a rare dominant gene with complete penetrance or a rare recessive gene of low penetrance?

Chapter **11**

STUDIES OF HUMAN TWINS

IN THE preceding Chapter it was concluded that, in general, penetrance and expressivity may be modified by the environment or by the genotype, or both. In organisms other than man, it is possible to standardize conditions experimentally, so that a standard genotype exposed to different environments would show to what extent environment was responsible for phenotypic variability, whereas a standard environment to which different genotypes were exposed would reveal to what extent these genotypes produced different phenotypes (cf. p. 6). Since neither the environment nor the genotypes of human beings are subject to experimental control, the question may be asked, how can it be determined to what extent a particular human trait is controlled by genotype (nature) and by environment (nurture)? Fortunately, this nature-nurture problem can be studied using the results of certain naturally occurring experiments. What are these?

An individual contains many different parts, all of which can be presumed to have the identical genotype. Accordingly, as mentioned in the last Chapter, one can attribute to nurture any phenotypic differences in expressivity or penetrance found among parts which are essentially duplicates of each other. So, for example, a polydactyly heterozygote with six fingers on one hand and five on the other illustrates the extent to which environment can affect this trait. When, however, a trait appears which involves the entire individual, or which occurs either in several

nonduplicated parts of the body or in a single part, the contribution of nurture can be learned only from comparisons of different individuals who have identical genotypes.

What is the probability that following sexual reproduction of human beings two individuals of identical genotype will be produced? On the assumption that the members of each pair of chromosomes in the two parents are genetically different in one respect, then, the chance of two offspring being genically identical is $\frac{1}{2}^{23} \times \frac{1}{2}^{23}$, or $\frac{1}{2}^{46}$. This is so because the chance a gamete will carry the same genotype as another gamete of that individual is $\frac{1}{2}^{23}$, since chromosome pairs segregate independently, and because gametes fertilize at random. Since each human individual is heterozygous for numerous genes, the chance of obtaining genetic identity in two *siblings* (brothers and/or sisters of the same parents) is, in effect, infinitely small.

However, two or more siblings with identical genotypes may be produced as a consequence of asexual reproduction in man. This kind of reproduction occurs in the following manner. A single fertilized egg starts its development normally by undergoing a series of mitotic cell divisions. At some time, however, the cells produced fail to adhere to each other, as they would normally do to form a single developing unit, but instead become separated into two or more parts, each of which may be capable of forming a complete individual. Each individual produced this way is genetically identical to all others formed from the same fertilized egg. The separation referred to may occur at the two-cell stage or it may occur later, at which time the number of cells may be unequal in the two or more groups formed. It is even possible for these separations to occur twice, at different times in the development of a particular zygote. Individuals produced this way are called *identical* or *monozygotic twins*, triplets, quadruplets, etc. We need only consider identical twins here, since multiple births of greater number are usually too infrequent to be useful for a general study of the nature-nurture problem.

Multiple human births may occur also as a consequence of sexual reproduction. In this case the twins produced start with two separate eggs, each fertilized by a separate sperm. Such twins are genetically different, being, in this respect, no more similar than siblings conceived at different times, and are, therefore, called *nonidentical* or *dizygotic* (*fraternal*) *twins*.

These two kinds of twins provide another natural experiment for determining the relative influence of genotype and environment upon the phenotype. For monozygotic twins furnish the identical genotype in two individuals, and both kinds of twins share very similar environments before birth and, when raised together, after birth.

Accordingly, the phenotypic differences between identical twins reared together are, barring the rare event of mutation, purely the consequence of environment (Figure 11-1). One can compare the average of these differences between identical twins with the average of the differences between identical twins who, for one reason or another, were reared apart, usually in separate families. This would yield information regarding the influence upon the phenotype of greater, as compared with lesser, environmental differences. Since nonidentical or identical twins reared together are exposed to environments which vary to the same extent on the average, a comparison of the average difference between identical twins and the average difference between nonidentical twins will give an index of the role of the genotype in causing the differences observed. However, in order to collect data from twin studies, you can see how essential it is to be able to recognize in each case whether the twins are monozygotic or dizygotic in origin.

The best way to identify twins as nonidentical is to compare the two individuals phenotypically. They should be compared with regard to a large number of traits known to have a basis in genes that are 100% penetrant and of fairly uniform expressivity. These would include such traits as sex, eye color, ABO, MN, Rh, and other blood group types. Naturally, only those traits for which at least one parent is heterozygous can be of use in testing the dizygotic origin of twins. Ignoring the rare event of mutation, any single difference in such traits would prove the twins nonidentical. Of course, two such differences would make your decision infallible for all intents and purposes, since two mutations occurring in the limited number of traits being followed in a pair of identical twins would be so rare as to be beyond any reasonable probability of occurrence. With these criteria, twins of opposite sex may be classified immediately as nonidentical.

Classification of twins as identical is based on the same procedure except that the greater the number of traits for which no difference at all is shown, the greater is the probability they are identical. For if the number of traits serving to test the genotypes of twins is sufficiently large, it becomes nearly certain that had they been dizygotic in origin they would have shown one or more differences, their failure to show any difference being attributable to their genotypes being identical because they were both derived from a single zygote.

We are now in a position to study the relative roles of genotype and environment in producing specific traits. What is done is to score the percentage of pairs of twins, reared together, in which one or both twins have the trait under consideration. Let us outline the procedure which we might actually follow. Suppose we wished to study the *blood group AB* in this respect. What we would do first is to eliminate from consideration all pairs of twins in which neither individual was type AB. We would have remaining, then, twins which had at least one member of AB blood type. Then, we would determine the percentage of *concordance*, that is, the percentage of cases where, given one twin to be of the specified phenotype, the other one is also. Now in the case of identical twins the concordance for AB blood type is found to be 100%.

In determining concordance for non-identical twins, we should usually include in our data only those cases where the twins are of the same sex. This is desirable because the postnatal environment of twins of opposite sex is likely to be more different than the environment of identical twins — which must be necessarily of identical sex on our criteria. (Were both genotype and environment different for the two kinds of twins, we would not be able to specify the cause of a given phenotypic difference which is greater among non-

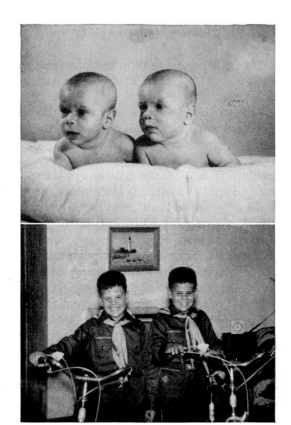

FIGURE 11–1. *Identical twins, Ira and Joel, at 3½ months, at 8 years, and at 16 years of age. (Courtesy of Mrs. Reida Postrel Herskowitz, July 14th, 1946.)*

identicals than identicals.) The precaution of using only twins of the same sex has been taken in all the twin studies discussed here.

The concordance of AB blood type is determined as approximately 64% for non-identicals. What conclusions can we draw? Had concordance been the same for both types of twins we would conclude that there is no genetic difference for AB blood group in the two types of twins. The concordances observed do differ, however, and do so in a particular direction. The 100% concordance for identicals is taken to mean that this trait is determined genetically with a penetrance of 100% despite the environmental fluctuations normally occurring between identical twins. The lower percentage of concordance for nonidenticals cannot be attributed in any part to environment, since an equivalent amount of environmental fluctuation caused no differences in the case of identicals. This lower concordance must be attributed, therefore, to the differences in genotype which nonidenticals have in this respect. Of course, we could have predicted such results from our previous discussion (Chapter 5), where it was shown that AB blood type is genetically determined and is known to have complete penetrance. The lower concordance for nonidenticals, therefore, must be due to their receiving different genotypes from parents, one or both of whom were heterozygous for I^A or I^B.

It should be noted that it is theoretically possible to obtain a result in which concordance is lower for identicals than it is for nonidenticals. Such a difference in concordance, if found, could be ascribed to environmental differences not being equivalent for both kinds of twins, being in fact greater among the identicals than among the nonidenticals.

Let us discuss the results of concordance studies for some physical traits in twins (Figure 11–2). Concordance for *clubfoot* is 32% for identicals, but only 3% for non-identicals. The extra concordance of 29% (32% − 3%) found among identicals must be attributed to their identical genotype. The 3% concordance found among nonidenticals might be due entirely to similarity in genotype or entirely to the environment, or to some combination of these two factors. Since we cannot decide this from these data, it is concluded that in twins or other individuals exposed to the same general environment as are twins, the occurrence of clubfoot can be attributed to genotype approximately 29% of the time, with 32% as the approximate upper limit.

In the case of the identicals, 68% of the time the second twin failed to have clubfoot when the first twin did. This failure of concordance is called *discordance*. The 68% discordance between identicals is attributable to differences in environment occurring between the partners of a set of twins. It is

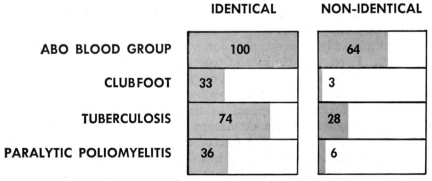

FIGURE 11–2. *Discordance (unshaded) and percentage concordance (shaded) for various physical traits in twins reared together.*

concluded, then, that in twins or other individuals exposed to the same general environment as are twins, the occurrence of clubfoot is the result of the environment approximately 68% of the time, with 71% as the approximate upper limit.

Concordance-discordance studies reveal only the relative contributions of genotype and environment to a particular phenotype (clubfoot, in the case just discussed). Such studies do not teach us anything about the kinds of environment involved when the genotype determines the phenotype under consideration, nor do they teach us anything about the genotypes involved when the environment decides the phenotype. The twin studies just discussed also offer no information on the effect upon penetrance of clubfoot caused by environmental differences greater than those found between twins reared together.

In the case of *tuberculosis*, concordance is 74% for identicals and 28% for nonidenticals. Accepting the supposition that both types of twins have the same average exposure to the tubercle bacillus, the susceptibility to this disease is determined genetically 46–74% of the time and environmentally 26–54% of the time. In support of the view that the extra concordance among identicals has a genetic basis are the findings that concordant identicals usually have the same form of this disease, attacking the same place, with the same severity, whereas these similarities are less frequent among concordant nonidenticals.

Paralytic poliomyelitis is 36% concordant for identicals and 6% concordant for nonidenticals. Here, as in the case of tuberculosis, the occurrence of the disease does not depend upon the infective organisms, because most human beings are exposed to these normally. Accordingly, the occurrence of this disease depends upon the rest of the environment 64–70% of the time and the genotype 30–36% of the time. In the case of *measles*, the fact that concordance is very

high among both types of twins simply means that any genetic basis for susceptibility to this disease is quite uniform throughout the population from which the twin samples were obtained.

The relative contributions of genotype and environment to personality and other mental traits may also be studied by the twin method. If a metronome is run at a series of different speeds, the tempo chosen as preferable will be different for different people. This *tempo preference* may be considered to be one aspect of the general personality. When tests are made to compare the preferred tempo of identical twins, the difference in their scores is found to be 7.8 of the units employed (Figure 11–3). This is, as might be expected, not significantly different from the difference in score of 8.7 units that is obtained by testing a given individual on different occasions.

INDIVIDUALS	DIFFERENCE IN SCORE
Same person on different occasions	8.7
Monozygotic twins	7.8
Dizygotic twins	15.0
Siblings	14.5
Unrelated	19.5

FIGURE 11–3. *Variation in tempo preference.* (*After C. Stern.*)

However, nonidenticals have a difference in score of 15 which is significantly different, being about twice that of the identicals. Since siblings born at different times have a difference in score of 14.5, they prove to be as similar in this respect as are nonidentical twins. Finally, unrelated persons show differences in score of 19.5 units. Since the greater the genetic similarity the smaller the difference in score, it may be concluded that there is a genotypic contribution to this personality trait.

Studies of twins for the mental disease *schizophrenia* show concordance of 86% for identicals and 14% for nonidenticals. However, it is likely that the environment is not the same for both types of twins, more discordance being produced by differences in social environment in the case of nonidenticals than in the case of identicals. Nevertheless, in support of the view that not all the concordance for identicals is attributable to their similar environment, and that there is some genotypic basis for concordance, are two cases of identical twins who were separated, grew up in different environments, yet were concordant at about the same age.

You are doubtless familiar with the fact that different people score differently on I.Q. examinations. We can use the differences in ability to answer questions on these examinations as a measure of what may be called *test intelligence*. While the scores of nonsiblings vary widely above and below 100, the difference between the scores of twins reared together is only 3.1 for identicals but is 8.5 for nonidenticals. Clearly identity in genotype makes for greater similarity in score. Tests of identicals reared apart show their scores differ by 6. In this case the greater difference in environment makes for a greater difference in performance of identicals, but this is still not so great a difference as is obtained between nonidenticals reared together. There are, therefore, both genotypic and environmental factors affecting the trait test intelligence.

Note that in the case of AB blood group we had previously discussed the nature of the genetic factors involved in the determination of the phenotype. We have not done this for the other traits studied in this Chapter. It should be re-emphasized, therefore, that though the twin methods used here tell whether there are genotypic differences associated with the occurrence and nonoccurrence of the phenotype under consideration, they do not offer any information regarding the nature of these gene differences. Whether or not the genotypic alternatives have any capacity for recombination, or whether or not they recombine in a regular predictable manner, cannot be determined from the data presented.

SUMMARY AND CONCLUSIONS

In human beings, the occurrence of essentially duplicate parts within an individual, and of identical and nonidentical twins, offers the opportunity to test the effect of environment and of genotype upon the appearance of a given phenotypic alternative.

A considerable number of physical and mental traits has been shown to be determined by the joint action of genotype and environment, sometimes the one and at other times the other having the greater influence.

The twin methods described do not study the transmissive properties of the genotypes involved. They do not, therefore, reveal anything regarding the recombinational properties of the genetic factors studied.

REFERENCES

Kallman, F. J., *Heredity in Health and Mental Disorder*, New York, Norton, 1953.

Montagu, A., *Human Heredity*, Cleveland, World, 1959.

Newman, H. H., *Multiple Human Births*, New York, Doubleday, Doran, 1940.

Osborn, F., *Preface to Eugenics*, Rev. Ed., New York, Harper, 1951.

Osborn, R. H., and De George, F. V., *Genetic Basis of Morphological Variation*, Cambridge, Mass., Harvard, 1959.

QUESTIONS FOR DISCUSSION

11.1. In determining whether or not twins are dizygotic, why must traits be studied for which one or both parents are heterozygotes?

11.2. Are mistakes ever made in classifying twins as being dizygotic in origin? Why?

11.3. When nonidentical twins are discordant for AB blood type, why must one or both parents have been heterozygous for I^A or I^B?

11.4. Invent a particular situation which would result in greater discordance for identical than for nonidentical twins.

11.5. What would be the probability of twins being dizygotic in origin if both had the genotype *aa Bb CC Dd Ee Ff*, each pair of alleles segregating independently, if the parents were genotypically *Aa Bb CC DD Ee Ff* and *Aa BB CC dd ee FF*?

11.6. How would you proceed to test whether, in women, there is a genetic basis for the maturation of more than one egg at a time?

11.7. In what way can you imagine that the paternal genotype could influence the frequency of twinning?

11.8. Is tuberculosis inherited? Explain.

11.9. What can twin studies by themselves tell you about genes? about genetic recombination?

11.10. Is it valid to apply the conclusions from twin studies to nontwin members of the population? Explain.

Chapter *12*

SEX–LINKAGE

WE HAVE already found that different pairs of genes segregate independently, and have hypothesized that this behavior is due to different pairs of genes being located in different pairs of chromosomes. You may now ask what the genetic basis for sex is. In the case of the garden pea we cannot obtain the answer from a study of just the two alternatives, maleness and femaleness, since all the pea plants dealt with were bisexual. So long as there are only two alternatives for the sex trait and both occur in every individual, there can be no phenotypic differences produced by segregation and recombination, and a genic basis for sex cannot be determined. We can, however, attempt a study of the genetic basis for sex, say in *Drosophila*, where the typical individual is either male or female (Figure 12–1). When normal males and females are mated, their progeny are in the approximate phenotypic ratio of male : female as 1 : 1. This permits the hypothesis that sex is determined by a single gene pair, and that one of the sexes of *Drosophila* is a homozygote and the other is a heterozygote. At the moment, however, we cannot say which sex carries which genotype. In accordance with our view that chromosomes contain the genes, there should be one pair of chromosomes concerned with sex. Let us call the homologous pair of chromosomes, which the homozygote for the sex genes carries, the XX pair, and the pair carried by the heterozygote, the XY pair. Segregation and random fertilization will produce equal numbers of XX and XY individ-

81

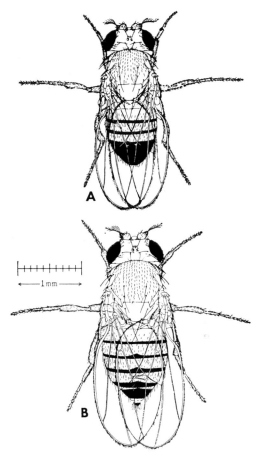

FIGURE 12–1. *Normal* (*wild-type*) Drosophila melanogaster *male* (*A*) *and female* (*B*). (*Drawn by E. M. Wallace.*)

uals. Since the X and the Y chromosomes carry the genes for sex, these can be called *sex chromosomes*, while the other chromosomes which an individual carries can be called *autosomes* (A). Since *Drosophila melanogaster* has a diploid chromosome number of four pairs, each individual can now be represented as either XX + 3AA or XY + 3AA.

Consider first crosses involving the recessives *cubitus interruptus*, *ci*, and *ebony body color*, *e*, and their dominant alleles *ci+* (*normal wing venation*) and *e+* (*gray body color*). Let one cross be *ci+ci e+e* × *ci ci e e*, in which one parent is dihybrid and the other parent is the double recessive (Figure 12–2).

The offspring appear in a 1 : 1 : 1 : 1 ratio, demonstrating that the two pairs of genes are segregating independently. The same result and conclusions obtain from the cross of $ci^+ci\ e\ e \times ci\ ci\ e^+e$. Consider next crosses in which sex and wing venation are studied simultaneously both in ci^+ci XX by $ci\ ci$ XY and in ci^+ci XY by $ci\ ci$ XX. The result found in both cases is a 1 : 1 : 1 : 1 ratio of cubitus male, cubitus female, normal male, normal female. Here, then, the sex genes segregate independently of the genes for cubitus. Therefore, by our hypothesis, the ci alleles are located autosomally.

Similarly, e^+e XX by $e\ e$ XY or e^+e XY by $e\ e$ XX also gives a 1 : 1 : 1 : 1 ratio, showing that *ebony* is located autosomally. It may be concluded also, since *ebony* and *cubitus* are found to segregate independently of each other, that they are located on different pairs of autosomes.

Note that the last two types of crosses could be described as backcrosses of a monohybrid which were made reciprocally, that is, one time the male was the hybrid parent, and the other time the female was, even though we cannot yet specify that male is XX or XY. In either case a 1 : 1 ratio is found among the

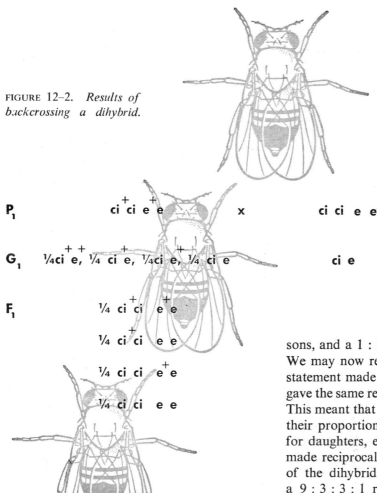

FIGURE 12–2. *Results of backcrossing a dihybrid.*

P₁ $ci^+ci\ e^+e$ x $ci\ ci\ e\ e$

G₁   ¼ci^+e^+, ¼ $ci\ e^+$, ¼ci^+e, ¼ $ci\ e$ $ci\ e$

F₁   ¼ $ci^+ci\ e^+e$

¼ $ci^+ci\ e\ e$

¼ $ci\ ci\ e^+e$

¼ $ci\ ci\ e\ e$

sons, and a 1 : 1 ratio among the daughters. We may now reconsider the meaning of the statement made earlier (p. 9), that all crosses gave the same results when made reciprocally. This meant that the observed phenotypes and their proportions were the same for sons as for daughters, even though the crosses were made reciprocally. So, for example, a cross of the dihybrids $ci^+ci\ e^+e \times ci^+ci\ e^+e$ gave a 9 : 3 : 3 : 1 ratio among the sons and a 9 : 3 : 3 : 1 ratio among the daughters be-

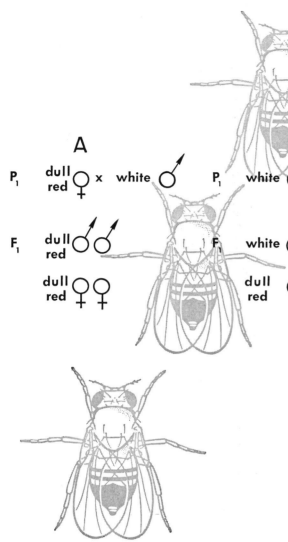

A

P₁   dull red ♀   x   white ♂

F₁   dull red ♂♂

  dull red ♀♀

B

P₁   white ♀   x   dull red ♂

F₁   white ♂♂

  dull red ♀♀

FIGURE 12–3. *Phenotypic results of reciprocal matings involving eye color.*

involving the *dull red* (w^+) and *white* (w) eye color alleles. Dull red ♀ × white ♂ (Figure 12–3A) produces all dull red sons and daughters in F₁, as expected, w^+ being dominant. However, the reciprocal cross (Figure 12–3B) of white ♀ × dull red ♂ gave only white sons and dull red daughters. Note that the first cross produced the same result for sons as for daughters, but the second, reciprocal, cross gave different results, sons resembling their mothers, and daughters resembling their fathers. Because of this difference in result from reciprocal matings, we must conclude that w^+ and its alleles are not located autosomally.

Let us assume that the gene for white eye is located in the sex chromosomes, being therefore *sex-linked*, and see what consequences this would have for its transmission relative to the sex phenotype.[1] In the rest of this Chapter we will not be particularly concerned with learning the genetic basis of sex in any greater detail, but will utilize principally the hypothesis that the two sexes are XX and XY.

[1] See T. H. Morgan (1910).

cause the sex genes were located on the sex chromosomes while the other genes happened to be autosomal. Therefore, in all previous work, we were dealing with autosomal transmission. This always showed independent segregation from the sex genes and permitted the statement that sex did not influence the results; that is, the results were the same among the sons as among the daughters even though reciprocal matings were made.

But consider now the results of crosses

Assume first that females are XY and males XX. The first cross is then dull red ♀♀ (females) $X^{w^+}Y^{w^+}$ by white ♂♂ (males) $X^w X^w$ (Figure 12–4, A–1), and the F_1 expected are $X^{w^+}X^w$ sons and $X^w Y^{w^+}$ daughters, all dull red-eyed, as observed. The reciprocal cross (Figure 12–4, B–1) is, then, white ♀♀ $X^w Y^w$ by dull red ♂♂ $X^{w^+}X^{w^+}$. The F_1 daughters ($X^{w^+}Y^w$) are expected to be dull red-eyed, as observed. However, the F_1 sons ($X^{w^+}X^w$) are expected to be dull red-eyed, whereas they are actually white-eyed. Therefore, we must reject this particular hypothesis for correlating sex chromosomes and eye color genes.

Let us assume next the reverse situation — that females are XX and males XY. The same crosses are represented now as dull red ♀♀ $X^{w^+}X^{w^+}$ by white ♂♂ $X^w Y^w$ producing $X^{w^+}X^w$ (dull red) daughters and $X^{w^+}Y^w$ (dull red) sons (Figure 12–4, A–2); reciprocally, white ♀♀ $X^w X^w$ by dull red ♂♂ $X^{w^+}Y^{w^+}$ gives $X^{w^+}X^w$ (dull red) daughters and $X^w Y^{w^+}$ (dull red) sons (Figure 12–4, B–2). The expected phenotype given last is contrary to fact, the phenotype of the F_1 sons being white, not dull red.

Since we cannot explain the observations merely by identifying maleness with XX or XY, we shall have to increase the number of assumptions used in an attempt to accomplish this. Let us test two hypotheses simultaneously, namely that *Drosophila* males are XY and that the Y chromosome can carry only w, and cannot carry w^+. The genotypes and results of the first cross given in the last paragraph remain the same (Figure 12–4, A–3). The reciprocal cross (Figure 12–4, B–3) becomes white ♀♀ $X^w X^w$ by dull red ♂♂ $X^{w^+}Y^w$ to produce $X^{w^+}X^w$ (dull red) daughters and $X^w Y^w$ (white) sons, as observed. Since these hypotheses fit the observations we may accept them.

There are a large number of other traits which, like white eyes, can be studied one at a time in *Drosophila*. Their transmission genetics also proves to be based upon a pair of genes on the sex chromosomes, each case giving different results in F_1 when pure lines of the two alternatives are crossed reciprocally. Moreover, each case can be explained by assuming that females are XX, males XY, with the Y carrying the most recessive and least effective allele known for the gene pair under test, as is the case for *white*. The finding, in dozens of different cases, that the Y chromosome always behaves as though it contains the least influential allele of the gene pair, tempts the hypothesis that for the gene pair under test the Y in fact contains no allele at all! The very fact that a partially or completely dominant allele of such a gene is normally never found on the Y of *Drosophila* must mean that such alleles cannot be formed there by mutation of the most recessive allele, most simply because this recessive allele does not exist on the Y. Accordingly, the Y can routinely be considered to lack an allele of a gene located on the X, and Figure 12–4, A–3 and B–3 should have Y substituted for each Y^w.

In all the cases where the Y carries no allele of a gene on the X, because sons receive their single X from their mother, they will show phenotypically whatever is contributed in the X they receive from their mother. With regard to these genes, therefore, a female is being test crossed whenever (or to whomever) she mates, since her genotype can be determined directly from the phenotypes of her sons. Genes present on the X chromosome and absent on the Y are said to be *hemizygous* in the *Drosophila* male, because half of the zygotes he produces will receive these alleles in the X he contributes, while the other half will not because they receive the Y. Note that the X of a *Drosophila* male is obtained from his mother and is transmitted to each of his daughters.

In the case of chickens, nonbarred feather ♀♀ × barred feather ♂♂ produces offspring which are all barred — *barred* (*B*) being dominant to *nonbarred* (*b*) (Figure 12–5A). In the

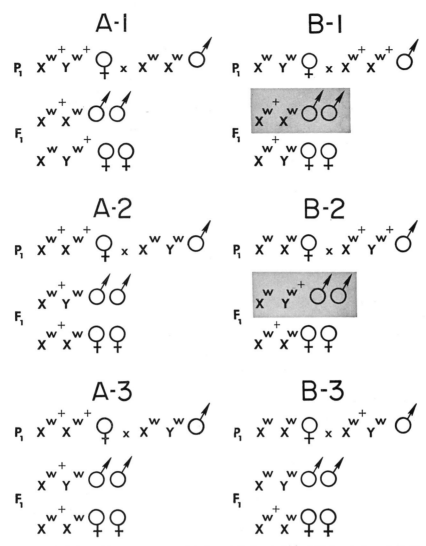

FIGURE 12–4. *Three attempts (A–1 and B–1, A–2 and B–2, A–3 and B–3) to represent matings A and B in Figure 12–3 genotypically. Shaded genotypes must be incorrect.*

reciprocal cross (Figure 12–5B) of barred ♀♀ × nonbarred ♂♂ all sons are barred and all daughters nonbarred. Here also the results of reciprocal matings differ, so that we are dealing again with sex-linkage. Note from the second cross that the exceptional individuals are the F_1 that show the recessive trait, as was the case in *Drosophila*. But in the present case the sex is opposite, since the

F_1 which are nonbarred are females, whereas the exceptional F_1 *Drosophila* were white-eyed males. In order to explain these results we can assume, as in *Drosophila*, that sex is determined by XX vs. XY, that the X chromosome does, and the Y chromosome does not, contain a gene for barred or nonbarred feathers, but that, contrary to the situation in *Drosophila*, males are XX and females XY.

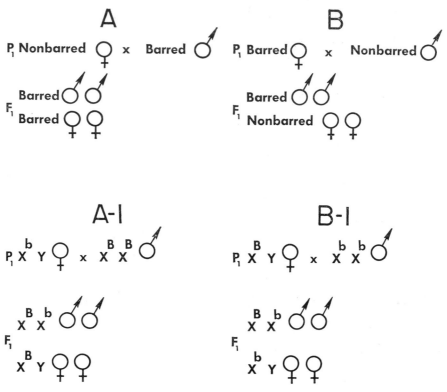

FIGURE 12–5. *Phenotypie (A and B) and genotypic (A–1 and B–1) results of reciprocal matings involving barred and nonbarred feathers in chickens.*

The genotypes of the bird crosses are, on these hypotheses, X^bY (nonbarred ♀) by X^BX^B (barred ♂) producing X^BY (barred ♀) and X^BX^b (barred ♂) in F_1; the reciprocal mating of X^BY (barred ♀) by X^bX^b (nonbarred ♂) produces X^bY (nonbarred ♀) and X^BX^b (barred ♂) in F_1, all as observed (Figure 12–5, A–1 and B–1).

You may be wondering if any clues can be obtained, from cytological observation of chromosomes, for the absence of alleles on the Y which are present on the X, both in the case of *Drosophila* and of poultry. It would be reasonable to expect, if the gene content for X and Y is so different, that this might be reflected in a difference in the cytological appearance of the two kinds of sex chromosomes. Note, however, our explanation of sex-linkage has been made independently of any cytological expectation.

It is found cytologically (Figure 12–6) in *Drosophila* that three pairs of chromosomes are the same in the male and the female, homologous chromosomes being very similar morphologically. In the female the homologs of the fourth pair are also similar morphologically, but in the male, while one member of the fourth pair is just like the homologs of the fourth pair in the female, its partner chromosome has a distinctly different morphology. Thus, the distinctive cytological appearance of this last chromosome is consistent with the genetic expectation for a Y chromosome, being present once in the male and not at all in the female. The other homolog in the male is then called the X, and is

FEMALE

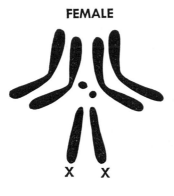

X   X

MALE

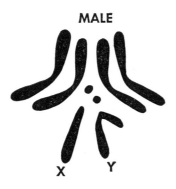

X   Y

FIGURE 12–6. *Silhouettes of chromosomes of* Drosophila melanogaster *as seen at mitotic metaphase.*

present twice in the female. Moreover, the reverse cytological picture is observed in poultry; here the males show that the homologs are similar for each pair of chromosomes, while the female has one pair that is *heteromorphic*, that is, one whose members are different from each other in appearance, one member being similar to, and one different from, the corresponding pair in the male.

In moths, as in birds, it is also found that males are XX and females XY. In human beings, genetic and cytological evidence shows XY to be male and XX to be female, as in *Drosophila*. It might be mentioned that in man a certain kind of red-green color-blindness is sex-linked, due to a recessive allele, *c*, present on the X and absent on the Y. Accordingly, color-blind women, X^cX^c, who

marry normal men, X^CY, have normal daughters, X^CX^c, and color-blind sons, X^cY. The classical bleeders' disease in human beings, hemophilia type A, is also due to an X-linked recessive gene, *h*, absent from the Y. This is a rare disease usually occurring in males; recently, however, a few hemophilic women have been discovered in England. These homozygotes are viable; they are extremely infrequent because they must have for parents a hemophilic father, X^hY, and a heterozygous mother, X^HX^h (Figure 12–7).

Let us consider certain additional experiments performed with the sex-linked gene for white eye in *Drosophila*.[1] When white ♀♀ (X^wX^w) are crossed to dull red ♂♂ ($X^{w+}Y$) and large numbers of progeny are scored, almost all F_1 are white sons (X^wY) and dull red daughters ($X^{w+}X^w$), as explained. But one or two F_1 per thousand do not show this typical result of sex-linkage, but are exceptional in being dull red-eyed sons or white-eyed daughters (Figure 12–8A). These exceptional flies cannot be explained as the result of careless scoring of phenotypes or contamination by strange flies. Moreover, they cannot be explained as being due to mutation, since the mutation rate from w^+ to w or the reverse is several orders of magnitude lower in frequency than that with which the two kinds of exceptional flies are obtained.

[1] Based upon work of C. B. Bridges.

FIGURE 12–7. *Pedigree showing a woman homozygous for the hemophilia gene.*

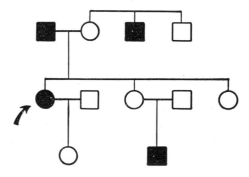

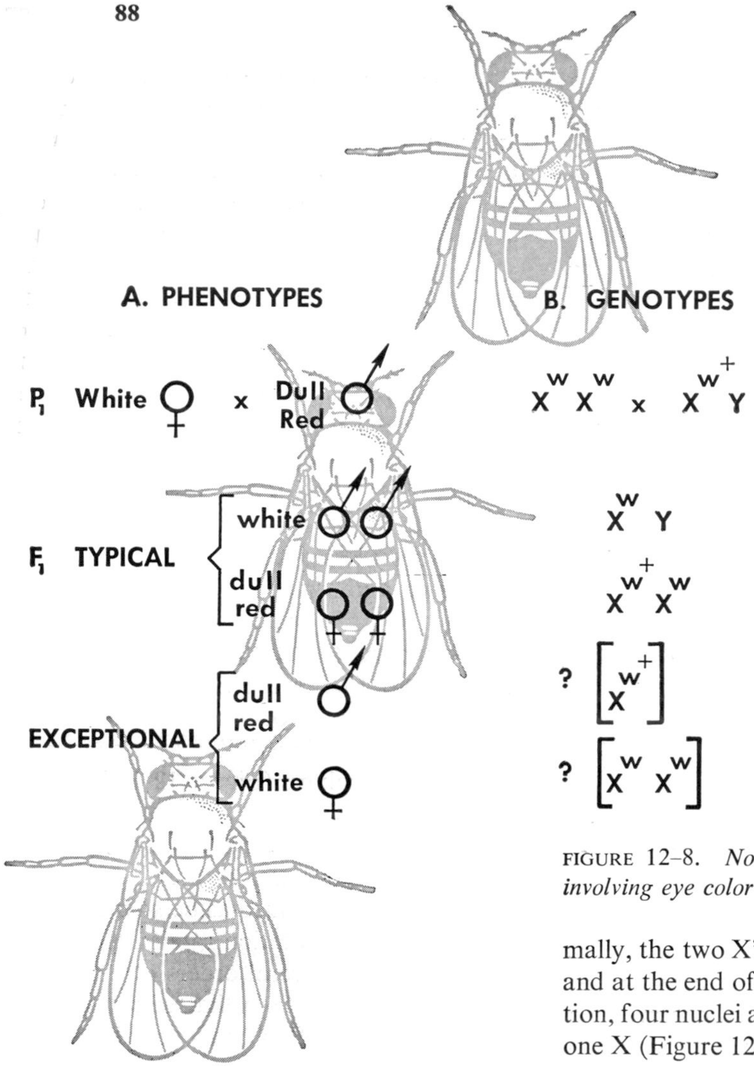

A. PHENOTYPES

B. GENOTYPES

P_1 White ♀ x Dull
Red ♂

$X^w X^w$ x $X^{w^+} Y$

F_1 TYPICAL {

white

dull
red

$X^w Y$

$X^{w^+} X^w$

EXCEPTIONAL {

dull
red

white ♀

? $\begin{bmatrix} w^+ \\ X \end{bmatrix}$

? $\begin{bmatrix} X^w X^w \end{bmatrix}$

FIGURE 12–8. *Nonmutant exceptions in crosses involving eye color in* Drosophila.

The following reasoning can be used to attempt to explain these results. Since the exceptional females are white-eyed they must contain $X^w X^w$ (Figure 12–8B). The only source for X's containing *w* was their mother. Accordingly, their father must have failed to contribute to them his X^{w^+} chromosome. The exceptional dull red-eyed sons must carry X^{w^+} which could have been received only from their father. In order to understand how this exceptional situation may come about, let us recall first the normal consequence of meiosis with regard to the sex chromosomes in the *Drosophila* female. Nor-

mally, the two X's synapse and form a tetrad, and at the end of meiosis, because of segregation, four nuclei are produced each containing one X (Figure 12–9A). Then one of the four nuclei becomes the gametic (egg) nucleus while the other three are discarded (in polar bodies).

Suppose, however, that occasionally separation of X chromosomal material in the tetrad fails to occur properly in either one of the two following ways. At anaphase I, instead of one dyad going to each pole, both dyads go to the same pole (Figure 12–9B). The nucleus containing no X dyad then proceeds through the second meiotic division and gives rise to two nuclei, neither of which contains an X. The other nucleus, containing two dyads, proceeds through the second division, during which the two members of each dyad separate and go to opposite poles at anaphase II. The result here will be two daughter nuclei each containing two X's, one from each dyad. Therefore, at the end of meiosis, the failure of dyads to disjoin at anaphase I will result ultimately in four nuclei, 2 with no X and 2 with two X's. The nucleus which becomes the gametic nucleus, therefore, has a 50% chance of carrying no X and a 50% chance of carrying two X's.

The second manner in which normal separation of X's may fail to occur during meiosis is as follows. In this case (Figure 12–9C), anaphase I is normal so that at telophase I

two nuclei are formed each containing one X dyad. In one of the two nuclei at metaphase II meiosis is completed normally, producing two telophase II nuclei, each containing one X. In the other metaphase II nucleus, however, the members of the X dyad fail to separate at anaphase II and go instead into the same telophase II nucleus. As a result of this failure to disjoin two nuclei are produced, one containing no X, and the other containing two X's. As a consequence of these events, the gametic nucleus has a 25% chance of carrying no X, a 25% chance of carrying two X's, and a 50% chance of carrying one X.

FIGURE 12–9. *Consequences of normal segregation of X chromosomes (A) and of its failure to occur (B and C).*

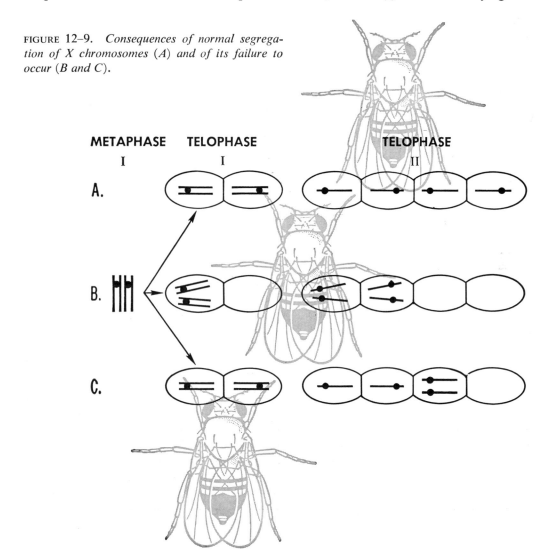

We have seen that the failure of normal separation of chromatids during meiosis, at either the first or second meiotic division, would have the consequence of producing some eggs containing either no X or two X's. Actually, this *nondisjunction* of chromosomes would represent a failure of the members of a pair of chromosomes to segregate. On our hypothesis that the X chromosome carries an allele for *w*, chromosomal nondisjunction can provide the mechanism by which a pair of genes can fail to segregate, so that after meiosis eggs are produced containing two members or neither member of the gene pair. Any egg produced following nondisjunction will usually be fertilized by a sperm carrying either an X or a Y in addition to a haploid set of autosomes. (Nondisjunction can also occur during meiosis in the male. We can ignore this here, because it would be an infrequent event, and the probability that an egg produced after nondisjunction would be fertilized by a sperm produced after nondisjunction is so small as to be negligible.)

If the hypothesis of chromosomal nondisjunction is valid, it should be consistent with the genetic results. After nondisjunction the exceptional eggs produced by a white (X^wX^w) female would be either X^wX^w or 0 (zero designating an egg carrying no X). The normal sperm produced by a dull red ($X^{w+}Y$) male would carry either X^{w+} or Y. The expected genotypes of F_1 from random fertilizations between these gametes are given in Figure 12–10.

Ignoring the sex of these exceptional offspring momentarily, and classifying them only for eye color, type 1 would be dull red-eyed, type 2 white-eyed, type 3 dull red-eyed, and type 4 of undetermined eye color. The genetic observations would be explained if types 1 and 4 were lethal, type 2 was female, and type 3 male. On the hypothesis that XX is female and XY is male, it is reasonable that types 1 and 4 would be neither, and might be, therefore, lethal. Even more specific re-

quirements need be fulfilled before accepting these hypotheses, namely, that each exceptional white female must prove to be XXY cytologically, that is, such females must have, in addition to the normal diploid chromosomes of a female, an extra chromosome which is Y; moreover, each exceptional male must have, besides the normal autosomes, one X but no Y. When the diploid cells of exceptional females and males are examined cytologically these chromosomal prescriptions are found to be fulfilled completely. It is also possible to show, moreover, that Y0 zygotes are lethal and that $X^{w+}X^wX^w$ individuals are dull red-eyed, but usually die before adulthood.

It should be noted that while XY individuals are fertile males, X0 flies are invariably sterile males. This means that the Y chromosome is necessary for male fertility, the trait being attributable to a gene on the Y which is absent from the X. Note also that our sex chromosome requirement for maleness must be modified to include XY and X0 individuals while that for femaleness includes XX and XXY individuals. The matter of the chromosomal and genetic basis of sex determination will be discussed in greater detail in the two Chapters which follow.

We should now take stock of our hypothesis that the chromosomes serve as the material basis for genes. In previous Chapters, a number of cases of parallelism had been found in the known or assumed properties and behavior of genes and of chromosomes, including the following: both come from pre-existing counterparts, both occur as pairs in all nondividing cells except gametes, both are replicated each mitotic division, both maintain their individuality from one mitotic division to the next, both are capable of mutation and subsequent replication of the new form, both segregate during gametogenesis so that they occur unpaired in the gamete, both combine at random at fertilization, both show independent segregation for different pairs. It has also been hypothesized that the chromosome is larger than a gene, since the latter is delimited also as the largest distance along the length of a chromosome within which a chiasma cannot form. Although these parallels still might be considered merely coincidental, the present Chapter provides additional tests of the idea that chromosomes function as the material basis for genes.

Sex-linkage, detected by the nonrandom association between gene transmission and sex, was found to be an exception to the mode of transmission of the autosomal genes heretofore discussed. This phenomenon could only be explained by assuming that certain genes did not have alleles in the homologous chromosome of a pair in one sex but did have alleles in the homologous chromosome of the other sex. This assumption of hemizygosity was necessary for the male of *Drosophila* and for the female of chickens. Such a genic aberration was exactly paralleled by the occurrence of a pair of heteromorphic chromosomes in the case of the *Drosophila* male and chicken female, one member of which was present as a pair in the *Drosophila* female and chicken male.

Finally, an exception to the exception of sex-linkage was found in *Drosophila* which could be explained genically as the failure of the members of a single pair of sex-linked genes under observation to segregate. This *genic nondisjunction* could be explained as being based upon *chromosomal nondisjunction*, the failure of the members of a pair of X chromosomes to segregate. The failure of these chromosomes to segregate predicted that the genetically exceptional individuals would have a specific and unique sex chromosomal composition, which further tests proved was indeed the case.

FIGURE 12–10. *Genotypic expectation from the fertilization of nondisjunctionally produced eggs by normal sperm.*

It must be concluded that the idea of the chromosome as the material basis of the gene should no longer be considered merely an hypothesis based upon limited, and therefore possibly circumstantial, evidence, but must now be accepted as a theory supported both by all the typical and all the atypical features of the transmission of genes and of chromosomes. Usually no comment will be made in subsequent Chapters when new tests of the theory further substantiate it, and you may assume henceforth that all tests do so unless note is made to the contrary.

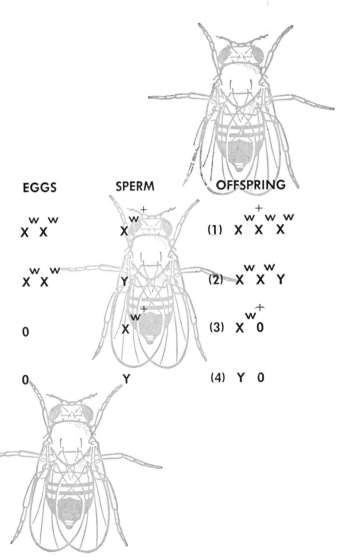

SUMMARY AND CONCLUSIONS

In previous Chapters the transmission of autosomally located genes was studied; their pattern of transmission is such that reciprocal crosses between different pure lines produce F_1 which are genotypically and phenotypically uniform; that is, there is no dependency between the traits which appear and the sex of the offspring.

In *Drosophila*, sex is determined by a single pair of genes located in the sex chromosomes. The facts stated in the preceding paragraph are to be expected, therefore, since whenever autosomal genes segregate they will do so independently of the sex genes.

For a number of other traits in *Drosophila*, however, crosses between different pure lines yield results which differ in reciprocal matings, the difference appearing in the phenotype shown by one of the sexes. Genes behaving in such a sex-linked way are not located autosomally. The results obtained for such genes can be explained on the basis that the Y sex chromosome carries no allele of these genes, while the X does.

In human beings and *Drosophila*, XY is male and XX female, while in birds and moths, it is the female which is heteromorphic, and, therefore, heterogametic with reference to sex chromosomes.

Occasionally, as a consequence of nondisjunction of sex chromosomes at meiosis, chromosome segregation fails, and gametes containing two or, complementarily, no sex chromosomes are formed. When this nondisjunction occurs in a *Drosophila* female homozygous for an X-linked recessive, and such a female is mated to a male carrying the dominant allele, some offspring appear that are simultaneously exceptions to sex-linkage and to sex chromosome content, the exceptional feature of the one accurately predicting the exceptional feature of the other, and vice versa.

Linkage and nondisjunction offer additional tests of the hypothesis that the material basis of the gene is in the chromosome, a view which is supported by so many and diverse lines of evidence, and contradicted by none, that it must be accepted as theory.

REFERENCES

Bridges, C. B., "Non-Disjunction as Proof of the Chromosome Theory of Heredity," Genetics, 1:1–52, 107–163, 1916.

Morgan, T. H., "Sex Limited Inheritance in Drosophila," Science, 32:120–122, 1910. Reprinted in *Classic Papers in Genetics*, Peters, J. A. (Ed.), Englewood Cliffs, N.J., Prentice-Hall, 1959, pp. 63–66.

CALVIN BLACKMAN BRIDGES (*1889–1938*). (*By permission of Genetics, Inc., vol. 25, p. 1, 1940.*)

QUESTIONS FOR DISCUSSION

12.1. Would you have phrased differently the statement on p. 84 that "sons receive their single X from their mother"? Explain.

12.2. What would you expect to be the genotypes of the zygotes produced, after sex chromosome nondisjunction occurs in both male and female *Drosophila*, in the cross $X^{w^+}Y$ by X^wX^w? What is the phenotypic outcome in each case?

12.3. If a trait is proved to be due to a gene unlinked to any autosome, does this mean the gene is linked to a sex chromosome? Explain.

12.4. A husband and wife both have normal vision, although both their fathers are red-green color-blind. What is the chance that the first child this couple has will be:

        a. A normal son?
        b. A normal daughter?
        c. A red-green color-blind son?
        d. A red-green color-blind daughter?

12.5. One twin is hemophilic while the twin brother is not.

        a. What is the probable sex of the hemophilic twin?
        b. Are the twins monozygotic? Explain.
        c. Give the genotypes of both twins, and of their mother.

12.6. A hemophilic father has a hemophilic son. Give the most probable genotypes of the parents and child.

12.7. A *Drosophila* male with cubitus interruptus wing venation, ebony body color, and white eye color is mated to a wild type female (normal wing venation, gray body color, and dull red eyes). The F_1 females are crossed to males like their father.

    Give the kinds and relative frequencies of genotypes and of phenotypes expected among the offspring of the last cross.

12.8. Are you convinced that all genes have their material basis in the chromosomes? Explain.

12.9. What reason can you give for believing in *Drosophila* that the Y chromosome is missing a gene present in the X chromosome? that the X is missing a gene present in the Y?

12.10. List evidences supporting the theory that chromosomes contain the material basis for genes.

12.11. Have we presented any evidence that a chromosome carries more than one gene? Explain.

12.12. What proportion of all genes for hemophilia type A are found in human males? Justify your answer.

Chapter **13**

SEX DETERMINATION (I)

UPPOSE reproduction had always occurred by asexual means. Even so the earth would now be populated by genetically different kinds of organisms, each variant having arisen by mutation in a pre-existing individual that was in turn produced from an unbroken line of descent. However, this method of direct descent is inefficient, at least in the respect that new mutations which confer a slight biological advantage would be wasted whenever they occurred in a genetically ill-adapted individual. For such an individual or its descendants would eventually become extinct, at which time the beneficial as well as the harmful genes would be lost simultaneously. Accordingly, biologically fit individuals could become more fit only by waiting until the rare event of mutation occurred in them.

The biological innovation of sexuality provides a tremendous genetic advantage over asexuality. Sexuality provides for genetic recombination (cf. p. 13), and this speeds up the process of the evolution of more adaptive organisms. For a more adaptive genotype may be produced by the combination in one individual of mutant and nonmutant genes originally located in different individuals who may have been less or even poorly adapted. Since genetic recombination normally occurs each generation for each gene pair, adaptive combinations of genes can originate much more rapidly than could be produced by mutation, which occurs much less frequently per gene than once a generation. In other words, sexuality provides numerous tests of

94

the adaptability of various combinations of genes, whereas equivalent tests in asexually reproducing lines would require an inordinately greater length of time, since these combinations would have to wait for successive mutations for their production. It should be clear, therefore, that sexuality, which produces more different adaptive genotypes in a given period of time than does asexuality, is primarily responsible for the great variety of adapted kinds of individuals that have appeared on earth in recent times.

You will agree that it is of interest to learn the basis of sex in view of its important role in biological evolution. The fundamental and unique feature of sex is the production of gametes. So our problem may be stated: What are the factors responsible for the production of gametes? Gametes are part of the phenotype just as are all other traits of the individual. Accordingly, since all traits of an organism have *some* genetic basis (in the genes that help create the organism, as an organism, and in whose absence there would be no organism and hence none of its traits), and since all genotypes must interact with the environment in order to produce phenotypes, it is clear that sex is also the consequence of the interaction between genotype and environment. We may be more specific, therefore, and seek to determine the relative importance of these two factors in the production of gametes. Let us evaluate these two factors insofar as they affect gamete formation in different kinds of organisms.

In certain organisms, male and female gametes are produced in the same individual. In animals, individuals of this type are called *hermaphrodites* (after Hermes and Aphrodite), while such plants are said to be *monoecious* ("one house"). In the case of the snail, *Helix*, there is only one type of sex organ, or *gonad*, which produces both eggs and sperm from cells which may lie very close together. In the earthworm, eggs and sperm are produced in separate gonads located in different segments of the body. Similarly, in certain mosses, egg and sperm-like gametes are produced in separate sex organs (located on the same haploid gametophyte individual).

In all these cases, the organism which produces the two types of gametes started its existence by containing but a single genotype. It might be supposed, at first, that the haploid genotype carried by eggs and by sperm is different, and is the cause of the difference in their phenotype and behavior. But, in the case of the gametophyte of mosses, the individual is haploid and so are both types of gametes it forms. Accordingly, we cannot expect differences in gene content to be the basis in such organisms either for the formation of gametes or for the different types of gametes produced.

Gamete formation in hermaphroditic and monoecious organisms, therefore, is dependent primarily upon environmental differences. These environmental differences must exist even between cells which lie close together, as is the case in *Helix*, and must often result from differences in the internal environment of an organism. We shall not pursue much further the matter of identifying the nature of the differences in the internal (or external) environment which result either in gamete formation or in the specific types of gametes formed. It will suffice, here, to point out that these sexual events are but specific instances of the general process of cellular differentiation that occurs in multicellular organisms. It is reasonable to suppose that the same kinds of environmental factors which can direct one group of cells to form muscle cells, and an adjacent group to form bone cells, could operate to direct the differentiation of still other cells into gonadal tissue in which adjacent cells might further differentiate as sperm and egg. You should note, however, that there is another problem of differentiation involved in sex, which is separate, at least in some organisms like the mosses, from

the production of gametes — the cells uniting in fertilization. This problem, which we shall not discuss further, concerns the genetic and environmental factors responsible for the onset of meiosis, which is, of course, the feature most fundamental to the success of the sexual process as it occurs at present.

The examples already mentioned dealt with the dependency of gamete differentiation upon the different positions which cells have within a single organism, as a consequence of which these cells are subject to differences in internal and external environments. In the marine annelid, *Ophryotrocha*, the two sexes are in separate individuals and the sex type formed is determined by the size of the organism. When the animal is small, because of youth or because it was obtained by means of amputating a larger organism, it manufactures sperm; when larger, the same individual shifts to the manufacture of eggs. In this case the environment of the gonad is changed by the growth of the organism. Finally, we can consider the determination of sex in the marine worm, *Bonellia*. In this organism the separate sexes are radically different in appearance and activity, females being walnut-sized and having a long proboscis, males being microscopic ciliated forms that live as parasites in the body of the female. Fertilized eggs develop into females when grown in the absence of adult females; they grow into males in the presence either of adult females or simply of an extract of the proboscis of females. In this case, then, differentiation as a whole, including sexual differentiation, is regulated by the presence or absence, as part of the environment, of a chemical messenger manufactured by females.

Nothing has been stated regarding the specific genetic basis for the determination or differentiation of sex in the examples so far discussed. Different sexes or gametes were determined not by genetic differences between cells, organs, or individuals, but by environmental differences acting upon a uniform genotype. In these cases, the genes neverthe-less played a role, one that made possible different sexual responses to differences in the environment.

Consider next the basis for gamete forma-tion in still other kinds of organisms. *Chla-mydomonas* is a unicellular plant with two flagella and with a chromatophore containing chlorophyll. It can reproduce asexually, by means of mitotic cell division, to produce cul-tures containing large numbers of individuals. When cultures are derived from a single ancestor no sexual reproduction is observed within them. If, however, the members of two such cultures are mixed together, one of two events is possible — either no mating occurs, or the individuals of one culture pair with members of the other culture, fuse, and produce zygotes. After two divisions of the zygote, four cells are produced. Each of these four cells can be grown separately and each will produce cultures within which there is no mating, as already explained. If now a sample from each of these four cultures is mixed with different portions of a fifth culture (also descended from a single individual), two cultures of the four will show mating (and since they do we can call these sexual type +) and two will not (being, therefore, of − sex). Moreover, when portions of the four cultures under test are combined in pairs, it is found that individuals of any + culture can mate to individuals in any − culture, while combi-nations of two + or two − cultures do not result in mating. Cytological examination shows no phenotypic difference between + and − individuals.

How may these results be explained? Note that among the first four cells produced from a zygote only two kinds of individuals are produced, exactly two being of + and two of − sex. This suggests that the zygote is diploid, carries a pair of genes for sex, which we can call + −, and that meiosis occurs in the next two divisions, as a consequence of which a 1 : 1 ratio of + : − is found among the haploid products. Therefore, it is pri-marily the genotype which determines sex in *Chlamydomonas*.

In certain kinds of grasshoppers, females have 14, and males 13, chromosomes, one of the seven kinds of chromosomes having no partner in the male. Thus, both sexes have 12 autosomes (6AA), females have two X's and males one X. After meiosis, all eggs contain 6A + 1X, while half of sperm carry 6A + 1X and half 6A. Sex determination is obvious, zygotes with one X forming males, those with two X's forming females. We could consider the function of the X, in sex determination in these forms, to be the pro-duction of the trait of femaleness, one X producing a tendency in this direction which appears as male, while two X's complete this tendency and produce female.

We have already discussed, in Chapter 12, the fact that the ordinary *Drosophila melano-gaster* female is 3AA + XX and the male is 3AA + X + Y. From this statement, how-ever, we cannot decide the chromosomal basis for sex determination in any greater detail, since there are two variables involved, the X's and the Y. Is the male a male be-cause he has a Y, or because he has only one X, or because he has both one X and one Y? A decision in this matter can be arrived at from the fact that flies have been obtained which were shown to contain, besides 3AA, either XXY, or XXYY, or X0; these were, respectively, female, female, and male, prov-ing that the Y is not sex determining in this organism. (We had already indicated the existence and sex of the first and third types of individual in Chapter 12, where it was also mentioned that the Y is necessary for fertility, X0 males having nonmotile sperm.)

On relatively rare occasions *Drosophila* in-dividuals appear which are abnormal in being part male and part female. These individuals are mosaic for the sex trait, and are called *gynandromorphs* or *gynanders* (Figure 13–1). The male and female parts are clearly demarcated in such flies, sometimes front and hind halves and other times right and left sides are of different sex. On the hypothesis that in *Drosophila*, as in the grasshoppers mentioned, XX makes for female and X for male, it would be predicted that in gynandromorphs each of the diploid cells in the female part would contain XX, and each of those in the male part X. If this is correct, then approximately half-and-half gynanders could originate in the following way. The individual starts as a zygote containing 3AA + XX, that is, as a female, and the zygotic nucleus divides mitotically to produce two nuclei. But, on this occasion, the first mitosis is abnormal. While one daughter nucleus is normal, containing 3AA + XX, the other daughter nucleus is defective, containing 3AA + X, because one of the X's it should contain failed to be included in this nucleus, degenerated, and was lost. Subsequently, however, nuclear division is normal, cells produced following mitosis of the XX nucleus and its descendents giving rise to female tissue, and cells derived from the X nucleus giving rise to male parts. In this case the gynander would have about half its body male and half female. If, however, the X

FIGURE 13–1. D. melanogaster *gynandromorph whose left side is female and right side is male.* (*Drawn by E. M. Wallace.*)

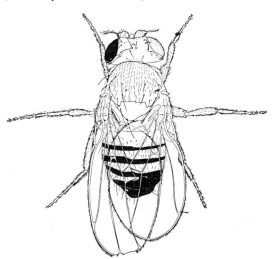

were lost at some later mitosis, a correspondingly smaller portion would be male. This would explain gynanders containing one quarter or less of the body as male.

What evidence can we obtain that this may sometimes be the correct interpretation? Let us make use of an X-linked gene which produces a phenotypic effect over a large portion of the body surface, that is, one affecting the size and shape of the bristles and hairs. This gene is *forked*, two of its alleles being f^{34b} and *f*. Homozygotes (females) and hemizygotes (males) for f^{34b} have bristles and hairs of normal length and shape, those for *f* have these shortened, split, and gnarled; f^{34b}/f heterozygotes have bristles and hairs slightly abnormal in these respects, showing a "weak forked" phenotype. If a cross is made so that the female offspring are heterozygotes as just indicated, the following predictions can be made regarding the phenotype of gynanders among the siblings. All gynanders having the origin postulated will be weakly forked in their female parts; on the other hand, the male parts will have either normal or strongly forked bristles and hairs depending upon whether the X carrying *f* or f^{34b}, respectively, was the one lost. The results actually obtained exactly confirm these expectations. Moreover, such a gynander may lay eggs if its posterior part is female, but it is sterile if its posterior half is male, as expected from X0 males.

While most *Drosophila* gynanders can be explained in this manner, there are some which originate another way. With extreme rarity, an abnormal egg is produced after meiosis, which contains not one but two haploid gametic nuclei. Now, because polyspermy takes place in insects, that is, because more than one sperm can enter an egg (although only one is used in fertilization), one of the two haploid egg nuclei may be fertilized by an X-carrying sperm, the other by a Y-carrying one. Resultant individuals would be approximately half-and-half gynanders. This type of origin may be identified if the gynander is concurrently mosaic for a sex-linked or autosomal gene for which the mother was heterozygous, or if it is concurrently mosaic for an autosomal gene for which the father was heterozygous.

Gynanders occur also in other insects. In moths, for example, where males may have large, beautifully colored wings and females small stumps of wings, gynanders have been found with wings like the male on one side and those like the female on the other side. The explanation of these exceptions is similar to that given for *Drosophila*. However, in the case of the moth, the gynander usually starts as a male zygote (XX). In insects, in general, gynanders usually have a sharp borderline between male and female parts because hormones play a relatively small role in differentiation, each body part forming largely according to the genotype it contains.

In man and the mouse, males are usually XY and females XX. In these organisms, X0 individuals are female (such human beings are usually underdeveloped females, demonstrating Turner's syndrome), while XXY individuals are underdeveloped males (such human beings having Klinefelter's syndrome). People who are otherwise diploid but are XXXY, XXYY, or XXXXY are abnormal males, while those who are XXX or XXXX are abnormal females. In man and the mouse, then, the presence of a Y chromosome determines the male sex; note that the chromosomal relation to sex is different from that found in *Drosophila*.

In the last group of organisms discussed (beginning with *Chlamydomonas*) we have seen that the genotype is primarily responsible for sex determination; in some cases the genetic basis for this is indicated by differences in the chromosomal make-up of the two sexes. In certain organisms the presence of one or of two chromosomes of a kind determines sex, in other cases sex is determined by the presence or absence of a single chromosome.

SUMMARY AND CONCLUSIONS

An understanding of the basis of sex requires the answer to two questions: What factors are responsible for the onset of meiosis? What is the basis for the formation of different kinds of gametes? Only the latter question was discussed here in any detail. It was found that in some cases the environment and in other cases the genotype is primarily responsible for sex determination. In the latter cases sexual differences can sometimes be correlated with differences in chromosome content.

REFERENCES

Hannah-Alava, A., "Genetic Mosaics," Scient. Amer., 202:118–130, 1960.

Lancet, No. 7075, Vol. 1, 1959, pp. 709–716.

Wilson, E. B., "The Chromosomes in Relation to the Determination of Sex in Insects," Science, 22:500–502, 1905. Reprinted in *Great Experiments in Biology*, Gabriel, M. L., and S. Fogel (Eds.), Englewood Cliffs, N.J., Prentice-Hall, 1955, pp. 254–257.

QUESTIONS FOR DISCUSSION

13.1. If sexual reproduction is as advantageous as discussed, why do so many organisms still reproduce asexually?

13.2. Does the study of sex determination offer any test of the theory that chromosomes furnish the physical basis for genes? Explain.

13.3. Is it possible to consider the factors responsible for the meiotic process separately from the factors responsible for gamete formation? Explain.

13.4. Why is meiosis the feature most fundamental for the success of sexuality?

13.5. Do you think the evidence presented is conclusive that sex in *Chlamydomonas* is based primarily upon a single pair of genes? Justify your answer.

13.6. Write the genotypes and phenotypes of the unexceptional, nondisjunctional, and gynandromorphic offspring from a mating of $f^{34b}/f \times f$ *Drosophila*.

13.7. Are there isoalleles for the genes determining the size and shape of the bristles and hairs of *Drosophila*? Explain.

13.8. Using first the autosomal alleles e and e^+ and then the X-linked alleles y and y^+, design crosses by which you could identify gynanders in *Drosophila* resulting from two fertilizations of a single egg.

13.9. Compare the genotypes and phenotypes of gynanders of flies, moths, and men.

13.10. "All human beings have the same number of chromosomes in each somatic cell." Discuss this statement, giving evidence in support of your view.

13.11. The following types of mosaics are known in human beings:

$$
\begin{array}{ll}
\text{XXX/X0} & \text{XXY/XX} \\
\text{XX/X0} & \text{XXXY/XY} \\
\text{XY/X0} &
\end{array}
$$

Explain how each of these could have originated.

13.12. In human beings, can the members of a pair of monozygotic twins ever be of different sexes? Explain.

Chapter **14**

SEX DETERMINATION (II)

WE HAVE already seen in the last Chapter that the genotype can be the principal factor in the determination of sex. It was found, in these cases, that sex can be correlated with the chromosomal alternatives of XX versus X, or Y versus no Y. The question now raised is, what is the detailed genetic basis for sex in terms of genes located in the X and Y chromosomes? The data so far presented have been analyzed as though a single pair of genes (in the cases of XX vs. X), or a single gene (in the cases of Y vs. no Y), was the total genetic basis for sex determination. There are several implications of this interpretation. The sex gene found in X chromosomes need have no alternative allele, the presence of one such gene producing one sex and the presence of two the alternative sex, there being, of course, no dominance involved. So, in *Drosophila*, for example, where an X may be considered to carry a gene producing femaleness, the presence of one such gene causes differentiation to proceed toward femaleness but stops at a point we label male, whereas two such alleles cause differentiation to proceed further toward femaleness whose end point we call female. In those cases where XX vs. X is sex determining and the Y though present has no influence in this regard, it must also be assumed that the Y carries no allele for the sex gene. However, two additional assumptions must be made in such cases in order to correlate the genetics with the cytology of sex. First, the sex gene must be located in a region of the X, which is

100

cytologically different in appearance from the corresponding region of the Y, and which is used to distinguish X from Y cytologically. Second, no chiasma may occur between X and Y within this cytologically different segment. These postulates are necessary to preserve the exact correspondence between the morphology of the X and its sex gene content. The consequence of these hypotheses is that even though chiasmata form between the X and Y, the resultant strands that appear X cytologically will carry the sex gene while those that appear Y will not. These requirements are not unreasonable in view of the known fact that synapsis does not occur between cytologically different regions in homologous chromosomes, and that, in the absence of synapsis, a chiasma cannot form.

Consider next the implication of the Y or no Y sex determining mechanism in human beings and mice. In this case the Y must carry a gene for maleness in that portion which makes it cytologically unique; this gene is absent from the X and has no alternative allele that produces femaleness. If you admit that the presence of the gene for maleness on the Y makes for male in these cases, what genetically is responsible for the femaleness produced in the absence of this gene? There may be some genetic factor present, other than in the Y chromosome, which determines femaleness. There may exist, therefore, some genetic factor in these cases which makes for femaleness but whose female tendency is overcome by the presence of the sex gene for maleness whenever a Y chromosome is present.

Let us consider certain crosses with *D. melanogaster*,[1] where it is found that for each 100 eggs laid, instead of approximately 50 forming males and 50 forming females, about 75 are males and 25 females (Figure 14–1A). Since just as many eggs become adult in this unusual case as in a strain giving a normal ratio of sexes, the abnormal results cannot

[1] Based upon work of A. H. Sturtevant.

FIGURE 14–1. *Abnormal sex ratio in* Drosophila.

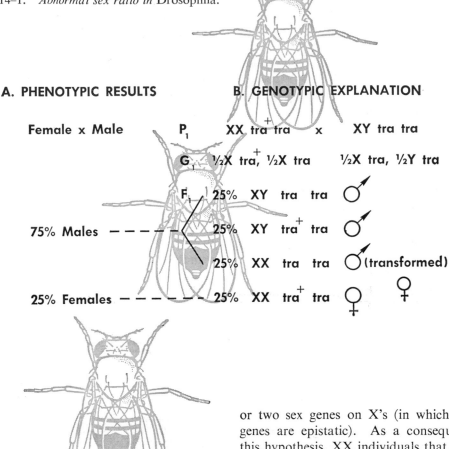

A. PHENOTYPIC RESULTS

B. GENOTYPIC EXPLANATION

| Female x Male | P_1 | XX tra^+ tra | x | XY tra tra |

G_1 ½X tra^+, ½X tra ½X tra, ½Y tra

F_1 25% XY tra tra ♂

75% Males — — — — — 25% XY tra^+ tra ♂

25% XX tra tra ♂ (transformed)

25% Females — — — — — 25% XX tra^+ tra ♀   ♀

be explained as being due to some gene producing a decreased viability for females. It may be hypothesized, in this exceptional case, that a pair of genes other than the gene on the X is exerting an effect on the determination of sex. In this case the gene is postulated to have two alleles, a dominant one, tra^+, and a recessive one, tra. Homozygotes for tra are presumed always to form males regardless of what X genes are present (tra tra is epistatic and the X genes hypostatic [2]), while heterozygotes or homozygotes for tra^+ have their sex determined by the presence of one

[2] These terms are defined in Chapter 7.

or two sex genes on X's (in which case X genes are epistatic). As a consequence of this hypothesis, XX individuals that are also tra tra will appear as males (transformed females), explaining the excess of males in the progeny. To further account for the specific numerical results it is necessary to postulate that the *transformer* gene is located autosomally (Figure 14–1B). Thus, a cross of XY tra tra (male) by XX tra^+ tra (female) would produce ¼ XY tra tra (males), ¼ XY tra^+ tra (males), ¼ XX tra tra (males, transformed females), ¼ XX tra^+ tra (females). All these assumptions have been tested in additional crosses, and are confirmed. These results prove, therefore, that autosomal genes are also concerned with sex determination. Note, however, that the tra allele is very rare, almost all *Drosophila* found in nature being homozygous tra^+.

FIGURE 14–2. *Normal (left) and triploid (right)* D. melanogaster *females.* (*Drawn by E. M. Wallace.*)

So far we have described only two sex types in *Drosophila.* Occasionally, however, individuals occur which have over-all an intermediate sexual appearance, being both male and female in certain respects. Such sexual intermediates are called *intersexes*, and are sterile. Intersexes are relatively frequent among the progeny of certain females. These females are slightly larger than normal females (Figure 14–2) and when examined cytologically prove to be *triploids*, individ-

uals having each chromosome threefold (Figure 14–3, where X's are filled in while autosomes are not and the Y is represented by a broken line). How can we explain the high proportion of intersexes in the progeny of these triploid females? Let us examine the process of meiosis in such individuals for clues to an explanation.

When triploids undergo meiosis, bundles of three homologous chromosomes (*trivalents*) may be formed at synapsis. This is

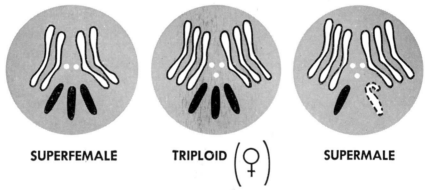

SUPERFEMALE   **TRIPLOID** (♀)   **SUPERMALE**

FIGURE 14–3. *Chromosomal complements of the sexual types found among the progeny of triploid females of* D. melanogaster.

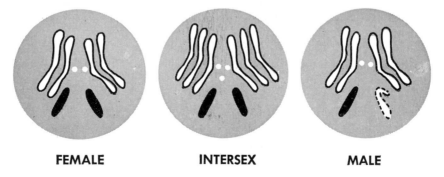

FEMALE   **INTERSEX**   **MALE**

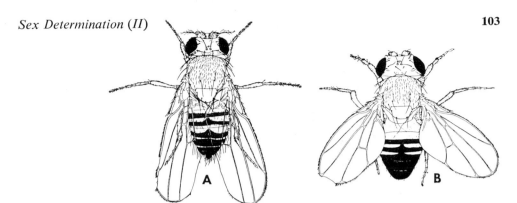

so because, at one place along the length of the chromosome, pairing is between two homologs, and, at another place, it is between one of these two and the third homolog. In this way, then, although pairing is two-by-two at any given level, all three homologs are held together as a trivalent. At the first meiotic division, the two homologs synapsed at their centromeric regions separate and go to opposite poles, while the third homolog goes to either one of the poles. At the end of the second meiotic division two nuclei each have one homolog of the trivalent and two nuclei each have two homologs. The same result obtains when synapsis is entirely between two homologs and excludes the third homolog. Since each of the four trivalents present at metaphase I segregate in this manner independently of the others, eggs may be produced which have each chromosome type singly, and so contain one complete genome (type 1), or contain two of each type, and so carry two genomes (type 2), or have any combination in which some chromosomes are represented once and others twice (type 3).

Type 1, being a haploid egg, will produce normal males and females when fertilized by sperm from a normal male. Eggs of type 2, being diploid, will produce triploid females when fertilized by X-bearing sperm. When the chromosomal content of intersexual survivors is determined cytologically, they prove to have three sets of autosomes plus either XXY or XX. The former type was derived from a type 2 diploid egg containing two sets of autosomes plus XX which was fertilized

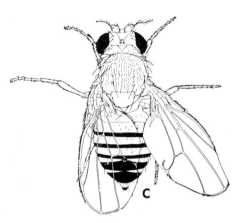

FIGURE 14–4. *Some abnormal sex types in* Drosophila: *A = superfemale; B = supermale; C = intersex.* (*Drawn by E. M. Wallace.*)

by a Y-bearing sperm; the latter type came from a type 3 egg containing two sets of autosomes plus X which was fertilized by an X-bearing sperm.

Close observation reveals two additional sex types among the progeny of triploid *Drosophila* (Figures 14–4, 14–3). These appear, not as intersexes, but as supersexes — some of these individuals show characteristic female traits even more strongly than do normal females (these are called *superfemales, metafemales,* or *ultrafemales*), the others show characteristic male traits even more strongly than do normal males (these are called *supermales, metamales,* or *inframales*). Chromosomally, superfemales contain two sets of autosomes and three X's, derived from a type

3 egg, carrying one set of autosomes plus XX, which was fertilized by an X-carrying sperm. These usually die before adulthood (see p. 90). Supermales prove to contain three sets of autosomes plus XY, derived from a type 3 egg, carrying two sets of autosomes plus X, which was fertilized by a Y-bearing sperm.

What conclusions can we come to, relative to sex determination, from a knowledge of the chromosomal composition of different sex types in *Drosophila*? [3] Since we already know that genes in the X and in the autosomes are sex-determining, let us tabulate for each sex type the number of X's and sets of autosomes present. This is done in Figure 14–5, which gives also the ratio of X's to sets of autosomes, as a kind of sex index. These sex indexes range from 0.33 for supermales up to 1.5 for superfemales. Note that an index of 0.50 makes for male, and that addition of a set of autosomes can be interpreted

[3] Based upon work of C. B. Bridges.

as making for more maleness, so that the supermale is produced. When the sex index is 1.0 essentially normal females are produced, as if the female tendency of one X overpowers the male tendency of one set of autosomes. But if the index is between 0.50 and 1.00 intersexes are produced because, on this line of reasoning, the effect of two X's is partially overpowered by the extra autosomal set present. Finally, when the sex index is 1.5 the female tendency of the X's becomes so strong as to make superfemales.

What we have postulated here is that sex determination is due to the balance of genes located in the X on the one hand and those in the autosomes on the other. According to this view, only the balance of the genes involved is important, so that a sex index of 1.0 should (and does) produce typical female, whether the individual is diploid (2X + 2 sets of A) or triploid (3X + 3 sets of A). Individuals carrying 4X + 4A sets (being tetraploid) and parts of individuals that car-

FIGURE 14–5. *Sex index and sexual type in* D. melanogaster.

PHENOTYPES		NO. X CHROMOSOMES	NO. SETS OF AUTOSOMES (A sets)	SEX INDEX $\dfrac{\text{No. X's}}{\text{No. A sets}}$
Superfemale		3	2	1.5
Normal Female	tetraploid	4	4	1.0
	triploid	3	3	1.0
	diploid	2	2	1.0
	haploid	1	1	1.0
Intersex		2	3	0.67
Normal male		1	2	0.50
Supermale		1	3	0.33

ried 1X + 1A set (being haploid) have been found. As expected from their sex index of 1.0, these individuals or parts were female. Since all known facts support the exact correspondence between chromosomal constitution and sexual types, we can accept chromosome balance as the typical basis of sex determination in *Drosophila*.

What is the relationship between X-autosome balance and *tra*, the sex transforming gene? Sex is determined by X-autosome balance when the individuals carry *tra+*, which they normally do. On those rare occasions when *tra tra* is present, the balance view does not apply, 2X + 2A sets, you recall, producing male.

We have seen in *Drosophila* that determination of sex is primarily genetic and that the sex type differentiated in different parts of an individual depends only upon the genotype carried by these parts (Chapter 13). Autonomous sexual development of each part of this organism is possible because of the absence of hormones affecting sexual differentiation. What is the situation in man?

In human beings sexual type is determined at fertilization, Y-bearing zygotes becoming males, Y-less zygotes females. The manner in which the appropriate sex phenotype is produced can be described briefly as follows. Early in its development, the gonad is neutral, i.e., there is no macroscopic indication whether it will later form testis or ovary. This early gonad has two regions, an outer one called the *cortex* and an inner one called the *medulla*. As development proceeds, the cortex degenerates in those individuals that carry a Y (males) and the medulla forms testis, while in those individuals genetically destined to be females the medulla degenerates and the cortex forms ovary.

Once the testis and ovary are formed, they take over the regulation of further sexual differentiation by means of the hormones they produce, so that these hormones direct the development or degeneration of various sexual ducts, the formation of genitalia, and other sexual characteristics. Since sexual differentiation is largely under the control of the sex hormones it should not be surprising to find genetically normal individuals who are morphologically abnormal with regard to sex. For any abnormal condition in the environment, which can upset the production of sex hormone and/or the response of tissues to it, may produce effects during development which result in an abnormal sex phenotype. Such abnormal sex phenotypes due to environmental factors could be intersexual, and theoretically could be produced either from genotypic males who have developed partially in the direction of female or from genotypic females partially differentiated in the direction of male. Some intersexes in humans prove to be due to an abnormal genotype present at fertilization, as is true for all intersexual *Drosophila*; other human intersexes result from genotypic mosaicism, which produces gynandromorphs in *Drosophila* where sex hormones are absent. Of course you realize that the phenotypes normally considered male and female show some variability. So, while it is sometimes easy to classify an individual as being an intersex, because that person is clearly between the two sex norms, other individuals at the extremes of normality may not readily be labeled as normal, or intersex, or supersex. It is debatable whether human beings that are X0 or XXY, but otherwise diploid, should be called intersexes, or whether they should be considered of normal but of underdeveloped sex.

Since we have just been discussing how the genotype may be related to the production of intersexes, consider how the genotype is related to the sex ratio, that is, the relative numbers of males and females born. On the average, 106 boys are born for each 100 girls. At first this might surprise you, since half of sperm are expected to carry X, and half Y, and all eggs an X, so that the sex ratio expected is 1 : 1 as boy : girl. Even if the four meiotic products of spermatogenesis are usually X, X, Y, Y, the possibility exists that during or after *spermiogenesis* (conversion of the telophase II cell into a sperm) some X-bearing sperm are lost. This is supported by a report that human ejaculates contain sperm heads of two sizes and shapes, the smaller type being in sufficient excess to explain an excess of males at fertilization, if the smaller sperm contains the smaller Y chromosome and the larger sperm carries the larger X chromosome. It is likely, then, that at conception males and females are unequal in number. A study of the sex ratio at birth has shown that the ratio of 1.067 : 1 is found only among young parents, and that it decreases steadily until it is about 1.036 : 1 among the children of older parents. How might this significant decrease be explained? It might be due to a greater chance for male babies to abort in older mothers. It might be due, in part, to the increased likelihood, among older mothers, for a chromosome to be lost, in the earliest mitotic divisions of the fertilized egg, by failing to be included in one of the daughter nuclei. For, if the chromosome lost was an X, and the zygote was XY, then the loss would be expected to be lethal, and what would have been a boy would be aborted, while if the zygote losing an X was XX, a girl would still be born. Moreover, if the chromosome lost in the XY individual was a Y, a girl might be born instead of a boy. Part of the effect must be due to the increase in meiotic nondisjunction with maternal age (zygotes of XXX type form viable females, while zygotes of Y0 type are expected to be lost before birth).

We must not preclude the possibility that the fathers are somewhat responsible for this shift in sex ratio. There may be an increase, with paternal age, in postmeiotic selection against Y-carrying sperm. Perhaps, as fathers become older, there is an increased chance for certain abnormal events to take place during the meiotic divisions preceding sperm formation. How could this be of significance? Suppose the XY tetrad undergoes nondisjunction in such a way that from a given prophase I cell, the four meiotic products, each forming a sperm, contain, respectively, X, X, YY, 0. The first two sperm listed would produce normal daughters, the last one an underdeveloped X0 daughter, while only the YY would be capable of producing maleness. Moreover, this "male" individual would be XYY and we do not know if such a genotype is viable. While still other genetic and nongenetic explanations for the shift in sex ratio with age are possible, the present discussion will suffice to demonstrate how the basic facts of sex determination, chromosome loss, and nondisjunction may be used to set up various explanatory hypotheses whose validity may subsequently be subject to test.

The sex ratio has been found abnormal in another respect. When pedigrees are examined for sex ratio, it occasionally is found that a dozen consecutive births are of the same sex. This could happen purely as a matter of chance if enough pedigrees are scored, just as it is possible (but unlikely) that you could have a coin fall with the same side up in a dozen consecutive tosses. But one family is reported to have had only boys in 47 births, and in another well substantiated case a family has had 72 births, all girls. In both these cases the result is so improbable that it is not reasonable to consider it to be merely due to chance! While we do not know the basis for such results in man, we can examine two different cases in *Drosophila* in which almost only female progeny are produced; these might suggest an explanation for those human pedigrees in which only one sex occurs in the progeny.

In the first case in *Drosophila*, the males were found to be responsible for the almost exclusive production of daughters. These males are XY but carry a gene called "sex

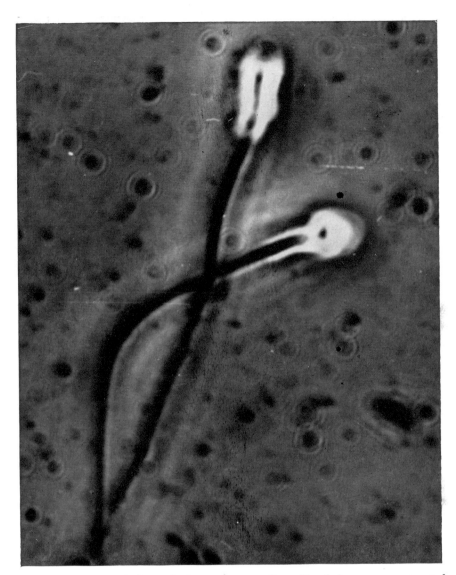

FIGURE 14–6. *Head shapes in human sperm. Round-headed sperm are reported to be smaller and more numerous than oval-headed sperm, suggesting these carry the Y and X chromosomes, respectively. (Courtesy of L. B. Shettles.)*

ratio." Because of this gene, almost all Y chromosomes degenerate during meiosis and almost all sperm carry an X. In the second case, the females were the important factor, for it was found that these females transmit a spirochaete microorganism to their offspring through their eggs. Such females, when mated to normal males, produce zygotes which initiate development. But very early in development the spirochaete kills XY individuals, so that almost all survivors are female.

Finally, when one talks about sex determination the question often comes up: Can sex be predetermined? In theory the answer is yes, in the sense that if we could control the genotypes of zygotes we would determine ahead of time what sex would be formed. And again, since X- and Y-bearing sperm of men apparently differ in cytological appearance (Figure 14–6; see also Figure 14–7), it should be theoretically possible to separate these, thereby leading to the control of the sex of progeny. Using various animal forms, experiments along these lines have been performed with some success by Russian, U.S., and Swedish workers using electric currents or centrifugation. Though these methods have given encouraging results, the results are not yet consistent and the techniques not yet suitable for practical use.

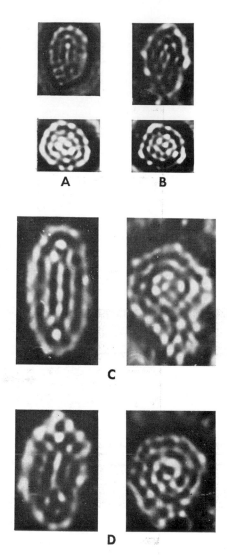

FIGURE 14–7. *According to L. B. Shettles, these phase-contrast photographs show a concentric arrangement of the chromosomes present in rounded and elongated types of sperm head. A, B, C, and D from different men. The light, lobulated chains are stained by the Feulgen-Rossenbeck procedure.*

SUMMARY AND CONCLUSIONS

Genes responsible for sex determination are located not only in the sex chromosomes, but in the autosomes as well. Although sex type may be changed through the action of a single pair of genes, a given sex is usually the result of the interaction of several, and probably many, pairs of genes. Sex is, therefore, a polygenic trait (Chapter 8), in which the usual chromosomal differences found among zygotes serve as visible manifestations of differences in the balance of genes concerned with sex, and by which one balance produces male and another female. Whenever, as in female *Drosophila*, genic balance is unaffected by the addition or subtraction of whole sets of chromosomes, sex also is unaffected. However, changes in chromosome content which make for intermediate genic balances produce intermediate sex types — intersexes; those which make the balance more extreme than normal produce extreme sex types — supersexes.

These principles of sex determination presumably apply also to human beings. In man and many other organisms, a large part of sexual differentiation is under the control of sex hormones produced by the gonads. While this type of control makes the occurrence of individuals who are typically male in one part and typically female in another part very unlikely, it may lead to the formation of abnormal sex types for nongenetic reasons.

REFERENCES

Bangham, A. D., "Electrophoretic Characteristics of Ram and Rabbit Spermatozoa," Proc. Roy. Soc., Ser. B, 155:292–305, 1961.

Bridges, C. B., "Sex in Relation to Chromosomes and Genes," Amer. Nat., 59:127–137, 1925. Reprinted in *Classic Papers in Genetics*, Peters, J. A. (Ed.), Englewood Cliffs, N.J., Prentice-Hall, 1959, pp. 117–123.

Goldschmidt, R. B., *Theoretical Genetics*, Berkeley and Los Angeles, University of California Press, 1955.

Shettles, L. B., "Nuclear Morphology of Human Spermatozoa," Nature, London, 186:648–649, 1960.

Shettles, L. B., "Nuclear Structure of Human Spermatozoa," Nature, London, 188:918–919, 1960.

Sturtevant, A. H., "A Gene in *Drosophila Melanogaster* that Transforms Females into Males," Genetics, 30:297–299, 1945.

Alfred H. Sturtevant (*in 1945*).

QUESTIONS FOR DISCUSSION

14.1. Does a gene have to have an alternative allele before it can be discovered? Explain.

14.2. Make a schematic representation of a trivalent as it might appear during synapsis. Suppose each carried a different allele, a^1, a^2, a^3, of the same gene.
Show diagrammatically the chromosomal and genetic content of the four meiotic products you might obtain from the trivalent you drew.

14.3. Ignoring chiasma formation, how many chromosomally-different kinds of eggs can a triploid *Drosophila* female produce? How many of these eggs have more than a 5% chance of occurring?

14.4. What explanations can you offer, other than those presented, which may pertain to the shift in sex ratio with age of human parents?

14.5. No Y0 human beings are known. Is this chromosomalconstitution considered lethal? Why?

14.6. List the types of human zygotes formed following maternal nondisjunction of the X chromosome. What are the phenotypes expected for each of the zygotes these may form in turn?

14.7. List specific causes for the production of abnormal sex types in human beings.

14.8. How can you account for the fact that one X0 individual is known who has had a successful pregnancy, whereas most known X0's are sterile?

14.9. Discuss the general applicability of the chromosomal balance theory of sex determination.

14.10. In *Drosophila*, why are gynanders not intersexes? Is this true in man also? Explain.

14.11. What chromosomal constitution can you give for a triploid human being who is "male"? "female"?
Which of these chromosomal constitutions would you expect to deviate most from its normal sex? Explain.

14.12. A non-hemophilic man and woman have a son who proves to be a hemophilic Klinefelter male. Describe the chromosomal content and genotypes of all three individuals mentioned.

Chapter 15

INTERGENIC LINKAGE

IT WAS reported in Chapter 6 (pp. 46–47) that each of the first seven pairs of genes studied in the garden pea segregated independently. This can be attributed to each pair of genes being located on a different pair of the seven pairs of chromosomes which this organism carries. What we should consider now are the results obtained when an eighth pair of genes, showing dominance and affecting an unrelated trait, is studied simultaneously with each of the other seven pairs in turn. When a dihybrid for a particular one of the seven and for the eighth gene pairs is made, a 9 : 3 : 3 : 1 phenotypic ratio is obtained when the dihybrid is self-fertilized, and a 1 : 1 : 1 : 1 phenotypic ratio is obtained when this individual is backcrossed to the double recessive. This demonstrates in two independent tests that the two pairs of genes involved are segregating independently and are located on nonhomologous chromosomes. The same ratios are obtained, from the same types of crosses, with dihybrids made with each of five other genes and this eighth gene pair, so that the same conclusion also applies for them. However, the results obtained from the dihybrid made with the remaining gene pair and the eighth will be described in some detail, since these results are radically different.

The seventh pair of genes happens to be the one concerned with the seed coat, a trait we have already studied in Chapter 6, whose allelic alternatives are *round* (R) and *wrinkled* (r). As mentioned earlier, we may use various symbols to represent genes. In the pres-

ent case, the first letter (or so) of the phenotype produced by the dominant allele (the one normally found in nature) has been used in upper and lower case to represent the dominant and recessive alleles, respectively. In other conventions (see Figure 15–1), the first letter (or so) of the recessive mutant (not normally found) allele is used in lower case for the recessive allele (*wrinkled* = w), while the normal dominant allele is given either the same symbol in upper case, or is given a $+$ symbol as a superscript or base to the lower case symbol, or is given as $+$ alone (so that *round* may be, respectively, W, w^+, $+^w$, $+$). Sometimes the hybrid $+w$ is represented as $\frac{+}{w}$ or $\frac{+}{w}$ or $+/w$ to show that these alleles are on different members of a pair of homologous chromosomes.

$$\frac{R}{r} \quad \frac{W}{w} \quad \frac{w^+}{w} \quad \frac{+^w}{w} \quad \frac{+}{w} \quad \frac{+}{w} \quad +/w$$

FIGURE 15–1. *Various ways of representing the round-wrinkled hybrid by gene symbols.*

The eighth pair of genes deals with the presence ($+$) and absence (t) of tendrils, threadlike structures used for attachment as the plant climbs. When a double recessive pea plant (wrinkled, no tendrils = $w\,w\,t\,t$) is crossed to a pure double dominant (round, tendrils = $+ + + +$), all F_1 are round with tendrils ($+ w + t$), as expected. (Notice we are using the $+$ system for symbols here.) When the F_1 are self-fertilized (dihybrid X dihybrid) the following results are obtained in F_2:

Phenotype	No. Individuals
round, tendrils	319
round, no tendrils	4
wrinkled, tendrils	3
wrinkled, no tendrils	123

Note that each gene pair shows segregation in the F_2 since round : wrinkled as 323 : 126 (a 3 : 1 ratio) and tendrils : no tendrils as

322 : 127 (a 3 : 1 ratio). Yet these 3 : 1 ratios are not produced independently of each other, for if they were they would give a 9 : 3 : 3 : 1 ratio, which is certainly not found here. Instead, there are in F_2 relatively too many plants phenotypically like the P_1 parents (wrinkled, no tendrils; round, tendrils), and relatively too few, new recombinational types (round, no tendrils; wrinkled, tendrils).

Examine also the phenotypic results obtained from backcrossing the dihybrid in question $(+ w + t \times w w t t)$:

Phenotypes	No. Individuals
round, tendrils	516
round, no tendrils	9
wrinkled, tendrils	7
wrinkled, no tendrils	492

The expectation according to independent segregation is a 1 : 1 : 1 : 1 ratio for each of the types obtained. Actually, there are relatively excessive numbers of gametes, produced by the dihybrid, containing the old combinations $(+ +$ and $w t)$ — that is, the combinations which came from the parents to form the dihybrid — and relatively too few new combinational or recombinational types, just as is true in the case where two of these dihybrids are crossed. We conclude again, therefore, that independent segregation does not obtain here.

The fact that we get some recombinational types in the present case confirms the earlier statement (which was really an assumption) that we are actually dealing with two separate pairs of genes. Let us assume that the two pairs of genes involved are located on the same pair of homologous chromosomes, a possibility which was introduced in Chapter 6 (p. 46). In this event, the *genes* are said to be *linked to each other* because they are on the same chromosome. Recall that the phenomenon of sex-linkage, already discussed in Chapter 12, dealt with a single gene (such as that for white eye) and its location on or linkage to a particular chromosome (the X

chromosome). We are now concerned with studying *intergenic linkage*, which involves all the nonallelic genes presumed to be located on the same chromosome. (Evidence bearing on this can only be obtained by studying the transmission genetics of more than one trait, other than sex, at a time.) For the first time, then, we shall be testing the hypothesis that a chromosome contains more than one gene.

Let us re-examine, by means of Figures 15–2 and 15–3, respectively, the results of the two kinds of crosses described. In these Figures we will use a horizontal line to represent a chromosome and indicate the presence of one member of each gene pair on each chromosome. In those cases where the genes could be either the normal or the mutant allele, a question mark is placed in the appropriate position. If linkage had been complete, that is, if the chromosome carrying $w t$ or $+ +$ was forever unchangeable (except for the rare event of mutation), then all results in Figure 15–2 down through the genotypes of the P_2 would be consistent with this view. However, the occurrence of seven recombinational individuals shows that linkage is not complete. These recombinational individuals have a chromosome which has kept one allele and received the nonallele present in the homologous chromosome. Moreover, the reciprocal type of recombinant is apparently equally frequent, as though a given pair of genes had switched positions in the homologs — that is, as though they had reciprocally crossed over. For this reason such recombinational individuals are said to carry a *crossover* chromosome produced by a process called *crossing over*. So, complete linkage between genes is prevented by a genetic process, crossing over, which produces genetic recombinations called crossovers.

What other rules, if any, can we establish for the crossing-over process and the crossovers it produces? Among the progeny obtained from backcrossing the dihybrid (Figure 15–3), 16 received crossovers in the gametes

P₁ **Wrinkled, no tendrils x Round, tendrils**

$$\frac{wt}{wt}$$ $$\frac{++}{++}$$

FIGURE 15–2 (*Left*). *Linkage between nonallelic genes in the garden pea.*

F₁ **Round, tendrils** $\dfrac{++}{wt}$

P₂ F₁ **Round, tendrils (self-fertilized)**

$$\frac{++}{wt}$$ x $$\frac{++}{wt}$$

F₂ **Round, tendrils** $\dfrac{++}{??}$ 319

Round, no tendrils $\dfrac{+t}{?t}$ 4

Wrinkled, tendrils $\dfrac{wt}{w?}$ 3

Wrinkled, no tendrils $\dfrac{wt}{wt}$ 123

TOTAL 449

FIGURE 15–3 (*Right*). *Linkage between nonallelic genes in the garden pea. The dihybrid parent was obtained from the F₁ in Fig. 15–2.*

P₂ F₁ **Round, tendrils x Wrinkled, no tendrils**

$$\frac{++}{wt}$$ $$\frac{wt}{wt}$$

F₂ **Round, tendrils** $\dfrac{++}{wt}$ 516

Round, no tendrils $\dfrac{+t}{wt}$ 9

Wrinkled, tendrils $\dfrac{wt}{wt}$ 7

Wrinkled, no tendrils $\dfrac{wt}{wt}$ 492

TOTAL 1024

contributed by the dihybrid and 1008 did not. The reciprocal crossover classes are apparently equally frequent. So approximately one crossover was produced for each 63 non-crossovers. The F₂ results in Figure 15–2 are consistent with this proportion, as you will find if you work it out.

It is also possible to make a dihybrid for these genes which receives one mutant and one normal (w +) from one parent, and one normal and one mutant (+ t) from the other parent. When this dihybrid is backcrossed, the crossovers ($w\,t$ or + +) and non-crossovers (w + or + t) also occur in the proportion 1 : 63. Apparently crossing over is a genetic phenomenon which occurs with the same frequency whether the two mutant genes enter the dihybrid from the same or from different parents. Crossovers, therefore, occur in the gametes of an individual with a frequency that is constant and independent of the specific way the alleles were carried by the gametes that fused to initiate that individual. If this is so, then it must follow that even in + +/+ + and $w\,t/w\,t$ individuals, one gamete in each 64 produced is a crossover for these genes, but is undetected because it carries no new combination of alleles. We see then that when two linked mutants enter a zygote together, because they are located on the same chromosome, they tend to stay together when transmitted to the next generation (*coupling*), but if they enter the zygote separately, being located on different members of a pair of homologous chromosomes, they tend to be transmitted separately to the next generation (*repulsion*).

In another species, the sweet pea, it is found that the trait purple flowers is due to a single gene (+) whose recessive allele (r) produces red flowers. Long pollen (+) is dominant to round pollen (ro). A pure line of purple long (+ +/+ +) crossed to red round ($r\,ro/r\,ro$) produces F_1 that are all purple long (+ +/$r\,ro$). Since self-fertilization of the F_1 produces too many P_1 phenotypes and too few, new, recombinational types (purple round and red long) for these two pairs of genes to be segregating independently, these genes also must be linked. But, as before, linkage is not complete. In this case, the crossovers obtained can be accounted for if the P_2 (F_1) dihybrid forms gametes in the relative proportions

$$10 + + : 10\,r\,ro : 1 + ro : 1\,r\,+.$$

This rate of crossing over is obtained no matter how the genes enter the dihybrid. Notice, however, that this constant rate ($\frac{1}{11}$) differs from the rate observed in the garden pea example previously discussed ($\frac{1}{64}$).

Consider also the rate of crossing over in two other cases. You recall, in *Drosophila*, that the mutant gene, w, for white eye is X-linked. So also is a different mutant gene which produces miniature wings (m). Using pure lines, a white-eyed, long-winged fly is crossed to a dull red-eyed, miniature-winged one. The F_1 female carries two X's and is, therefore, w +/+ m. This female is then mated to any male and the sons are scored phenotypically. Any male can be used as parent, since any male will transmit to his sons a Y chromosome that is devoid of the genes under consideration. In fact, it can be shown that the Y is lacking most of the genes known to be present on the X, the gene *bobbed bristles*, bb, being a notable exception. (Besides a bb allele, the Y contains several genes for male fertility which have no alleles on the X.) Since the sons will receive their X from their mother, they will show by their phenotype directly which of these alleles each received in the gamete she provided. It is found among the sons of this mating that about one crossover type appears for every two that are noncrossovers.

Finally, in man, *color-blindness* (c) and *hemophilia type A* (h) are recessive X-linked mutant genes absent on the Y chromosome. Though rare, there are some women with the genotype + h/c +, i.e., having one of these mutants on each X. Available data indicate that crossover ($c\,h$ or + +) and non-crossover (+ h or c +) sons occur in the approximate ratio of 1 : 9.

These results show that when linkage between genes fails to be complete, the percentages of crossovers formed between any two given pairs of genes is constant, but that this frequency can be quite different in cases studied in different organisms.

SUMMARY AND CONCLUSIONS

When independent segregation fails, the nonallelic genes involved tend to be inherited in a linked manner. Recombination between linked genes offers proof that a chromosome contains more than one gene. Just as linkage is an exception to independent segregation, crossing over is an exception to linkage and causes linkage to be incomplete. In any given case, the degree to which linkage is incomplete, that is, the rate of crossing over, is constant and independent both of the specific alleles which are present for the two different genes and of the combinations these were in when they entered the individual forming the gametes. Moreover, reciprocal crossover types are equally frequent. The crossover frequency in different cases, as studied in different organisms, is found to vary considerably.

REFERENCES

Morgan, T. H., "Random Segregation Versus Coupling in Mendelian Inheritance," Science, 34:384, 1911. Reprinted in *Great Experiments in Biology*, Gabriel, M. L., and S. Fogel (Eds.), Englewood Cliffs, N.J., Prentice-Hall, 1955, pp. 257–259.

QUESTIONS FOR DISCUSSION

15.1. Distinguish between sex linkage and the linkage of nonalleles.

15.2. Does the linkage of two pairs of genes prove that they are located on the same chromosome? Explain.

15.3. Discuss the advantages and disadvantages of linkage and crossing over with respect to the fitness of individuals carrying certain genotypes.

15.4. In *Drosophila*, *y* and *spl* are X-linked. A female genotypically $+ +/y$ spl produces sons of which 3.0% carry either $y +$ or $+ spl$.

What are the genotypes and relative frequencies of gametes produced by the mother? Is the father's genotype important? Explain.

15.5. Name all the processes so far discussed which lead to genetic recombination.

15.6. Do you think that one of the main principles demonstrated in the present Chapter is that chromosomes contain more than one gene? Explain.

15.7. How would you proceed to state a "law of independent segregation" in the light of your present knowledge?

15.8. What evidence do you have that crossing over does not involve the unilateral movement of one gene, from its position in one chromosome to a position in the homologous chromosome?

15.9. Does crossing over always result in genetic recombination? Explain.

15.10. In what respect do you think the development of the principles of genetics in this text would have been affected had the first two pairs of genes, simultaneously studied in crosses, been linked?

15.11. Assume the gene for woolly hair (p. 34) is located autosomally. A nonwoolly haired nonhemophilic man marries a woolly haired nonhemophilic woman. They have a woolly haired hemophilic son. Give the genotypes of all three individuals. Give the genotypes and frequencies of the gametes usually produced by the son.

Chapter *16

CROSSING OVER AND CHIASMA

YOU HAVE already seen how the study of cross-fertilizing species demonstrated that the genetic material was divisible first into a single pair of genes (because of segregation), then into a number of gene pairs (because of independent segregation), and then into still more genes (because those in the same chromosome are not forever bound together, or completely linked, but become separated and may produce new combinations). Linked genes may form these new combinations when the genes of a pair mutually switch their position in a pair of homologous chromosomes by a process named crossing over (Chapter 15). The strength of linkage was found to vary in different cases studied in different organisms. Let us continue to study linkage and crossing over by means of a number of examples taken from the same organism, *Drosophila melanogaster*.

Two mutants *b* (black body color) and *vg* (vestigial wings) are studied simultaneously. A P_1 cross between *vg +/vg +* (vestigial[1]) ♀♀ and *+ b/+ b* (black) ♂♂ produces all normal F_1, *vg +/+ b*. As shown in Figure 16–1A, a backcross of the F_1 female (*vg +/+ b* ♀ × *vg b/vg b* ♂) produces only 20% of F_2 with recombinant chromosomes (all F_2 carry *vg b* from the father, their maternal chromosome being 40% of the time *vg +*, 40% *+ b*, 10% *+ +*, 10% *vg b*). Since these results are independent of sex, we conclude that *b* and *vg*

are linked autosomally. (For comparison, recall from the last Chapter that the X-linked genes *m* and *w* showed 33% crossing over.)

When, however, the reciprocal cross is made with the F_1, the dihybrid being the male (*vg +/+ b* ♂ × *vg b/vg b* ♀), 50% of offspring are *vg +/vg b* (vestigial) and 50% *+ b/vg b* (black) (Figure 16–1B). This demonstrates no offspring with crossovers, so that linkage is complete for these genes in the male *Drosophila*. Of course, had linkage been complete in the female also, we should not have had any evidence that *vg* and *b* are separable and are therefore two genes instead of one. It develops, moreover, that in *Drosophila* any genes which show incomplete linkage in the female show complete linkage in the male, so this sex, therefore, does not undergo the process of crossing over.[2] It may be noted that in animals, in general, the heterogametic sex has reduced or no crossing over.

What will be the consequence of crossing two *Drosophila* which are dihybrid *vg +/+ b*? The female will produce gametes in the following frequencies: .4 *vg +*, .4 *+ b*, .1 *+ +*, .1 *vg b*; the male .5 *vg +*, .5 *+ b*. Combining these by means of a branched track produces the results shown in Figure 16–2. The 2 : 1 : 1 : 0 phenotypic ratio obtained is easy to distinguish experimentally from a 9 : 3 : 3 : 1 ratio, which would be expected according to independent segregation. We can generalize the results to be expected in *Drosophila*. Let the two linked mutants be *a* and *b* and each dihybrid *a +/+ b*. Let 2p equal the frequency of noncrossover eggs (*a +* plus *+ b*), and 1 − 2p the frequency of crossover eggs (*a b* plus *+ +*). When linkage is incomplete, p < .5. The results are shown in Figure 16–3. We see there that no matter what value, below .5, p is permitted to have, the phenotypic ratio will be 2 : 1 : 1 : 0. If

---

[1] The convention used here, and usually on subsequent occasions, is to describe the phenotypes of individuals only with respect to the appearance of mutant traits, all traits not mentioned being of the normal type.

[2] A special kind of "crossing over" does occur on very rare occasions in the germ line (see p. 118) of male *Drosophila*, but is not of the kind that typically occurs in females.

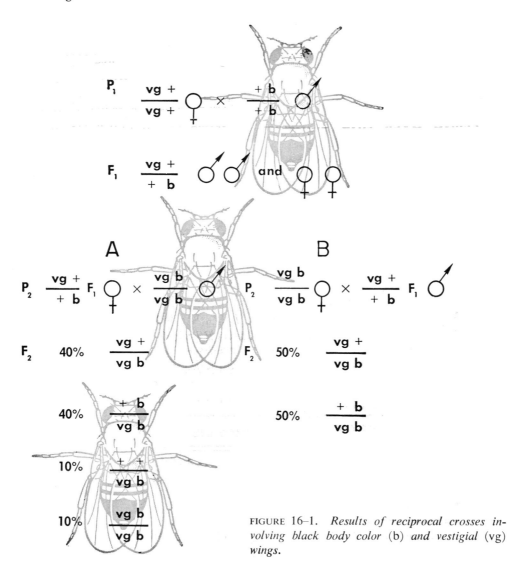

FIGURE 16–1. *Results of reciprocal crosses involving black body color* (b) *and vestigial* (vg) *wings.*

the dihybrids are $ab/++$, however, this ratio is not obtained.

Thus far, two cases in *Drosophila* have been studied and different crossover rates found in each, one case involving the X, the other an autosome. The question may now be asked: What is the strength of linkage between a given gene and several others located in the same chromosome? This can be studied readily for certain X-linked genes. Females are constructed with the genotypes shown in Figure 16–4. The frequencies of crossover combinations, as detected in their sons, are shown in the other column of the Figure. The recombination rates given are those found between the gene for yellow body color (*y*) in each instance and for white eye (*w*), crossveinless wings (*cv*), cut wings (*ct*), minia-

FIGURE 16–2. *Derivation of the phenotypic ratio obtained in* Drosophila *from mating together two dihybrids for linked genes.*

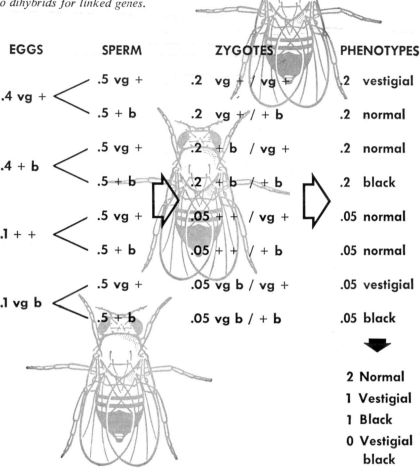

EGGS	SPERM	ZYGOTES	PHENOTYPES
.4 vg +	.5 vg +	.2 vg + / vg +	.2 vestigial
	.5 + b	.2 vg + / + b	.2 normal
.4 + b	.5 vg +	.2 + b / vg +	.2 normal
	.5 + b	.2 + b / + b	.2 black
.1 + +	.5 vg +	.05 + + / vg +	.05 normal
	.5 + b	.05 + + / + b	.05 normal
.1 vg b	.5 vg +	.05 vg b / vg +	.05 vestigial
	.5 + b	.05 vg b / + b	.05 black

2 Normal

1 Vestigial

1 Black

**0 Vestigial
black**

ture wings (*m*), and forked bristles (*f*). For example, the female dihybrid for *y* and *cv* produces about 13 eggs of each 100 which carry crossovers (+ + or *y cv*). What does this value, and what do the other still different linkage values, mean in terms of meiosis?

Recall from what was discussed in the present Chapter and the one preceding that no commitment was made as to where or when the genetic event of crossing over takes place. Since we have been concerned with complete and incomplete linkage as studied in successive generations of individuals, let us consider only crossing over that occurs in the cell line giving rise to the gametes (the *germ line*), ignoring the possibility that crossing over occurs in *somatic* (nongerminal, p. 23) *cells*. Although the possibilities still remain that crossing over is premeiotic, meiotic, and postmeiotic in occurrence, we shall presume that all crossovers are produced during meiosis. We have already discussed (pp. 44–46) the theoretical genetic consequences of a chiasma between two pairs of genes during meiosis, and we shall suppose that a chiasma represents physical cytological evidence that a genetic crossing over has occurred.

The genetic events theoretically associated

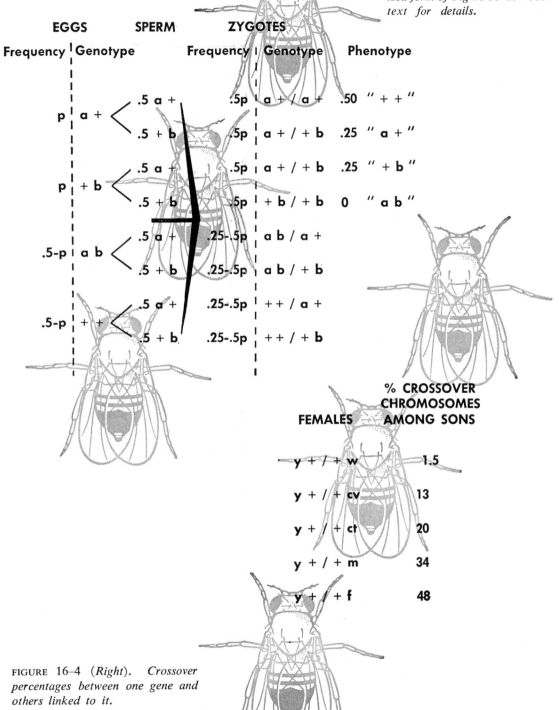

FIGURE 16–3 (*Left*). *Generalized form of Figure 16–2. See text for details.*

EGGS		SPERM	ZYGOTES		
Frequency	Genotype		Frequency	Genotype	Phenotype
p	a +	.5 a +	.5p	a + / a +	.50 " + + "
		.5 + b	.5p	a + / + b	.25 " a + "
p	+ b	.5 a +	.5p	a + / + b	.25 " + b "
		.5 + b	.5p	+ b / + b	0 " a b "
.5-p	a b	.5 a +	.25-.5p	a b / a +	
		.5 + b	.25-.5p	a b / + b	
.5-p	+ +	.5 a +	.25-.5p	+ + / a +	
		.5 + b	.25-.5p	+ + / + b	

FEMALES	% CROSSOVER CHROMOSOMES AMONG SONS
y + / + w	1.5
y + / + cv	13
y + / + ct	20
y + / + m	34
y + / + f	48

FIGURE 16–4 (*Right*). *Crossover percentages between one gene and others linked to it.*

with a chiasma are depicted in Figure 16–5 in somewhat more detail than those which are shown in Figure 6–8B (p. 46). Stage I shows a pair of homologous chromosomes, one member (hollow bar) carrying the recessives *a* and *b*, and the other (solid bar) carrying their normal alleles. The black dots represent centromeres. The homologs synapse, form a tetrad (each univalent now represented by two *sister strands*), and give the appearance at diplonema depicted in stage II. Here there is a chiasma between the *a* and *b* *loci* (the places in a chromosome containing the genes). Note, when the univalents are initially identical in appearance, that a chiasma results in the physical exchange of

exactly equivalent segments between two non-sister strands of a tetrad, the strands exchanging segments being just as long after the exchange as they were before. Stage III shows the dyads present after the first meiotic division is completed. Note that the upper cell contains one + + noncrossover strand and one + *b* crossover strand, while the bottom cell contains the reciprocal crossover strand *a* + and the noncrossover strand *a b*. Stage IV shows the four haploid cells produced after the dyads form monads and the second meiotic division is completed. Notice that if one chiasma occurs in any position between the loci of *a* and *b*, two haploid nuclei are produced, containing noncrossover, parental

FIGURE 16–5. *The genetic consequences expected following a chiasma between linked genes.*

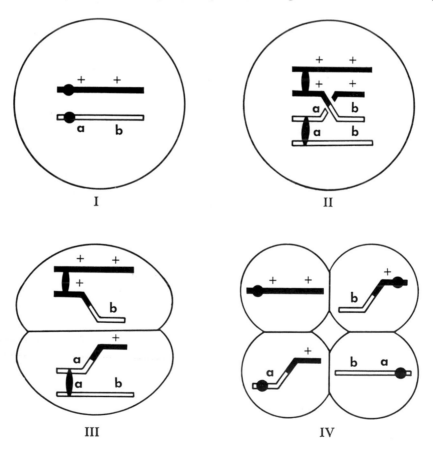

I

II

III

IV

combinations, while the other two haploid nuclei contain crossover, nonparental recombinations.

Evidence that the crossovers found in gametes have this origin is ordinarily difficult to obtain. This is so because, in females, typically only one of the four haploid products, from each nucleus starting the meiotic divisions, is retained as the nucleus of a functional gamete, the others being lost (often as polar body nuclei). Even in those cases where each of the four haploid products becomes a gamete, as in sperm or pollen formation, the four gametes, produced from a cell containing a given chiasma, mix with those produced from other meiotic cells which may or may not have had a similar chiasma. As a consequence, therefore, only one of the four meiotic products from a given chiasma is observed or identified at a time. Note that the chiasma explanation for crossing over would provide equal numbers of the two reciprocal kinds of crossovers, and also equal numbers of the two types of noncrossovers, as is required from the crossover data already presented. However, crossing over during the two-stranded stage I would also satisfy these requirements.

Can we obtain genetic evidence as to whether crossing over occurs in the two-strand or four-strand (tetrad) stage? One possible way to determine this would be to use a genetic system whereby not one but two strands of the four in a tetrad are retained in a single gamete. If such a gamete carried one strand which is a noncrossover and another homologous one which is a crossover, this would support the four-strand hypothesis exclusively. This possibility becomes a reality through the use of *Drosophila* females whose two X's are not free to segregate from each other because they share a single centromere. Such attached-X's are V-shaped at anaphase. During meiosis the attached-X replicates once and the four arms synapse to form a tetrad, yielding two meiotic products

each of which carries attached-X's and two devoid of X chromosomes. From a genetic analysis of the female progeny, of females whose attached-X's are dihybrid, evidence favorable to the four-strand view has been obtained (Figure 16–6).

In pursuit of additional evidence regarding the time crossing over takes place during meiosis, the red bread mold *Neurospora* can be investigated. *Neurospora* ("nerve spore") is usually haploid and comes in two different sexes. In the sexual process, so-called fruiting bodies are formed, composed of cells each containing two haploid nuclei, each of which was derived originally from a different parent (Figure 16–7). Two such haploid nuclei fuse to form a diploid nucleus containing seven pairs of chromosomes, and the cell elongates to form a sac. The diploid nucleus immediately undergoes meiosis, in the manner shown, so that at completion of meiosis the four haploid products are arranged in tandem, i.e., the topmost two nuclei come from one first division nucleus, the bottom two from the other first division nucleus. Subsequently, each haploid nucleus divides once mitotically, in tandem, so that each meiotic product is present in duplicate within the elongated sac, and each of the eight nuclei becomes encased to form a football-shaped spore. Each haploid spore (*ascospore*) can be removed from the sac (*ascus*), grown individually, and its genotype determined directly. You see, therefore, that these events and procedures make it possible to obtain and identify all of the products of meiosis derived from a single diploid nucleus.

Using the same symbols as were used in Figure 16–5, let us follow, in Figure 16–8, the genetic consequences of a single chiasma that occurs between the loci under study. This will provide us with the results expected from four-strand stage crossing over. Since only one pair of the seven pairs of chromosomes present are being traced, the others are omitted from the Figure. As a consequence

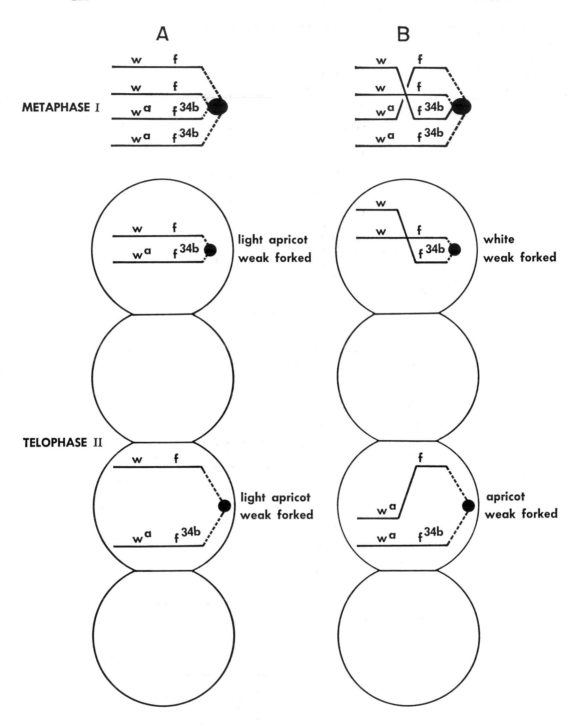

FIGURE 16–6. *Genotypic and phenotypic consequences of no chiasma (A) and of one type of chiasma (B) between marker genes in an attached-X female of* Drosophila.

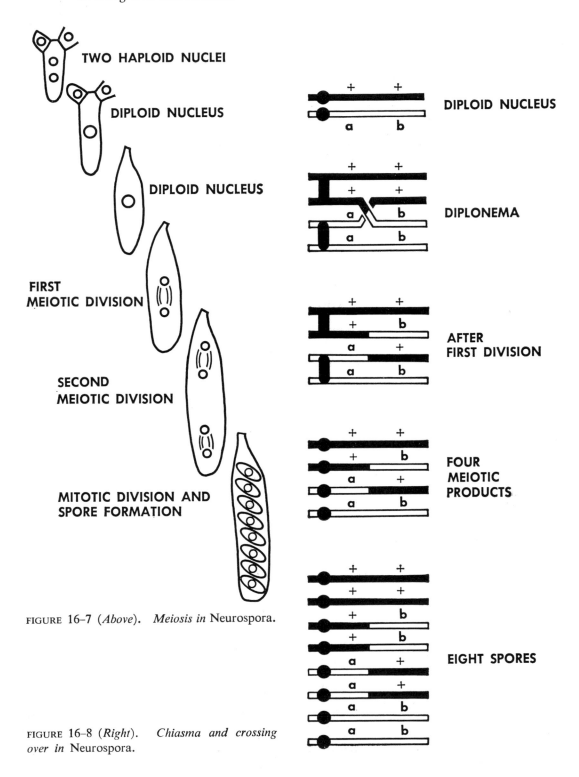

FIGURE 16–7 (*Above*). *Meiosis in* Neurospora.

FIGURE 16–8 (*Right*). *Chiasma and crossing over in* Neurospora.

exactly two of the four meiotic products are crossovers and exactly two are not. Note on the other hand, that had crossing over occurred in the two-strand stage (in the topmost nucleus), all the meiotic products in a single sac would be recombinant.

The result actually observed in some cases is that either none of the eight spores in an ascus is a crossover between *a* and *b*, or exactly four of the eight are; never are all eight spores, from a single sac, crossovers. This demonstrates conclusively that crossing over occurs in the four-strand stage, as shown in Figure 16–8.

It has already been implied that chiasma formation is a normal part of meiosis (p. 26). One of the consequences of chiasma formation is to prevent the premature separation of dyads by holding them together as a tetrad until anaphase I. (There is usually at least one, and there may be as many as six chiasmata, per tetrad.) Therefore, crossing over too is a normal part of meiosis. The fact that there are numerous places along a chromosome where a chiasma can form has a very interesting consequence. A single chiasma formed at any position between two loci will result in crossovers for these loci. Accordingly, it is reasonable to believe that the greater the distance between two loci, the greater will be the chance for a chiasma to occur between them, and the greater will be the frequency of crossovers for them. Reciprocally, the closer two loci are, the smaller will be the chance a chiasma will occur between them, and the smaller will be the number of crossovers for them. According to this view, the frequency of crossovers can be used as an indication of the relative distances between loci. (The results presented in Figure 16–4 should now have additional meaning for you.)

Suppose, in our model, that no chiasma occurs in 80% of spore sacs in the genetically marked region we have been considering. These sacs would produce 80% of the total number of spores carrying only parental, noncrossover genotypes. From the 20% of spore sacs which do contain such a chiasma, one would find half of the spores to be of the parental types and half to be recombinational. So, a chiasma frequency of 20% would result in 10% of all spores being of crossover type. We can express the distance between the loci of *a* and *b* as being 10 crossover map units, where a *map unit* is that distance which gives one crossover per hundred (spores, in the present case). It is generally true, then, that in the simple case (where the genes are sufficiently close together, as in the present example), crossover frequency (map distance) is just one-half chiasma frequency.

What procedures may be used to measure crossover frequency in *Neurospora*? There are several. First, this can be done in terms of spore sacs. As many spores are tested from each sac as are required to decide whether or not the sac carries a crossover in the region tested. (No more than five spores need to be tested per sac.) Speaking in terms of the *a-b* model already discussed, 20% of sacs would have crossovers, 80% would not. And since each sac containing crossovers has four spores that are crossovers and four that are not, crossing over frequency would be 10%. Second, all the spores from many sacs are mixed and then a random sample of spores is taken and tested. This method would give 10% recombination with our model, and is like the sampling procedure involved in determining crossover frequency in animal sperm. A third procedure would be to test one randomly chosen spore from each sac and discard the others. Again, 10% recombination would be obtained. This method resembles the situation in many females (including *Drosophila* and human beings) where, normally, one random product of meiosis enters the egg, the others being lost.

In what has been discussed relating chiasmata and crossing over, no study was described that directly correlated a genetically detected crossover with some cytologically detectable event involving a particular chromosome region. Such a connection cannot be made if both members of a pair of homologous chromosomes are identical in cytological appearance. This is true because a crossover strand, having exchanged a cytologically identical segment with its homolog, would appear the same as a noncrossover strand (cf. p. 120). But it is possible to construct a dihybrid for linked genes in which one homolog differs cytologically from its partner on both sides of the loci being tested. Such a genetic dihybrid is, simultaneously, cytologi-

cally dihybrid in the way specified (Figure 16–9). In this case, it is possible to collect noncrossover progeny and show cytologically that they invariably retain the original chromosomal arrangement, while crossovers always show cytologically a new chromosome arrangement that is explained by a mutual exchange between the homologs of specific chromosome regions.[3]

[3] In such a way, genetic crossovers were correlated exactly with cytological crossovers by Stern (1931) using *Drosophila*, and by Creighton and McClintock (1931) using maize.

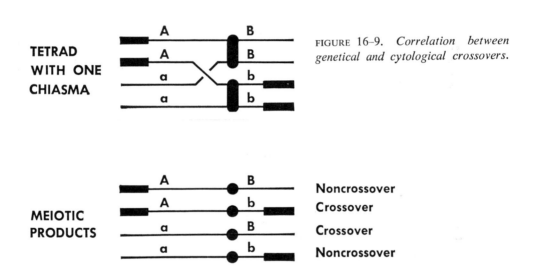

FIGURE 16–9. *Correlation between genetical and cytological crossovers.*

SUMMARY AND CONCLUSIONS

A crossover chromosome carried by a gamete is derived from a tetrad in which a chiasma, involving only two of the four strands, has occurred between the linked genes showing recombination. For closely linked genes, crossover frequency is one-half the frequency with which a chiasma occurs between their loci.

It is hypothesized that crossover frequency is directly related to distances between genes on a chromosome. One unit of crossover distance between genes is defined as one crossover per one hundred postmeiotic cells (spores or gametes). Since different genes linked to the same gene show different percentages of crossing over with this gene, they are presumably different distances from it.

Maize workers (l. to r.) at Cornell University in 1929: C. R. BURNHAM, M. M. RHOADES, G. W. BEADLE *(crouched)*, R. A. EMERSON, *and* BARBARA MCCLINTOCK.

CURT STERN, *in the early 1930's.*

REFERENCES

Creighton, H. S., and McClintock, B., "A Correlation of Cytological and Genetical Crossing-over in Zea Mays," Proc. Nat. Acad. Sci., U.S., 17:492–497, 1931. Reprinted in *Classic Papers in Genetics*, Peters, J. A. (Ed.), Englewood Cliffs, N.J., Prentice-Hall, 1959, pp. 155–160; also in *Great Experiments in Biology*, Gabriel, M. L., and S. Fogel (Eds.), Englewood Cliffs, N.J., Prentice-Hall, 1955, pp. 267–272.

Stern, C., "Zytologisch-genetische Untersuchungen als Beweise für die Morgansche Theorie des Faktorenaustauschs," Biol. Zbl., 51:547–587, 1931.

QUESTIONS FOR DISCUSSION

16.1. Does the Summary and Conclusions section contain one or more statements which have not been made in essentially the same terms earlier in the Chapter? If your answer is yes, give an example.

16.2. In a species where both sexes undergo crossing over with equal frequency, what is the percentage of crossing over between two loci if a mating between identical dihybrids (*Ab/aB*) gives four equally viable classes of offspring, the smallest class comprising 1% of all offspring?

16.3. How would you proceed to prove genetically that the last division in a spore sac of *Neurospora* is a mitotic one?

16.4. Could you determine, in the absence of crossing over, whether the alternatives for two different traits were due to a single pair of genes or to two pairs of linked genes? Explain.

16.5. Draw an attached-X chromosome of *Drosophila* heterozygous both for *y* and for *m*. Show the kinds of gametes which could be obtained following:

        a. No chiasma.
        b. One chiasma between the nonallelic genes.
        c. One chiasma not between the genes mentioned.

16.6. Suppose a plant has a long pair of chromosomes, one member of which has a large knob at one end of the chromosome while the other member has a small knob at the opposite end of the chromosome. Suppose, moreover, there is also a shorter pair of homologs, one member terminating with a large knob, while the other member terminates at the other end with a small knob.

With respect to these chromosomes, what combinations and configurations would you expect to find readily in the gametes of this individual?

16.7. What reasons can you present for believing that germ-line crossing over is based neither upon premeiotic nor upon postmeiotic events?

16.8. Translate into English the title of the article written by C. Stern.

Chapter 17

GENE ARRANGEMENT
AND CHIASMATA

IT WAS found in the preceding Chapter that the frequency of crossing over between genes may be considered in terms of distance measured in map units. Different genes linked to a given gene were found to have different crossover distances from it. The question arises, how are these different genes related to each other spatially? It may be that the crossover distances between a number of linked genes represent physical distances from one gene to another which would describe either some three-dimensional configuration (like a sphere, cube, prism, or polyhedron) or some two-dimensional one (like a circle, ellipse, triangle, or line). In order to determine if this is so, it is necessary to determine all the map distances for a minimum of three linked loci. (The crossover distance between two genes defines only two points; two points are insufficient to tell us whether linked genes occur in a specific geometrical arrangement.)

The arrangement of linked loci can be investigated in *Drosophila* using the three X-linked genes, *y* (for yellow body color), *w* (for white eyes), and *spl* (for split bristles). Dihybrid females of each of the following types are obtained, *y w/+ +*, *y spl/+ +*, *w spl/+ +*, and each is backcrossed to the appropriate double recessive male. The crossover percentages, or map distances, obtained from these crosses are, respectively, *y* to *w* 1.5, *y* to *spl* 3.0, and *w* to *spl* 1.5. These data describe a simple arrangement for these three genes, namely a linear one, since the crossover dis-

128

tance between the end genes *y* and *spl* equals the sum of the crossover distances from the middle gene *w* to the end ones. We shall presume, henceforth, that crossover distance is proportional to physical linear distance between genes.

It is also possible to study a fourth and then all other X-linked genes, and to map their positions relative to these three. When this is done, it is found that all are arranged in a linear order. In such a crossover or genetic map, *y* is arbitrarily assigned the position, or locus, 0. A standard crossover map for the *Drosophila* X would have the genes *y*, *w*, *spl*, *cv*, *ct*, *m*, and *f* lined up at the respective positions, 0, 1.5, 3.0, 13, 21, 36, 56.7. From this standard map one can read that *ct* and *m* are 15 map units apart (36–21). Since one map unit equals one crossover per hundred gametes, the dihybrid for *ct* and *m* (Figure 17–1) should produce 15% crossovers (7.5% + + and 7.5% *ct m*). However, such a result is obtained only when certain conditions are met.

The crossover rates actually observed will depend upon several factors. One of these is the number of individuals making up the sample. Standard distances are arrived at only after scoring large numbers of progeny. In small samples it is very likely that, by chance, the observed values will deviate considerably from the standard map distance in both directions. The larger the size of the sample, the closer will the observed value approach the standard one.

Another factor influencing observed crossover rates concerns the fact that different phenotypic classes may have different viabilities (cf. p. 9). Usually the phenotypic expression of a + allele is more viable than that of its mutant forms. So, in Figure 17–1, for example, phenotypically *ct m* sons are not as viable as normal (wild-type) sons, and though both types are equally frequent as zygotes, the former fail to complete development more often than the latter, and are, therefore, relatively less frequent among the adults scored for crossovers. It should be noted also that zygotes destined to become either miniature or cut are also discriminated against more than are zygotes destined to produce the wild-type. Whenever pheno- types are scored after some long develop-

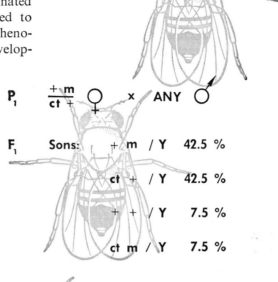

P_1 $\dfrac{+\ m}{ct\ +}$ ♀ x ANY ♂

F_1 Sons: $+\ m$ / Y 42.5 %

$ct\ +$ / Y 42.5 %

$+\ +$ / Y 7.5 %

$ct\ m$ / Y 7.5 %

FIGURE 17–1. *Crossover rate for two X-linked genes in* Drosophila.

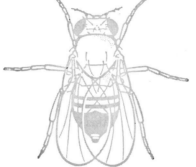

mental period, much of the error due to differential viability may be avoided by pro- viding optimal culture conditions. Another way to avoid most of this kind of error is to obtain progeny carrying the chromosome to be scored for crossovers, in which the homolo- gous chromosome contains the normal alleles of all genes under crossover test. Since such progeny are phenotypically normal they will all have approximately the same viability and can be scored as to chromosome type from the offspring each produces when individually test crossed. Thus, for example, the female in Figure 17–1 is crossed to wild-type males

and the daughters (all phenotypically normal) are individually mated to any male. Daugh- ters which carry, in addition to $+ +$ on one X obtained from their father, a homologous X of one of the following types, $+ m$, $ct +$, $+ +$, $ct m$, will produce sons, of which, respectively, some are miniature but none cut, some cut but none miniature, all normal and some miniature and cut. In this way the generation being tested for crossover rate is protected from differential viability and its genotypes are detected in the generation fol- lowing. For some purposes the extra labor entailed by the use of this method is justified.

Variability in crossover rates may be due also to factors influencing the process of crossing over itself. Such factors include temperature, nutrition, age of the female, and the presence of specific genes.

In order to understand better the relationships between crossing over and chiasmata, consider the properties of the following, oversimplified model (Figure 17–2). Assume that a chromosome (ignoring the centromere) is divided into five *equal* segments marked by

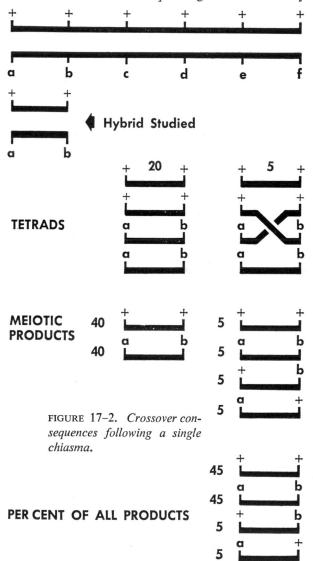

TETRADS

MEIOTIC PRODUCTS

FIGURE 17–2. *Crossover consequences following a single chiasma.*

PER CENT OF ALL PRODUCTS

six genes. Assume further that each tetrad with this chromosome contains one, and only one, chiasma which can occur at random among these segments. What would be observed if only the region between *a* and *b* was followed in the hexahybrid shown in the Figure? The chance that the chiasma will occur in the *a-b* region is 20%. From each 25 tetrads 100 haploid meiotic products are produced. Of each 25 tetrads, 20%, or five tetrads, will have the chiasma in the *a-b* region. These will produce 10 crossover and 10 noncrossover strands. The latter 10, when added to the 80 noncrossover strands from the other 20 tetrads, give 90 noncrossover strands. So, in this region, 20% chiasmata gives 10% crossovers, as explained in Chapter 16. Similarly, were only the *b-c* region followed, 10% crossovers would be observed.

If now only the *a-c* region is followed, the chiasma will fall within it 40% of the time and 20% of all haploid meiotic products will be crossovers between *a* and *c*. Note that in this model the sum of the distances *a-b* and *b-c* equals the distance as measured between *a* and *c* directly. So the model aligns the genes linearly, just as was observed in the experiment described near the beginning of this Chapter.

Note also, from the way the model was described, that the occurrence of a chiasma in one region automatically excludes its occurrence in some other region. We find, then, that the chance for a chiasma in the *a-c* region is equal to the sum of the separate chances for a chiasma in the *a-b* and *b-c* regions. It is a general rule that *the total probability that any one of a series of mutually exclusive events will occur is equal to the sum of their separate probabilities of occurrence.* Accordingly, the chance of a chiasma occurring between *a* and *f* is, of course,

$$100 (20 + 20 + 20 + 20 + 20)\%,$$

so that recombination is 50%, and the number of map units in our model is fifty.

You should be dissatisfied, however, with the ability of this model to represent reality, in view of the fact, previously noted, that a given tetrad usually contains more than one chiasma. This complication prompts the following question: What is the relationship between two chiasmata in the same tetrad? Two possible relationships come to mind. First, the frequency with which two chiasmata occur simultaneously within a certain region may be larger or smaller than that expected by chance. Second, the frequency with which the two chiasmata involve the same two strands of the tetrad may be larger or smaller than that which would be expected by chance. Consider the second relationship first.

Let us specifiy the strands in the tetrad of the model as 1, 2, 3, 4, where 1 and 2 are the normal sister strands and 3 and 4 the mutant sister strands (Figure 17–3). Suppose one chiasma occurs between strands 2 and 3 in the *a-b* region. There are six combinations of strands possible for a second chiasma which occurs in the *b-c* region, namely, 1 with 2, 3 with 4, 2 with 3, 2 with 4, 1 with 3, and 1 with 4. These positions are indicated in the Figure. Note, for this second chiasma, that the first two combinations listed would involve sister strands which are, naturally, genetically identical. Since sister-strand crossing over would have an effect upon the production of new genetic combinations only under other, very special, circumstances, such crossing over need not be considered further for our purposes. Each of the last four types

of chiasma involves nonsister strands in the *b-c* region, and together with the single chiasma in the *a-b* region, forms *double chiasmata* of three types, respectively: *2-strand* (the same two strands exchange in both chiasmata), *3-strand* (one of the two strands of the first chiasma exchanges in the second; there are two ways this can occur), and *4-strand* (the strands exchanging in the second chiasma are those which did not exchange in the first).

Restricting our attention to the *a-c* region, let us examine the genetic consequences of the nonsister double chiasmata described. Figure 17–4 shows, at the left, the configurations of these four nonsister types of double chiasmata. The middle column shows the meiotic products of each, and the right column describes whether these products are noncrossovers, single crossovers, or double crossovers for the *a-c* region. Notice that following 2-strand double chiasmata two of the four meiotic products are genetic noncrossovers ($+ + +$ and $a\ b\ c$) and two are double crossovers ($+ b +$ and $a + c$) recognizable because the middle gene is switched in position relative to the end genes. A 3-strand double chiasmata produces one double crossover, two single crossovers (recognizable because each has one end gene switched), and one noncrossover. The 4-strand double chiasmata produces four single crossover strands. Two things may be noted, namely, that each type of double chiasmata produces some strands with a new genetic combination,

FIGURE 17–3. *Chromatid combinations possible in a double chiasmata. (See text for details.)*

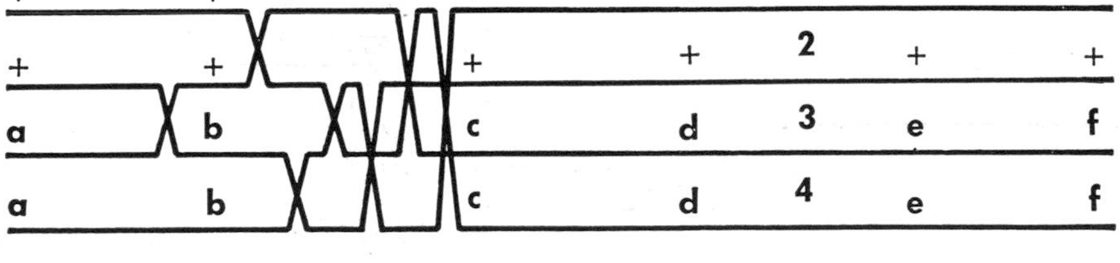

i.e., which are crossover, and that each of the three different types produces a characteristic pattern of noncrossover and crossover types. Note further that the genetic consequences of these double chiasmata are different from what would be obtained following a single chiasma (which, you remember, produces two noncrossovers and two singles).

In view of the preceding discussion, it should be possible by using an organism like *Neurospora*, in which all the products of meiosis are recoverable and testable, to learn from the genotypes of the meiotic products the relative frequency with which the four types of double chiasmata occur. If all four types occur with equal frequency, this would mean that the strands forming one chiasma are uninfluenced by those which form an adjacent chiasma. Indeed, work performed with *Neurospora* shows that all four types do occur. In some experiments the four types occur with equal frequency, and, for our purposes, we can accept the view that there is usually *no chromatid interference* in chiasma formation, i.e., the chromatids which enter into a chiasma do so uninfluenced by which strands have or have not undergone chiasma formation in an adjacent region.

Let us consider now the second possible relationship, already mentioned, between adjacent chiasmata. Does the occurrence of one chiasma increase or decrease the probability that an adjacent chiasma will occur, regardless of which strands are involved? Suppose, in a genetic system as in Figure 17–4, the probability of a single chiasma between *a* and *b* is 0.2 and between *b* and *c* is also 0.2. Having presumed that each of two regions under observation has a 20% chance of forming a single chiasma, let us again make use of the observation that more than one chiasma can form in a tetrad. If the occurrence of a chiasma in the *a-b* region is uninfluenced or independent of a chiasma in the *b-c* region, then, of all tetrads, 20% of the 20% with an *a-b* chiasma will simul-

taneously have a *b-c* chiasma, or 4% will contain double chiasmata. (And from what has been discussed before these 4% will be comprised of the four nonsister types in equal frequency.) It is a general rule that *the probability for the simultaneous occurrence of two or more independently occurring events is obtained by multiplying together their separate probabilities.*

If an experiment studying these regions actually gave 4% double chiasmata, one would conclude there was no *chiasma interference*; that is, the fact that homologous chromosomes form one chiasma has no effect upon the likelihood of their forming another one in an adjacent region. If, on the other hand, only 2% double chiasmata were observed, this would represent interference of one chiasma with the formation of another in an adjacent region.

The degree of chiasma interference can be expressed by the fraction:

$$\frac{\text{double chiasmata observed}}{\text{double chiasmata expected}} = \frac{.02}{.04} = .5$$

This fraction is called the *coefficient of coincidence* and expresses the frequency with which the expected coincidence of two chiasmata is actually observed. So, a coefficient of coincidence of 0 would mean one chiasma completely prevented the other one from occurring, while a value of 1 would mean that the one chiasma did not interfere at all with the occurrence of the other.

In practice, however, one does not determine the actual rates of occurrence and the positions of double chiasmata, since it is not feasible cytologically to score chiasmata in these ways. We are led, therefore, to examine the genetic event of crossing over to see whether it can be used to measure interference. Since we can be sure that each double crossover observed came from a double chiasmata, let us see if such crossovers can be used to calculate the coefficient of coincidence. The expected frequency of double crossovers in our example can be calculated in the following way: since each region has a 0.2 chance for a single chiasma, each has a 0.1 chance for a single crossover, and the expected chance for a double crossover is 0.1 × 0.1, or 0.01. If, as before, the actual double chiasmata in our example occurred with a frequency of .02, then, since only 4 of the 16 meiotic products appear as double crossovers (Figure 17–4), the observed fre-

quency of double crossovers would be .02/4 = .005. The coefficient of coincidence determined from double crossovers (observed frequency/expected frequency) would be .005/.01, or .5, which is the same as the value previously obtained using chiasmata frequencies. In practice, therefore, one can determine the coefficient of coincidence by dividing the observed frequency of double crossovers by their expected frequency, the

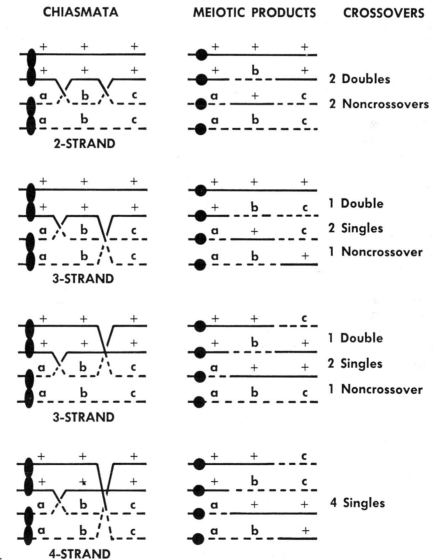

FIGURE 17–4.
Double chiasmata types and their genetic consequences.

latter value equaling the product of the observed frequencies of single crossovers in the two adjacent regions.

It is found, in general, that the coefficient of coincidence is 0 for short map distances and becomes larger as the distances do. This means that a tetrad in which one chiasma forms is somehow inhibited from having a second one occur in a region close by, this inhibition becoming less the farther away this second region. In *Drosophila*, for example, the coefficient of coincidence is 0 for map distances up to 10–15 map units, so that no double chiasmata (hence no double crossovers) occur within such distances. As the distance increases beyond 15 map units, the coefficient increases gradually to 1, at which time there is no interference with the formation of double chiasmata.

You remember that, if every tetrad in our model had a single chiasma located somewhere between *a* and *f*, the maximum frequency of recombination for these end genes would be 50%. What happens to the frequency of recombination for the end genes when our model is also permitted to have double chiasmata? If, now, each tetrad has one or more chiasmata (and hence crossovers), you might think, at first, that the end genes would form new combinations more than 50% of the time. However, examination of Figure 17–4 will show you, because each type of double chiasmata is equally likely, that, on the average, there will be eight products which would switch the end genes (being those which are single crossovers) and eight products which would not (being composed of four double crossovers, in which an interstitial gene switches but end genes retain their original order, plus four noncrossovers). Accordingly, even if every tetrad has double chiasmata, the maximum recombination for the end genes is again 50%.

If four genes are studied and three chiasmata occur in each tetrad, one in each region, it turns out that per each 64 meiotic prod-

ucts 32 will be recombinational for the end genes and 32 will not. One can work out the fact that for cases where there are four or more chiasmata between end genes, the number of meiotic products bearing odd numbers of crossovers (1, 3, 5, etc.) is 50%. In each of these cases one end gene is shifted relative to the other. However, the remaining strands contain either even numbers of crossovers (which do not cause the end genes to shift relative to each other) or no crossovers. Accordingly, there is still a maximum of 50% recombination for the endmost genes (and, therefore, of course, for any genes between them).

If two genes are located far apart in a chromosome and multiple chiasmata normally fall between them, their rate of recombination will be near 50%. Since 50% recombination is taken to mean independent segregation of gene pairs, you might not be able to conclude from the recombination rate that these two genes are linked (cf. p. 46). Whenever genes are known to be linked, however, their correct order relative to each other may be determined without concern about the correctness of the distances involved. Moreover, this may be decided from the results of a single cross. Suppose the trihybrid $+ + +/a\,b\,c$ is test crossed, and the frequencies of phenotypes in the progeny are as shown at the left in Figure 17–5. These frequencies, you recall, represent the frequencies of the corresponding genotypes in the gametes of the trihybrid. The middle gene would be the one which switches least often from the original gene combinations ($+ + +$ and $a\,b\,c$), for only it requires two chiasmata to switch. Accordingly, this gene is identified as *c*, and the actual gene order is *a c b* (or *b c a*). You may understand this more readily by examining the data when the genes are listed in their correct order, as shown at the right in Figure 17–5. Here the frequency of observed crossovers between the *a* and *c* loci is 30%, and between *c* and *b* 10%. (The

+ + +	0.31	+ + +	0.31
a b c	0.31	a c b	0.31
+ b c	0.14	+ c b	0.14
a + +	0.14	a + +	0.14
+ + c	0.01	+ c +	0.01
a b +	0.01	a + b	0.01
+ b +	0.04	+ + b	0.04
a + c	0.04	a c +	0.04
	1.00		1.00

FIGURE 17–5. *Determination of gene order from a test crossed trihybrid.*

expected frequency of double crossovers would be 0.3×0.1, or 0.03, so that the coefficient of coincidence is .02/.03, or 0.66.) For the *a-b* region the percentage of crossovers is 40% (the double crossovers are counted twice since each represents two crossovers between the end genes).

Having established the order of these genes, would it be satisfactory to use these data to construct a standard map for the distances between these genes, assuming

large numbers of progeny had been scored and standard experimental conditions had obtained? The observed distance between *c* and *b* is acceptable for this purpose, since in such a short distance only a single chiasma can be produced. However, the situation is otherwise for the *a-c* region, which is at least 30 map units long. For in such a distance double chiasmata could occur and the double crossovers these produce would be undetected, since there are no genetic markers between *a* and *c* whose switch would enable us to detect them. You see, then, from this and from what has been discussed previously, why the crossover rates observed for large distances are less than the standard map distances. For standard map distances are always obtained by the summation of short distances within which only a single chiasma can occur.

You should also realize, even though end genes can show at most 50% recombination, that the length of the crossover map may be more than 50 units. For example, if each tetrad contained an average of two chiasmata (see Figure 17–4), there would be a total of 100 crossovers among 100 meiotic products and the map length would be 100 units (even though end genes recombined 50% of the time). In fact, the length of the standard map can be predicted to be equal to the mean number of chiasmata per tetrad × 50.

Map length = chiasmata x̄ /tetrad x50

SUMMARY AND CONCLUSIONS

Using crossover frequency as an indication of distance, it is found that linked genes are arranged linearly. Observed crossover rates may fluctuate because of sample size and because of factors acting either after crossing over (differential viability), or on the crossover process itself (temperature, age, nutrition, genotype). Standard crossover maps are made under standard conditions.

The presence of one chiasma interferes with the occurrence of a second one nearby in the same tetrad, this chiasma interference diminishing as the distance between the two regions increases. Whenever double chiasmata do occur, the chromatids of one chiasma typically have no influence upon which chromatids form the other chiasma, so that there is no chromatid interference.

Recombination between end genes is 50% maximally, no matter how many chiasmata occur per tetrad. While the order of linked genes is easily determined by test crossing trihybrids, the distance between two genes will be underestimated when they are far apart.

REFERENCES

Sturtevant, A. H., "The Linear Arrangement of Six Sex-Linked Factors in Drosophila, as Shown by Their Mode of Association," J. Exp. Zool., 14 : 43–59, 1913. Reprinted in *Classic Papers in Genetics*, J. A. Peters (Ed.), Englewood Cliffs, N.J., Prentice-Hall, 1959, pp. 67–78.

See Supplement II.

QUESTIONS FOR DISCUSSION

17.1. Does the linear arrangement of the genes offer any evidence for or against the view that the chromosomes are carriers of genes? Explain.

17.2. How many gene pairs must be heterozygous to detect (1) a single crossover; (2) a double crossover in *Drosophila*? in *Neurospora*?

17.3. Suppose a pair of homologs in *Neurospora* had the genotypes $A B/a b$. Draw an ascus, containing 8 spores, derived from a cell that had:

a. No chiasma between these homologs.
b. One chiasma between the centromere and the gene pair closest to it.
c. One chiasma between the two pairs of genes.
d. One two-strand double chiasmata between the two pairs of genes.

17.4. What advantages has *Neurospora* over *Drosophila* as material for genetic studies?

17.5. Under what conditions would segregation of a pair of alleles occur during the first meiotic division? the second meiotic division?

17.6. What indications would you have that differential viability was having a role in modifying the crossover distances obtained experimentally?

17.7. For how many linked gene pairs must an individual of *Drosophila* and of *Neurospora* be hybrid, in order to determine from the crossovers it produces whether these genes are arranged in a linear sequence? Explain.

17.8. A test cross proves that one of the parents produced gametes of the following genotypes: 42.4% *PZ*, 6.9% *Pz*, 7.0% *pZ*, and 43.7% *pz*. List all the genetic conclusions you can reach from these data.

17.9. The trihybrid *Aa Bb Cc* is backcrossed to the triple recessive, *aa bb cc*. The following phenotypic results were obtained: abc 64, abC 2, aBc 11, aBC 18, AbC 14, Abc 17, ABc 3, ABC 71.

a. Which of these loci are linked? Why?
b. Rewrite the genotypes of both parents.
c. Determine the observed map distances between all the different pairs of linked genes

17.10. Describe one practical use of the fact that linked genes are arranged linearly.

17.11. How can you determine the position of a centromere in a linkage group of *Neurospora?*

17.12. Discuss the statement on p. 124 that "never are all eight spores, from a single sac, crossovers."

Chapter 18

CHANGES INVOLVING
WHOLE GENOMES AND
SINGLE WHOLE CHROMOSOMES

IN THE preceding Chapters marked by asterisks we used recombination to study the genetic material. This operation permitted us to divide the genetic material into genes whose properties are expressed in terms of their recombinational behavior. The present Chapter and others to follow (especially Chapters 19, 23, 25) deal with the study of the genetic material by means of the operation of mutation. We shall be especially interested to learn to what extent the genetic material can be partitioned into mutational units; that is, we will be concerned with the possibility of describing a gene in terms of its mutational behavior.

It has been possible for us to learn the recombinational properties of genes only because the genetic material exists in more than one alternative state and is apparently capable of replicating itself and certain of its modifications. You can readily see that a gene, which is present in homozygous condition in all organisms, is not detectable, since all individuals would have the same genotype, and, therefore, the same range of phenotypic expression. A gene can be detected only if it occurs either in different numbers in different individuals, or if it has an alternate allele, or both, provided such a genetic difference produces a detectable phenotypic change.

A great deal of genetic variation exists among living organisms (Chapter 1). We have seen that some of the phenotypic varia-

tion attributable to genes arises via sexuality, by means of which new combinations of already present genes may be produced by segregation, independent segregation, crossing over, and fertilization. These mechanisms of recombination shuffle the genes, just as shuffling a deck of playing cards produces the great variety of different combinations obtained with the same cards. However, the genetic differences found in a population today were not always present in it.

What we are concerned with now is how the genetic differences arise whose shuffling produces phenotypic variation by recombination. Before we can study this, however, we must have some way to distinguish the origin of *mutants, really new genetic forms*, produced by the process of mutation, from the recombination of old, pre-existent genes. Consider a case, involving *Drosophila*, that illustrates how this distinction may be made. None of the flies in laboratory strains of *Drosophila*, regardless of origin and crossbreeding, have an appendage on the anterior-dorsal part of the thorax. Suppose a single fly occurs with an appendage in this region (Figure 18–1), and this trait appears in approximately one half of this fly's progeny. How is the new phenotypic variation, called *Hexaptera*, to be explained? It cannot be due to environmental factors alone. Hexaptera cannot be due to the interaction of particular members of a pair of genes, already present in the population, which happened to become combined in the same zygote at fertilization. For if the occurrence of Hexaptera depended upon such a combination, this would have to be so rare that, following segregation, this phenotype would not be expected to appear in any appreciable number of the progeny. Hexaptera cannot be due to the rare combination of two previously existing unlinked nonalleles, since at most only one quarter of the progeny would have the novel phenotype. So, neither segregation nor independent segregation is responsible

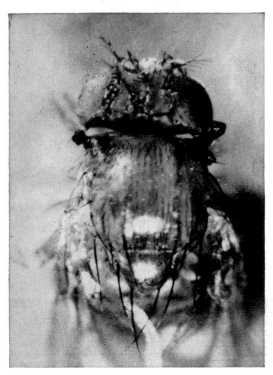

FIGURE 18–1. *The Hexaptera phenotype in* D. melanogaster. (*By permission of Genetics, Inc., vol. 34, p. 13, 1949.*)

for Hexaptera. However, such a new phenotype could have arisen by genetic recombination, due to the occurrence of a crossover chromosome, which was very rare because the nonallelic genes involved were extremely close together. Once produced, this combination of linked genes would remain intact and be transmitted to one half of the progeny. But suppose also that the chromosomes of the parents of the first Hexaptera were suitably marked with genes, and it was found that the chromosome region whose presence is essential for the production of the new phenotype was of a noncrossover type. Then crossing over would not explain the results. The only reasonable explanation remaining would be that a novel change had occurred in the genetic material, a mutation, which produced a dominant phenotypic effect. You see, then, that under certain circumstances it

may be possible, without great difficulty, to identify a novel phenotype as being due to mutation rather than to genetic recombination, when the mutant produces a dominant phenotypic effect.

When, however, the novel phenotype requires the mating of two particular individuals for its appearance in progeny, it is much more difficult to decide whether the genetic recombination required for its appearance involves old genes or a recently arisen mutant which is apparently completely recessive. Note, after the mutational origin of a completely recessive autosomal gene, that its detection is postponed for that number of generations which is required for two heterozygotes to mate and produce a mutant homozygote. Under certain conditions, many generations may elapse before the recessive mutant becomes homozygous, during which period the mutant allele may become relatively widespread in the population in heterozygous condition. In this event, one cannot decide when the mutant first arose, and it may be considered part of the old pool of genes present in the population. It would be easier to identify a phenotype as the result of a recessive mutation if the genotype of the population was known to be uniform prior to this. You see, therefore, why the detection of mutants, both of recessive and of dominant types, is made relatively easy by the employment of pure lines. The pure line procedure for detecting mutants was used with self-fertilizing beans, as described in Chapter 1. As mentioned there, sudden phenotypic changes, not due to environmental fluctuation, are occasionally found which clearly represent mutations, not recombinations from genotypically different parents. In cases where completely pure lines cannot be obtained because self-fertilization does not occur, detection of mutations is facilitated when they involve genes for which both parents are homozygous or completely known genotypically.

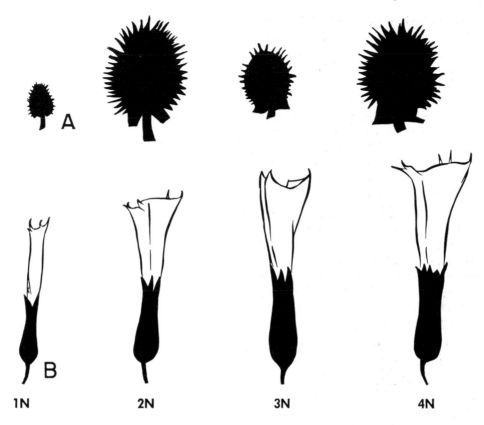

FIGURE 18–2. *Ploidy in* Datura (*N = 12*) (*silhouettes*).

Once a phenotype is proved to result from a mutation, the basis for the genetic change has still to be determined. Let us start our study of the basis and character of mutation with some examples taken from plants.

In the evening primrose, *Oenothera*, a giant type called *gigas* is found to be a mutant. Other *Oenothera*, like most sexually reproducing species, are diploid, having two sets of chromosomes, or genomes — one genome having been contributed by each of the gametes. In the *gigas* type, cytological examination shows that there are three genomes, so that such individuals are *triploid*. Studies of other groups of diploid plants have revealed related types which prove to have four genomes and so are *tetraploid*,

others may have six sets (*hexaploids*) or eight (*octaploids*). Triploidy has been found even in human beings. The occurrence of any ploidy greater than diploidy is called *polyploidy*, although this term may also be used for multiples of the haploid number when monoploidy is the normal condition.

Different forms of the Jimson weed, *Datura*, are found to carry different ploidies.[1] Some are haploid, others diploid, triploid, or tetraploid. The appearance of the flowers each type produces is shown in Figure 18–2 line B, and their respective seed capsules are shown above in line A of the Figure. Note that the flower size increases with ploidy. The seed capsules illustrated are those which might

[1] Based upon work of A. F. Blakeslee and J. Belling.

have been obtained had the individual under test been fertilized by pollen from a diploid. (In this case each pollen grain would contribute one genome to the development of the zygote in the seed.) The differences in size of the seed capsules is due partly to the number of seeds that have set or developed.

Polyploidy is also found in animals, for example, in *Drosophila*. Female *Drosophila* have been found that are triploid ($3X + 3$ sets of A) and tetraploid ($4X + 4$ sets of A) (cf. pp. 102–104). Parts of individuals have been found to be haploid ($1X + 1$ A set). You recall that triploid females produce gametes many of which are genomically abnormal. Since two tetraploid *Datura* can be crossed, and a sufficient number of fertile seeds are set to form a tetraploid race, the question arises, can a tetraploid race of *Drosophila* be produced?

The tetraploid *Drosophila* female forms gametes that more often contain complete genomes than do the gametes of triploids. (The number of genomes present must be even, not odd, if each chromosome is to have a partner at meiosis. So, in tetraploids, where genome number is even, the four homologous chromosomes often segregate 2 and 2, but sometimes segregate 3 and 1.) So this sex presents no difficulty for the continuity of a tetraploid race. However, the tetraploid male would have to carry $2X + 2Y + 4$ sets of A in order to be of normal sex. Unfortunately, during meiosis in such a male the X's would synapse with each other and so would the Y's, so that after meiosis each sperm would carry $1X$ and $1Y$ in addition to 2 A sets. Such sperm fertilizing eggs of $2X + 2$ sets of A constitution, from tetraploid females, would produce zygotes with $3X + 1Y + 4$ sets of A which would develop as sterile intersexes. Thus, a tetraploid race of *Drosophila*, which is self-maintaining, cannot be established. In fact, it becomes clear that any species containing a heteromorphic pair of sex chromosomes (like X and Y)

cannot form polyploid races, since the correct balance between sex chromosomes and autosomes will be upset by the meiotic divisions. This factor probably explains why polyploid races and species are rarer among animals than among plants, where sexuality is often not associated with such chromosomal differences (Chapter 13).

Nevertheless, polyploid races of animals are sometimes found. For example, tetraploids of the water shrimp, *Artemia*, of the sea urchin, *Echinus*, and of the roundworm, *Ascaris*, are known. In the moth, *Solenobia*, some females may produce haploid eggs and others diploid eggs. Both types of eggs start development without fertilization, i.e., start development *parthenogenetically*. During development, however, nuclei of the respective individuals fuse in pairs to establish the diploid and tetraploid conditions. Polyploid larvae of salamanders and of frogs also have been obtained, although races are not formed.

One way that ploidy can increase is by the addition of genomes of the same kind as are present, that is, by *autopolyploidy*, as was the case in the *Datura* discussed. Autopolyploidy can arise several different ways. An organism capable of asexual reproduction may fail to have a normal mitotic anaphase so that the doubled number of chromosomes becomes incorporated into a single nucleus, which thereafter divides normally to produce daughter polyploid nuclei and eventually polyploid progeny. Sometimes two of the haploid nuclei produced by meiosis may fuse to form a diploid gamete which, after fertilization with a haploid gamete, forms a triploid zygote. Or haploid individuals may undergo meiosis, and, while this usually results in gametes containing only part of a genome, a complete haploid gamete may sometimes be produced which, upon fertilization with another haploid gamete, forms a diploid zygote.

By interfering with mitosis and meiosis,

drugs like colchicine (which destroy the spindle, so that the anaphase movement of chromosomes is prevented) and environmental stresses like starvation and cold can artificially induce autopolyploidy. We have already mentioned the normal occurrence of parthenogenesis in *Solenobia* and the subsequent fusion of haploid and of diploid nuclei to establish diploidy and tetraploidy, respectively. In other organisms, parthenogenesis may be artificially induced and haploid development initiated. In such cases, development as a haploid, of an individual that is ordinarily diploid, is usually abnormal. The abnormality produced must be due sometimes to the expression of detrimental genes which would not be expressed in a diploid because of the presence of their normal alleles on homologous chromosomes. That this is not always the case is evidenced by the fact that if chromosome doubling, naturally or artificially induced, occurs at an early stage, a normal diploid (and homozygous) embryo may be produced. Such a chromosome doubling has produced parthenogenetic salamanders and rabbits (which are female). In these cases, at least, abnormal development when haploid must often have its basis in quite a different factor. This factor probably involves the surface-volume relationships within the nucleus and between the nucleus and the cytosome, which are disturbed when cells adapted to contain a diploid number of chromosomes carry only a haploid set.

Autopolyploidy occurs normally in certain somatic cells, such as liver cells in man, and may be induced by the irradiation of cells in tissue culture. In the autopolyploid cells we have so far discussed, each chromosome lies separately in the nucleus and proceeds to the mitotic metaphase independently. There are other cases of autopolyploidy in which all homologous chromosomes are synapsed even though the cell is part of somatic tissue. Let us examine an example of this as found in the giant salivary gland cells of *Drosophila* larvae.

Note, first, that in the usual cell of *Drosophila*, the metaphase chromosome is sausage-shaped, containing chromatids coiled tightly in a series of spirals like those in a lamp filament, and that during interphase the chromatids have largely unwound. The chromosomes in the salivary gland cell nucleus are also in an unwound state, perhaps even more so than in ordinary interphase, and have undergone three special changes. First, each chromosome present has replicated synchronously a number of times in succession, so that one chromosome produced two, two produced four, four produced eight, eight formed 16, 16 formed 32, etc. This replication can occur as many as nine times, producing 512 chromosomes. Second, all sister strands, instead of separating, remain in contact with the homologous loci apposed, giving the appearance of a many-threaded, *polytene*, cable. Third, since the original members of a pair of homologous chromosomes are paired at homologous points, by what is called *somatic synapsis*, a double cable is formed which can contain as many as 1024 chromosomes. When seen under the microscope (Figure 18–3), these double cables have a cross-banded appearance. Because of differences in density along the length of the unwound chromosome, a band is formed by a dense part of one chromosome being synapsed to the homologous region of all the other strands of that type (Figure 18–4). The pattern of bands is sufficiently constant and so characteristic that it is possible to identify not only each chromosome but different regions within a chromosome (Figure 18–5). The giant size of salivary chromosomes, long because they are unwound, and thick because of synapsed polytenes, offers a unique opportunity to correlate genetical and cytological events.

While we have so far discussed only autopolyploidy, there is a different way by which ploidy may increase. It is sometimes found that the genomes in a given species have been

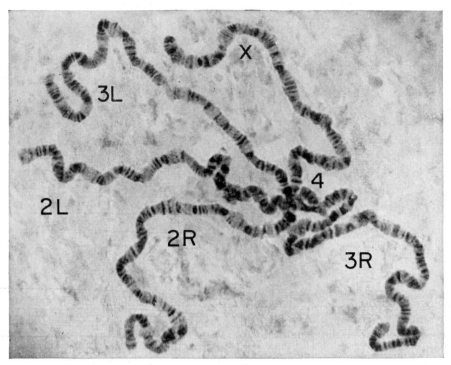

FIGURE 18–3. *Salivary gland chromosomes of a female larva of* D. melanogaster. *(Courtesy of B. P. Kaufmann; by permission of The American Genetic Association, Journal of Heredity, Frontispiece, vol. 30, No. 5, May, 1939.)*

FIGURE 18–4. *A band (at top) and interband (below) region of a stretched* Drosophila *salivary gland chromosome. Photographed with the electron microscope at a magnification of approximately 12,200×. Present enlargement is about 13,000×. (By permission of The American Genetic Association, Journal of Heredity, vol. 43, p. 231, 1952.)*

FIGURE 18–5. *The pair of fourth chromosomes, drawn to the same scale, as seen in salivary gland nuclei (each homolog is highly polytene) and at mitotic metaphase (arrow). (By permission of The American Genetic Association, C. B. Bridges, "Salivary Chromosome Maps," Journal of Heredity, vol. 26, p. 62, 1935.)*

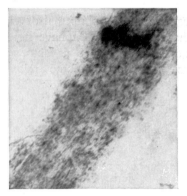

SCALE |←5 μ→|

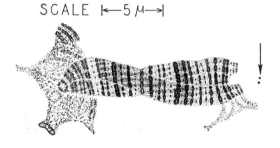

derived from different species. These cases represent examples of *amphiploidy*, or allo-polyploidy, in which two or more genomes have come from each of the different species. Cultivated wheat is an amphiploid. Amphiploids often show a combination of characteristics of their different parent species, just as you would expect. This type of polyploidy is discussed in more detail in Chapter 29.

Changes in genome number represent the class of mutational events which involves the largest amounts of genetic material. While many plants are polyploid, this type of mutation does not occur many times in succession, for chromosome number would become unwieldy in nuclear division. It should be noted also that certain other classes of mutation, like those involving a single locus, would have a greater difficulty expressing themselves in polyploids than they would have in haploids or diploids where there is no other, or just one other, homologous locus capable of masking the mutant effect.

Changes in genome number preserve the same ratios that genes or chromosomes have to each other in the normal diploid. Such changes are said to be *euploid* ("right-fold").

The next category of mutations to be discussed in the present Chapter involves the addition or subtraction, not of whole chromosome sets, but of single whole chromosomes. Such mutations upset the normal balance referred to and produce *aneuploid* ("not right-fold") genetic (chromosomal) constitutions. By what mechanisms can single whole chromosomes be added to or subtracted from a genome? We have already discussed two ways in previous Chapters, in the phenomena of chromosomal nondisjunction in normal diploids (Chapter 12) and of chromosomal segregation in autopolyploids (triploids in Chapter 14).

You recall that nondisjunction in the germ line of *Drosophila* can produce offspring, otherwise diploid, that are X0, XXX, and XXY. Nondisjunction of the small fourth chromosome can lead to the production of individuals with one fourth chromosome (haplo-IV individuals) or three (triplo-IV individuals), as pictured in Figure 18–6. Even though addition or subtraction of a chromosome IV makes visible phenotypic changes from the normal diploid condition, as you can see by referring to the Figure, both changes are viable. This is not true for

FIGURE 18–6. *Haplo-IV (left) and triplo-IV (right) females of* D. melanogaster. *The haplo-IV is smaller than the wild-type female shown in Fig. 12–1.* (*Drawn by E. M. Wallace.*)

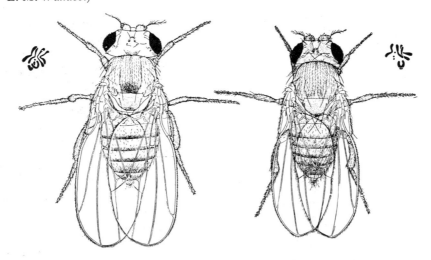

individuals that are haploid or triploid with respect to either one of the two large autosomes, such individuals dying during the egg stage before they can hatch as a larva. In these cases, death is attributable to the genetic imbalance of having the numerous genes present in a long autosome in excess in individuals triploid in this respect, or to the deficiency of these genes in individuals haploid in this respect.

We have seen (Chapter 14) how the diploid individual contains, in its two sets of chromosomes, a proper balance of genes for the determination of male and female sex. There is, therefore, every reason to expect that the production of other phenotypic traits is also dependent upon proper genic balance. It is not surprising, then, that a haploid animal mated to a diploid produces very few progeny, since after fertilization most zygotes are chromosomally unbalanced by the absence of one or more chromosomes needed to make two complete genomes. The triploid animal mated to a diploid also produces zygotes that are imbalanced, but in the opposite direction, having one or more chromosomes in excess of two genomes.

However, in matings with diploids, the triploid animal usually produces more offspring than the haploid one. This can be explained as the result of the lesser imbalance wrought by the addition of chromosomes to the diploid condition than by the subtraction of chromosomes from it. You can visualize this by comparing how far from normality (diploidy) each of the two abnormal conditions is. In the former case, in which one chromosome is in excess, the abnormal chromosome number of three is one and a half times larger than the normal number of two. In the latter case, in which one chromosome is missing, the abnormal chromosome number of one is two times smaller than the normal number. Thus, the addition of a chromosome makes for a less drastic change in balance than does its subtraction. (Accord-

ingly, knowing in *Drosophila* that the triple dose of a large autosome is lethal, we would have predicted the single dose would be also.)

Chromosome addition and subtraction can also be studied in *Datura*.[2] The haploid number of chromosomes here is 12. It is

[2] Based upon work of A. F. Blakeslee and J. Belling.

FIGURE 18–7. *Silhouettes of the capsules formed by the twelve kinds of trisomic* Datura.

possible to obtain 12 different kinds of individuals, each having a different one of the 12 chromosomes in addition to the diploid number. Each of these kinds is said to be *trisomic* for a different chromosome (the triplo-IV *Drosophila* being trisomic for chromosome IV), and is given a different name. The normal seed capsule and those produced by these 12 trisomics are shown in Figure 18-7. It is also possible to obtain viable plants that are diploid but missing one chromosome of a pair; these are *monosomics* or *haplosomics* (just as is a haplo-IV *Drosophila*). Individuals that have two extra chromosomes of the same type (tetrasomics) or have two extra chromosomes of different types (doubly trisomic) are also found.

Datura permits us to test again our ideas relative to the phenotypic consequences of disturbing the normal balance among chromosomes. Compare, by means of Figure 18-8, the seed capsules produced by the normal diploid (2N), with those of diploids having either one extra chromosome (2N + 1), of the type producing Globe (Figure 18-7), or two of these (2N + 2).

The latter two are *polysomics*, which can be called trisomic diploid and tetrasomic diploid, respectively. Although the tetrasomic is more stable chromosomally (each chromosome having a partner at meiosis) than is the trisomic, the tetrasomic phenotype is too abnormal to establish a race, since it has a still greater genetic imbalance than the trisomic; and produces a still greater deviation from the normal diploid phenotype.

In comparison, the tetraploid (4N) individual is almost like the diploid phenotypically, as might be expected since chromosomal balance is undisturbed. The tetraploid which has the "Globe" chromosome extra once (4N + 1, making it a pentasomic tetraploid) deviates from the tetraploid in the same direction as the 2N + 1 already mentioned deviates from 2N, but does so less extremely. Hexasomic tetraploids (4N + 2) deviate from 4N just about as much as 2N + 1 deviates from 2N. You see, then, that addition of a single chromosome to a tetraploid has less phenotypic effect than its addition to a diploid, since there is a relatively smaller shift in balance between chro-

FIGURE 18–8. *Effect upon the capsule of* Datura *of the presence of one or more extra "Globe"* (*Figure 18–7*) *chromosomes.*

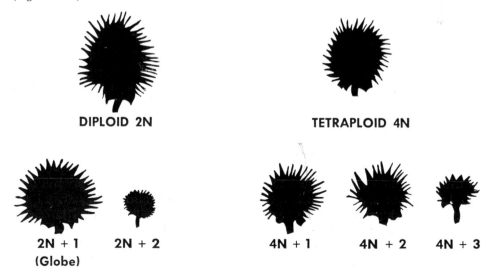

DIPLOID 2N   TETRAPLOID 4N

2N + 1   2N + 2   4N + 1   4N + 2   4N + 3
(Globe)

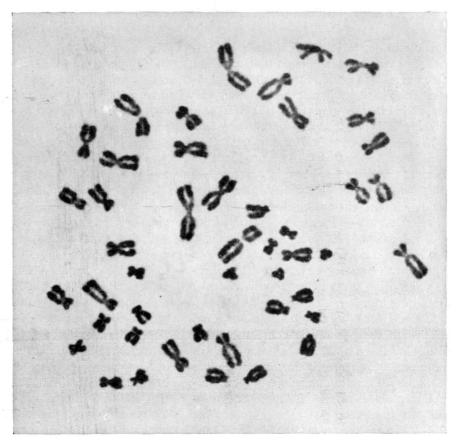

FIGURE 18–9. *The chromosomal complement of a normal human female. Cell was in mitotic metaphase (hence chromosomes appear double) when squashed and photographed. (Courtesy of T. C. Hsu.)*

mosomes in the former than in the latter case. Thus, polyploids can stand whole chromosome additions and subtractions better than can diploids.

We have already mentioned in Chapter 13 some of the phenotypic consequences of whole chromosome subtraction and addition in human beings — otherwise diploid individuals may be X0 (Turner's type female) or XXY (Klinefelter's type male). Mongolian idiocy is known to be sometimes the result of a trisomic diploid chromosomal constitution. In this case, the trisomic is the third smallest of all human chromosomes (the smallest being the Y) (Figures 18–9, 18–10). Trisomics for seven other autosomes are also known, each producing its own characteristic

set of congenital abnormalities. It is a reasonable expectation that the haploid condition of these or of any other autosome would be lethal before birth, in line with the view that chromosome subtraction is even more detrimental than chromosome addition.

Although we have not always specified the particular manner in which each of the genomes aneuploid for whole chromosomes originated, you will recall that we have already indicated two general mechanisms by which such aneuploidy may arise in the germ line. It should also be mentioned that nondisjunction may also occur in somatic cells, as occurs when both daughter chromosomes proceed to the same pole at mitotic anaphase. This produces, in a diploid, one daughter cell

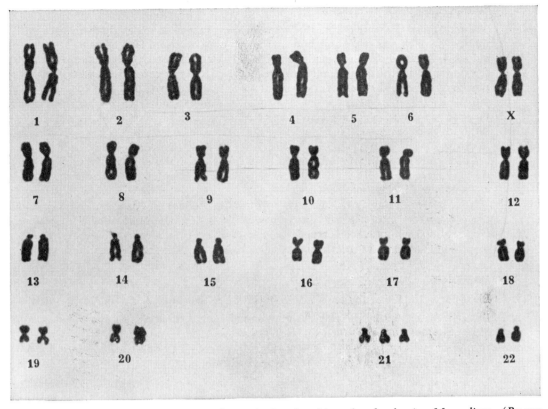

FIGURE 18–10. *Chromosomal constitution found in a female showing Mongolism. (By permission of M. A. Ferguson-Smith and A. W. Johnston, and The Annals of Internal Medicine, vol. 53, p. 361, 1960.)*

that is monosomic and one that is trisomic, each giving rise to patches of tissue of these respective types when this "misdivision" or "mitotic dislocation" is followed by normal mitosis.

While chromosome addition and subtraction may occur as a result of spontaneous nondisjunction and of the meiotic processes that normally take place in triploids, pentaploids, etc., we should not conclude that these are the only mechanisms for their origin. Moreover, it is known that the incidence of nondisjunction can be increased by means of high energy radiations, such as are released by radium or involved in X rays. Carbon dioxide, other chemical substances, and

certain diploid genotypes can increase the nondisjunction rate in *Drosophila*. In human beings, the fact that older women are more apt to have Mongoloid children suggests that some metabolic defect occurs with age which increases the chance for nondisjunction (cf. p. 106), and, therefore, the frequency of eggs carrying the appropriate chromosome in addition to the 23 chromosomes of a haploid set.

Because of the large genetic unbalance produced, we would expect that addition and subtraction of whole chromosomes is a class of mutation which involves too drastic a phenotypic change to be very useful in evolution.

SUMMARY AND CONCLUSIONS

The mutational events involving the largest amount of genetic material are changes in the number of whole sets of chromosomes. The modes of origin and the breeding behavior of autopolyploids are discussed, and the origin and structure of the giant chromosomes of the salivary gland of *Drosophila* larvae are described. Ploidy can increase also via amphiploidy.

Polyploidy is more common among plants than among animals. When an individual possesses an odd number of genomes, many of the gametes it produces have an incomplete set in which a chromosome is more detrimental to survival when missing than when present in excess.

Chromosome addition or subtraction results in aneuploidy, and is a type of mutation that produces too drastic a phenotypic change to be as important in evolution as euploid changes in whole chromosome sets.

Loss or gain of single whole chromosomes can be produced by means of nondisjunction and the segregation of chromosomes in polyploids possessing an odd number of genomes. Not only do such mutations occur in the germ and somatic lines spontaneously, but they may be initiated or have their frequency enhanced by physical and chemical factors.

REFERENCES

Blakeslee, A. F., "New Jimson Weeds from Old Chromosomes," J. Hered., 25:80–108, 1934.

Blakeslee, A. F., and Belling, J., "Chromosomal Mutations in the Jimson Weed, Datura Stramonium," J. Hered., 15:194–206, 1924.

Bridges, C. B., and Brehme, K. S., *The Mutants of Drosophila Melanogaster*, Washington, D.C., Carnegie Institution of Washington, Publ. 552, 1944.

Dobzhansky, Th., *Genetics and the Origin of Species*, 2nd Ed., New York, Columbia University Press, Chap. 7, pp. 223–253, 1941.

Heitz, E., and Bauer, H., "Beweise für die Chromosomennatur der Kernschleifen in den Knäuelkernen von *Bibio hortulanus* L. (Cytologische Untersuchungen an Dipteren, I)," Z. Zellforsch., 17:67–82, 1933.

Painter, T. S., "A New Method for the Study of Chromosome Rearrangements and Plotting of Chromosome Maps," Science, 78:585–586, 1933. Reprinted in *Classic Papers in Genetics*, J. A. Peters (Ed.), Englewood Cliffs, N.J., Prentice-Hall, 1959, pp. 161–163.

Patau, K., Smith, D. W., Therman, E., Inhorn, S. L., and Wagner, H. P., "Multiple Congenital Anomaly Caused by an Extra Autosome," Lancet, 1:790–793, 1960.

White, M. J. D., *Animal Cytology and Evolution*, 2nd Ed., Cambridge, Cambridge University Press, 1954.

QUESTIONS FOR DISCUSSION

18.1. How do we know that the genetic differences found in a population today were not always present in it?

18.2. From the present Chapter, what have you learned about the characteristics of mutation?

18.3. What is the relation between mutants and genes? mutants and recombination?

18.4. From your present knowledge, how would you modify the statements on p. 21 relative to the ploidy of gametes?

18.5. Describe at least two different ways that the trisomy causing Mongolism may originate.

18.6. Give a possible chromosomal formula for human individuals who are:

        a. Triploid males.
        b. Klinefelter's type of male.
        c. Mongolian idiot.
        d. Both b. and c.

    Which of these are trisomic diploid, tetrasomic diploid, doubly trisomic diploid? Which are euploid, and explain?

18.7. Discuss the statement: "All somatic cells from diploid zygotes are chromosomally identical."

18.8. Klinefelter's males and Mongolian idiots rarely have children. Each of these abnormalities occurs in about 0.2% of individuals at birth. What would you calculate to be the minimal frequency of zygotes that are trisomic diploid for any chromosome?

18.9. Do you suppose that the human species will benefit from the discovery that certain members of it are trisomic? Explain.

18.10. What are the advantages of autopolyploidy? of amphiploidy?

18.11. What can you conclude about the mutational basis for Hexaptera from the fact that its salivary gland chromosomes are apparently indistinguishable from normal?

18.12. What genetic explanation can you offer for the fact, demonstrated in Figure 18–2, that the seed capsule of the haploid *Datura* is smaller than that of the triploid?

Chapter *19

STRUCTURAL CHANGES
WITHIN CHROMOSOMES

T HE TWO classes of mutation discussed in Chapter 18 dealt with
changes in chromosomal con-
tent involving whole chromosomes, either
individually or in sets. Sometimes, genetically detected mutations are found to be
based upon the gain, loss, or shift of a part
of one or more chromosomes. It is these
structural changes in chromosomes, comprising our third category of mutations, that we
shall now consider.

All such structural changes in chromosomes
are preceded by chromosome breakage.
When a chromosome is broken, the two ends
produced are "sticky" and are capable of
joining to each other. When the ends produced by several breaks join together the
chromosomes formed are never branched,
demonstrating that each broken end can join
only to one other broken end. However, any
broken end can join to any other broken end.
Moreover, an end produced by breakage
cannot join to the normal (unbroken) end of a
chromosome. Thus, originally free ends of
chromosomes are not sticky, having genes
called *telomeres* that serve to seal them off
and make it impossible for normal ends to
join to each other or to ends produced by
breakage.

The ends produced by one break usually
join together, in what is called *restitutional*
union, even when ends produced by other
breaks coexist in the same nucleus, indicating
that proximity of broken ends favors their
joining together. Although restitutional

150

union usually occurs, so that the original
linear order of the chromosome is reconstituted, under certain conditions, to be described more fully, the ends uniting may be
such that a gene arrangement other than the
original one is produced. The latter union
is, therefore, of a *nonrestitutional*, or *exchange*, or *cross-union* type. Let us see how
nonrestitutional unions produce various structural changes in chromosomes.

Consider first the consequences of a single
chromosome break (Figure 19–1). Diagram
1 represents a normal chromosome whose
centromere is indicated by a black dot. In
diagram 2 this chromosome is broken. If
these broken ends join together, i.e., restitute,
no chromosomal rearrangement is produced.
Although, as was said, restitution is the rule,
on some occasions it may fail to occur. Perhaps restitution sometimes fails because following breakage the new ends spring apart or
are moved apart by Brownian movement or
protoplasmic currents. In that case, if the
chromosome replicates preparatory to a
subsequent nuclear division, a daughter
strand will be produced just like the parent
strand, i.e., with a break in the same position.
This is shown in diagram 3, in which the two
broken sister strands are indicated. The union
of piece a, containing no centromere, to piece
b′, the centromere-bearing piece of the
other sister chromosome, would be, in effect,
restitution, as would be the joining of a′ to b.
(Sometimes, only one of these restitutional
unions may occur.)

But, if no restitution occurs either before
or after the chromosome replicates, the ends
closest together will usually join together,
these being the corresponding ends of the
sister strands (a with a′ and b with b′). The
results of such nonrestitutional unions are
shown in diagram 4. Shown there is one
chromosome without a centromere (an *acentric chromosome*) and one that has two centromeres (a *dicentric chromosome*). Note that
both the acentric and dicentric chromosomes

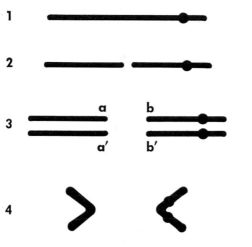

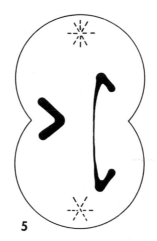

FIGURE 19–1.   *Conse-quences of a single non-restituting chromosome break.*

are composed lengthwise of identical halves, each being termed, therefore, an *isochromosome*. This diagram shows these chromosomes contracting preparatory to metaphase.

Diagram 5 shows that in mitotic anaphase the acentric is not pulled to either pole while the dicentric is pulled toward both poles at once. The acentric chromosome is, therefore, not included in either daughter nucleus and so is lost to both. (The acentric pieces in diagram 3 will be lost in any subsequent division, whether they join to each other or do not join at all.) The dicentric isochromosome, being pulled to both poles at once, forms a bridge that may prevent any of the chromosome from entering either daughter nucleus, so that the dicentric is lost. Alternatively, the centric regions of the dicentric piece may enter the daughter nuclei, and either the bridge may snap at any one of a number of places between the centromeres, so that the daughter nuclei are free of each other, or the bridge may persist so that the daughter nuclei are joined together.

The amount of phenotypic detriment that a single nonrestituting break will produce in the daughter cells and their progeny cells will depend upon the particular chromosome involved, the place of breakage, and the fate of the dicentric piece. Suppose first, for example, that chromosome IV of *Drosophila*

(which you recall is often viable as a haplo-IV individual) is the chromosome involved. The break may occur at any locus in IV and the loss of the genes in the acentric piece, though detrimental, will not usually cause inviability, nor will the loss of the entire dicentric fragment if excluded from both daughter nuclei. The phenotypic consequences would probably be the same should the bridge between daughter nuclei snap (in which case, you recall, each daughter nucleus certainly will be deficient at least for the genes in the acentric piece). However, note what happens when a bridge, involving a dicentric isochromosome linearly differentiated as a.bcddcb.a, snaps other than between the d segments. If it snaps between b and c, one fragment would be still more deficient, yet viable in the present example, while the other would contain an extra dose of the genes in the cd segment (most probably viable). Regardless of where the bridge snaps, however, both daughter nuclei would carry an unjoined centric fragment which, after replicating, would usually form a new dicentric isochromosome which, at the next mitotic division, would again form a bridge. It is possible, then, to have a cycle of bridge-breakage-fusion-bridge events in the course of successive mitotic divisions.

If, however, the bridge does not break, and

the two daughter nuclei are tied together, the entanglement of the nuclei may interfere with subsequent attempts at nuclear division, even though, as in our example, the presence or absence of the genes located in the bridge may not be of paramount importance to the functioning of these cells.

Suppose, next, that the chromosome broken is one of the large autosomes of *Drosophila*. Detriment or death to one or both daughter cells may occur because of the genes lost, when either the acentric piece or the dicentric fragment is left out of one or both daughter nuclei. In addition, successive bridge-breakage-fusion-bridge cycles may harm future cell generations via the aneuploidy produced as the result of the off-center breakage of dicentric isochromosomes. It would be expected, other things being equal, that shorter dicentrics would usually break and that longer dicentrics would be more likely not to. Of course, any bridge between nuclei that does not break would be expected to have the effect already mentioned.

Single chromosome breaks may occur either in the somatic or in the germ line. In the latter case, aneuploid gametes may be produced. In the case of animals, since the genes have been found to be physiologically inactive in the gametes, aneuploid genomes can enter the egg and sperm without impairing their functioning. Accordingly, in animals, aneuploid genomes can be carried by unaffected gametes into the zygote, which subsequently may suffer dominant detrimental or lethal effects. In most plants, however, the products of meiosis (pollen, for instance) perform certain physiological functions that require the action of the haploid genome they contain. So, in this case, aneuploidy is usually more lethal or detrimental before fertilization than it is after.

Having completed our discussion of the consequences of a single nonrestituting break, let us now consider the consequences of two breaks that occur in the same chromosome.

Such breaks can be located either *paracentrically*, in which case both are to one side of the centromere, or *pericentrically*, where the centromere is between the breaks (Figure 19–2).

Consider a chromosome linearly differentiated as ABCDEFG.HIJ, the centromere being between G and H. When the breaks are paracentric in position (between A and B, and F and G), the fragments may unite to produce a centric chromosome (AG.HIJ, Figure 19–2a) deficient for the acentric interstitial piece (BCDEF). The ends of the latter may join to produce a *ring chromosome*, which, in any event, is lost in the next nuclear division. When the breaks are pericentric (between D and E, and H and I), the end pieces are lost, whether or not they join together (Figure 19–2c). The centric middle piece can survive if its ends join to form a ring, and if the deficient sections are not extensive. Even if a ring can survive because it is not too *hypoploid* (the aneuploid condition in which genes or chromosomal regions are missing), it is at a disadvantage in that a single chiasma either with a nonring (called a *rod*) homolog or with another ring results in a dicentric rod or ring, respectively, as you can see by drawing the configurations for these situations yourself.

Chromosomes with small *deficiencies* may act as recessive lethals and may have a lesser detriment than this when heterozygous; those with large deficiencies usually act as dominant lethals in the next cell generation. Of course, the nucleus, in which breakage or other events occur which lead to a deficient chromosome or, for that matter, any other structural change, is still euploid. It is only after a nuclear division that the daughter cells become hypoploid or *hyperploid* (aneuploid because of an excess of genes or chromosome parts). The preceding portion of this paragraph should be reread with this consideration in mind.

It should be realized, in describing the

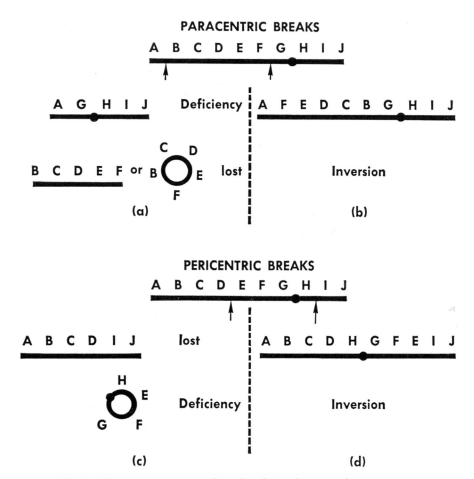

FIGURE 19–2. *Some consequences of two breaks in the same chromosome.*

production of deficiencies, that we have ignored the usual consequence of two breaks, which is that the ends from both breaks restitute. Again, only the consequences of the failure of breaks to restitute will be described in the discussion that follows regarding the production of other types of structural change.

Another structural consequence of two breaks in the same chromosome is represented in Figure 19–2b and d. In this case, the middle piece is inverted relative to the end pieces and undergoes exchange unions with them. The result is either a paracentric or a pericentric *inversion* (Figure 19–2b and d, respectively), which can occur by having the middle portion move while the ends are relatively stationary, or the reverse. Note that an inversion is a euploid rearrangement, and is of no phenotypic consequence from this standpoint.

How would you expect an inversion to behave during meiosis? If an inversion occurs by mutation and is retained in the germ line of a population, it may become homozygous in some individuals. In these individuals, meiotic behavior will be normal whether or not the tetrad is involved in chiasma formation, since all the strands involved are identically inverted. Other individuals, however, may possess one inverted homolog and a noninverted one, being heterozygous for the inversion. If the inversion is very small the homologs will pair properly everywhere but in the inverted region. Here, because the homologs cannot, in so short a region, twist enough to make homologous loci meet, they will fail to synapse, no chiasma will be formed and no crossing over will occur. Insofar as crossing over can lead to more adaptive recombinants, such inversion heterozygotes are at a disadvantage from this standpoint, as compared to noninversion or inversion homozygotes, because of the absence of re-combination among genes within the inverted region. Nevertheless, very small inversions may survive in any species.

But consider now the meiotic behavior of heterozygotes for larger paracentric inver-sions. In this case (Figure 19–3A), synapsis between homologs is made possible in all regions, with the exception of the parts near the points of breakage, by one homolog looping in the inverted region while the other does not. It happens that this Figure shows the inverted chromosome looping, but the reverse is equally likely to occur. Note that only two nonsister strands are shown; the other two naturally do not have a chiasma where these two have formed one. If one or more chiasmata occur outside the inverted region the four meiotic products will each be *eucentric* (having one centromere), as usual. If, however, one chiasma occurs anywhere within the inverted region, as shown between C and D, two strands of the tetrad will be eucentric (one with and one without the in-version, being those strands of the tetrad not shown in the Figure) and two will be *aneu-centric* (having no centromere or more than one). One of the aneucentrics will be acentric (duplicated for A and deficient for G.HIJ) while the other will be dicentric (having duplicated and deficient segments that are the complement of the acentric's). If the inversion is only moderately long, only one chiasma may occur within it, but if it is

sufficiently large, some 2-strand double chias-mata may occur within it, in which case the crossover strands will be eucentric.

Regardless of the length of a paracentric inversion, a single chiasma within the inverted region in an inversion heterozygote will pro-duce two aneucentric, aneuploid meiotic prod-ucts, as we have just seen. In animals that undergo crossing over each of these products will enter a gamete, which will function but usually have a dominant lethal effect after fertilization. This means that such individ-uals are at reproductive disadvantage, and this often leads to the elimination of the inversion from the population soon after it arises as a mutant. In certain species where there is no crossing over in one sex (the *Drosophila* male, for example), any homolog, inverted or not, has the same chance of being included in the gametes produced by that sex. There is a special factor to consider, however, with regard to meiosis in the *Drosophila* fe-male (the sex in which crossing over does occur), where it has been found that the two meiotic divisions occur in tandem, just as in *Neurospora* (see p. 123). In the *Drosophila* oocyte heterozygous for a paracentric inver-sion, a single chiasma within the inverted region produces a dicentric at anaphase I which orients the dyads at metaphase II so that the two eucentric monads proceed to the outermost of the four poles at anaphase II. At the end of telophase II, the four meiotic products, therefore, are arranged in a row: eucentric, part of dicentric, remainder of dicentric, eucentric — one of the two end eucentric-containing nuclei becoming the egg nucleus, the others degenerating. In this way the dicentric strand is shunted away from the egg nucleus, which therefore receives one of the two eucentric, noncrossover strands. In *Drosophila*, therefore, paracentric inversions of any size rarely cause aneuploid gametes in either sex and can become established in nature. Note, however, that in this species, the production of crossover-containing

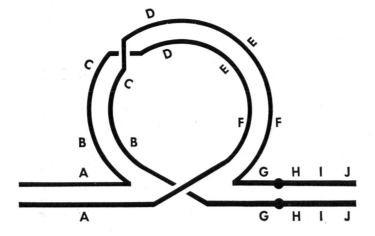

A. PARACENTRIC INVERSION

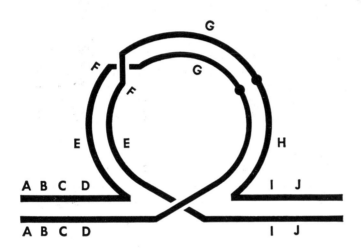

B. PERICENTRIC INVERSION

FIGURE 19–3. *A single chiasma in an inversion heterozygote. (See text for explanation.)*

gametes is suppressed in the paracentric inversion heterozygote female either because of nonsynapsis, or, in cases of synapsis, because of the exclusion from the egg of crossovers within the inverted region.

What is the effect of a chiasma within the inverted region in a heterozygote for a larger pericentric inversion? As seen in Figure 19–3B, a single chiasma, such as between F and G, produces four eucentric strands: two are noncrossovers (one with, and one without, the inversion, these being, again, those strands of the tetrad not included in the

Figure), one has a duplication (for ABCD) and a deficiency (for IJ), the other has a deficiency and a duplication of these same regions, respectively. These two aneuploid strands will enter the gametes of males, if crossing over occurs in the male. They will also be present in the gametes of females that have crossing over, even in the case of *Drosophila*, since all meiotic products are eucentric and there is, therefore, no shunting of euploid strands into the egg nucleus. So, the aneuploidy resulting from crossing over within a pericentric inversion always puts the heterozygote at a reproductive disadvantage. For this reason, it is expected, after arising by mutation, that only the smallest pericentric inversions, which do not synapse when heterozygous, will usually be able to survive in a population.

Following two breaks in the same chromosome, the last type of possible rearrangement to be discussed is *duplication* (Figure 19–4). If joining is delayed until after the broken chromosome reproduces, the two interstitial pieces may join, and, with the appropriate end pieces, produce a eutelomeric chromosome with the interstitial region repeated (neither, either, or both of these regions may be inverted with respect to the original arrangement). (The two remaining end pieces may or may not join to form a deficient chromosome.) Provided the duplicated region is small enough and acentric, such a duplication may survive in the population.

We shall consider now what is expected to happen when two breaks occur, one in each of two different chromosomes. In the first case to be considered, the two chromosomes may be homologs (ABCDEFG.HIJ). Usually, the breaks will be at different places, say between A and B in one, and D and E in the other. Exchange unions can occur one way

to produce a dicentric and an acentric chromosome, whose fate you can readily predict. Other exchange unions can produce two eucentric chromosomes in which BCD is deficient in one and duplicated in the other.

In the second case of this kind, the two chromosomes broken are nonhomologous (Figure 19–5). If the two centric pieces unite, a dicentric is formed. The two acentric pieces are lost in the next division, whether they join each other or do not join at all. If all pieces join as indicated, what is accomplished is a mutual exchange of segments between nonhomologous chromosomes; this is called a segmental interchange, or usually, a *reciprocal translocation*, and is of the aneucentric type. This type often acts as a dominant lethal in a subsequent division, particularly when the dicentric is pulled toward both poles at once.

It is often just as likely, however, that union occurs between the centric piece of one chromosome and the acentric piece of the nonhomolog, with, vice versa, the centric piece of the second joining the acentric piece of the first. This reciprocal translocation is of the eucentric type. In individuals heterozygous for such an exchange, having two nonhomologs translocated and two nontranslocated,

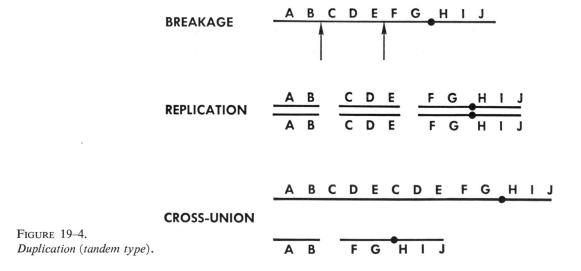

FIGURE 19–4.
Duplication (tandem type).

gametes will be formed with deficiencies and duplications if segregation results in their receiving one but not both members of the reciprocal translocation.

In nuclei in which the chromosomes are compacted in a relatively small volume, no broken end is very distant from any other broken end, and usually if one of the two unions needed for reciprocal translocation occurs, so does the other. This is the situation in the nucleus of the sperm of *Drosophila* just after it has been involved in fertilization. In oocytes, and probably in other cells that have a relatively large nuclear volume, the distances between the broken ends of nonhomologs are so great that reciprocal translocations are comparatively rare, and even if one cross union occurs the two other broken ends usually fail to join to each other, so that only half of a reciprocal translocation —

called a *half-translocation* — is produced. The loss or behavior of the unjoined fragments usually causes descendent cells to die or to be abnormal, as you would expect. Half-translocations are sometimes found as the result of segregation in heterozygotes for a eucentric reciprocal translocation (see the previous paragraph). Half-translocations having this origin are known to occur in human beings, for example.

In view of the preceding discussion of translocations, you can predict that such mutants would tend to be eliminated from the population. There is one exception to this, however, involving eucentric reciprocal translocations in which both chromosomes are broken close to their centromeres. In these cases, almost a whole arm of each chromosome has been mutually exchanged. Such *whole arm reciprocal translocations* when heterozygous in *Drosophila*, and probably most other species, undergo synapsis and disjunction in such a regular manner that euploid gametes (containing both or no pieces of the translocation) are usually formed, so that translocation heterozygotes of this type are not at an appreciable reproductive disadvantage.

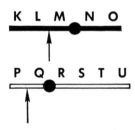

FIGURE 19–5. *Reciprocal translocation between nonhomologous chromosomes.*

ANEUCENTRIC TYPE

EUCENTRIC TYPE

Structural changes may result also after three breaks. When all three occur in one chromosome, the two interstitial pieces may exchange positions, producing what is called a *shift*. Two breaks in one chromosome and one in a nonhomolog can result in the interstitial piece of the first chromosome being inserted into the second. This result is called *transposition*.

In this and in the preceding Chapter, it has been pointed out that a change in ploidy may survive in nature when it either causes no shift in chromosome balance (because it deals with whole genomes), or involves eucentric aneuploidy in which small segments of chromosomes are hypo- or hyperploid. For, in the latter case, the deficient or duplicated genes are limited in number and produce only moderate phenotypic effects. On the reasonable assumption that the greater the amount of chromosomal material, the greater the complexity possible in an organism, and correspondingly, the greater the possible diversity in its phenotype and adaptiveness, viable changes in ploidy are particularly important in organic evolution. In view of this it becomes desirable to consider the different ways in which small numbers of genes may be added to a genome following breakage.

Two methods of increasing gene number following breakage have already been described. One of these dealt with two breaks in the same chromosome. After breakage, the entire chromosome replicated, after which the broken ends joined so as to form a chromosome with the interstitial piece duplicated (cf. p. 156). The other method involved a pair of homologs each having one break in a different region, followed by eucentric cross union (cf. p. 156). A third mechanism involves the heterozygote for a shift. If, in this case, the homologs pair in the region of the shift and a chiasma forms within it, you will see, by tracing the resultant strands, that one of the crossovers has a section in duplicate.

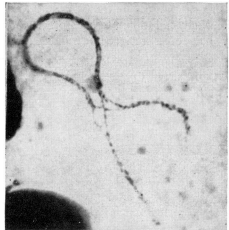

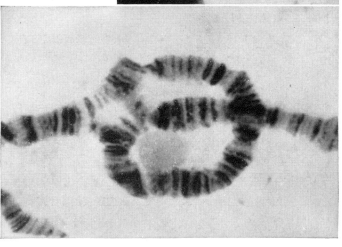

FIGURE 19–6. *Inversion heterozygotes in corn (pachynema) (courtesy of D. T. Morgan, Jr.) and in* Drosophila *(salivary gland) (courtesy of M. Demerec).*

Finally, it should be mentioned that a chromosome containing a transposition may come to be present, in subsequent generations, not with the nonhomologous, deficient, chromosome from which the piece was transposed, but with two normal chromosomes of that type. In this way an individual is produced containing a pair of normal homologs, part of which is present in hyperploid condition in a nonhomolog.

The preceding paragraph illustrates how the same type of structural change (duplication) may result following different types of breakage events. Accordingly, by observing the rearrangement produced, one cannot always specify the particular number of breaks originally involved. Usually, the simplest explanation is proposed. You should also note that cells which are missing an entire chromosome may be produced consequent to breakage; thus, not all such cells are the result of nondisjunction. Breakage events can also produce the monosomics discussed in the preceding Chapter, but not the trisomics.

During the course of the present Chapter it is very likely that you have wondered how the structural changes in chromosomes we have discussed are detected. Such mutants may be detected by direct cytological examination of cells. Or they may first be noted by their effects on the phenotype in general, after which genetic tests are made to detect their specific nature and fate in the population. So, identification of the type of structural change involved may be made genetically or cytologically, or by both methods.

Deficiencies may sometimes be recognized genetically when heterozygous, since they permit the expression of any allele of all genes present in this region in the nondeficient chromosome. Inversions and translocations may be suspected when mutant heterozygotes show a marked reduction in offspring carrying crossovers. Using appropriate marker genes, inversion homozygotes will show certain genes in an order the reverse of normal, while in translocations genes normally not linked, will be found linked. These types of mutants may also be identified cytologically; sometimes the cytological method is preceded by genetic studies that indicate which types of structural changes are likely to be involved and/or the particular chromosomes concerned. Of course, detailed knowledge of the appearance of the normal genome is a prerequisite for such cytological work.

The prophase of meiosis of some organisms, and the giant salivary gland chromosomes of Diptera, are particularly suited for cytological studies, because synapsis between

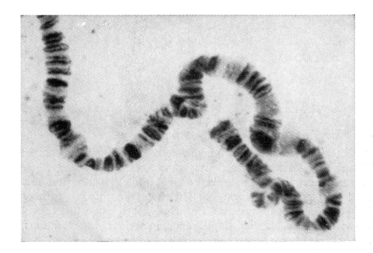

FIGURE 19–7. *Salivary gland chromosomes heterozygous for a shift within the right arm of chromosome 3 of* Drosophila melanogaster. *A piece from map region "98" is inserted into map region "91." The rightmost buckle is due to the absence of the shifted segment; the leftmost buckle is due to its presence. (Courtesy of B. P. Kaufmann.)*

homologs helps locate the presence, absence, or relocation of chromosome parts. For example, in inversion heterozygotes, there will be one reversed segment which does not pair with its nonreversed homologous segment (if the region is small), or which shows one homolog forming a loop in order to synapse (if the inversion is larger) (Figure 19–6). A deficiency heterozygote will buckle in the region of the deficiency. Since a chromosome with a duplication may also buckle when heterozygous, careful cytological study is needed to distinguish this case from deficiency (see Figure 19–7). Heterozygotes for reciprocal translocations (Figure 19–8) will show two pairs of nonhomologous chromosomes associated together in synapsis.

This discussion should suffice to introduce you to the origin, nature, and consequences of the more common types of structural changes in chromosomes, and to the methods used to identify such mutations.

FIGURE 19–8. *Heterozygous reciprocal translocation in corn (pachynema) (courtesy of M. M. Rhoades) and Drosophila (salivary gland) (courtesy of B. P. Kaufmann).*

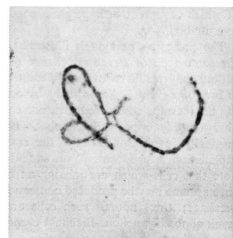

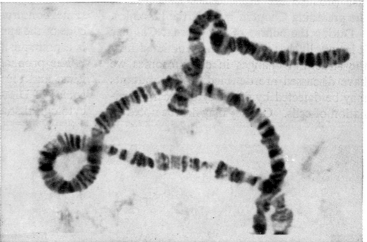

SUMMARY AND CONCLUSIONS

Structural change in chromosomes is a type of mutation involving the gain, loss, or relocation of chromosome parts. All such mutations are preceded by chromosome breakage. Since proximity of broken ends favors their union, most broken ends restitute. Nonrestitutional unions give rise to structural changes in chromosomes. The occurrence of one, two, or three nonrestituting breaks in one or two chromosomes is discussed in relation to the production of whole chromosome losses, deficiencies, duplications, inversions, translocations, shifts, and transpositions.

The chromosomes that have undergon estructural change may be euploid or aneuploid. The cells in which these mutations arise are euploid but may become aneuploid following mitosis, segregation, or crossing over. The structural changes most likely to be retained in the population are the smallest ones, those directly or indirectly causing an increase in gene number being most likely to be important in evolution.

REFERENCES

Bearn, A. G., and German III, J. L., "Chromosomes and Disease," Scient. Amer., 205, No. 5:66–76, 1961.

Muller, H. J., "The Nature of the Genetic Effects Produced by Radiation," in *Radiation Biology*, A. Hollaender (Ed.), New York, McGraw-Hill, 1954, Chap. 7, pp. 351–473.

QUESTIONS FOR DISCUSSION

19.1. The terms *euploid* and *aneuploid* (hypo- or hyperploid) have been applied both to individual chromosomes and to whole nuclei. Give an example of:

a. A hypoploid chromosome in a euploid nucleus.
b. A hyperploid chromosome in a hyperploid nucleus.
c. An aneuploid nucleus containing all structurally normal chromosomes.

19.2. Could a reciprocal translocation occur between homologous chromosomes? Explain.

19.3. What does the term *eutelomeric* mean, as used on p. 156?

19.4. While most Mongolian idiots are trisomic for a particular small autosome, some are known that have 46 chromosomes. In the latter cases, all chromosomes seem of normal composition except that one of the homologs of a different autosome has one arm that is exceptionally long. Discuss the origin and cause of Mongolian idiocy in these exceptional cases.

19.5. Given the chromosome AB/CDE/F.GHI/J, where the period indicates the centromere and the slanted lines the positions of three simultaneously produced breakages, draw as many different outcomes as you can. Indicate which one is the most likely to occur.

19.6. The loss of a given chromosome in *Drosophila*, resulting in monosomy, is approximately 3–5 times as frequent as its gain, resulting in trisomy. Explain.

19.7. Discuss the frequency of monosomics among human zygotes.

19.8. Discuss the detectability, in human chromosomes at mitotic metaphase, of a:

a. Paracentric inversion.
b. Pericentric inversion.
c. Deficiency.
d. Duplication.
e. Half-translocation.

19.9. What advantages may inversion provide?

19.10. What characteristics of cells undergoing oogenesis favor the production and viable transmission of half-translocations?

19.11. In *Drosophila*, a male, dihybrid for the mutants *bw* and *st*, when backcrossed to *bw bw st st*, normally produces offspring whose phenotypes are in a 1:1:1:1 ratio.
    On exceptional occasions, this cross produces offspring which are clearly of only two of the four phenotypes normally obtained. How can you explain such an exception?

19.12. Is the telomere a gene? Why?

Chapter 20

CYTOGENETICS OF OENOTHERA

A T THE close of the last Chapter you were introduced to some of the genetic and cytological methods for detecting and identifying structural changes in chromosomes. In still earlier Chapters you have learned the characteristics and some of the properties of other types of mutational events, as well as the basic principles of transmission genetics. Let us take the opportunity to use this information in toto in an investigation [1] of a plant called the evening primrose, *Oenothera*, which has until now been mentioned only on one occasion (p. 139).

Oenothera (Figure 20–1) is a common weed found along roadsides, railway embankments, and in abandoned fields. It is self-fertilizing in nature, where it exists in a number of pure breeding strains, each having a characteristic phenotype. These strains can be cross-fertilized in the laboratory, however, and progeny obtained. If the two strains crossed are *Lamarckiana* and *biennis*, a surprising result is obtained in F_1. In the first place, the F_1 are not all uniform in phenotype, as we would expect from previous experience with crossbreeding two pure lines, but are of three distinct types which we can call A, B, C. In the second place, each of these three F_1 types is thereafter pure breeding upon self-fertilization. If the F_1 were hybrid, we would expect self-fertilization to produce recombinants of more than one phenotype. These

[1] Based upon work of H. DeVries, O. Renner, R. E. Cleland, F. Oehlkers, A. F. Blakeslee, J. Belling, S. Emerson, and A. H. Sturtevant.

162

FIGURE 20–1. Oenothera. (*Courtesy of R. E. Cleland.*)

two peculiarities are summarized in Figure 20–2, where the typical results obtained from similar crosses with garden peas are indicated side by side.

What conclusions can we draw from this information? We must conclude, contrary to any such impression which might have been gained in Chapter 1, that self-fertilizing strains cannot automatically be considered to be pure, homozygous lines. In order to obtain three different genotypes in F_1, either *Lamarckiana*, or *biennis*, or both, must be heterozygous. Let us make the simplest assumption, namely that *Lamarckiana* is heterozygous for a single pair of genes. If so, how can this strain produce only *Lamarckiana* upon self-fertilization? This would require that the heterozygote produce only heterozygote progeny. But suppose that self-fertilization does, as expected, produce the two homozygotes, but that these are never observed because both types are lethal. (Recall that for yellow mice, see p. 65, only one

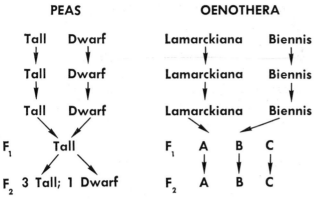

PEAS   OENOTHERA

FIGURE 20–2 (*Above*). *Comparative breeding results from garden peas and* Oenothera.

FIGURE 20–3 (*Below*). *Balanced lethal systems that enforce heterozygosity.*

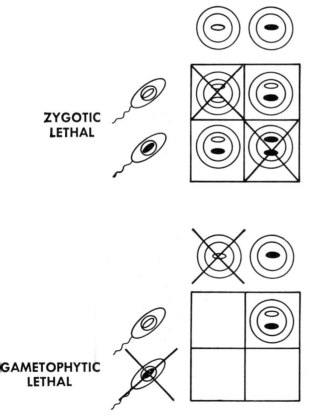

ZYGOTIC
LETHAL

GAMETOPHYTIC
LETHAL

homozygote is lethal, the other is viable. In the present case the two different alleles would have to act as recessive lethals.) This hypothesis would require that of all zygotes, one half die before becoming mature *Lamarckiana*. This view is supported by finding that approximately one half of the ovules regularly fail to produce seed upon self-fertilization, and this is evidence that *Lamarckiana* in nature is a permanent heterozygote in this respect, as the result of a *balanced lethal system*. In this case, since ovules fail to produce seed, the lethals must kill prior to this stage. In fact, the lethal may kill at the time of fertilization, or very soon thereafter, being in effect a *zygotic lethal* (Figure 20–3).

But, we have ignored another possible time for lethal action. Recall that in some plants, including *Oenothera*, there is a haploid gametophyte generation. Permanent heterozygosity could be maintained also, if one allele were lethal to the male gametophyte and the other to the female (Figure 20–3). So *gametophytic lethals* can also provide a balanced lethal system. Further study shows that half of the ovules fail to produce seed in *biennis* also, and, in general, in all strains of *Oenothera* found in nature, and that, in fact, both zygotic and gametophytic lethals are involved in these balanced lethal systems.

Does the establishment of the existence of a balanced lethal system in *Oenothera* explain how it is that the phenotype, say of *Lamarckiana*, is the only one produced in the progeny from self-fertilization? Since all sexual organisms so far studied have many pairs of genes, it would not seem reasonable that *Oenothera* has only a single pair of recessive lethal genes whose pleiotropic (manifold) effects produce the entire phenotype. It is more reasonable to believe that there are many gene pairs but that these form a single linkage group, so that the diploid has one genome whose genes are all linked to one recessive lethal, and another genome whose genes are all linked to the allelic lethal.

In other words, *Lamarckiana* behaves as though it contains two *complexes* of linked genes. Within a strain these genes are completely linked by some mechanism that prevents recombination, so that only two kinds of genotypes are found in the gametes. The two gene complexes are so constant in natural populations of a strain that they are given, in the case of *Lamarckiana*, the names *gaudens* and *velans*, so that this strain can be identified as *gaudens.velans*, whereas *biennis* can be described by its gene complexes as *albicans.rubens*. Figure 20–4 shows how these balanced lethal gene complexes are distributed

FIGURE 20–4. *Balanced lethal gene complexes in* O. biennis *and* O. Lamarckiana.

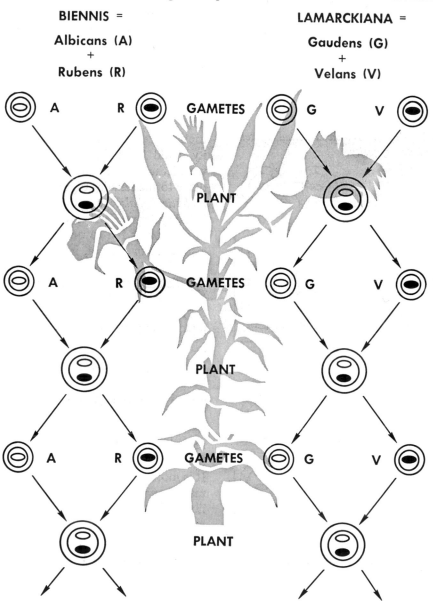

BIENNIS =

Albicans (A)
+
Rubens (R)

LAMARCKIANA =

Gaudens (G)
+
Velans (V)

generation after generation in *biennis* and *Lamarckiana*. It is a simple matter for you to work out that all the recessive lethal alleles in the one strain cannot be identical to those in the other of these two strains, for the F_1 from crossing them would be of only two different phenotypes, whereas three types were actually obtained. We can conclude, therefore, that the balanced lethal system in *Oenothera* in general involves either a multiple allelic series, or several pairs of genes, or both.

While each of the three different hybrids obtained in F_1 from crossing *Lamarckiana* and *biennis* breeds true upon self-fertilization,

showing in this way that each contains two completely linked gene complexes, this may or may not be true of the breeding behavior of hybrids obtained from certain other interracial crosses. This ambivalence is illustrated in Figure 20–5. In this Figure, the gene complexes present in the different hybrids are shown at the left. The distribution in their gametes of the various genetic markers shown at the top of the Figure was determined by breeding tests. So, for example, the *curvans.velans* hybrid bred in such a way that all marker genes behaved as though they were still linked (the marker genes and their alleles being distributed in gametes in a total

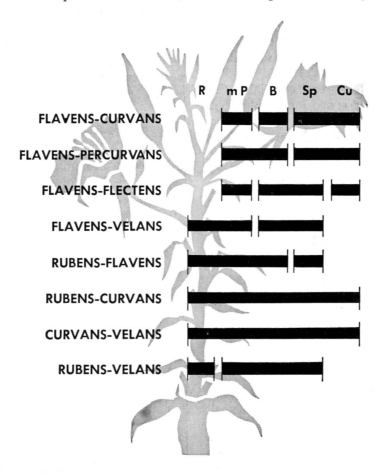

FIGURE 20–5. *Linkage groups in hybrids from interracial crosses.*

of only two combinations). On the other hand, the *flavens.velans* hybrid produced four kinds of gametes, the genes for *R*, *m*, and *P* (all still linked to each other) segregating independently of the genes for *B* and *Sp* (both still linked to each other), so that half of the gametes contained one of the two parental combinations, the other half carried one of the two recombinations. In this case, therefore, genes that belonged to a single linkage group in the parent races behaved as two linkage groups during the gametogenesis of their hybrid. (The fact that 50% recombination occurred in the gametogenesis of the hybrid means that we cannot explain these results by postulating that *flavens* (or *velans*) is always a single linkage group, which cannot crossover with the partner gene complex of the parent race, but which can do so when its partner is *velans* (or *flavens*).)

Other tests of the hybrid containing *flavens.curvans* showed *m* and *P* still linked but separate from *B*, which was, in turn, separate from *Sp* and *Cu*, so that there were now three linkage groups, and perhaps more would have been found had additional genetic markers been employed. In all cases, however, the same hybrid combination always showed the same linkage groups in its gametogenesis.

In view of the fact that at least three linkage groups can be identified in certain hybrids (even though under certain conditions these act as one), it is to be expected that the diploid would have at least three pairs of chromosomes. Cytological examination confirms this genetic expectation, there being seven pairs of chromosomes in all of the *Oenothera* strains discussed in the present Chapter. (*Oenothera gigas*, the triploid mentioned in Chapter 18, has 21 chromosomes.) According to our assumption that the balanced lethal system is based upon a single pair of genes located on a single pair of homologs, this pair of chromosomes must necessarily remain heterozygous to be viable in F_1. But this would not be expected to be true for the other

six pairs of chromosomes, which should segregate independently. So, for example, gametes of *biennis* which carry the *albicans* recessive lethal should be equally likely to carry the *rubens* or the *albicans* homolog in each of the other six cases of independent segregation. But this is not found. It is theoretically possible, however, to have seven pairs of chromosomes each heterozygous for a different recessive lethal which would, upon self-fertilization, produce only viable F_1 like itself. Since this explanation would predict that only about $\frac{1}{2}^7$ of all ovules would develop as seeds, it cannot be the correct one for *Oenothera*.

FIGURE 20–6.   *Circle of 14 chromosomes in* Oeno-thera. *Chromosome number is clear in upper cell where the circle has broken open. (Courtesy of R. E. Cleland.)*

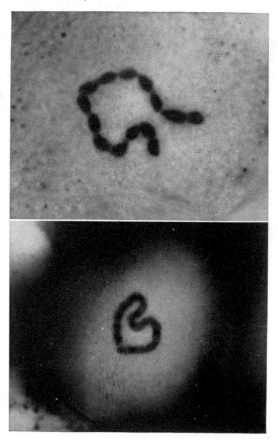

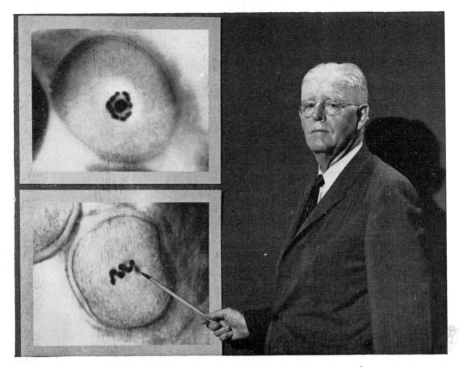

FIGURE 20–7. RALPH E. CLELAND *points to zig-zag chromosomal arrangement at the start of anaphase I of an* Oenothera *having a circle of 14 chromosomes at metaphase I.* (*Photograph courtesy of The Calvin Company.*)

A clue to the orderly segregation of complete gene complexes is found in the study of meiosis in *Oenothera*. Here it is found that the typical *Oenothera* in nature does not form seven separate bivalents, but, as seen clearly at metaphase I, forms a closed circle of 14 chromosomes, synapsed end to end (Figure 20–6). At anaphase I, moreover, chromosomes that are adjacent to each other in the circle go to opposite poles of the spindle, so that at the start of the separation the chromosomes assume a zigzag arrangement (Figure 20–7). If you make the assumption that paternal and maternal chromosomes alternate in the circle, then all paternal chromosomes go to one pole, and all maternal chromosomes to the other. The complete linkage of all genes in a complex would be explained (if crossing over is rare) by such a manner of chromosome segregation, and the gametes produced by an individual would be identical to those which united to form it (Figure 20–8).

If the alternate segregation procedure separates maternal and paternal genomes, a circle should always contain an even number of chromosomes. Moreover, we could make the prediction that when a genome no longer behaves as a single linkage group it would also no longer form, with the other linkage group, a single circle of 14 chromosomes. Theoretically, there is a total of 15 different ways that 14 chromosomes can be arranged in circles (composed of even numbers of chromosomes) and pairs, as shown in Figure 20–9. And when various race hybrids are made, indeed all 15 types and no others are found in the metaphase I stage, any particular

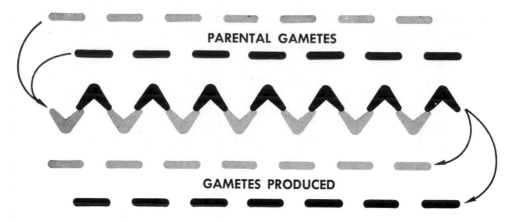

FIGURE 20–8.   *Manner of chromosome segregation during meiosis of* Oenothera.

FIGURE 20–9.   *Circle and pair arrangements possible for* Oenothera *chromosomes.*

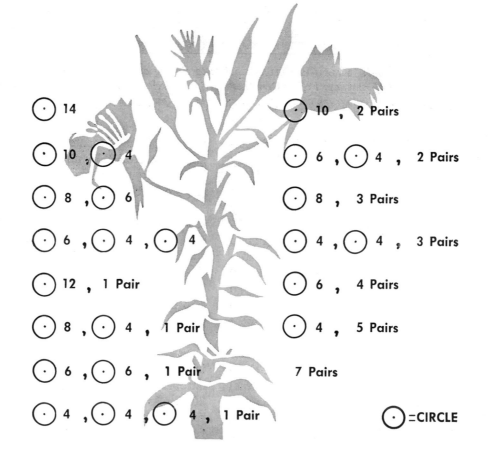

hybrid always giving the same meiotic configuration. (The top cell in Figure 20–7 shows an inner circle of four and an outer circle of ten chromosomes.) If what has been supposed is true, it also ought to follow that while alternate chromosomes within a circle show complete linkage with each other, such linkage groups would not be prevented from segregating independently from those linkage groups made up of chromosomes either in separate circles or in separate pairs. This expectation can be tested by comparing the number of linkage groups found in the different hybrids of Figure 20–5 with the chromosome arrangements seen cytologically during their meiosis. When this is done, it is found that the number of separate groups of chromosomes observed in meiosis is always equal to, or greater than, the number of linkage groups detected genetically. In fact, whenever enough genetic markers are used, the number of linkage groups always equals the number of chromosome groups.

While all of the preceding satisfactorily demonstrates that segregation of alternate chromosomes in a circle to the same pole and the presence of balanced lethal systems can explain most of the unusual genetic behavior of *Oenothera*, other matters still need explanation. What causes these chromosomes to form circles in the first place? A clue to this is contained in the observation made near the end of the last Chapter, namely, that two pairs of nonhomologs will be associated together during synapsis if a reciprocal translocation is present between two of the nonhomologs and absent in their homologs, i.e., if these nonhomologs are heterozygous for a reciprocal translocation. This can be illustrated in *Oenothera* by means of Figure 20–10. In *Oenothera* all chromosomes are small, of the same size, with median centromeres. To help us identify homologous chromosomes, the ends of each chromosome in a genome are given different numbers. Suppose, some time in the past, a eucentric reciprocal translocation occurred between the tips marked 2 and 3 (top left of Figure). This rearrangement in heterozygous condition (middle left) would produce an X-shaped configuration at the time of synapsis in prophase I (bottom left), and a circular appearance at metaphase I — early anaphase I. In this way a circle of four chromosomes would be produced.

If now a second reciprocal translocation

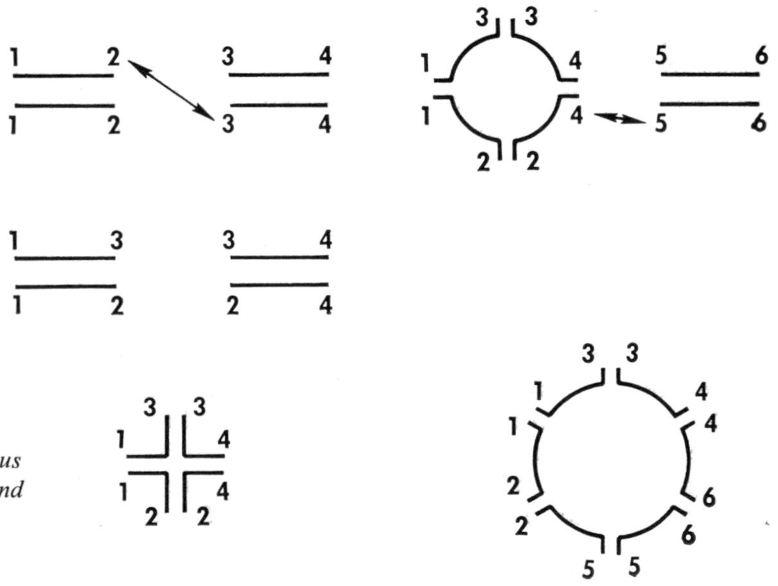

FIGURE 20–10. *Heterozygous reciprocal translocations and circle formation.*

occurred between any chromosome tip in a circle of four and a tip of some other pair of chromosomes, a circle of six chromosomes will form in the heterozygote for both reciprocal translocations. This is illustrated at the right of Figure 20–10 where the upper diagram shows the configuration before tips 4 and 5 exchange, and the lower diagram shows the circle of six following this exchange. Still larger circles can be formed by successive interchanges of this type, six being required to form a circle of 14. The presence of reciprocal translocations in heterozygous condition could explain how various sized circles containing even numbers of chromosomes are produced in *Oenothera*.

We have not yet completed our analysis of *Oenothera*, however. One of the questions remaining is: By what mechanism is it arranged that alternate chromosomes in a circle proceed to the same pole during meiosis? The answer to this is unknown. A second question stems from the fact that almost all the different races of *Oenothera* found in nature form a circle of 14. Are the six translocations involved the same in all races? No, for if they were, viable hybrids between races would form either circles of 14 or seven pairs at meiosis. The very fact that all the configurations in Figure 20–9 are found in such hybrids must mean that different gene complexes must differ from each other in the specific ways that their chromosome ends have become translocated. There are many thousands of ways, theoretically, that 14 ends can be arranged in seven groups of two. How can we determine how many of these different arrangements are found in nature?

Let us start by taking a particular gene complex, calling it the standard, and labeling its chromosome ends 1–2, 3–4, 5–6, 7–8, 9–10, 11–12, 13–14. (Normally, i.e., in nature, this complex would form a circle of 14 with the other gene complex, which would therefore have no chromosome with the same pair of ends as has the standard.) Now a series of interracial hybrids is formed with the standard as one of the complexes, and their meiotic arrangements scored. Suppose in one case the hybrid forms 5 pairs and a circle of 4. This must mean that the ends of 5 chromosomes are in the same order in the complex under test as in the standard, but that they are in a different order in the remaining two chromosomes. Until now there was no reason to assign ends 1–2, 3–4 of the standard to any particular chromosomes. But now we can arbitrarily assign these ends to the two standard chromosomes in the circle of 4, and, therefore, the chromosomes in the circle from the complex under test can be called 2–3, 4–1. In this way, the composition of ends of two pairs of chromosomes is specified permanently. Figure 20–11 (top) shows the standard and tested complexes in our example synapsed according to numbers.

Let us call the complex just tested A. Suppose next another complex, B, is made hybrid both with the standard and with A. You can see that an appropriate result will specify other ends of standard, A, and B. Such procedures can be carried out until all of the standard's chromosomes are specified and the complete order of all 14 ends determined for any other complex. In this manner, it is discovered in nature that a circle of 14 is produced in many different ways, a theoretical and an actual example being shown in the central and lower parts of Figure 20–11. In fact, of 350 complexes analyzed, more than 160 different segmental arrangements have been found. All these results are consistent with the hypothesis that during the course of evolution the ends of *Oenothera* chromosomes have been shuffled many times in different ways by reciprocal translocation. Finally, a most convincing test of the reciprocal translocation interpretation would be the ability to predict the meiotic chromosomal arrangement to be found in a hybrid not yet formed. This has been done many times and

A. COMPLEXES DIFFERING BY ONE RECIPROCAL TRANSLOCATION

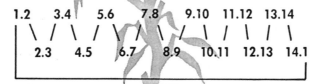

B. COMPLEXES DIFFERING BY SIX RECIPROCAL TRANSLOCATIONS

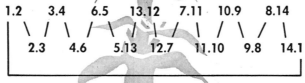

C. MURICATA RACE'S ACTUAL COMPOSITION OF ⊙14

A and B are theoretical

FIGURE 20–11. *Arrangement of chromosome ends in different* Oenothera *complexes.*

all such predictions came true. We see, then, that the cytogenetic behavior of *Oenothera* becomes understandable in view of its (1) long previous history of reciprocal translocation, (2) method of chromosome segregation, (3) balanced lethals, and (4) self-fertilization.

At various points in this discussion *Oenothera* seemed to behave exceptionally, apparently violating our concepts of pure lines and independent segregation. More complete analysis has shown, however, that the failure of *Oenothera* to behave in the ways expected was due to the operation of other, already known, genetic events. *Oenothera* is an exception which should be treasured, for in the exact correspondence between its atypical genetics and its atypical cytology, it furnishes an outstanding example of the validity of the chromosome theory of transmission genetics.

SUMMARY AND CONCLUSIONS

Both the genetics and the cytology of *Oenothera* are exceptional. This, however, is found to be the normal consequence of the simultaneous operation of certain already known cytogenetic phenomena. In this way, *Oenothera* provides an outstanding confirmation of the validity of the chromosome theory of transmission genetics.

REFERENCES

Cleland, R. E., "Some Aspects of Cyto-Genetics of Oenothera," Bot. Rev., 2:316–348, 1936.

QUESTIONS FOR DISCUSSION

20.1. What evidence can you present that the genes comprising the balanced lethal system in *Lamarckiana* are different from those in *biennis*?

20.2. Discuss the statement: "All evening primroses in nature are constant hybrids."

20.3. With respect to chromosomes, how does the origin of a circle differ from the origin of a ring?

20.4. Can circles contain an odd number of chromosomes? Explain.

20.5. What new investigations regarding the genetics and/or cytology of *Oenothera* does the present Chapter suggest to you?

20.6. List the principles of genetics you could have arrived at had *Oenothera* been the only organism so far studied.

20.7. If this Chapter contains no new principles of genetics, for what purpose do you suppose it was written?

20.8. Curly winged *Drosophila* mated together always produce some non-curly offspring. Plum eye colored flies mated together always produce some non-plum offspring. But, when flies are mated that are both curly and plum only flies of this type occur among the offspring.

Defining your gene symbols, explain all three kinds of results.

20.9. Draw a diagram representing the appearance of a heterozygous whole-arm translocation in *Drosophila* at the time of synapsis. Number the arms of the chromosomes involved.

What else would you require in order that a mating of two flies with this configuration produce only offspring of this type?

20.10. Do you suppose that the preservation of heterozygosity has an adaptive advantage in *Oenothera*? In other organisms?

HUGO DE VRIES (*1848–1935*), *pioneer in the study of* Oenothera *genetics.* (*By permission of Genetics, Inc., vol. 4, p. 1, 1919.*)

Chapter **21**

NATURAL AND INDUCED CHROMOSOMAL CHANGES

CHAPTER 19 dealt primarily with different types of structural change within chromosomes and the manner in which their origin depended upon chromosome breakage. However, little was said there concerning the factors responsible for the production of the key events of breakage and of union. This is one of the matters to be taken up in the present Chapter. Also, in that earlier Chapter, relatively little detail was given concerning the types of structural change actually found in nature. We did learn subsequently, in Chapter 20, that reciprocal translocations have played an important role in the evolution of *Oenothera*. It might be claimed, however, that *Oenothera* does not furnish a representative test of the importance of chromosomal rearrangements in evolution, since its cytogenetical behavior is so unorthodox. For the specific reciprocal translocations in *Oenothera* involve the ends of chromosomes and are retained in natural populations in heterozygous condition.

There are hundreds of different species of *Drosophila* in nature. These species can be compared ecologically, morphologically, physiologically, serologically, and biochemically. They can also be tested for ability to interbreed, and when they do crossbreed, their genetics can be compared; they can be compared relative to the banding patterns of their salivary gland chromosomes and the appearance of their chromosomes at metaphase. And when all known information of this kind

173

is taken into account, it becomes possible to arrange these species on a chart so that those closest together are more nearly related in descent, in evolution, than are those farther apart.[1] This has been done in Figure 21–1, which shows the haploid set of chromosomes at metaphase, including the X but not the Y chromosome, for different species or groups of species of *Drosophila*. For example, the chromosomes of the *melanogaster* species group are drawn in row 2, column 1, the bottom chromosome being the rod-shaped X, the two V's being the two large autosomes (II and III) and the dot representing the tiny chromosome IV. In the other metaphase configurations, chromosomes or their parts which are judged to be homologous are placed in the same relative positions. What can we learn from a comparison of these metaphase plates?

Since the amount of detail in a metaphase chromosome is limited to size and shape, we cannot expect to detect any rearrangements of small size at this stage. So, regardless of their importance, small rearrangements involving duplications, deficiencies, shifts, transpositions, inversions, and translocations cannot be detected in the Figure. Even a large paracentric inversion is undetected here, since it does not change the shape of the chromosome. However, other gross structural changes can be detected. In row 4, the chromosome patterns in columns 2 and 3 seem identical, except that a pericentric inversion has changed a rod to a V, or the reverse. (Pericentric inversions will always change the relative lengths of arms when the two breaks are different distances from the centromere.) Compare the plate for *melanogaster* (r.2, c.1) with the plate to its right (r.2, c.2). A V-shaped autosome in *melanogaster* appears as two rods in its relative. (Note also that the dot chromosome is missing.) In the next plate to the right (r.2, c.3), two rods have combined

[1] Based upon work of C. W. Metz and others.

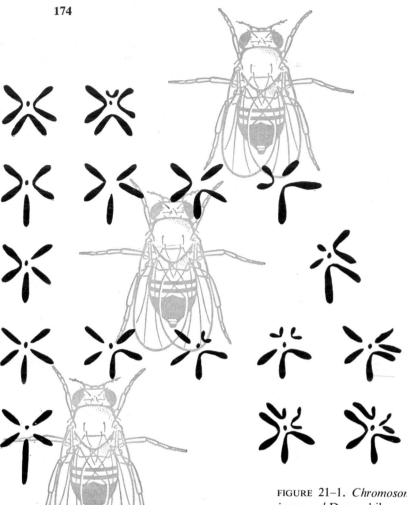

FIGURE 21–1. *Chromosome configurations in several* Drosophila *species.*

to form a V that is different from either of the two V's in *melanogaster*.

There are other examples in this chart of two rod-shaped chromosomes forming a V-shaped chromosome, or of a V forming two rods. Let us see how these changes can come about. Consider first how a V can originate from two rods (Figure 21–2). It should be recalled that a rod-shaped chromosome has two arms, although one is very short. The short arm may not be noticeable at metaphase or anaphase, but may be demonstrable either cytologically at an earlier or later stage of the nuclear cycle, or by genetic means via the genes it carries. Suppose two rods are broken near their centromeres, one break being in the long arm of one chromosome, the other break being in the short arm of the other chromosome. If the long acentric arm of the first chromosome joins to the long centric piece of the second chromosome, a V is formed. Notice that this involves the joining of two whole or almost-whole arms in a eucentric half-translocation. The remaining pieces may join together to form a short eucentric chromosome, thereby completing a reciprocal translocation, or they may not join. In either case, if these short pieces are lost in a subse-

FIGURE 21–2 *(Left)*. *Formation of a V-shaped chromosome from two rod-shaped chromosomes.*

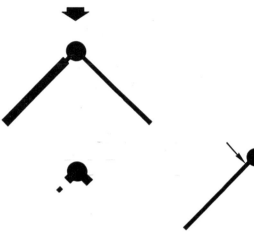

HALF (OR RECIPROCAL) TRANSLOCATION

RECIPROCAL TRANSLOCATION

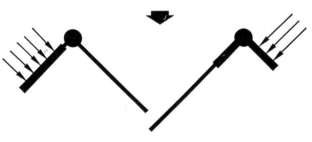

FIGURE 21–3 *(Right)*. *Formation of two rod-shaped chromosomes from a V-shaped chromosome and a Y chromosome.*

PARACENTRIC DELETIONS

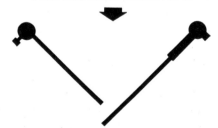

quent nuclear division and if the number of genes lost in these pieces is small enough, the absence of these parts may be tolerated physiologically.

The reverse process, the formation of two rods from a V, necessitates the contribution of a centromere from some other chromosome. This second chromosome may be the Y (Figure 21–3). Suppose the V is broken near its centromere and the Y is broken anywhere. If a eucentric reciprocal translocation then occurs, two chromosomes are produced each having one arm that is derived largely from the Y. Then, later, if paracentric deletions occur in these Y-containing arms, the rod shapes will be attained, completing the change from a V to two rods. Note that almost all but the centromere of the Y chromosome is eventually lost in this process. But this may have little or no disadvantage since the Y carries relatively few loci and is primarily concerned with sperm motility. For example, this series of mutations may be initiated in the male germ line so that two Y-containing rods are produced. Deletion of Y parts can occur without detriment if these chromosomes happen to enter the female germ line, or they may stay in the male germ line provided a regular Y chromosome is added to the chromosome complement in due time. The small IV chromosome in *melanogaster*, whose monosomy is tolerated in either sex, may also serve to contribute a centromere in changing a V to two rods by an identical or similar series of mutational events.

The metaphase plate observations confirm expectation in the case of *Drosophila* (Chapter 20), in that whole arm translocations are capable of persisting in natural populations. Such rearrangements and pericentric inversions are very useful in helping us establish evolutionary relationships among different species. But it should be emphasized that this kind of information by itself does not prove either that the formation of different species is a primary consequence of the occurrence of these rearrangements, or that these rearrangements are of secondary importance in species formation, or that these mutational events occur after species formation is completed. As exemplified by *Oenothera* and *Drosphila*, we have seen that gross rearrangements of somewhat different types have persisted in the course of the evolution of different groups of organisms. For this reason it would be prudent to refrain from predicting, except in the general way we have done in Chapter 20, which, if any, structural changes would be found associated with the

evolution of other particular groups of organisms.

Let us turn our attention now to the factors which produce the breaks leading to structural change. Chromosomes do break spontaneously; that is, they occasionally break during the normal course of events. However, because spontaneous breaks occur relatively rarely, the study of them and their consequences would be greatly enhanced by the application of external agents capable of producing breaks in great numbers. One of these agents is radiation, and our attention will be restricted to this agent in the present Chapter (Figure 21–4). The process of breaking a chromosome is a chemical reaction requiring energy. Radiation may supply energy in three different forms: *heat, activation or excitation,* and *ionization*. The biochemical effect of a radiation depends upon the type and amount of energy it leaves in tissue, less energetic radiations (like visible light) leaving energy in the form of heat, more energetic radiations (like ultraviolet light) leaving energy also in the form of activations (in which an electron is moved from an inner to an outer orbit). The more energetic the radiation, the greater is the likelihood that the energy absorbed will lead to chemical change. For example, visible light does not produce as many breaks in chromosomes as does ultraviolet light. Radiations of still higher energy (like X rays, gamma rays, and alpha, beta, neutron, proton, and other fast-moving particulate radiations) are most likely to cause breaks. Although such high-energy radiations can heat and activate, most of their energy is left in cells in the form of ionizations, and it is these which produce most of the breaks. Let us consider first what ionization is and how it is produced, and then how it is connected with the production of breaks.

X and gamma rays are electromagnetic waves like visible light, but have relatively shorter wave lengths, and can penetrate tissue more deeply before they are stopped, at

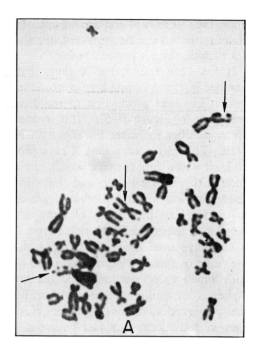

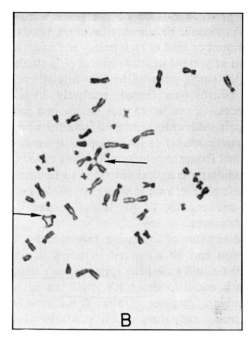

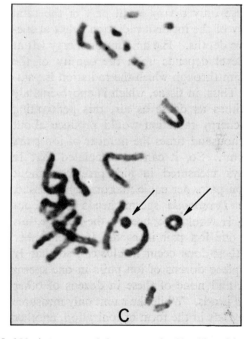

which time their energy is absorbed. Energy is transferred into ionization when some of these rays are stopped by an atom which subsequently loses an orbital electron. This electron, torn free of the atom, shoots off at great speed and can, in turn, cause other atoms to lose electrons in a similar manner. All atoms losing electrons become *positively charged ions*. The freed electrons are finally captured by other atoms which become negatively charged, or *negatively charged ions*. Since each electron lost from one atom is eventually gained by another atom, ions occur as pairs. In this way a *track of ionizations* is produced which often has smaller side branches. The length of a primary track and its side branches, and the density of ion pairs within these, will differ depending upon the type and energy of radiation involved. Suffice it to say that all known ionizing radia-

FIGURE 21–4. *Structural changes X-ray-induced (75–150 r) in normal human male fibroblast-like cells* in vitro. *Arrows show: (A) broken chromosomes, (B) translocation (center) and dicentric (lower left), (C) ring chromosomes. A, B are in metaphase (see Fig. 18–9), C is late prophase. (Courtesy of T. T. Puck, Proc. Nat. Acad. Sci., U.S., 44:776–778, 1958.)*

tions produce clusters of ion pairs within submicroscopic distances. In other words, no amount or kind of high-energy radiation is known at present which produces only single ions, or single pairs of ions, evenly spaced over microscopic (hence relatively large) distances. Since we cannot obtain one ion or a pair sufficiently separated from the next, the genetic effects of ionization must be determined from the activity of clusters of ions. Ions undergo chemical reactions to neutralize their charge, and, in doing so, clusters of them are capable of producing breaks in chromosomes.

The amount of ionization produced by a radiation can be measured in terms of an ionization unit called the *roentgen, or r unit,* which is equal to about 1.8×10^9 ion pairs per cubic centimeter of air. A sufficiently penetrating radiation, which produces this 1.8×10^9 ion pairs in a cm³ of air, may also produce this amount in successive cm³ of air because only a very small part of the total energy of the incident radiation is left at successive depths. The amount of energy left at any level depends upon the density of the medium through which the radiation is passing. Thus, in tissue, which is approximately ten times as dense as air, this penetrating high-energy radiation would produce about one thousand times the number of ion pairs per cm³. So, it can be calculated that 1r (always measured in air) produces about 1.5 ion pairs per cubic micron (μ^3) of tissue. Since *Drosophila* sperm heads are about $0.5\mu^3$, 1r would produce, on the average, less than one ion pair in each. But remember that these ions occur in clusters, so that 1r may place dozens of ion pairs in one sperm head, and none of these in dozens of other sperm heads. While the r unit only measures energy left in the form of ionization, another unit, the *rad*, measures the total amount of energy of the radiation which is absorbed by the medium. In the case of X rays, about 90% of the energy left is in the form of ioniza-

tions, the rest as heat and excitations. Ultraviolet radiation can be measured in rads, but not r units, since it is nonionizing.

It has been found, for X rays, that the number of chromosome breaks produced increases in direct proportion to the dose expressed in r (Figure 21–5). This means that break number increases linearly with X-ray dose. This also means that X rays produce at least some ion clusters which are large enough to cause a break, and that different clusters of ions do not combine their effects to do so. (Had there been such a cooperation between clusters, the break rate at low doses would have been lower than found, due to the waste of smaller clusters having no others with which to cooperate, while the rate at higher doses would have been higher, due to the cooperation among smaller clusters.) Certain radiations, like fast neutrons, produce fewer breaks per r than do X rays. This is explained by the fact that one r of these radiations produces larger (and hence fewer) clusters of ions than do X rays, these larger clusters more often exceeding the size needed to produce a break, and being, therefore, relatively less efficient in this respect.

Ion clusters may produce breaks either directly, by attacking the chromosome itself, or indirectly, by changing oxygen-carrying molecules, which in turn react with the chromosomes, or by influencing chemicals which affect oxygen-carrying molecules. In any case, this indirect pathway must be of submicroscopic dimensions, otherwise there would be cooperation among the chemical effects of different ion clusters to cause breakage. Thus, only ion clusters in or very close to the chromosome can produce breaks in it. This has been visibly demonstrated by the use of beams of radiation of microscopic dimensions. Such a beam passing through a metaphase chromosome breaks it, but fails to do so when directed in the plasm just adjacent to the chromosome.

From what has been stated in the previous

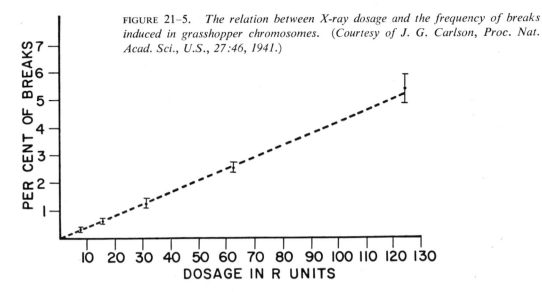

FIGURE 21–5. *The relation between X-ray dosage and the frequency of breaks induced in grasshopper chromosomes. (Courtesy of J. G. Carlson, Proc. Nat. Acad. Sci., U.S., 27:46, 1941.)*

paragraph, it should be no surprise to you that the number of breaks produced by the direct action of a given dose of a particular radiation will depend upon the volume which a chromosome occupies; this volume may be different at different times in the nuclear cycle, and the same chromosome may occupy different volumes in different tissues or sexes. It is also reasonable, in view of the fact that breakage is energy-requiring, that the number of breaks produced indirectly is increased, if during irradiation either the amount of oxygen is increased or the cell's reducing substances are poisoned. As expected, therefore, replacement of oxygen by nitrogen during irradiation reduces the number of breaks produced.

With this preliminary discussion of some of the factors influencing the production of radiation-induced breaks as a background, consider next the factors influencing the fate of the ends produced by breakage. Just as breakage involves a chemical reaction, so does the union between two broken ends. It has been shown that the joining of broken ends also requires energy, being enhanced by the presence of oxygen (and prevented by nitrogen) when present after irradiation. So,

restitution is prevented if nitrogen has replaced oxygen after irradiation. This increases the time that the ends from the same break stay open, and this often increases their chance for cross-union later in the presence of oxygen. (You see, therefore, that oxygen has two contrary effects on rearrangements, its presence during irradiation increasing the number of breaks and its presence after irradiation increasing restitution.)

Since, under a given set of conditions, the number of breaks increases linearly with dose, each part of the dose independently producing its proportional number of breaks, it is clear that the number of breaks produced is independent of the rate at which a given total dose of radiation is administered. It also follows, then, that all structural changes consequent to single breakages are also independent of the radiation dose rate. Radiations, like fast neutrons, which produce tracks that are long and dense with ionizations, may frequently produce two breaks with the same track. In this case, if the same chromosome is broken twice because, having coiled tightly, it lay in the path of the track twice, large and small structural changes of inversion, deficiency, and duplication types may be produced. The frequency of these will increase linearly with neutron dose, and be independent of the dose rate. The same track of ionizations may, as in the case of fast neutrons, break two different chromosomes; this would be possible when these chromosomes are closely packed together, as they are in the sperm head. The fact that the total frequency of reciprocal translocations increases linearly with fast neutron dose when sperm are treated is evidence both of this and of the view, already presented in Chapter 20, that proximity of broken ends favors their union. For such a result would be obtained only if both breaks were produced by the same track, and only if the broken ends capable of exchange union were restricted to those located near each other, broken ends produced in the course of different tracks being too far apart.

When, however, ordinary X rays are involved, the clusters are smaller, and the track of ionizations is shorter. In this case, two breaks will be produced by the same track less frequently, and if they do occur, they will usually be in the same chromosome at places quite close together. For example, the two breaks may occur within submicroscopic distances in successive gyres of a coiled chromosome, so that only minute to small structural changes will be produced by such breaks. In the case of X rays, two breaks occurring microscopic distances apart in the same nucleus are usually the result of the action of two clusters, each one derived from an independently arising track, so that one break has no dependence upon the other for its production. For this reason, X-ray-induced gross rearrangements can be dose dependent. For when a low enough dose is given, some nuclei contain only one track and only one break, and no gross two-break rearrangements can occur in them. But when the dose is raised high enough so that these nuclei are traversed by two separate tracks, the two breaks required for such rearrangements can be pro-

duced in the same nucleus. The higher the dose of X rays, then, the greater is the efficiency in the utilization of breaks to produce gross rearrangements. Accordingly, for doses causing some cells to have two independently produced breaks, and for doses higher than this, the frequency of these mutations increases, not in direct proportion to the dose, but faster than this. There is, however, a small proportion of single X-ray tracks that will, in the treatment of sperm, for example, cause two breaks, each in a different chromosome. Therefore, for doses of X rays that produce fewer than two tracks per sperm, gross rearrangement frequency will increase linearly with dose. So, there is actually no dose of X rays to sperm which would not have some chance of producing a gross rearrangement, which means that no dose is safe in this respect.

X-ray-induced rearrangements, produced by two or more independently arisen breaks, may also be dose-rate-dependent. When a suitably large dose is given over a short interval, the ends produced by separate breaks are present simultaneously and can undergo cross-union. But when the same dose of this radiation is given more slowly, the pieces of the first break may restitute before those of the second are produced, in this way eliminating the opportunity for cross-union. In this event, the same dose, given in a protracted manner, would produce fewer gross rearrangements than it would when given in a concentrated manner. While this dose-rate-dependence for X rays holds true for most cells, it does not obtain, however, for mature sperm of animals, probably including man. In these cells the broken pieces cannot join each other and are, therefore, accumulated. For this reason, it makes no difference how quickly or slowly the dose is given to the chromosomes in a sperm head, for the breaks remain unjoined until after fertilization when the sperm head swells.

We have already mentioned that the spatial

arrangement of chromosomes relative to each other will influence the number of breaks and the kinds of structural changes these produce. It should be noted, specifically, that when the chromosomes are packed into the tiny head of a sperm, the possibilities for multiple breakages and for later joinings may be quite different than they are for chromosomes located in a large nucleus. But even within a given type of cell, there are a number of other factors which may influence breakage or rejoining. These include the presence or absence of a restrictive and insulating nuclear membrane, the degree of spiralization of the chromosomes, the stress or tension under which the parts of a chromosome are held, the degree of hydration, the amount of matrix in which the genes are embedded, protoplasmic viscosity and the amount of fluid and particulate movement around the chromosomes, gravity effects, centrifugal forces, and vibrations. One special restriction to the movements of broken pieces occurs in cells whose chromosomes have just divided, and in meiotic cells where homologs synapse. For under these conditions, the forces, which keep like parts of one strand apposed to the like parts of its sister or homolog, may prevent the pieces newly produced by breakage from moving apart freely, so that the unbroken strand or strands serve as a splint for the broken one, reducing the opportunities for cross-union. All these factors determine to what degree chromosome fragments may move or spring apart; those affecting the distances between different chromosomes, or the parts within a chromosome, may also affect chromosome breakability.

The frequencies and types of structural changes will depend also upon the total amount of chromosomal material present in a nucleus and the number and size of the chromosomes into which this is partitioned. The rearrangements occurring in different cells of a single individual will depend upon whether the cell is haploid, diploid, or polyploid, and whether or not the chromosomes are in the process of replication and are metabolically active.

Finally, there are two different types of chromosomal material and each has a different capacity to produce structural changes. Most of the chromosomal material in the genome reacts similarly to certain staining procedures, and is said, therefore, to be *euchromatic* (truly or correctly colored). Other portions of the chromosomes stain either darker or lighter than this, and are said to be *heterochromatic*. Although some heterochromatin may be located at various places along the chromosome arm, it is normally found in both arms adjacent to the centromere and, to a lesser extent, near the telomeres. The genes in heterochromatin function to produce large blocks of chromosomal material in mitotic and meiotic chromosomes, so that their contribution to the size of the chromosome, as seen at metaphase, is relatively greater per gene than it is for genes located in euchromatic regions.

Besides its special stainability, location, and function, heterochromatin has a fourth characteristic, in that it is less specific in synapsis than is euchromatin; heterochromatin located at different places along a chromosome or in nonhomologous chromosomes is often found synapsed. (Thus, for example, in the salivary gland nuclei of *Drosophila* larvae, the heterochromatic regions proximal to the centromeres of all chromosomes synapse to form one mass, called the *chromocenter*. Also, the heterochromatic regions near the telomeres are sometimes found in synapsis with the chromocenter.) Relative to the number of loci present, the fifth fact is observed, that radiation-induced structural changes more frequently involve heterochromatic regions than they do euchromatic ones. Whether this excess is to be attributed to a greater breakability or lesser restitutability, or both, of heterochromatin, as compared to euchromatin, cannot be decided. Nevertheless, this means that in many rearrangements, at least one of the breakage points is located in the heterochromatin near the centromere. It is not unexpected, therefore, that whole arm reciprocal translocation (which is involved in forming a V-shaped chromosome from two rods) is the most frequent type of reciprocal translocation. Moreover, the likelihood of the change from a V to two rods is enhanced in *Drosophila* by the fact that the Y is almost entirely heterochromatic, as is one entire arm of chromosome IV.

You should recall that our motivation for studying energetic radiations was based upon their ability to induce many breaks and subsequently many structural changes. It was because this great supply of rearrangements was readily available that many of the other factors influencing breakage and joining, which we have just been discussing, were originally discovered. Other important discoveries were made possible by the study of structural changes, including, for instance, that the

centromere has a genetic basis and that crossing over near it is always reduced, that the telomere has a genetic basis, and that there are genetic elements (called *collochores*) near the centromere which are especially important for synapsis. Perhaps the most fundamental contribution was the finding, via structural changes, that the genes have the same linear order in the chromosome as they have in crossover maps. However, the spacing of these is different in the two cases (Figure 21-6). Thus, in view of the reduction of crossing over near the centromere, the genes nearest the centromere, which are spaced far apart in the metaphase chromosome, are found to be close together in the crossover map.

While we have restricted our attention to the factors influencing the production and fate of breaks produced by ionizing radiation, these factors would be expected to operate upon breaks produced by any other spontaneously occurring or induced mechanism. For, in general, broken ends produced in different ways all possess the same properties.

SUMMARY AND CONCLUSIONS

Pericentric inversions and whole arm reciprocal translocations have been frequent in the past evolutionary history of *Drosophila*, the former changing chromosome shape, the latter leading to changes in chromosome number.

The components of structural change, breakage and exchange union, are readily studied through the use of ionizing radiations. Such radiations induce breaks primarily by means of the clusters of ion pairs they produce. These clusters form tracks of ionization, whose thickness and length determine the number and location of the breaks. Tracks of ionization must occur very close to, or inside of, the chromosome that is broken. Whether they result from one or from two breaks, all chromosomal rearrangements produced by a single track increase linearly with radiation dose, have no threshold dose, and show no effect of protracting or concentrating the dose. Two-or-more-break structural changes, produced by ion clusters in separate, independently initiated tracks, increase in frequency faster than the dose, and have a threshold dose. If joining of ends produced by breakage can take place during the course of the irradiation, the latter types of rearrangement are reduced in frequency by protracting the delivery of the total dose.

Since both the breakage and joining processes involve chemical changes, their frequencies

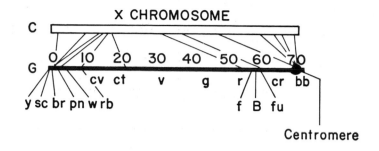

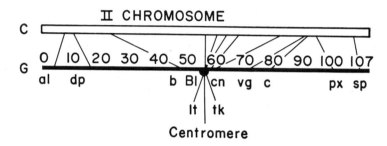

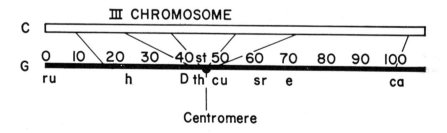

FIGURE 21–6. *Comparison of crossover or genetic (G) and chromosome (C) maps.*

are modifiable by the metabolic state of the cell. All types of rearrangement are expected to be affected by the physical and chemical state of the chromosome, the amount and location of its euchromatin and heterochromatin, its position relative to other chromosomes, the number and arrangement of the other chromosomes present, the presence or absence of a nuclear membrane, and the movements of broken ends as influenced by cellular particulates, fluids, and extracellular factors.

REFERENCES

Bacq, Z. M., and Alexander, P., *Fundamentals of Radiobiology*, 2nd Ed., New York, Pergamon Press, 1961.

Chu, E. H. Y., Giles, N. H., and Passano, K., "Types and Frequencies of Human Chromosome Aberrations Induced by X-rays," Proc. Nat. Acad. Sci., U.S., 47:830–839, 1961.

"Ionizing Radiation," Scient. Amer., 201:No. 3 (Sept.), 1959.

Muller, H. J., "General Survey of Mutational Effects of Radiation," in *Radiation Biology and Medicine*, Claus, W. D. (Ed.), Reading, Mass., Addison-Wesley, Chap. 6, pp. 145–177.

Puck, T. T., "Radiation and the Human Cell," Scient. Amer., 202, No. 4:142–153, 1960.

Sparrow, A. H., Binnington, J. P., and Pond, V., *Bibliography on the Effects of Ionizing Radiations on Plants, 1896–1955*, Brookhaven Nat. Lab. Publ. 504 (L–103), 1958.

QUESTIONS FOR DISCUSSION

21.1. Why should tissue, which is only about ten times as dense as air, have about one thousand times the number of ionizations in it as has air, when both are given the same radiation exposure?

21.2. What evidence can you give to support the view that the ions causing breakage need not always attack the chromosome directly?

21.3. Does the observation that the volume of a chromosome is variable under different conditions mean that it has an inconstant gene content? Explain.

21.4. Do you suppose that chromosomes exposed to X rays are more likely to undergo structural change when they are densely spiralized than when they are relatively uncoiled? Why?

21.5. Discuss the role of heterochromatin in changes involving chromosome number and chromosome shape.

21.6. Do you suppose the oxygen content of a space capsule could affect the mutability of *Drosophila* passengers? Explain.

21.7. Discuss the relative efficiency, per r, of small doses of X rays and of fast neutrons in producing structural changes in chromosomes.

21.8. Do you suppose that the mutability of ultraviolet light threatens man's survival? Explain.

21.9. Compare the breakages and their consequences caused by the same dose of X rays administered to:

        a. A polyploid and a diploid liver cell in man.
        b. A diploid neuron in man and *Drosophila*.
        c. A sperm and a spermatogonium in man.

21.10. How could you locate the position of the gene for white eye in the salivary X chromosome of *Drosophila* using:

        a. Different small deletions?
        b. Overlapping inversions?

Chapter 22

POSITION EFFECT
AND ALLELISM IN DROSOPHILA

WE HAVE already mentioned a number of discoveries made possible by the abundance of structural changes in chromosomes induced by ionizing radiations (Chapter 21). In the course of irradiation studies with *Drosophila*, the same kind of two-break rearrangement has been produced time and again, in which both of the breakage points have occurred at the same, or nearly the same, positions. In many of these cases it is found that there is a phenotypic change which occurs simultaneously with the rearrangement, and that the same kind of phenotypic effect is produced by each nearly identical rearrangement. Further study shows that the phenotypic effect is transmitted whenever the rearrangement is, and that, in many cases, this effect is similar to that of a known allele of a gene located at, or very near, one of the points of breakage. In these cases, then, the change in phenotype seems to be directly connected with the mutation of a gene known to be located at or near a point of breakage.

To explain this effect, you might at first think that the very fact that a break took place in or adjacent to this gene automatically changed it to this allelic form. But this cannot be the explanation since other breaks at this locus, which go into different kinds of rearrangement, do not produce such a change in phenotype. For the same reason, it is not tenable to presume that the track of ionizations which produced the break simultaneously produced a minute deficiency or duplication of the affected locus. We may conclude, therefore, that an important feature of this phenotypic change is that it is not based upon what occurs at the time of breakage; this suggests that the change is due to the nature of the broken ends that join. Moreover, this change takes place only when the broken end, which joins to the broken end carrying the affected locus, comes from certain specific loci in the genome. So, the gene affected at the broken end is not mutant and will not change its effect if it joins to some broken ends, but will do so, and in the same way, if it joins to certain others. In other words, we can hypothesize that the phenotypic effect, the functioning, of the same gene may be modified when its linear neighbors are changed. This type of phenotypic change is said to be due to *position effect*. Would we be justified in calling position effect a mutation? Mutation was defined on page 5 as a change in the genes, not in their phenotypic expression. Note that all the types of mutation discussed hitherto, from Chapter 18 on, have been based upon material changes in the genome, such as gains, losses, or rearrangements of chromosomal material, and all novel phenotypic changes so far discussed could be attributed to such mutations. However, in the case of position effect we are presumably dealing with *a change in gene effect in which the gene itself has been unchanged!* Position effect, therefore, can be one of the phenotypic consequences of mutations involving structural rearrangements, but is not in itself a mutation. Position effect is no more to be called mutation than is dominance, although both require a prior mutation for their detection.

You may be dissatisfied with our presumption that the gene showing position effect is chemically and physically unchanged in any permanent way. You might suppose that when the gene in question joins to certain genes it does so by means of one kind of chemical or physical connection, leading to

185

one type of functioning, whereas, when it joins to other genes, it does so in another way, leading to a different type of functioning. This kind of explanation would be a mutational one, but is made extremely unlikely by the fact that genes located some distance from a point of breakage sometimes show position effects. You will agree that it is unreasonable to believe that a change in the kind of connection between genes at the point of breakage would somehow spread along the chromosome to affect the configuration of a gene whose adjacent genes had not been substituted by others. (This spreading effect is additional reason for dismissing explanations of position effect based upon breakage itself or upon other mutational changes connected with tracks of ionization.)

If the physico-chemical nature of a gene showing position effect is unchanged, then two other predictions should prove true. The gene in a position-effect rearrangement should return to its old functioning upon being placed near its old genic neighbors. This can be done in two ways. Rearrangement-carrying individuals can be irradiated and progeny examined for structural changes that reverse this rearrangement. Or the gene showing position effect can be moved to a normal chromosome by means of crossing over. In both cases it is found that the gene, returned to its old position, returns to its old way of functioning. A second prediction is that when a normal gene is placed in the rearranged position via crossing over, it should then cause the position effect. It does.

In *Drosophila*, the organism most studied in this respect, position effects often accompany rearrangements that bring genes in euchromatin near those in heterochromatin. Placing a gene normally located in a euchromatic region near or in a heterochromatic one often produces a special, wavering, position effect which is expressed in the phenotype in a mosaic or variegated way. Thus,

for example, if the gene for dull-red eye color on the X chromosome, w^+, normally located in euchromatin, is placed in the heterochromatin proximal to the centromere by means of a paracentric inversion, the eye color produced is mottled, being composed of speckles of white and dull red. Such variegation is reduced, however, if, by breeding, an extra Y chromosome or another heterochromatin-rich chromosome is added to the genotype. It is not yet known how this suppression of variegation is produced.

We have seen that the only requirement for the occurrence of position effect is an appropriate shift in the kind of linear neighbors a gene has. Breakage merely provides us with a way of obtaining such shifts. The possibility should be entertained that position effects could also be detected with the aid of some other mechanism for changing the relative positions of genes. We already know that crossing over can do this. Let us see if we can devise a particular crossover system [1] whose operation might produce a position effect.

An X-linked mutant is known in *Drosophila*, which has the effect of reducing the number of *facets* (*ommatidia*) in the compound eyes. Because it changes the eye from round to a slit shape it is called *Bar* (*B*). When the normal and the *Bar*-containing chromosomes are studied in larval salivary gland nuclei, it is found that about six successive bands in the normal chromosome are duplicated in tandem in the *Bar* chromosome. Let us designate as 123456 each such region of six bands, so that a normal female would contain 123456/123456 and a homozygous Bar female 123456 123456 /123456 123456. In normal $(+/+)$ females the two homologs would pair with homologous numbers (parts) together, and crossing over could take place between corresponding numbers. In homozygous *Bar* (*B/B*)

[1] Based upon investigations of A. H. Sturtevant, H. J. Muller, C. B. Bridges, and others.

females, proper pairing (*eusynapsis*) could also occur and normal crossing over follow; but this case potentially offers a different sequence of events in which synapsis occurs incorrectly (*aneusynapsis*), the left region in one chromosome pairing with the right region of the second (as in Figure 22–1), leaving the other two regions unpaired. If this incorrect synapsis is followed by normal crossing over anywhere in the paired region (as shown between 2 and 3 in the Figure), the crossover strands will be 123456 and 123456 123456

123456; the former strand has this region only once and will therefore be normal (+), while the latter has this region thrice. If an egg containing the crossover with one region is fertilized by an X-bearing sperm of a normal-eyed male, the zygote would produce a daughter having normal eye shape, demonstrating that *Bar* has reverted to +. This could also be checked in a subsequent generation by examination of the salivary gland chromosomes.

If an egg containing an X with this region

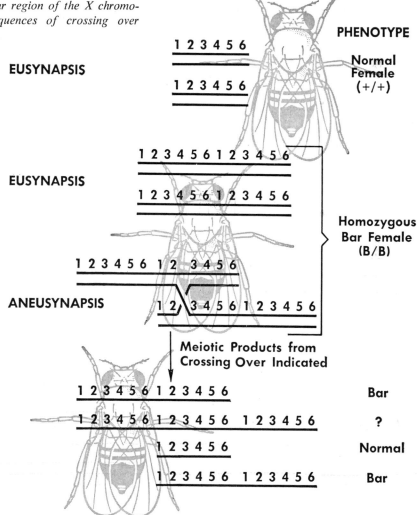

FIGURE 22–1. *Diagrammatic representation of the normal and the Bar region of the X chromosome and the consequences of crossing over following aneusynapsis.*

in triplicate is similarly fertilized, a female would be produced having four of these regions, three in one homolog and one in the other. The question is: What would be the phenotype of such a female? Could it make any phenotypic difference whether these regions are positioned two by two (as in homozygous *Bar*) or three by one? Note that the genic neighbors of the four regions are different, when two regions are present on each homolog, from what they are when one homolog has three regions and the other has one region. Knowing that position effect does occur, it is possible that the differences in neighbors, when these four regions are arranged in the two different ways, could make for different phenotypic effects.

While we do not know precisely what the potential position effect phenotype will be, we can direct our attention to the number of facets in the eye and look for any change from the number expected. The normal round eye of females and males ($+/+$ and $+/Y$) contains more than 200 facets, or ommatidia. The homozygous *Bar* female (B/B) and hemizygous *Bar* male (B/Y) have about 68 ommatidia per eye. The heterozygous female ($+/B$) has about 150, *Bar* on one chromosome being incompletely dominant to the $+$ condition in the homolog. From the cross $+/Y$ ♂ $\times$ B/B ♀, then, the usual F_1 females are $+/B$ with about 150 ommatidia per eye. Reversions to the $+$ condition, by means of crossing over in an aneusynaptic tetrad, could be detected as a $+/+$ female, as mentioned. The complementary crossover chromosome having the

triple region together with a normal chromosome would produce a female which might have less than 68 facets, or more than 68 but less than 150 facets, per compound eye.

The experimental design is not yet complete, however. Since we do not know how often the chromosomes showing the potential position effect will be produced in meiosis, we must eliminate two other possible causes of change in eye shape which would be classified as exceptional. If the cross made is $+/Y \times B/B$, a sperm carrying two X's (because of nondisjunction in the father) fertilizing an egg with no X (because of nondisjunction in the female) will produce a $+/+$ female which would be counted as one of the exceptional types we are seeking. Such zygotes would be extremely rare. Nevertheless, we would be able to recognize them if the $+$ chromosome carried the gene for yellow body color, y, as a marker, since such nondisjunctionally produced females would be yellow, not gray, in body color. (In this way we would also recognize any female progeny resulting from the contamination of our cultures by flies of the yellow stock.) So the cross we should make is $y +^B/Y \times y^+ B/y^+ B$. For clarity, the genic symbol for round eye is now given as $+^B$.

The other event we must eliminate from confusing our results is mutation at or near the *B* locus. The exceptional phenotypes (round and an unknown shape of eye) we are looking for would always be produced following a crossing over in the region of *Bar*. All we need do is to make the B/B female dihybrid for genes near to, and on

FIGURE 22–2. *Compound eye of* Drosophila. *Left: Ultrabar; center: Bar; right: normal.*

either side of, *B*, near enough (closer together than ten crossover units) so that no double crossovers could occur between them. *Bar* is located at 57.0, *forked bristles* (*f*) at 56.7, and *carnation eye color* (*car*) at 62.5 on the X chromosome linkage map. We, therefore, construct females that are

$$y^+ f^+ B\ car/y^+ f\ B\ car^+.$$

Any unusual eye shape that is noncrossover between the loci for *f* and *car* can be eliminated immediately from consideration. All exceptional phenotypes of interest will be crossovers between *f* and *car*; crossovers in this region will normally be present in 5.8% (62.5–56.7) of F_1 daughters. Of course, the males used will now have to be $y f +^B car/Y$ in order to identify the crossover daughters (which will be either nonforked noncarnation, or forked carnation). The cross then is: $y f +^B car/Y\ \male \times y^+ f^+ B\ car/y^+ f\ B\ car^+\ \female$.

When the experiment is performed it is found that about one female in two thousand is round-eyed and carries a crossover between *f* and *car*; a similar number of females, that are crossovers in this region, have very narrow eyes, called *Ultrabar* (Figure 22–2), each eye containing about 45 facets. Note that the reciprocal types of exceptional flies are equally frequent, as would be expected if they were the reciprocal products of a crossing over in an aneusynaptic tetrad. Moreover, Ultrabar females can be bred, and the salivary glands of their F_1 larvae prove they contained the triple region in one X and a single region in the other X, as predicted. You might still maintain that the Ultrabar individual is a mutant and not a position effect, the production of the mutation somehow being dependent upon a simultaneously occurring crossover. That this is not the case can be demonstrated by taking the two different exceptional types of X, placing them together in a female, and occasionally obtaining perfectly typical *Bar* chromosomes. These are found to carry two regions pro-

duced by crossing over between the single region of one chromosome and the middle region of the triple-dose homolog (Figure 22–3, on p. 190).

We conclude, therefore, that four regions, aligned in different positions, produce different phenotypes. The alignments were shifted by crossing over and not by mutation-producing chromosome breaks, as was the case in the rearrangement experiments previously described. This discussion should lead you to appreciate the fact that in the advancement of genetic knowledge, while the theory and the preparations to test it experimentally are often complicated as in physics, the data obtained are simple and unambiguous.

One other possibility presents itself for the detection of position effects using crossing over. If the genotype of a *Drosophila* female were *y a b spl/y⁺ a b spl⁺*, a crossover between *a* and *b* would produce no new positions of the *a* and *b* genes relative to each other, and no position effect would be expected, or found. But, suppose the genotype was *y a⁺ b spl/y⁺ a b⁺ spl⁺*. In this case both the *a* and *b* loci are heterozygous; the mutants are on different homologs, being "across" from each other, or in *trans position* (Figure 22–4). If crossing over occurs be-

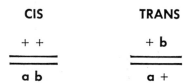

FIGURE 22–4. *Cis and trans positions for dihybrid linked genes.*

tween these loci we obtain *y a⁺ b⁺ spl⁺* and *y⁺ a b spl* as the crossover chromosomes. If these two crossover chromosomes were present in the same individual, then both mutants (*a* and *b*) would be together on one homolog and their normal alleles both would be on the other homolog, so that these genes now are

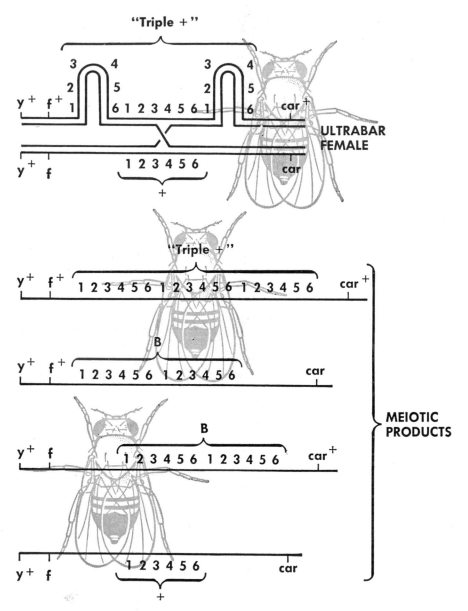

FIGURE 22–3. *Production of Bar chromosomes by crossing over in Ultrabar females.*

in the *cis position*. Note that the trans heterozygote and cis heterozygote have the same number of genes on each chromosome, but, in the former case, *a* has *b*+ for its linear neighbor (and *a*+ has *b*) whereas in the latter case *a* has *b* for its linear neighbor (and *a*+ has *b*+). If the trans dihybrid has one phenotypic effect and the cis dihybrid, obtained from it by crossing over, has a different phenotypic effect, then position effect will be considered proven if the cis form can, by crossing over, revert to the trans form and restore the old phenotypic effect.

This *cis-trans test for position effect* should

have the best chance of yielding a positive result if the two pairs of genes concerned are adjacent or very close to each other. But this also means that if the genes are very close together crossing over will rarely occur between them, and large numbers of progeny will have to be observed to be sure at least one exchange between them has been included among the results! What particular genes should we use in our test? Should we use linear neighbors that apparently perform very different functions, or shall we use those having similar effects? If the effect of one gene is to be modified by the effect of its linear neighbor, it would seem reasonable to use neighboring genes that have similar effects, for in this case changing the allele of the neighboring gene might be expected to produce a change in its own effect. Suppose, on the other hand, the two neighbor genes affected totally different traits. In this case, while changing the allele of the neighboring gene would mean that the neighboring allele now present affects the totally different trait in a different way, this would not be expected to have any effect on the functioning of its linear neighbor.

The best source of genes which have very similar effects is, of course, the members of a multiple allelic series, for instance, the members of the white series on the X chromosome of *Drosophila*. But you immediately might say that these cannot be used in our experiment, since only one is present on each homolog, and we need two pairs of genes to perform a cis-trans test for position effect. Moreover, all these alleles of *white* are located at 1.5 on the crossover map. When the "trans" hybrid for w^a (apricot) and w (white) is made, it is found to produce pale apricot eye color. However, such a phenotype does not prove w^a and w are alleles. Alleles are alternatives of the same gene; genes are most properly identified as alleles because they occupy the same site on homologous chromosomes and cannot be recombined as the con-

sequence of crossing over, and because, barring nondisjunction, the members of a pair of alleles always segregate. The statement that w^a and w are located at position 1.5 may be incorrect! Suppose these two are really nonallelic but similarly acting genes located close together, one at position 1.49 (w^a) and one at 1.51 (w). The crossover data, being finite and somewhat variable, could have accidentally placed them both at locus 1.5. If w^a and w are, in fact, close but not allelic to each other, the trans heterozygote for them should yield the cis heterozygote by crossing over. But if these genes are only .02 of a crossover unit apart, only one such crossover would occur among 5,000 tested chromosomes. If only a few hundred flies are scored in a search for such crossovers, it is very likely none of this type will be found. Such an experiment would have to be done on a very large scale to serve as a test for nonallelism.

Let us examine the plan and results of a large scale experiment [2] actually designed to test the nonallelism of w^a and w. *Drosophila* females were constructed carrying an attached-X chromosome containing $y \, w \, spl$ on one arm and $y^+ \, w^a$ and spl^+ on the other. Recall that the use of attached-X's permits one to recover two strands of the four involved in each crossover (cf. p. 122). The present genetic system even permits both complementary crossover types to appear simultaneously in the same gamete. The left part of Figure 22–5 shows schematically a portion of this attached-X as it would appear in the tetrad stage at the time of the crossing over, and indicates the standard genetic map location of the y and spl markers. The female carrying this chromosome has a pale (dilute) apricot phenotype. If such a female is crossed to a *Bar*-containing male, the non-Bar F_1 daughters (who carry a Y from their father) are usually noncrossovers and have pale apricot-colored eyes like their mother. Crossovers which occur between the white

[2] Based upon work of E. B. Lewis.

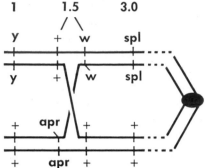

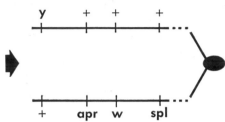

FIGURE 22–5. *Crossing over between* apricot *and* white *in attached-X chromosomes.*

locus and the centromere produce either white daughters or apricot daughters. Barring mutation, these are the only phenotypes expected if w^a and w are allelic.

But if apricot is not allelic to w, it should be distinguished by giving it a new kind of symbol, *apr*. In this case, if *apr* lies to the left of w, as shown in the left part of the Figure, a rare crossover could occur between these loci, as indicated there, producing the crossover attached-X shown at the right of the Figure. Note that if *apr* and w are nonallelic, each must have its own + allele in the other arm of the parental attached-X, so that these female parents are trans heterozygotes with respect to these loci. As a result of the crossing over mentioned, these nonallelic genes would be placed in the cis position. If the cis position also produces light apricot eye color, we will not be able to distinguish such a crossover from any other one between y and *spl* that does not occur between *apr* and w, and we will be forced to conclude (for lack of evidence) that *apr* and w are really alleles. (Two genes are considered allelic, then, when they actually are allelic and cannot be recombined by crossing over, and when they are nonallelic and undergo crossing over but give the same phenotype in both the cis and trans positions.)

When large numbers of daughters from the attached-X females were examined, six were found with dull-red eyes. To determine whether these flies were mutant or the result of a change from the trans to the cis form, the attached-X's found in the dull-red-eyed exceptional flies were detached (by collecting the products of the occasional crossing over that occurs between the attached-X and the Y in the heterochromatic regions near their centromeres). The genes carried in each detached arm were determined and it was found that one arm always could be represented as y apr^+ w^+ spl^+ and the other arm always as y^+ apr w spl. Such results offer strong support for the view that the dull-red exceptional females were cis heterozygotes which produced dull-red eye color; they also demonstrate that if *apr* and w are separate loci, *apr* lies to the left of w on the X, as shown in the Figure. (You should work out the distribution of the markers following crossing over between *apr* and w on the assumption that *apr* is to the right of w.)

Proof that the exceptional dull-red females were the result of a position effect rather than some mutational phenomenon was completed by mating these exceptional females and obtaining occasional daughters which were pale apricot. These new exceptional daughters were then shown to contain the original gene arrangement, this order having been restored by crossing over.

The phenotypic difference between pale apricot and dull red is undoubtedly the result of position effect, since the only difference between the cis and trans conditions is the arrangement which the same genetic material takes. This phenomenon is therefore called a *cis-trans position effect*. In order to detect such an effect it was necessary to separate two very closely linked genes. The genes used in the experiment had previously been considered alleles because of their closeness on the genetic map and their similar phenotypic effects. But the fact that the cis and trans positions of them gave different phenotypic effects made it possible to prove they are nonalleles, occupying different loci. You may next ask about the other genes making up the "white multiple allelic series" (Chapter 9). Are some allelic to *w* and others allelic to *apr*? The answer is yes. Moreover, some are allelic to neither, and appropriate crossing over studies have shown that the "white region" on the X is a nest of four (perhaps five) separate, linearly arranged loci with similar effects.

In view of the result obtained with the white region, you may correctly ask next whether there are other regions in the genome where two or more genic alternatives have been considered allelic by the same criteria as were originally used in the white region, but which prove to be *pseudoallelic*, that is, prove to be nonallelic when subjected to the cis-trans test. Again the answer is yes. Numerous examples of such pseudoallelism have been found in diverse organisms including, for example, cases involving color in cotton, taillessness in mice, lozenge and also vermilion eye colors in *Drosophila*, and other cases found in *Aspergillus*, other microorganisms, and corn.

Another case of pseudoallelism in *Drosophila* will be discussed [3] briefly, in which the nonalleles differ in their functioning somewhat more than do *apr* and *w*. The normal (wild-type) fly (Figure 22–6A) has small club-shaped *balancers* (*halteres*) located on the posterior part of the thorax. One of the pseudoalleles, *bithorax* (*bx*), converts the haltere into a large wing-like structure

³ Based upon work of E. B. Lewis.

(Figure 22–6B), another called *postbithorax* (*pbx*) appears to do much the same thing (Figure 22–6C). But close examination reveals that these two recessive pseudoalleles really do different things, *bithorax* converting the front portion, and *postbithorax* the hind portion, of the haltere into wing-like structure. This is verified by obtaining the double mutant combination (*bx pbx*, hence the cis form) by crossing over (at a rate of .02%), and observing the phenotypes of flies made homozygous for the double mutant combination. Such flies (Figure 22–6D) have a fully developed second pair of wings.

What are the cis-trans effects for *bx* and *pbx*? The cis form (+ +/*bx pbx*) has normal balancers, while the trans form (*bx* +/+ *pbx*) shows a slight postbithorax effect, providing another example of cis-trans position effect and demonstrating the non-allelism of these genes.

You may have already tried to visualize how cis-trans position effects are produced. One model, but not necessarily the only one possible, compares the two homologous chromosomes to assembly lines, each of which makes its products independently. The cis form can make all the products in turn, in the strand containing the two normal alleles. (The strand with both mutants makes less or no end product.) So, over all, much end product is produced by the cis form. In the trans form, however, because each strand contains a mutant (defective machine), the total end product produced is zero or relatively little. (It should be noted, however, that detection of a cis-trans position effect requires only that the phenotypes produced by the two arrangements be different — it does not require or specify that cis appear phenotypically normal.)

Why should cis-trans position effects be produced? It is reasonable to think that the products of genes which are linear neighbors would be more likely to depend upon each other than they would be to depend upon the

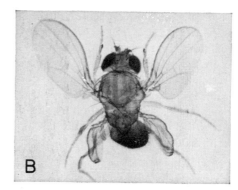

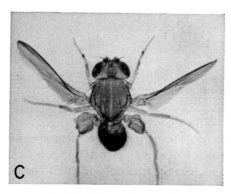

FIGURE 22–6. Drosophila melanogaster *males: normal (A), bithorax (B), postbithorax (C), and bithorax postbithorax (D).* (*Courtesy of E. B. Lewis; reprinted by permission of McGraw-Hill Book Co., Inc., from* Study Guide and Workbook for Genetics *by I. H. Herskowitz. Copyright, 1960.*)

products of their alleles in the homologous chromosome, for this homolog is usually located a considerable distance away. Consider also cases of position effect brought about by structural changes. The same reasoning could explain position effects following shifts in the relative positions of heterochromatin and euchromatin via breakage. In fact, position effects from structural changes would be expected to be particularly common in species whose chromosomes or chromosome parts are not located at random in the nucleus, but take on special positions relative to each other. The facts that during nuclear division *Drosophila* chromosomes show somatic synapsis, and that

somatic synapsis is found in the interphase nuclei of salivary gland and other cells, suggest that at the time of gene action different chromosomes and their parts are arranged so that the products of gene action may be formed or used in particular sequences. Intra- and interchromosomal rearrangements which change these sequences might be expected to produce position effects. The fact that *Oenothera* chromosomes form a circle of 14 during meiosis (Chapter 20) demonstrates a very orderly arrangement of chromosomal parts involving heterozygosity for reciprocal translocations. Here also, a new arrangement of chromosomal parts might be expected to disturb functional sequences and produce position effects. And, in fact, position effect is known to occur in *Oenothera.*

Finally, let us consider the morphology of chromosome regions found to contain pseudoalleles. The white series is associated with a *double band (doublet)* in the salivary gland chromosome; *apr* may be in one band, *w* in the other. The vermilion series is associated with a doublet on the X chromosome, while the bithorax series (composed of five separate pseudoallelic loci) is connected with two doublets. (This indicates, what is proved by other data, that a band may contain more than a single gene.) Since there are many doublets in salivary chromosomes, this suggests that genes located in these regions will be found to be pseudoallelic.

How can we explain the origin of apparently adjacent loci with similar types of action? There are several possible ways in which this situation may have come about. One explanation is that during the course of evolution, adjacent genes, having different effects, mutated to alleles which performed similar functions, and therefore were advantageous. A second explanation invokes a selective advantage of rearrangements which brought together widely separated non-alleles with similar functions. While both of these mechanisms may explain some of the cases found, it seems more likely that most adjacent and similar genes arose as duplications that occurred once, or more times (as in the bithorax case), in the ways already described in Chapter 19. Following duplication, the linear array of originally identical genes would become somewhat different from each other functionally because of mutation, thereby fostering evolution.

SUMMARY AND CONCLUSIONS

The same genic matter arranged in different ways may have different phenotypic consequences. The shuffling of genes which produces position effects may be accomplished by means of structural changes in chromosomes and by means of crossing over preceded either by aneusynapsis or eusynapsis. While position effect may be one of the consequences of mutation, it itself does not represent mutation.

While the decision is usually valid that two genes located in totally different parts of the genome are nonallelic whether or not they have similar or different phenotypic effects (on the presumption that one is not an allele which was transported to a new location via structural change), statements made in earlier Chapters that two genes are allelic may often have been invalid. To properly apply the term *allele* to two similarly acting genes, apparently at the same map locus, it is necessary to perform exhaustive tests to recombine them via crossing over. Recombination is demonstrated by the detection of a cis-trans position effect, which proves the genes to be pseudoallelic and, therefore, nonallelic. Failure to obtain a cis-trans position effect after exhaustive trials is taken to mean the genes involved are alleles, though this necessarily includes possible cases of separable nonalleles which fail to give this effect.

Linear nests of genes with similar effects have probably arisen by one or more duplications *in situ* of an ancestral gene, followed by mutations that led to differentiation in their effects.

Position effect is attributed to some dependency which exists between the gene products of adjacent nonalleles.

REFERENCES

Bridges, C. B., "The Bar 'Gene' a Duplication," Science, 83:210–211, 1936. Reprinted in *Classic Papers in Genetics*, Peters, J. A. (Ed.), Englewood Cliffs, N.J., Prentice-Hall, 1959, pp. 163–166.

Lewis, E. B., "The Pseudoallelism of White and Apricot in Drosophila Melanogaster," Proc. Nat. Acad. Sci., U.S., 38:953–961, 1952.

Muller, H. J., Prokofyeva-Belgovskaya, A. A., and Kossikov, K. V., "Unequal Crossingover in the Bar Mutant as a Result of Duplication of a Minute Chromosome Section," C. R. (Dokl.) Acad. Sci., U.R.S.S., N.S., 1(10):87–88, 1936.

Sturtevant, A. H., "The Effects of Unequal Crossingover at the Bar Locus in Drosophila," Genetics, 10:117–147, 1925. Reprinted in *Classic Papers in Genetics*, Peters, J. A. (Ed.), Englewood Cliffs, N.J., Prentice-Hall, 1959, pp. 124–148.

QUESTIONS FOR DISCUSSION

22.1. If a novel phenotypic change is associated with a qualitative or quantitative change in the genetic material, how can you decide whether to attribute the effect to mutation or to position effect?

22.2. Do you expect that position effects will be found in most sexually reproducing organisms? Why?

22.3. Is there any evidence that crossing over is ever unequal? Explain.

22.4. Should pseudoalleles be considered to be subgenes (parts of one gene) rather than separate, nonallelic genes? Explain.

22.5. Does position effect require pseudoallelism for its detection? Explain. Is the reverse true? Explain.

22.6. What is the minimum number needed, of genotypic alternatives for a "locus," in order to test whether it shows a cis-trans position effect? Explain.

Can one of the alternatives be a deficiency for all or part of the region under investigation? Why?

22.7. Can position effect occur in haploids? Why?

22.8. How would you proceed to test whether two recessive mutants in *Drosophila* that are apparently alleles of the X-linked gene, v^+ (normal allele of vermilion eye color), are pseudoalleles?

*Chapter *23*

GENE AND POINT MUTATIONS

WHAT have we learned, beginning with Chapter 18, about the mutational units of the genetic material? We have seen that the unit of mutation in the genotype may be a whole genome, single chromosomes, and parts of chromosomes. Even though each of these units involves more than one gene, it is possible that our study of these larger units can tell us something about the mutational characteristics of a single gene. It is also possible that our knowledge concerning the recombinational properties of individual genes will shed light in this direction. Accordingly, we shall begin the present discussion by considering what can be revealed about single gene mutation by what we have already learned.

It has been demonstrated that the genes in a chromosome are arranged linearly. This linear order could be formed in two ways, that is, either by having the genes attach to each other directly, or by having some nongenic material serve to connect adjacent genes. In either event, the fact remains that a chromosome is invariably linear, being either a rod or a ring, but never branched. For not only are all ordinarily observed chromosomes linear, but, even when chromosomes have been observed immediately after crossing over, or after they have been broken more than once and the pieces have joined together, no case has ever been observed of an authentic branched chromosome. This is almost conclusive evidence that the gene cannot be joined, directly or

197

indirectly, to other genes at more than two places, and that a mutation of this kind cannot occur either spontaneously or inductively in genic material. The fact that this change is never observed, regardless of the organism studied, can be interpreted to mean either that the gene never had this property, or that it is lost to all presently existing genes. We are led to conclude, therefore, that all interstitial (nonterminal) genes are *bipolar*, and that mutation is incapable of causing the gene to be more than bipolar.

Almost all mutations retain the bipolarity of genes, as evidenced by the "stickiness" of both ends produced by a break in a chromosome. However, in some relatively rare cases broken ends are known to become permanently healed, so that mutation from bipolarity to unipolarity does occur. That mutation must possess this property of changing genes from a bipolar to a *unipolar* type, or the reverse, is evidenced also by the presence of telomeres, unipolar genes that serve to seal off the normal ends of chromosomes.

You may be acquainted with the fact that a change from genic bipolarity to unipolarity is a regular phenomenon in the life history of certain animals, as in certain species of the roundworm *Ascaris*. Here, in nuclei which remain in the germ line there is a single pair of chromosomes, but in those nuclei which enter the somatic line these chromosomes break up into a number of smaller linear fragments, each of which has sealed-off ends and behaves normally during mitosis. (The latter behavior is made possible by the fact that, in these cases, the germ line chromosome has a number of centromeres along its length, and each fragment of the chromosome in a somatic cell has one of these centromeres. This is an exception to our statement, on page 19, that normal chromosomes are unicentric, and involves a polycentric chromosome which in the germ line has the action of all but one centromere suppressed.)

Because this chromosome fragmentation takes place only in somatic cells, these polarity changes can be ascribed to some physiological difference between cells entering the somatic line and cells remaining in the germ line. Should such changes be considered mutational? They should not, because the changes from bipolarity to unipolarity in *Ascaris* are numerous and simultaneous, and lack the novelty required of mutations.

It should be noted that while no unambiguous case has ever been reported of a mutation from unipolarity to bipolarity, the chance of detecting and proving such a change is very small indeed. Accordingly, the capacity of mutation to change a gene in this manner cannot, at present, be denied with any assurance. Thus, although there are bipolar and unipolar genes, a change in polarity via mutation is clearly known to proceed only from the former to the latter. Does this mean that mutations to nonpolarity do not occur or cannot occur? We cannot give a definite answer at this point, since, thus far, we have restricted our attention to genes all of which have been localized in chromosomes. It must be evident that a unipolar or bipolar gene that mutates to a nonpolar alternative must necessarily drop out of the chromosomal line-up. If this happens, then the freed, not-at-all-sticky gene will not be linked to any chromosome. From what has already been presented, there has been no evidence for the existence of genetic material which has been liberated from its chromosomal locus in this way. Since the only kind of gene we have so far identified is the chromosomally located one, we must accept the simplest explanation, and conclude that genes cannot occur singly, two of them comprising the smallest group possible.

The gene was discovered by studying sexually reproducing individuals, in which many of its recombinational properties were revealed because of synapsis and the events consequent to this process. Synapsis is the result of the attraction which exists between corresponding segments of homologous chromosomes. It is a remarkable fact that corresponding loci located on homologous chromosomes do attract each other in synapsis even though the particular alleles contained may be identical or somewhat different. Let us assume that synapsis is directly dependent upon the genic content of a chromosome. Is this synaptic attraction between genes restricted to alleles only? It is probable (see Chapter 22) that what are nonallelic genes, at present, were at some time, in the remote past, allelic. Accordingly, mutation must be capable of changing the synaptic specificity of the gene, and it must follow, at least in a general way, that identical genes attract each other more than do nonidentical ones. That different degrees of specific attraction exist between genes is illustrated by the genes located in heterochromatin (cf. p. 181), which synapse much less specifically than those found in euchromatin. Other genes are known (for example, one in maize called *asynaptic*) which either (1) not only lack synaptic attraction for their alleles but also destroy this attraction between pairs of genes at other loci, or (2) cause general desynapsis. Apparently, the gene is unrestricted mutationally in the way it can affect synaptic force.

It should be clear from what has been learned (in Chapter 22, for example) that different genes do exist, mutations in them not being explicable merely in terms of their complete loss or inactivation, since each gene can usually mutate to a number of different allelic forms, which comprise a series of multiple alleles. Because different genes exist, it is obvious that mutations occur involving single genes. Since the gene is submicroscopic (a single band in the salivary gland chromosome of *Drosophila* can contain more than one gene), so also is a change produced in a single gene. The only way we have of detecting changes in individual genes, therefore, is by the phenotypic changes these produce. Since, at present, we recognize a gene operationally as the smallest unit of genetic material whose recombination can be detected phenotypically, we must determine the characteristics of mutation in single genes from the phenotypic changes produced in recombinationally detected genes. Accordingly, it is clear that we shall not be able to determine from such phenotypic changes whether single gene mutation involves the recombinational gene *in toto*, or one portion or site within it, or many different sites within it. If gene mutation requires a change in the entire gene, then the material composition of the genes detected by recombination and by mutation would be identical. If, on the other hand, the recombinationally detected gene contains within it one or more sites at which mutation can occur, the basic recombinational unit of genetic material would be larger than the basic mutational unit of the genetic material. In the absence of critical evidence as to which of these alternatives obtains, *we shall continue to consider the mutational and recombinational genes to be materially equivalent*, as we have assumed since page 14, where we invoked the law of parsimony.

As already mentioned in Chapter 1, any given gene is rather stable, being faithfully replicated many thousands of times before a detectable mutation occurs in it. You should recognize, however, that the greater the sensitivity of our tests for detecting mutations, the larger will be the rate of mutation observed (recall the detection of isoallelism on p. 65). It remains probable, therefore, that there are transmissible modifications of single genes which escape our present modes of detection. Nevertheless, within the limits of our present methods of analysis, the gene appears to be a very stable entity.

The studies to be considered next started with the collection of all detectable mutants of genes which were being investigated singly or in combinations. The mutants obtained were then analyzed. Some of the mutations involving a given locus proved to be based upon ploidy changes, not involving chromosome breakage; others proved to be associated with gross or small chromosomal rearrangements. These types were eliminated from further consideration. Then, sometimes, all genetic and cytological tests known were applied in order also to eliminate the minutest chromosomal rearrangements, including, for example, tiny duplications or deficiencies. The remainder of mutations was then assumed, for lack of evidence to the contrary, to comprise in considerable portion mutations involving a single gene (*gene mutations*) or involving at most only a few genes (*intergenic mutations*). The mutations remaining, then, behaved as though they occurred at a single point in the genetic and cytological maps, and they were, therefore, called *point mutations*. (Note that gene mutation includes losses of single whole genes.)

Let us discuss now those discovered characteristics of spontaneous and induced point mutations which are likely to apply to gene mutation. Point mutation can occur in a vast number of different genes, so that this process is not restricted to a very limited type of gene. It might be thought that the conditions causing point mutation could be of such a nature that, in the diploid cell, both members of a pair of alleles would tend to respond by mutation. But, when point mutation does occur in a diploid cell, it is found that only one gene of the pair present is affected. The fact that only one member of a pair of genes mutates, though both are located in the same nucleus, demonstrates that the point mutation process is a very localized, submicroscopic event.

Is point mutation a rapid or a gradual change? If it were typically a gradual change, or one which involved an instability of the gene for more than one cell generation, then point mutations would usually occur in clusters, even if within a cluster the same gene did not always mutate to the same allele. But many point mutants occur singly, and others, which appear in a cluster and seem to be identical, can usually be accounted for on the basis that a single cell containing the mutant gene divided a number of times before the tests to detect the mutant condition were made. While such data do not prove that point mutation is instantaneous, they indicate that it is usually completed within one cell generation and is, in this respect, more a quick than a gradual change. However, the number of point mutations obtained from X ray or ultraviolet ray treatments is reduced, if a posttreatment of certain types of visible light or of chemical substances is given immediately. Such posttreatments produce *photo-* or *chemorecovery* from point mutation. This proves that the point mutation process is often not completed for some minutes. It is only after the point mutation process is completed that the new genetic alternative is about as stable as the old.

While the point mutants which arise at the present time are just about as stable as their parent genes, or other genes in the genotype, this should not be taken to mean that all allelic and nonallelic genes have the same spontaneous mutation rate. A representative sample of specific loci in *Drosophila* gives an average of one point mutation at a given locus in each 200,000 germ cells tested. In mice, the per locus rate is about twice this, or one in 100,000. In man, scoring mutants that are detected when in heterozygous condition, the per locus rate is one per 50,000 to 100,0000 germ cells per generation. Within each species, the different loci studied had about the same order of mutability. Nevertheless, some genes are definitely more mutable than others, and those that seem to be very mutable are called "mutable genes." The latter will be discussed in Chapter 25. The average spontaneous point mutation

rate per genome has been estimated for *Drosophila*, mouse, and man. In *Drosophila*, one gamete in twenty (or one zygote in ten) contains a new detectable point mutant which arose in that generation. In mice, this frequency is about one in ten gametes, while in man this rate is about one in five gametes (or two in five zygotes).

The point mutations which occur spontaneously — that is, during the course of observations made under natural conditions — bear no obvious relation to the environment, either with respect to the locus affected or to the type of alternative produced. However, modifications in the environment do influence point mutation rate. For example, changes in temperature can change point mutation rate, each rise of 10° C, in the range of temperatures to which individuals are usually exposed, producing about a fivefold increase in mutation rate. This rate of increase is similar to, though somewhat higher than, what is obtained in ordinary chemical reactions with an increase in temperature. Violent temperature changes in either direction produce an even greater effect upon point mutation rate. Actually, it is found that detrimental environmental conditions of almost any kind cause an increase in point mutation rate.

Certain physical and chemical agents which raise the mutation rate enormously are called *mutagens*. All high-energy radiations (see Chapter 21) are mutagenic as are many highly reactive chemical substances, including mustard gas and its derivatives, and also peroxides, epoxides, and carbamates. The point mutation rates obtained with mutagens may be 150 times the spontaneous rate, and the loci affected and the types of mutant alternatives produced are not radically different from those which are involved in spontaneous mutation. One can speak of a spectrum of spontaneous point mutations, however, in that certain loci are normally somewhat more mutable than others. Ionizing radiations produce a mutational spectrum much like the spontaneous one, as would seem reasonable from the fact that the radiant energy involved is more or less randomly distributed in the nucleus and generally enhances chemical reactions of all kinds. However, the point mutational spectrum is somewhat different for different chemicals, and is different from that for natural or radiation mutation agents. This can be attributed to either the nonrandom penetration of these chemical substances into the nucleus, or the specific capacities that these have of combining with different nuclear chemicals, or both. Nevertheless, the frequency of point mutations, which increases linearly with the dose of ionizing radiation (although the rate is influenced by the amount of oxygen present), probably also increases linearly with the nuclear dose of many different chemical mutagens. So point mutations show no threshold dose with these mutagens, and the number of point mutations produced by a given total dose is constant, regardless of the rate of delivery. However, in the case of ultraviolet light, which is not a highly energetic radiation, the situation is otherwise. Here the individual quantum of energy has a probability of inducing point mutation which is considerably less than 100 per cent. This means that several quanta can cooperate to produce mutation, so that the point mutation rate increases faster than linearly with dose, at least at low doses, and an attenuated dose is less mutagenic than a concentrated one.

Point mutation is not restricted to the genes of any particular kind of cell. It occurs in males and females, in somatic tissues of all kinds, and in the diploid and haploid cells of the germ line. It has been found that *perifertilization stages* (later stages in gametogenesis and very early developmental stages) are relatively rich in spontaneous point mutations. It is not surprising that despite the very great differences in life span, there is not a greater difference in spontaneous mutation rate between flies, mice, and men. For, if most germ line mutations occur in the perifertilization stages, these rates would be quite similar, since these different organisms are not very different in the length of time occupied by these stages. A further similarity exists among these species, in that there is not a very great difference in the number of cell divisions required to go from a gamete of one generation to a gamete of the next. In fact, the differences in mutation rate for these organisms are approximately proportional to the differences in the number of germ cell divisions per generation.

This brings to mind the following questions: When, during the history of the gene, does the event of mutation occur? Can the old gene itself undergo mutation whether it is or is not in the process of synthesizing a new one? Can "mutations" occur during the course of synthesis of what is to be the new gene? The fact already mentioned, that point mutation rates in *Drosophila*, mouse, and man are proportional to the numbers of cell divisions that occur, suggests that some of these mutations occur at the time of synthesis of the new gene, although this does not specify whether it is the old or the new gene that becomes mutant. It has been found that the aging of spermatids and sperm of *Drosophila* increases their point mutation rate. Since these nondividing cells do not have their viability impaired when they are aneuploid, the increase in point mutations may be due to an effect upon the old gene, which is physiologically quiescent and probably not actively synthesizing new genes. The occurrence of mutation in the old gene would mean that point mutational changes can occur while a gene is linearly attached to its genic neighbors. However, the higher mutation rate observed after cells are aged may also be explained as resulting from the accumulation, with time, of a mutagen which acts on the old or new gene once gene replication is resumed. Finally, the possibility still remains that changes can occur in the steps leading to gene synthesis, before the new gene is completed and attached to its linear neighbors; these changes may be detected later as point mutants.

SUMMARY AND CONCLUSIONS

The mutational units in a genotype are, in order of size, the genome, the chromosome, chromosomal segments involving more than one gene, and the gene. *to the site.* Since a number of different alleles occur per gene, gene mutation may involve the entire gene, or one mutational site within the gene which has many alternatives, or many mutational sites which have one or more alternatives. It is possible that the genes operationally delimited by recombination and by mutation are not exactly equivalent materially. However, in the absence of critical evidence on this, we shall continue to assume that they are identical.

Gene mutation is not limited in any way with regard to the effect it can have on synapsis. It is also in no way restricted by ploidy, type of cell or gene, but is limited with respect to the effect it can have on a gene's polarity. Tripolar genes are excluded, bipolarity being the usual, and unipolarity the less usual, alternative.

Point mutations are the remainder of all mutations which are not known to involve intergenic changes. Since point mutations include changes in single genes they may be employed to determine the mutational characteristics of the gene. The frequency of point mutations increases linearly with the dose of high energy radiations, there being no effect of dose protraction, and no threshold dose below which the gene is safe from such change. Such mutations indicate that a given gene is relatively stable over many cell generations, changes in it being the result of very localized physico-chemical events which are completed in a matter of minutes, after which the new gene is similarly stable. Changes in the gene are enhanced or induced by temperature changes, aging, gene replication, and physical and chemical mutagens. It is possible that changes resulting in gene mutation can take place in the old gene, or in the new gene, or during the formation of the new gene.

REFERENCES

Alexander, P., "Radiation-Imitating Chemicals," Scient. Amer., 202, No. 1:99–108, 1960·

Muller, H. J., "Variation Due to Change in the Individual Gene," Amer. Nat., 56:32–50, 1922. Reprinted in *Classic Papers in Genetics*, Peters, J. A. (Ed.), Englewood Cliffs, N.J., Prentice-Hall, 1959, pp. 104–116.

Muller, H. J., "Artificial Transmutation of the Gene," Science, 66:84–87, 1927. Reprinted in *Classic Papers in Genetics*, Peters, J. A. (Ed.), Englewood Cliffs, N.J., Prentice-Hall, 1959, pp. 149–155, and also in *Great Experiments in Biology*, Gabriel, M. L., and S. Fogel (Eds.), Englewood Cliffs, N.J., Prentice-Hall, 1955, pp. 260–266.

QUESTIONS FOR DISCUSSION

23.1. Is there a dose of X rays and/or of ultraviolet radiation which is safe, in that it cannot cause some point mutations? Explain.

23.2. Can we be sure that any given mutation involves a single gene change rather than an intergenic one? Explain.

23.3. Would we know of the existence of genes if all genes had the identical mutational capacity? Explain.

LEWIS JOHN STADLER *(1896–1954) is noted for his studies on the nature of mutation and of the gene (see p. xi). He and H. J. Muller discovered independently the mutagenic effect of X rays. (By permission of* Genetics, Inc., *vol. 41, p. 1, 1956.)*

23.4. Would you expect the mutation rate to polydactyly, *P*, from normal, *p*, to be greater among normal individuals in a pedigree for polydactyly than it is among normals in general? Explain. How might you proceed to test this hypothesis?

23.5. Do the mutational properties discussed suggest any limitations with respect to the chemical composition of genes? Explain.

23.6. When a chromosome is broken, is the breakage point within a gene or between genes, or can both occur? Justify your answer.

23.7. Point mutations are sometimes called gene mutations. Do you think this is permissible? Why?

23.8. In what way is the study of mutation dependent upon genes? In what way is the reverse true?

23.9. What is your opinion with regard to the validity of applying principles of point mutation directly to gene mutation?

Chapter **24**

POINT MUTANTS —
THEIR DETECTION AND
EFFECTS IN INDIVIDUALS

Point mutants comprise the remainder of all genetically detected mutants for which no association with intergenic changes can be demonstrated. It is not only of historical importance, but also of current and future interest, to understand something about the genetic methods that are used for collecting point mutants. We shall consider two elegant procedures [1] using *Drosophila melanogaster*, one for the detection of mutants that are recessive lethals, the other for "visible" mutations, at specific loci, which are viable when heterozygous.

The technique for detecting recessive lethals is called "*Basc*" (see Figure 24–1), and is designed to discover such mutants that arise in the germ line of the male, in X chromosome loci which are hemizygous, i.e., have no allele in the Y chromosome. The males used are wild-type, having all normal characteristics, including round, dull-red compound eyes. The females employed have X chromosomes homozygous for Bar eye (B), for apricot eye color (*apr*), and for a paracentric *inversion* (*In*) of almost the entire left arm (*In sc^{S1} sc^8* whose right breakage point is designated *sc^{S1}* and left *sc^8*) inside of which is a smaller inversion (*InS*). "*Basc*" derives its name from *B*ar, *a*pricot, *sc*ute inversion. *Basc* females (or males) have nar-

row-Bar eyes of apricot color. The genotype of the *Basc* female is written

$$sc^{S1}\ B\ InS\ apr\ sc^8/sc^{S1}\ B\ InS\ apr\ sc^8.$$

A wild-type male is mated to a *Basc* female and the F_1 daughters are obtained. These daughters are $+/sc^{S1}\ B\ InS\ apr\ sc^8$ and appear heterozygous (wide) Bar (being otherwise wild-type).

Since the very short right arm of the X is entirely heterochromatic, it is of no concern here. Because each F_1 female is heterozygous for two paracentric inversions, any crossing over between the left arms of her X's produces dicentric or acentric crossover strands which fail to enter the gametic nucleus (see Chapter 19). Accordingly, F_1 females produce eggs having an X that is, for our purposes, either completely maternal

$$(sc^{S1}\ B\ InS\ apr\ sc^8),$$

or completely paternal ($+$). If this F_1 daughter mates with her *Basc* brothers, half of the sons in the next generation (F_2) receive the $+$ maternal X, and half receive the *Basc* maternal X. So, if the progeny of a single F_1 female are examined, it is a simple matter to recognize the presence of both types of sons, since it is usual to obtain more than forty sons per female. Note that each wild-type F_2 son carries an identical copy of the X in the sperm that fertilized the egg which developed as his mother (the F_1 female). Even when the sperm used to form the F_1 female carries an X-linked recessive lethal mutant, the F_1 female will survive because she carries the $+$ allele of it in her *Basc* chromosome. However, each $+$ F_2 son will carry this mutant in hemizygous condition and will usually die before adulthood, so that no $+$ sons appear in F_2! It becomes clear, then, since an F_1 female is formed by fertilization with a $+$ X-carrying sperm, that the absence of $+$ sons among her progeny is proof that the particular P_1 sperm carried a recessive lethal mutant.

---

[1] These were invented by H. J. Muller.

Such a lethal mutant must have occurred in the germ line after the fertilization that produced the P_1 male, for if it were present at fertilization, he would not have survived. It is unlikely that many of the lethals detected in sperm originate very early in development, for in this case a large portion of the somatic tissue would also carry the lethal and this would usually cause death before adulthood. Usually, the X-linked lethal present in sperm arises in a small portion of the germ line so that even when a few hundred sperm, of the several thousand sperm ejaculated, are tested, only one is found to carry a mutant. Occasionally, however, the mutation occurs early enough in the germ line so that several sperm tested from the same male carry what proves to be the same recessive lethal.

When a thousand sperm from normal untreated males are tested for X-linked reces-

FIGURE 24–1.   *The breeding scheme used in the Basc technique.*

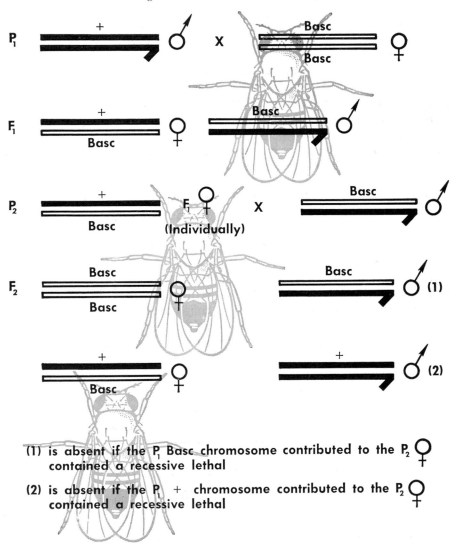

(1) is absent if the P_1 Basc chromosome contributed to the P_2 ♀ contained a recessive lethal

(2) is absent if the P_1 + chromosome contributed to the P_2 ♀ contained a recessive lethal

sive lethals by means of a thousand separate matings with F_1 females, as described, approximately two of these matings are found to yield no + sons, so that the recessive lethal mutation rate of 0.2% is a fairly typical one. For each dose of 1000 r of X rays to which the adult male is exposed, approximately 3.1% more sperm are found to carry X-linked recessive lethals.

The Basc technique has certain disadvantages. When used as described, it detects only those recessive lethals which cause 100 per cent mortality before adulthood. Other recessive lethals that produce sterility or cause death of the adult before it can mate are not detected. No recessive lethals are detected unless they are hemizygous in the F_2 male, as mentioned, and a considerable number are known to occur whose lethality is reduced by genes normally present in the Y chromosome.

On the other hand, the advantages and applications of the Basc technique are numerous. A few can be mentioned here. The presence or absence of + males in F_2 is easily and objectively determined. Since the recessive lethal which is detected in F_2 is also carried by the heterozygous-Bar F_2 females, this permits further study of the recessive lethal in that generation and subsequent ones. In such studies it can be discovered whether the lethals are associated with intergenic changes; those that are not are designated as recessive lethal point mutants. The Basc technique can also be used to detect recessive lethals that occur in a P_1 *Basc* chromosome, the absence of *Basc* males among the F_2 progeny indicating such a mutation. Moreover, using standardized environmental conditions, it becomes possible to detect hemizygous mutations which either lower the viability of the males without being lethal or raise their viability above normal. Most important is the additional possibility of studying the viability effects of recessive lethals when in heterozygous condition.

Although the Basc technique may be used also to detect X-linked mutants producing a visible morphological change when hemizygous, all those "visibles" which are also hemizygous lethals are missed. The *"Maxy"* technique (refer to Figure 24–2) overcomes this difficulty. The males used carry an X chromosome containing two medium sized paracentric inversions, *In49* (having no obvious phenotypic effect) and B^{M1} (having a dominant effect like *Bar*). The X also carries a minute paracentric inversion (of negligible phenotypic effect) associated with the recessive lethal *lJ1* (located to the left of *yellow body color*, *y*), which is also present. This X also carries the recessive mutant *ocelliless* (*oc*) which removes the ocelli (simple eyes). The males are able to survive *lJ1* because they carry the normal allele, *lJ1*+, as a mutant duplication in the longer arm of the Y chromosome. The genotype of the male may be written as: *lJ1 In49 oc B^{M1}/lJ1+.Y*.

One of the female's X's is the same as the one in the male. The second X carries *lJ1*+ and a recessive lethal mutant *l* (located between *scute bristles*, *sc*, and *white eye*, *w*), for which the other X carries the normal allele, *l*+. This second X also carries the long inversion *In sc^{S1} sc^8* (as in *Basc*), plus recessive genes for yellow body color (*y*), outstretched wings and small eye (*odsy*), echinus, rough eyes (*ec*), forked bristles (*f*), singed bristles (*sn*), dusky wings (*dy*), cut wings (*ct*), and recessive genes for the following eye colors: carnation (*car*), garnet (*g*), vermilion (*v*), raspberry (*ras*), carmine (*cm*), ruby (*rb*), white (*w*), and prune (*pn*). The arrangement of all the markers in this X is as follows: *y l sc^{S1} car odsy f g dy v ras sn ct cm rb ec w pn sc^8*.

Since, by convention, only mutants are indicated in the genetic formulae for these X's, you must realize that the B^{M1}-containing X carries *l*+ as well as the normal alleles of all the other recessives in the second kind of X. Similarly, the X carrying the multiple recessives also carries lJl^+, though this is not indicated in the formula.

Females of this stock do not produce gametes containing X chromosome crossovers, since these are eliminated in the same manner as in the $Basc/+$ heterozygote. When females and males of this stock are mated together, only two kinds of male zygotes are produced. However, the half receiving the l-containing X die, while the other half, which live, are genotypically exactly like their father. The female zygotes are also of two equally frequent types, the homozygotes for lJl dying, the ones surviving being identical in genotype to their mother. This stock is self-perpetuating because it contains a *balanced lethal system* (see Chapter 20) in which the females are permanent heterozygotes and the males are of only one type. Note that if nondisjunction produces an X0 zygote, this will die because of the hemizygosity either of lJl or l. There are three possible types of nondisjunctional XXY females. One type which is homozygous for X's carrying lJl, lives, because of the lJl^+ on the Y, but it cannot breed because females that have oc in homozygous condition are sterile; the XXY type homozygous for l dies. The third type of XXY lives and breeds, but since it is heterozygous for the two kinds of X's, the usefulness or continuity of the stock is not impaired.

Phenotypically, males are ocelliless and bar-eyed, while females are slightly bar-eyed, but otherwise wild-type. You can readily see that mutations in the X of the male which involve any of the fifteen normal loci affecting the eyes, body color, wings, or bristles, for which the female has recessive alleles, may be detected in their daughters. For example, if a sperm carries a mutation from y^+ to y, this will produce a yellow daughter when it fertilizes an egg carrying the multiple recessive X. This stock is, therefore, called "Maxy" because it was designed for the finding of "visible" mutations in the *male*'s

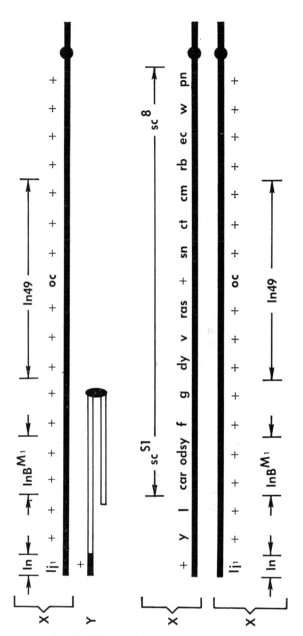

FIGURE 24–2. *The sex chromosomes of the males and females used in the Maxy technique.*

X at specific loci, including y. The Maxy stock permits the detection of any mutation, spontaneous or induced, involving the normal alleles of the fifteen recessives, provided the mutant does not produce the normal phenotype when heterozygous with the recessive allele, and provided it is not a dominant lethal. Once such mutants are obtained, they can be screened for point mutants.

The study of recessive lethals on the X chromosome and on the autosomes shows that there are hundreds of loci whose point mutations may be recessively lethal. It should be noted that the recessive lethals detected by Basc, and the visibles detected by Maxy, are not mutually exclusive types of mutants, for some Maxy-detected visibles are lethal when hemizygous, and about 10 per cent of Basc-detected hemizygous lethals show some morphological effect when heterozygous. It can be stated, in general, that any mutant in homo- or hemizygous condition which is a "visible" will be found to produce some change in viability, and, conversely, that any mutant which affects viability will be found to produce a "visible" effect, "visible" at least at the biochemical level.

What, in general, is the nature of the phenotypic effect of point mutants when homozygous or hemizygous? A mutant's biological activity is best described in terms of its effect upon *reproductive potential*, i.e., the capacity to produce surviving offspring. These terms include the mutant individual's capacity to reach the reproductive stage, its fertility and fecundity during this period, as well as the viability of its offspring until sexual maturity. We already know that each mutant has manifold effects due to a pedigree of causes (Chapter 10). It has been found that point mutants with small phenotypic effects are much more frequent than those with large effects. For instance, using the Basc technique, it is found that recessive mutants, which lower the viability of males without being lethal, are at least three to five times more frequent than those that are lethal (Figure 24–3).

The vast majority of point mutants produce a detrimental effect on the reproductive potential, those that are beneficial being extremely rare. For example, the great majority of mutations affecting a trait or organ cause its degeneration. This is understandable in terms of the past evolutionary history of a species. All the genotypes in a species have been subjected to selection for many generations, and those which produced the greatest reproductive potential were retained. Although point mutation at any locus is a rare event, many of the alternatives possible for each gene must have occurred at least several times in the past history of the species. Of these alternatives only the more advantageous alleles were retained, and these are the ones found in present populations. So, when point mutation occurs today, it is likely to produce one of the genetic alternatives which had already occurred in the past and had been eliminated because it produced a lower biological fitness, that is, a lower reproductive potential. It should be realized, moreover, that reproductive potential is the result of coordinated action of the whole genotype. The genotype may be likened to the machinery that makes modern automobiles, the environment furnishing the raw materials for this process, with the automobile representing the phenotype. Just as it is true for present genotypes, the machinery that manufactures automobiles is complex and has had a long evolutionary development. The chance that a random local change in the present machinery will result in a better automobile is just as small as the chance that a newly occurring point mutation will increase reproductive potential.

In what way does the phenotypic effect of a point mutant differ from that of its normal alternative? This can be studied by examining the effect of increasing the relative number of doses of the mutant present in the genotype. In *Drosophila*, for example, the normal fly has long bristles when the dominant gene bb^+ is present. There is a mutant

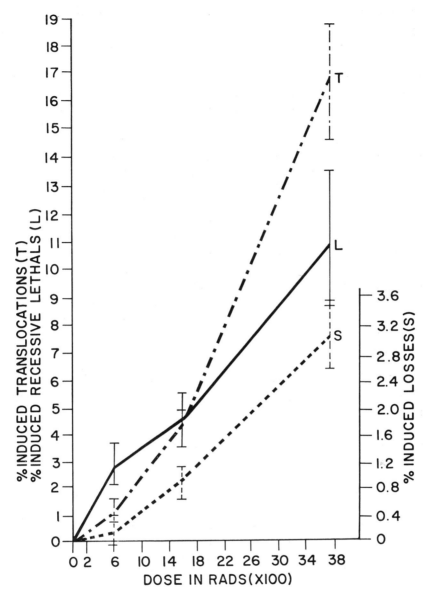

FIGURE 24–3. *Percentage of mutations, ±2 × standard error, recovered from* Drosophila *sperm exposed to different dosages of 18 mev electrons. The sex-linked recessive lethal frequencies (L) are joined by solid lines and are adjusted for the control rate; sex chromosome loss frequencies (S) are connected by broken lines and are corrected for the control rate; reciprocal translocation frequencies (T) between chromosomes* II *and* III *are connected by dot-dash lines. (From I. H. Herskowitz, H. J. Muller, J. S. Laughlin, Genetics, 44: 326, 1959.)*

strain with shorter, thinner bristles due to the recessive allele *bb* (*bobbed bristles*). Now, *bb* has a locus that happens to be present both in the X and the Y chromosomes. You might suppose that the male, or female, homozygous for *bb* has bobbed bristles because this allele results in thinning and shortening the normal bristle. Since it is possible to obtain otherwise diploid XYY males and XXY females which carry three doses of *bb*, one would expect, according to this view, that the bristles formed would be still thinner and shorter. But, on the contrary,[2] in the presence of three doses of *bb*, the bristles are almost normal in size and shape. This demonstrates that *bb* functions in the same way as does *bb*+, but to a lesser degree. Mutants having a similar but lesser effect than the normal gene are called *hypomorphs*. Many point mutants are hypomorphs, since the addition of further doses of them causes the phenotype to become more normal.

Of the remainder of point mutants, most are *amorphs*, producing no phenotypic effect, even when present in extra dose. *White eye* (*w*) in *Drosophila* is an example of this. Cases are also known of mutants which function as *neomorphs*; these produce a new effect. Adding more doses of such a mutant causes more departure from normal, while adding more doses of the normal alternative has no effect.

We can represent the relationship between the normal gene and its hypomorphic mutants diagrammatically, as shown in Figure 24–4.[3] The vertical axis represents phenotypic effect, the normal effect being indicated by +. The horizontal axis refers to the dosage of the normal gene or of a hypomorphic mutant. Notice that a single + gene by itself almost produces the full normal phenotypic effect (and often the difference between its effect and the normal effect is not readily detected). Two + genes reach the + pheno-

typic level. But, in the case of the hypomorphic mutant, even three doses may not reach the phenotypic level produced by one + gene (recall the discussion of *bb*). Note also that genetic modifiers or environmental factors, which would shift the position on the horizontal axis and thereby shift the phenotypic effect, have less and less influence as one proceeds from individuals carrying only one dose of mutant toward individuals carrying two + genes. You can see that natural selection would favor alleles resulting in phenotypic effects close to +, that is, near the curve's plateau, for this would insure phenotypic stability. Any mutant which produced such a phenotypic effect would, in the course of time, become the normal gene in the population and would automatically be dominant when heterozygous with a hypomorphic gene alternative. This model illustrates how the heterozygote with one + and one mutant gene has practically the same effect as the normal homozygote, and seems to be the best explanation for most cases of complete or almost complete *dominance*. This scheme also illustrates why so few mutants are beneficial, other things being equal, for the normal gene alternative already produces an amount of phenotypic effect near optimum.

In view of what was just discussed, you can understand that hypomorphic and amorphic mutants are usually detrimental when pure (homo- or hemizygous). But you may wonder what their effects will be when heterozygous with the normal gene. If they are amorphs, the single + gene may fall short of producing the full phenotypic effect, and so such mutants would be expected to be slightly detrimental when heterozygous. Hypomorphs would be expected to be less detrimental or not at all detrimental when heterozygous, at least with respect to the trait for which they are classified as hypomorphic. But it should be recalled that each gene affects many different biochemical processes, and a mutant which

[2] As shown by C. Stern.
[3] Adapted from H. J. Muller.

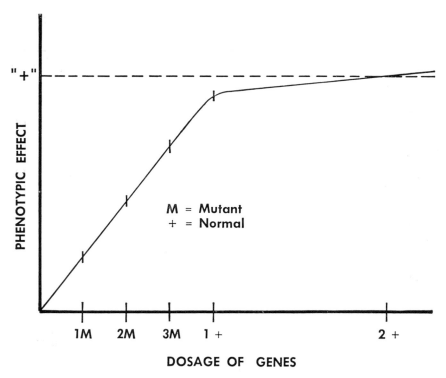

FIGURE 24–4. *The relationship between dosage of normal and mutant genes and their phenotypic effect.*

is hypomorphic with regard to one trait may be amorphic with respect to another one. Thus, in *Drosophila*, the normal allele *apr*+ results in dull-red eye color and also pigments the Malpighian tubules. One of its alleles, *apr*, results in a lighter eye color (being hypomorphic in this respect) but no color in the Malpighian tubules (being amorphic in this respect).

Experience confirms expectation in this regard. It has been shown that most "recessive" lethal point mutants result in some detrimental effect on reproductive potential when heterozygous. Such mutants are not completely recessive, therefore, and it has been found, in *Drosophila*, that when heterozygous, they are cause of death before adulthood of about four per cent of individuals. Mutants, which are detrimental but not lethal when pure, also usually show such a detrimental effect when heterozygous, this effect being somewhat less than that produced by heterozygous lethal point mutants. The principles of phenotypic action discussed here apply both to spontaneous and to induced point mutants.

SUMMARY AND CONCLUSIONS

The details of the Basc and Maxy genetic schemes for the detection of recessive lethal and recessive visible mutants in *Drosophila* are described. The study of point mutants of these types and others reveals that almost all are detrimental to the reproductive potential of individuals when pure (not hybrid), and to a lesser extent when hybrid. Accordingly, most point mutants are not completely recessive to their normal genetic alternatives. Most normal genes fail to produce the full normal phenotypic effect in single dose, and most point mutants act on the phenotype in a hypomorphic or amorphic manner.

REFERENCES

Muller, H. J., "A Semi-automatic Breeding System ('Maxy') for Finding Sex-linked Mutations at Specific 'Visible' Loci," Drosophila Info. Serv., 28:140–141, 1954.

Muller, H. J., "The Nature of the Genetic Effects Produced by Radiation," in *Radiation Biology*, Hollaender, A. (Ed.), New York, McGraw-Hill, 1: Chap. 7:351–473, 1954.

Schalet, A., "A Study of Spontaneous Visible Mutations in Drosophila Melanogaster," Proc. X Intern. Congr., Genetics, Montreal, 2:252 (Abstr.), 1958.

See Supplement III.

H. J. MULLER, *at Cold Spring Harbor, 1941.*

QUESTIONS FOR DISCUSSION

24.1. Are all of the mutants detected by the Basc or Maxy techniques point mutants? Explain.

24.2. Suppose, in the Basc technique, an F_2 culture produced both expected types of daughters, but no sons at all. To what would you attribute this result?

24.3. How might you proceed to test whether a recessive lethal detected in the F_2 of the Basc technique was associated with an inversion or a reciprocal translocation?

24.4. A wild-type female produces 110 daughters but only 51 sons. How could you test whether this result was due to the presence, in heterozygous condition, of a recessive X-linked lethal?

24.5. How can you explain the phenotype of a rare female in the Maxy stock that produces only the usual Maxy type of progeny, but which has both compound eyes distinctly lighter than normal?

24.6. Can the Maxy stock be used to detect the occurrence of visible mutants which arise in the female germ line? Explain.
        Can the Maxy stock be used to detect the frequency of recessive lethal mutations that arise in the male germ line? Explain.

24.7. Compare the relative suitability of man and *Drosophila* for the determination of mutation rates.

24.8. The genes in the X chromosomes are incompletely linked in the females of the Basc stock, but completely linked in the females of the Maxy stock. Do you agree with this statement? Why?

24.9. Do you suppose that the general conclusions regarding the phenotypic effects of mutants in *Drosophila* also apply in the case of man? Why?

24.10. Reread the main part of this Chapter and write a Summary and Conclusions section of less than 200 words without consulting the one given. Compare the two sections critically and objectively.

24.11. What is the relation between the gene and the phenotypic effect by which it is detected?

Chapter *25

THE GENETIC CONTROL
OF MUTABILITY

IN SEVERAL Chapters preceding this, we have become familiar with the characteristics of different units of mutation, ranging from the largest changes, genomic changes, to the smallest, gene changes. We have seen, moreover, that various externally applied environmental agents can produce mutations of all kinds. What is the nature of the role that the genotype plays in mutability? A few moments of reflection will lead you to realize that in several respects the very nature of the genotype influences its mutability.

The fact that mitosis and meiosis occur in the precise way they do is evidence that the genotype normally prevents genomic and single whole chromosome changes in successive generations of cells and individuals, respectively. There can be no doubt that these processes are under genic control — even if we cannot specify in each case, or in any particular case, the specific genes responsible for these orderly mechanisms for mutation-prevention. The synthesis of new genes must usually be so orderly as to prevent improper gene components from substituting for the proper ones, on the presumption that both types are present in the cell at the same time. The process of synapsis between homologous loci is adequately specific so that a chiasma typically occurs at precisely corresponding points of the two nonsister strands, and crossovers resulting in deficiencies and duplications are avoided. (We have already mentioned some evidence for the genetic control

of synapsis in the existence of collochores, in Chapter 21, and in the case of asynaptic maize in Chapter 23.)

It might be argued, however, that such examples only serve to demonstrate that the processes mentioned reduce mutability as an inevitable consequence of their normal operation. While it would be true in these cases that the present genotype appears to play a passive role, it must be admitted, since mitosis and meiosis are not intrinsic properties of genes, that during the course of evolution, the selection of genes to carry out these activities was an active process aimed at reducing mutability, or, in other words, aimed at maintaining genetic stability, while permitting replication and genetic recombination via sexuality.

While the genetic controls so far mentioned lead to a reduction in mutability, it should be recognized that the genotype also permits genetic changes to occur in controlled or regulated ways. This is demonstrated by the very process of sexuality, whose ploidy changes, from diploid to haploid and back again, must be under genetic control. Since mutational changes increase with mitotic activity (Chapter 23), and because mitosis and mitotic rate are known to be under genetic control (many cancer cells are mutants whose mitotic rate is increased), the genotype controls mutability in this way. We have already mentioned (Chapter 18) certain modifications of meiosis, doubtless also under genic control, which lead to ploidy changes in the next generation. Even within the somatic tissues of a multicellular organism, controlled genetic change is permitted in cells whose chromosomes become polyploid (as in human liver) or polytene (as in the Dipteran salivary gland). We have also already noted (Chapter 23) in *Ascaris* that changes from bipolarity to unipolarity occur in somatic tissues, as a result of which a number of small chromosomes are formed from a single large one. (The genotype sup-

presses mutation in a polycentric chromosome by suppressing the action of all but one
centromere.) The frequency of nondisjunction, which leads to aneusomy, has been
shown to be dependent upon both the
amount and distribution of heterochromatin,
and also upon the types of chromosomal
rearrangements present. So, insofar as the
genotype regulates its heterochromatin and
rearrangements, it is also regulating the incidence of nondisjunction. Similarly, the
arrangement of meiotic nuclei in the oogenesis
of *Drosophila* (Chapter 19) eliminates dicentrics produced by crossing over in paracentric inversion heterozygotes. Finally, the
arrangement of the chromosomal material
and the metabolic activity of the cell (amount
of water and oxygen present, for example)
are other ways in which mutability is regulated by the genotype itself.

The preceding discussion has dealt largely
with the prevention or regulated occurrence
of intergenic changes. Is there other, specific
evidence that the genotype regulates the occurrence of point mutation? Compare the
spontaneous point mutation rates of two
lines of the same species of *Drosophila*, one
living in a tropical and the other in a temperate climate. If the genotype was at the mercy
of temperature, in nature, the tropical form
would be expected to have a higher rate of
spontaneous point mutation than the temperate form. However, when both lines are
grown in the laboratory at the same temperature, the tropical form has a lower mutation
rate than the temperate one. This is good
evidence that the tropical form has genetically
suppressed (or the temperate form has genetically enhanced) its mutational response to
temperature. Accordingly, the two forms, in
nature, probably show less difference in mutation rate than expected from the temperature difference. Other strains of *Drosophila
melanogaster* collected from different regions
have different spontaneous point mutation
rates. Some of this difference may be due to

differences in mutability of the isoalleles
(cf. p. 65) that are present and which result in
the same wild-type appearance in each case;
but part may be due also to a general control
of mutability by the genotype. For some
strains are known to contain *mutator genes*
in whose presence the general point mutation rate is increased as much as tenfold. Of
course, other alleles of mutator genes may
therefore act as general suppressors of point
mutability. Certain organisms (bacteria, for
example) have mutants which make the individual generally less mutable when exposed
to a given mutagen. Note also that the organisms most advanced in evolution contain
more chromosomal material per cell than do
less advanced forms, and they have probably
selected genotypes that reduce their spontaneous mutation rate to avoid overmutation.

Consider next certain results in maize.[1]
The kernels of some plants are white, others
are colored, while still others are white with
colored speckles. At first, it appears as
though we are dealing with a high rate of
mutation of the "colorless" gene. It was
found, however, that the white phenotype is
the result of the presence of two genes adjacent to or very near each other on the same
chromosome. If these two loci become dissociated from each other, as when a particular one is removed via a two-break deletion,
for example, the mutant cell and all its
daughter cells containing the remaining locus
are colored. The locus removed is called
Dissociation, Ds; this locus can be the cause
of breakage in chromosome regions near it,
and was shown to be a heterochromatic portion of the chromosome. If *Ds* is never dissociated from the adjacent locus, the kernel is
white; if it is dissociated during kernel formation, the kernel has colored sectors or dots on
a white background; if *Ds* is moved before
the kernel forms, the kernel and later generations of plants are completely colored. The
mutation described here is the loss or removal

[1] Based upon work of B. McClintock.

of *Ds* via breakage. This is not synonymous with the change in color, though the change in color is the phenotypic event which led to the detection and proof of the mutational event. The change in color is apparently a position effect (Chapter 22); the presence of *Ds*, next to the gene for color, suppresses color formation; its absence permits the gene for color to produce color.

It was possible to prove that the very capacity of *Ds* to cause breakages nearby is under genic control. These latter genes, since they activate *Ds* to break the chromosome, thereby leading to the removal of *Ds* from its original position, are called *Activator*, *Ac*, genes. *Ac* does not have to be on the same chromosome as *Ds*, and usually is not.

FIGURE 25–1. *The effect of* Activator *on the action of* Dissociation. *(A) No* Ac *is present. The kernel is colorless due to the continued presence of* Ds, *which inhibits the action of a neighboring pigment-producing gene. (B) One* Ac *factor is present. Breaks at* Ds *occur early in kernel development, leading to large colored sectors. (C) Two* Ac *factors are present. Time of* Ds *action is delayed, producing smaller sectors which appear as specks. (D) Three* Ac *factors are present.* Ds *action is so delayed that relatively few and tiny specks are produced. (Courtesy of B. McClintock.)*

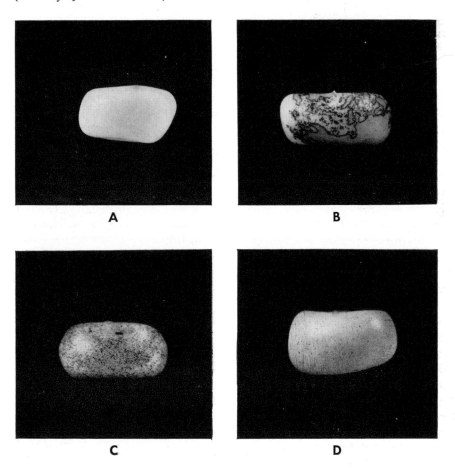

A

B

C

D

It was found that the colored speckles were large in some plants, while in other plants they were small in size. The large speckles were due to the movement of *Ds* early in development, while the small speckles meant the movement of *Ds* later in development, when very few additional cell divisions had yet to take place. It was possible to obtain cells containing one, two, and three *Ac* genes, the spots becoming smaller the greater the number of *Ac* genes present. Thus, *Ac* also acts to delay the time of *Ds* action. Here, then, is a case where the genotype regulates its own mutability — *Ac* not only determines the capacity of *Ds* to produce breakages but regulates the time when breakage is to occur (Figure 25–1).

The breaks which *Ds* causes are usually near to *Ds* in the chromosome, but are not always at the same locus. Because of this property, and because breaks can occur simultaneously in other chromosomes (due to spontaneous events, or to the presence of other *Ds* genes located in them), *Ds* need not be lost following breakage, but can become transported from one position in a chromosome to another in the same or a different chromosome, and the number of *Ds* factors present can increase in successive generations. When the number of *Ds* genes increases in a given region of a chromosome, that region breaks more and more frequently, while a *Ds* transposed to another chromosome can cause breaks near it in its new location. Whenever *Ds* moves its location, a mutation has occurred. Such relocations of *Ds* often cause a suppression of the phenotypic effect of a gene located near the new locus of *Ds*. As long as *Ds* remains in its new position, the new phenotype is produced, and this simulates a stable point mutation of the gene near *Ds*. Moreover, each time *Ds* is lost from such a location, the new phenotype of the adjacent gene reverts to the old phenotype. If these last transportations are frequent, they may be incorrectly scored as point mutations of an unstable, mutable allele of the neighboring gene.

Let us next consider in some detail how another case of what originally appeared to be an unstable gene was analyzed in maize.[2] The pericarp of a corn kernel encloses the seed which contains the embryo. While embryo tissue is of the offspring generation, the pericarp is formed by the parental generation. Some plants are completely red and produce fully red pericarps in their kernels, others are striped with red, this striping being seen also in the pericarp, and others are completely nonred. A plant which shows medium variegation of red, therefore called *medium variegated*, produces kernels of the type shown in Figure 25–2. Note in the random sample of kernels shown that about six per cent have full red color. From this result and others it was decided that a medium variegated pericarp parent has about six per cent of kernels that are mutant. Genetically, the results were interpreted as being due to mutation at a locus *P* on chromosome 1. Nonred individuals were

[2] Based upon work of R. A. Brink and coworkers.

FIGURE 25–2. *A random sample of kernels from a medium variegated pericarp ear. (Courtesy of R. A. Brink; photograph by The Calvin Company reprinted by permission of McGraw-Hill Book Co., Inc., from* Study Guide and Workbook for Genetics *by I. H. Herskowitz. Copyright, 1960.)*

$P^W P^W$, while the medium variegated individuals that produced some full red kernels were only heterozygous for P^W, the other allele, P^V, being an unstable one which frequently mutated in somatic cells to a red-producing alternative. According to this view, large red sectors are due to mutations of this unstable allele early in development of the shoot, and small sectors are due to mutations which occur later.

It was found, however, that medium variegateds produce not only red mutants but light variegated ones, also. The parental type and the two mutant types can be seen in the ears shown in Figure 25–3. The *light variegated kernels* ("*lights*") have about half as many sectors mutant as have *medium variegated kernels* ("*mediums*").

The results of test crossing mediums ($P^V P^W$) are shown in Figure 25–4. As expected, half of the offspring are nonred ($P^W P^W$). Of the remaining half, which have various degrees of red, 90% are mediums ($P^V P^W$), about 6% are *full red* ("*reds*"), and

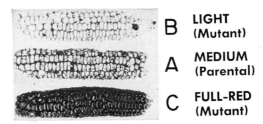

B	LIGHT (Mutant)
A	MEDIUM (Parental)
C	FULL-RED (Mutant)

FIGURE 25–3. *Corn ears showing medium variegated pericarp (parental type) (A), and the mutant types light variegated (B) and full red (C). (Courtesy of R. A. Brink; reprinted by permission of McGraw-Hill Book Co., Inc., from* Study Guide and Workbook for Genetics *by I. H. Herskowitz, Copyright, 1960.)*

4% are lights. The similar frequency of reds and lights suggests that these two mutants are related in some way in their origin. Reds × $P^W P^W$ produce offspring which, if colored, are all red, the red allele being a stable one. While this result is readily understandable, the following one is not. Lights × $P^W P^W$ sometimes produce about equal numbers of

FIGURE 25–4. *Results of test crossing medium variegated pericarp with colorless pericarp.*

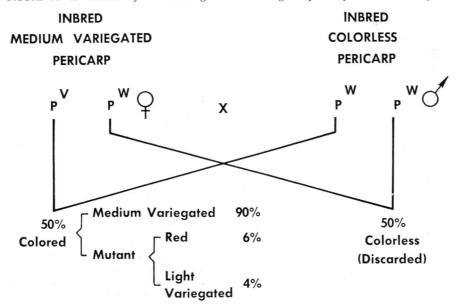

INBRED
MEDIUM VARIEGATED
PERICARP

INBRED
COLORLESS
PERICARP

P^V P^W ♀   X P^W P^W ♂

50% Colored
- Medium Variegated 90%
- Mutant
  - Red 6%
  - Light Variegated 4%

50% Colorless (Discarded)

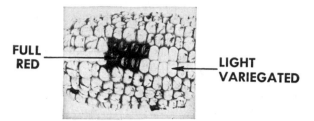

FULL RED — **LIGHT VARIEGATED**

FIGURE 25–5. *Twin patch of mutant kernels, full red and light variegated, in a medium variegated pericarp ear.* (*Courtesy of R. A. Brink; photograph by The Calvin Company reprinted by permission of McGraw-Hill Book, Co., Inc., from* Study Guide and Workbook for Genetics *by I. H. Herskowitz, Copyright, 1960.*)

lights and mediums among the colored offspring, plus a few reds (which can be considered new mutants from variegated). We shall return to this result shortly.

Occasionally, medium ears show the two mutants, light and red, as twin patches of kernels (Figure 25–5). This suggests that reds and lights are not merely related in origin, but that these mutants are complementary; that is, in the mutation process, one has gained something the other had lost. In view of the results with *Ac* and *Ds*, a new genetic hypothesis can be presented to explain this pericarp variegation (Figure 25–6). Note that the gene symbols have been changed. Because of the way these strains are carried and crossed, all variegated genotypes are heterozygous for P^w, the stable gene on chromosome 1 for nonred pericarp. The variegated allele is considered to be a dual structure, containing P^r, the top dominant allele for red, and *Mp*, *Modulator*, which suppresses red pigment production.

$\overline{P^r\ Mp}$ together suppress red pigmentation, so that mediums are produced. P^r alone produces stable, full red. $\overline{P^r\ Mp}$, plus an additional *Mp* somewhere else (*transposed Modulator*), produces lights. This would explain the results, given in the next to last paragraph, from backcrossing lights ($P^w\ P^w \times \overline{P^r\ Mp}/P^w$ plus transposed *Mp*). Half of the offspring would be nonred ($P^w\ P^w$), the colored being about half lights (genetically like the light parent) and half mediums (like the light parent but lacking the transposed *Mp*) and a few reds (cases where *Mp* was transposed from $\overline{P^r\ Mp}$, leaving P^r alone). How can the mechanism for transposing *Mp*

away from $\overline{P^r\ Mp}$ be visualized? The same kind of process that transposes *Ds* can be considered to apply here, also. This can be illustrated with Figure 25–7, where the medium parent cell has chromosomes ($\overline{P^r\ Mp}$ and P^w) which are shown already divided, daughter strands still being connected at the centromere. A normal division would produce two daughter cells each carrying $\overline{P^r\ Mp}/P^w$, and each would give rise to medium sectors. But when mutation occurs, presumably involving two or more breaks, the *Mp* in one daughter strand may be transposed into a nonhomologous chromosome (hollow bar), and it is possible that the daughter cell which receives the transposed *Mp* will be the one carrying $\overline{P^r\ Mp}$, in which case the other daughter cell will carry only P^r. Subsequent normal mitosis, of the cell containing P^r alone, will produce reds, and of the sister cell, lights, these cells becoming adjacent mutant patches in a medium background (see again Figure 25–5).

Red × nonred ($P^r/P^w \times P^w/P^w$) should produce about half nonred and about half red. We have already mentioned that it does. Reds do not have *Mp* adjacent to P^r. Light × nonred ($\overline{P^r\ Mp}/P^w$ plus transposed *Mp* × $P^w\ P^w$) should produce half nonred. It does. If, in the last cross, transposed *Mp* is located in a nonhomologous chromosome, one quarter of F_1 will be light and one quarter will be medium. But *Mp* can move from $\overline{P^r\ Mp}$, yet still remain in the same chromosome but at a new position. Lights may therefore have their transposed *Mp* on chromosome 1. In this case, backcrossing will produce more than one quarter of F_1 that are lights and correspondingly fewer that are medium.

Other properties of *Mp* have been discovered. *Mp* may become fixed at the *P* locus, so that a medium becomes a stable nonred form. Transposed *Mp* may occupy a variety of sites, two of which have already been mentioned (linked, and no longer linked, to chromosome 1). In 57 of 87 cases, transposed *Mp* was still linked to chromosome 1, having moved less than 50 crossover units from *P*. In the remaining cases *Mp* was transposed to any one of five different nonhomologous chromosomes. Of the 57 cases where transposed *Mp* was still linked to chromosome 1, 37 cases showed *Mp* within five crossover units of *P*, 10 were between

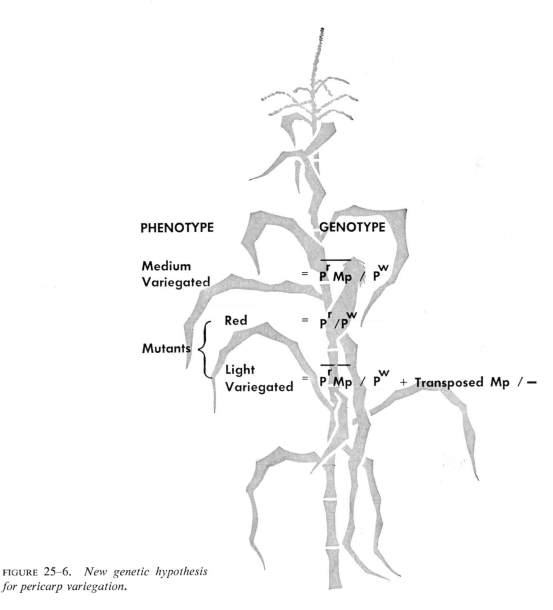

FIGURE 25–6. *New genetic hypothesis for pericarp variegation.*

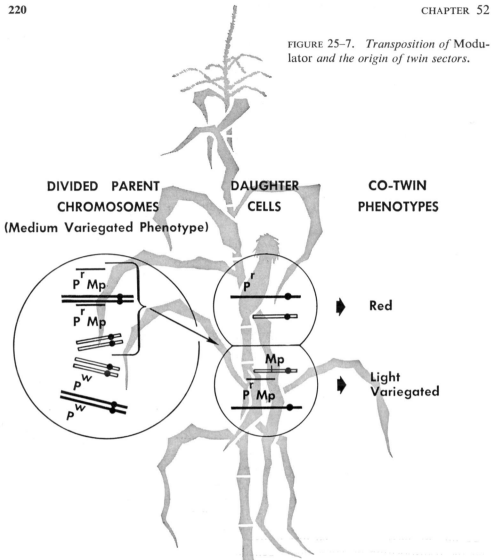

FIGURE 25–7. *Transposition of* Modulator *and the origin of twin sectors.*

DIVIDED PARENT
CHROMOSOMES
(Medium Variegated Phenotype)

DAUGHTER
CELLS

CO-TWIN
PHENOTYPES

Red

Light
Variegated

five and 15 units, and the remainder were farther away. Hence, *Mp* tends to move from the *P* locus by a short, rather than a long, jump. This suggests that contact between old and new sites may be required for shifts and transpositions of *Mp*.

Sometimes reds revert to variegated. In such cases, a transposed *Mp* is found to have been transposed near to *Pr*.   In fact, the frequency of such reversions from red to variegated can be studied by introducing into a chromosome containing *Pr*, a transposed

Mp located various distances from *Pr*. As shown in Figure 25–8, the closer transposed *Mp* is to *Pr*, the greater the frequency of reversions. In summary, then, medium mutates to red by loss of *Mp* from its position near the *Pr* locus. In this process, complementary lights are produced which possess an extra *Mp*, transposed *Mp*. The medium type is reconstituted by the movement of a transposed *Mp* back near the *Pr* locus.

Two additional points need to be made. The changes in phenotype involving reds, mediums, lights, and nonreds are not really mutations at the *P* locus. These changes are the phenotypic consequences of mutations involving the transposition of *Mp*, and are in this respect like the changes consequent to the transposition of *Ds*. Transposition of *Mp* to another locus may change the phenotype produced by the recipient locus. Thus, in a particular medium red carrying an allele on chromosome 9 that resulted in the starchy phenotype, a "mutation" to the waxy phenotype was observed. The waxy phenotype was unstable and frequently "mutated" back to starchy. Tests showed that *Mp* had been transposed to the starchy locus which then gave the waxy phenotype, and that the reversions to starchy were the result of *Mp*'s being transposed away from this locus. All the phenotypic changes consequent upon the movement of *Ds* and *Mp* strongly resemble position effects.

So far, we have not offered any evidence that the transposition of *Mp* is under genetic control. If *Mp* transposes away from $\overline{Pr\ Mp}$ 100 times in the absence of a transposed *Mp*, the presence of one transposed *Mp* reduces this frequency to about 60, while the presence of two transposed *Mp*'s further reduces this value to about 5. Thus, the transposition of *Mp* from $\overline{Pr\ Mp}$ is controlled by the presence of transposed *Mp*! Note that while breakability by *Ds* is regulated by a different factor *Ac*, breakability and its regulation are the consequence of a single kind of factor in the case of *Mp*.

Factors like *Ds* and *Mp* are known to be

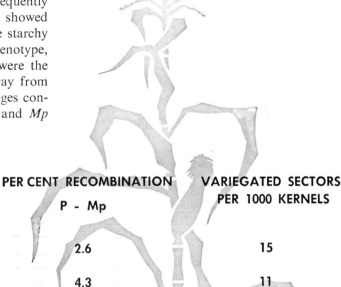

FIGURE 25–8. *Effect of distance of* Mp *from* P *upon transposition rate of* Mp *to* P.

PER CENT RECOMBINATION
P - Mp

VARIEGATED SECTORS
PER 1000 KERNELS

P - Mp	Variegated sectors per 1000 kernels
2.6	15
4.3	11
7.6	8
12.0	3
42.0	0.2

fairly common in maize, and the phenotypic instability of various loci in other flowering plants, ferns, fungi, and bacteria may be due to similar factors. A genetic control of spontaneous "breakability" of chromosomes that resembles the *Ac-Ds* system has been found also in *Drosophila melanogaster*. We do not know to what extent transmissible changes are due, not to point mutations of the "mutable" and "less mutable" loci, whose phenotypic effects we are following, but to the removal of some neighboring gene whose presence can cause a position effect. However, not all point mutations can be such position effects, of course, since different genes must first arise by mutation in order to obtain position effects with them.

ROYAL ALEXANDER BRINK *in 1961.*

SUMMARY AND CONCLUSIONS

The spontaneous occurrence of genomic and of single whole chromosome mutations is suppressed by the genotypic control of the processes of mitosis and meiosis. Structural rearrangements in chromosomes are suppressed by the precision of synapsis. All these controls are possible only because genes are linearly arranged in chromosomes with sealed-off ends, such structural features themselves being primary properties of genes. Genetic change is genotypically regulated in certain cases involving the production of polyploid and polytene chromosomes, and of several monocentric chromosomes from a polycentric chromosome.

Point mutation frequencies also are regulated genotypically. This is evidenced by the general control of mutation response to temperature changes or to mutagenic agents, by the occurrence of mutator genes, and of genes which produce breakages in chromosomes that lead to losses, shifts, and transpositions which may cause position effects, and by the occurrence of genes which regulate the operation of the genes causing the breakages.

REFERENCES

Brink, R. A., "Very Light Variegated Pericarp in Maize," Genetics, 39:724–740, 1954.

McClintock, B., "The Origin and Behavior of Mutable Loci in Maize," Proc. Nat. Acad. Sci., U.S., 36:344–355, 1950. Reprinted in *Classic Papers in Genetics*, Peters, J. A. (Ed.), Englewood Cliffs, N.J., Prentice-Hall, 1959, pp. 199–209.

McClintock, B., "Controlling Elements and the Gene," Cold Spr. Harb. Symp. Quant. Biol., 21:197–216, 1956.

Peterson, P. A., "The Pale Green Mutable System in Maize," Genetics, 45:115–133, 1960.

Sandler, L., Hiraizumi, Y., and Sandler, I., "Meiotic Drive in Natural Populations of Drosophila Melanogaster. I. The Cytogenetic Basis of Segregation-Distortion," Genetics, 44:233–250, 1959.

van Schaik, N. W., and Brink, R. A., "Transpositions of Modulator, a Modifier of the Variegated Pericarp Allele in Maize," Genetics, 44:725–738, 1959.

QUESTIONS FOR DISCUSSION

25.1. How is the precision of the mitotic and meiotic processes related to the mutability of the genetic material?

25.2. Defend the statement that meiosis and mitosis are not intrinsic properties of genes.

25.3. If whole genome changes represent a class of mutation, should the changes in ploidy which occur in gametogenesis and fertilization be considered mutations? Why?

25.4. Does *Dissociation* itself provide evidence for the genetic control of mutability? Explain.

25.5. What evidence can you present that variegation is not due to the effect of a single pair of genes, one of whose alleles is unstable?

25.6. Could you detect the transposition of a transposed *Modulator* to a locus near P^w? Explain.

25.7. Why does a light variegated individual of maize, that has a transposed *Modulator* on the same chromosome as $\overline{Pr\ Mp}$, produce more than one quarter of F_1 offspring that are lights and less than this that are mediums, when this individual is backcrossed to nonred ($P^w\ P^w$)?

25.8. Could *Modulator*like genes be the cause of relatively rare "mutants" of amorphic, hypomorphic, or neomorphic types? What is the basis for your opinion?

Chapter **26**

THE GENE POOL IN
CROSS–FERTILIZING POPULATIONS

THE study of cross-fertilizing individuals has led to our understanding of the recombinational and mutational properties of genes. We have studied the nature of these genetic units and their phenotypic consequences in terms of the traits produced within individuals and their relatives. However, cross-fertilizing individuals exist not only as individuals or as parts of families, but also as members of a general population. In such a general population each individual usually has an opportunity to mate with numerous other individuals. The gametes of all individuals mating furnish a pool of genes, or *gene pool*, from which the genes of the next generation will be drawn. What we are concerned with, on this occasion, is the fate of a particular gene in the gene pool of successive generations. Let us construct a gene pool and see what will happen to a gene in it in successive generations.

Suppose, in the not too distant future, it is decided to colonize Mars with human beings from the Earth. Suppose that the population arriving there is sufficiently large, and that with respect to eye color genes, only the

B (brown) allele and the completely recessive *b* (blue) allele are present, in such frequencies that the gene pool from the fathers and mothers is comprised of gametes that are .2*B* and .8*b*. On the presumption that the marriages which occur will be uninfluenced by eye color phenotype, what will be the genotypes of the F_1 generation? What will be their phenotypes? Of what will the F_1 gene pool consist?

The answer to the first question may be obtained from Figure 26–1. As the result of the random union of gametes, .04, or 4%, of children will be *BB*, .32, or 32%, will be *Bb*, and .64, or 64%, *bb*. Phenotypically, the F_1 population will be composed of 36% brown- and 64% blue-eyed people. (Since this eye color gene is located autosomally, the same proportions occur among boys and girls.) When, barring mutation, the F_1 marry, what

FEMALE GAMETES

	.2 B	.8 b
.2 B	.04 BB Brown Eyes	.16 Bb Brown Eyes
.8 b	.16 Bb Brown Eyes	.64 bb Blue Eyes

MALE GAMETES

The F₁ Population

.04 Brown (BB) + .32 Brown (Bb) + .64 Blue (bb)

The F₁ Gene Pool

FIGURE 26–1. *F₁ genotypes and the gene pool these produce.*
224

B = .04 + .16 = .2
b = .16 + .64 = .8

will the gene pool be in their gametes? The 4% of *BB* individuals will furnish 4% of all gametes and these will be *B*, and the 32% of *Bb* individuals will furnish 32% of all gametes of which half, or 16%, will be *B* and half, or 16%, *b*. So, in the total gene pool there will be 20%, or .2, gametes with *B*. The *b* gametes comprise 80%, or .8, of the gene pool (16% from the 32% *Bb* heterozygotes and 64% from the 64% of *bb* individuals). Note that the gene pool of the F_1 is identical to that of the P_1. It follows that in the F_2 and all subsequent generations the same genotypic and phenotypic ratios will be found, because the frequencies of *B* and *b* in the gene pool will remain constant in every subsequent generation.

What would be the consequence if, instead of starting the Martian colony with 80% *b* and 20% *B*, some other proportion had obtained? We can generalize the analysis by letting p equal the fraction of male and of female gametes in the population which carries *B*, and q equal the fraction of male and of female gametes which carries *b*. Naturally, for eggs, p + q = 1, as is true also for sperm. These sex cells will combine at random to produce the result shown in Figure 26–2. The resultant offspring population will be, then, p^2 *BB* + 2pq *Bb* + q^2 *bb*. The fraction of individuals who are brown-eyed will be p^2 + 2pq, while q^2 will be the blue-eyed fraction. The frequency of *B* and *b* among the gametes produced by the offspring population will be:

$$B = p^2 + pq = p(p + q) = p$$
$$b = q^2 + pq = q(q + p) = q.$$

Thus the gene frequencies will remain the same as they were in the gametes of the previous generation, and all future generations will have the same gene pool and the same relative frequencies of genotypes. The formula

$$p^2 \ BB + 2pq \ Bb + q^2 \ bb$$

describes the genotypic equilibrium produced by a static gene pool.[1]

It should be noted that this equilibrium principle is not dependent upon either the presence or the absence of dominance. Moreover, the *B* and *b* in the formula can represent any two alleles whose frequency in the gene pool is known, even if the sum of their frequencies is less than 1.

If this equilibrium principle applied indefinitely, gene frequencies would remain unchanged, and the evolution of different genotypes (and accordingly of new phenotypes) would not occur. In the Martian model described, however, certain conditions had to be fulfilled in order to maintain genic equilibrium. One condition was met by barring mutation. If *mutation* is permitted to occur, to allelic states other than *B* and *b*, it is clear that the frequency of these two alleles in the population will become reduced, upsetting the equilibrium. Moreover, the frequency of any allele will be changed if

[1] This is called the *Hardy-Weinberg equilibrium principle* (see references at the end of this Chapter).

EGGS

	p B (Brown)	q b (Blue)
p B (Brown)	p^2 BB (Brown Eyes)	pq Bb (Brown Eyes)
q b (Blue)	pq Bb (Brown Eyes)	q^2 bb (Blue Eyes)

SPERMS

FIGURE 26–2. *The types and frequencies of genotypes produced by a gene pool composed of p* B *and q* b.

the mutation rates to and from it are different. In either or both events, the genetic equilibrium will be shifted until a new one is attained. Thereafter, the new equilibrium will be maintained until some new factor acts on mutation rate in a directional way.

We have also presumed in our model that the reproductive potential is the same regardless of what the genotype is with respect to eye color. But it is possible, under certain conditions, that persons with blue (or those with brown) eyes are preferred as mates, in which case the reproductive potential of an individual would not be independent of the alleles under consideration. Accordingly, if individuals with a certain genetic endowment produce more surviving offspring than do those of a different genetic endowment, the genes which confer this higher biological fitness will tend to increase their frequency in the population, while those genes with lower fitness will tend to decrease. In this way, *selection*, operating on genotypes of different biological fitness, causes changes in gene frequencies, and shifts in the genotypic frequencies found at equilibrium.

We have also presumed that the Martian population was a large one. When populations are very large, oscillations that occur by chance in the number of children produced by different genotypes do not matter for they do not change the gene pool. In small populations, however, such chance oscillations can change gene frequencies. Suppose, for example, the Martian population whose gene pool is $.8b$ and $.2B$ runs short of food, so that only one couple, determined by chance, can have children. The chance that this husband and wife will be blue-eyed is $.64 \times .64$, or about $.41$, or 41%, which is the chance that the gene pool will drift at random in this particular manner, to produce the new gene frequencies of 1.0 for b and 0 for B. This *random genetic drift* can be illustrated also in a less extreme situation. If the Martian population is very large, and

a certain family chances to produce a relatively large number of children for several generations, then the proportion of all individuals having this family name will still be very small. But if the Martian population decreases while the reproductive rate of this family is unchanged, the proportion of all people with this surname will be increased.

Finally, we have not mentioned the possibility that the Martian colony will have emigrants or immigrants. If the emigrants have gene frequencies that differ from those in the population gene pool, the gene frequencies in the remaining population will be changed. If the immigrants have a different gene frequency from the natives and interbreed with them, this also will change the gene pool. In this way *migration* can shift gene equilibrium.

We see then that a cross-fertilizing population will remain static, in genetic equilibrium, in the absence of mutation, selection, random genetic drift, and differential migration. The occurrence of one, another, or all of these will change the frequencies of genes in the gene pool and thereby shift the frequencies of genotypes at equilibrium. Different species possess different gene pools, and it is natural to presume that they are different species because of their different gene pools. In accordance with this view, since these four factors serve to change gene frequencies, they may be considered to be the principal causes of species formation. Insofar as the formation of higher taxonomic categories is, like speciation, based upon change in gene pools, mutation (which supplies the raw materials), selection (which shapes these raw materials into the biologically fit genotypes of races and species), random genetic drift (which can produce rapid changes in gene frequency in small populations), and differential migration (which can shift gene frequencies via interchange of individuals between populations) are the principal causes of biological evolution.

SUMMARY AND CONCLUSIONS

The gametes which function to produce the next generation in cross-fertilizing populations comprise a gene pool. If the population (gene pool) size is very large, if mutation does not occur in any direction preferentially, if there is no differential selection for genotypes, and if migrants are genotypically just like the natives, the gene pool in successive generations will remain forever unchanged, as will also the relative frequencies of genotypes. However, if any of these conditions fails to obtain, there will be a shift in the nature of the gene pool, that is, gene frequencies will change, and so will the frequencies of different genotypes, until a new equilibrium is attained.

It is suggested that not only species formation, but all of biological evolution is based upon changes in the gene pool.

REFERENCES

Dobzhansky, Th., *Evolution, Genetics, and Man*, New York, John Wiley & Sons, 1955.

Dobzhansky, Th., *Genetics and the Origin of Species*, 3rd Ed., New York, Columbia University Press, 1951.

Hardy, G. H., "Mendelian Proportions in a Mixed Population," Science, 28:49–50, 1908. Reprinted in *Classic Papers in Genetics*, Peters, J. A. (Ed.), Englewood Cliffs, N.J., Prentice-Hall, 1959, pp. 60–62, and in *Great Experiments in Biology*, Gabriel, M. L., and S. Fogel (Eds.), Englewood Cliffs, N.J., Prentice-Hall, 1955, pp. 295–297.

Li, C. C., *Human Genetics*, New York, McGraw-Hill, 1961.

THEODOSIUS DOBZHANSKY *in 1957.*

SEWALL WRIGHT *is noted for his research in physiological genetics and in the mathematics of population genetics. Photograph was taken in 1954.*

Rasmuson, M., *Genetics on the Population Level*, Stockholm, Sweden, Svenska Bokforlaget Bonniers; London, Heinemann, 1961.

Weinberg, W., "Über den Nachweiss des Vererbung beim Menschen," Jahresh. Verein f. vaterl. Naturk. in Württemberg, 64:368–382, 1908. Translated, in part, in Stern, C., "The Hardy-Weinberg Law," Science, 97:137–138, 1943.

QUESTIONS FOR DISCUSSION

26.1. Does evolution have the same causes in populations reproducing only asexually, as in those reproducing sexually? Explain.

26.2. Suppose, in a population obeying the Hardy-Weinberg rule, mutation occurred for one generation, thereby changing the composition of the gene pool. How many additional generations would be required before a new genetic equilibrium would be established? Explain.

26.3. Discuss the statement: "The Hardy-Weinberg Law is the cornerstone of evolutionary genetics."

26.4. Assuming the Hardy-Weinberg principle obtains, what is the frequency of the gene R, if its only allele R' is homozygous in the following percentage of individuals in the population: 49%? 4%? 25%? 36%?

26.5. About 70% of Americans get a bitter taste from the drug phenyl thiocarbamide (PTC), and are called "tasters." The remaining 30% of the people get no bitter taste from PTC, and are "nontasters."

All marriages between nontasters produce all nontaster offspring. All results support the view that a single pair of nonsex-linked genes determines the difference between tasters and nontasters, that dominance is complete between the only two kinds of alleles that occur, and that penetrance of the dominant allele is complete.

    a. Which of the two alleles is the dominant one?
    b. What proportion of all marriages between tasters and nontasters have
       no chance (barring mutation) of producing a nontaster child?
    c. What proportion of all marriages occurs between nontasters? tasters?

26.6. The proportion of AA individuals in a large crossbreeding population is .09. Assuming all genotypes with respect to this locus have the same reproductive potential, what proportion of the population should be heterozygous for A?

26.7. What do you suppose would happen to a population whose gene pool obeyed the Hardy-Weinberg rule for a very large number of generations? Why?

26.8. Can the same population obey the Hardy-Weinberg rule for one locus and not for another? Explain.

MUTATION AND SELECTION —
NONRANDOM MATING
AND HETEROSIS

THE composition of the gene pool is dependent upon several factors, including mutation and selection (Chapter 26). Selection acts at the phenotypic level to conserve in the population those genotypes which provide the greatest reproductive potential. Selection takes place at all stages in the life cycle of an individual. If a particular stage has been produced under the action of a haploid genotype, selection will favor the most adaptive phenotypes and thereby conserve the most adaptive haploid constitutions. If other stages in the life history involve the action of a diploid constitution, selection will favor the most adaptive phenotypes and therefore the diploid genotypes they contain. Several implications of these statements need to be specified, namely, that selection acts not upon single genes, but upon genotypes, sometimes acting upon the phenotypes produced by single genomes, and at other times, in sexually reproducing organisms, acting upon the combined phenotypic effect of two genomes. It should be noted also that what is a relatively adaptive genotype at one stage of the life cycle may be relatively ill-adaptive at another stage, regardless of whether or not these stages have the same or different ploidies. It is, of course, the total adaptiveness of all these separate features which determines the overall reproductive potential of an individual. Finally, it should be noted that in crossfertilizing populations selection favors geno-

229

types which produce maximal fitness of the population as a whole. Because selection acts this way, it may be that some portion of the population may receive genotypes which are decidedly disadvantageous to the individuals receiving them. If this is so, the same genetic components would be expected to be advantageous when present in other, more probable combinations.

Since the human being is primarily of one ploidy, diploidy, it is upon his diploid-produced phenotype that selection principally operates. If we ask, "What is the fate of mutants in the gene pool?" our answer must include knowledge of the frequency with which the mutants arise and of their effects upon reproductive potential in a diploid genotype. The phenotypic effect of a mutant gene will depend, not only upon the nature of its allele, but also upon its relationship with the nonalleles in the genotype (Chapter 7). Let us consider, in human beings, the fate in the gene pool of mutants whose over-all phenotypic effect is dominant lethal, or dominant detrimental, or recessive lethal, or recessive detrimental, insofar as selection and mutation influence their fates.

Dominant lethal mutations are lethal when heterozygous, and are eliminated from the gene pool in the same generation in which they arise. Accordingly, the *biological fitness*, *adaptive value*, or *reproductive potential* of such mutants is zero. If the normal homozygote (A_1A_1) is considered to have a selective disadvantage of 0, then the dominant lethal has complete selective disadvantage, its *selection coefficient*, s, being therefore 1. You can readily see that the *mutation frequency* or *rate*, u, to this dominant lethal condition must be equal to one half the frequency of affected individuals (A_1A_2), since each affected individual has one mutant and one normal gene. In the absence of special medical treatment, *retinoblastoma*, a kind of cancer of the eye, is an example of such a dominant lethal in man.

Achondroplastic (chondrodystrophic) dwarfism is characterized by normal head and trunk size, but shortened arms and legs, making for disproportionate dwarfism. This rare, fully penetrant (see p. 71) disease is due to the presence of a gene in heterozygous condition, which acts, therefore, as a dominant detrimental mutant. Such dwarfs (A_1A_2) produce only 20 per cent as many children as are produced by normal people. This lower reproductive potential is expressed by assigning the A_1A_2 genotype a selection coefficient, s, of .8.

The frequency of A_1A_2 in the population was found to be 10 dwarf babies in 94,075 births. This frequency must be due to the occurrence of dwarf children from normal parents, who carry new mutations to A_2, in addition to dwarf children, one of whose parents was dwarf. The gene frequency, p, of A_2 in the population must be 10/2(94,075), or .000053. From the incidence of dwarfs who were known to have normal parents, the

mutation rate, u, to A_2 was determined to be .000042. If the value s = .8 is correct, p = u/s, or .000042/.8, or .0000525, which is in excellent agreement with the value of p observed. Note that for a dominant lethal p = u because s = 1. In the present case s is less than 1, so that p is larger than u. The fact that for dwarfism p is not very much larger than u illustrates the efficiency of natural selection in eliminating such mutants from the gene pool.

The gene for *juvenile amaurotic idiocy* (a_2) has no apparent effect when heterozygous (A_1a_2), but causes homozygotes to die as children. It is, therefore, a recessive lethal mutant. Affected individuals (a_2a_2) are found with a frequency of 1/100,000, or .00001. What is the frequency of a_2 in the gene pool? As shown in Figure 27–1, the frequency at equilibrium of a_2a_2 individuals is equal to q^2. Accordingly, the frequency of a_2 (q) must be equal to $\sqrt{q^2}$, or $\sqrt{.00001}$, or about .003, while the frequency of A_1 must be 1 − .003, or .997. Note that the heterozygous carriers are 600 times more frequent than afflicted individuals. What is the mutation rate from A_1 to a_2? We have presumed that the gene pool is at equilibrium, that is, the rate at which a_2 enters the population by mutation must be equal to the rate at which it leaves the population in a_2a_2 homozygotes. Accordingly, u to a_2 must be .00001. The selection coefficient for normal individuals (A_1A_1 and A_1a_2) is 0 and for a_2a_2 is 1. We see, therefore, that at equilibrium the frequency in the gene pool of a recessive mutant

GENOTYPE	$A_1 A_1$	$A_1 a_2$	$a_2 a_2$
PHENOTYPE	Normal	Normal	Dies
FREQUENCY AT EQUILIBRIUM	p^2	$2pq$	q^2

u = Mutation rate from $A_1 \longrightarrow a_2$

$q = \sqrt{u/s}$ Here s = 1, hence $q = \sqrt{u}$

$u = 10^{-5} = 0.000{,}01$ Hence $q = \sqrt{0.000{,}01} = 0.003$

ACTUAL FREQUENCY AT EQUILIBRIUM	(p^2)	($2pq$)	(q^2)
	$(0.997)^2$	$2(0.997)(0.003)$	$(.003)^2$
	0.994	0.006	0.000,01

FIGURE 27–1.
Juvenile amaurotic idiocy.
(*See text for explanation.*)

can be expressed as $q = \sqrt{u/s}$, where s = 1 in the case of a recessive lethal. If the recessive mutant is detrimental without being lethal, s becomes less than 1 (but more than 0) and the frequency of the mutant in the gene pool becomes higher for the same mutation rate. Thus, if in the present example, s is ¼ instead of 1, q is twice as large.

In deriving the types and frequencies of genotypes in a population at equilibrium, it was presumed that marriages were at random with respect to the genotypically determined trait under consideration. What happens if the different genotypes do not marry at random? Consider the disease *phenylketonuria* (Figure 27–2) which involves a type of feeblemindedness in individuals, homozygous for a recessive gene, who cannot properly metabolize the amino acid phenylalanine. The frequency in the gene pool of the normal gene (*A*) is .99, and of the abnormal gene (*a*) is .01. In the population at equilibrium, therefore, *AA* : *Aa* : *aa* individuals will have frequencies of

9801/10,000 : 198/10,000 : 1/10,000,

respectively. Notice that *Aa* individuals are 198 times more frequent than *aa*, so that even if every *aa* did not reproduce, only one per cent of the *a* genes present in the gene pool would be eliminated each generation. This illustrates the inefficiency of selection against homozygotes for rare recessive genes, insofar as lowering the frequency of such genes is concerned. *AA* and *Aa* individuals apparently marry each other at random.

However, it is also true that feebleminded people do not marry in the population at random. But this has little effect on the distribution of genotypes in successive generations, since *aa* people have so few of all the *a* genes present in the population. You can see that it is only marriages between *Aa* individuals that are of consequence, since those are the major source of *aa* offspring.

The example of phenylketonuria shows that, when a gene is rare and apparently completely recessive, nonrandom marriage has little influence upon its frequency, or the diploid genotypes in which it is found in the population. When the mutant is relatively frequent in the population, however, it is obvious that nonrandom marriages will raise the frequencies of certain genotypes and lower others. Moreover, if there are adaptive differences for the different genotypes, the composition of the gene pool may be changed in a different direction, or at a different rate, from what would be predicted for a population mating at random. Consider two ways in which mating may be nonrandom. The first involves the tendency of phenotypically similar individuals (disregarding the sex differences) to mate, and is referred to as *assortive mating*. This kind of

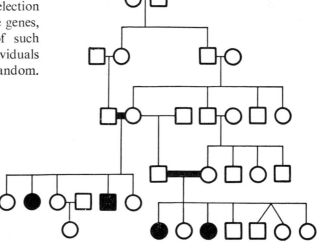

FIGURE 27–2. *Pedigree showing the occurrence of phenylketonuria among the offspring of cousin marriages (denoted by thick marriage lines)*

breeding pattern is generally true in animals and in human beings, also. The genetic result is the production of more homozygotes than would occur by chance matings.

The second departure from random mating involves *inbreeding*, the tendency for mates to be more closely related in descent than they would be, were selection of mates made at random in the population. What is the effect of inbreeding when carried out for a single generation? We can estimate this by studying what happens to the genes that are heterozygous in the parent generation. There are various degrees of inbreeding, the closest form being *self-fertilization*, which occurs in many plants. In self-fertilization, the heterozygote for a given pair of genes, *Aa*, produces progeny one half of which are homozygotes, so that heterozygosity is reduced by one half with respect to this pair of heterozygous genes. The decrease in heterozygosity due to self-fertilization can be expressed in general, as follows: the chance that an offspring will receive a particular allele in the male gamete is $\frac{1}{2}$ and the chance it will receive the same allele in the female gamete is $\frac{1}{2}$. The chance the offspring will be a homozygote for that allele, therefore, is $\frac{1}{4}$. But there is an equal chance the offspring will become homozygous for the other allele, so that there is a total chance of 50% for homozygosis attributed to this type of inbreeding. If all members of the population self-fertilize, then in each successive generation, half of the genes that were heterozygous become homozygous.

Suppose, in a portion of a population that mates at random, X% of the progeny are homozygotes. These come from matings between two heterozygotes, between two homozygotes for the same or for different alleles, and between a homozygote and a heterozygote. If the gene pool is at equilibrium, the matings that tend to increase homozygosis are counterbalanced by others which decrease it, so that X% homozygosis

remains constant generation after generation. Consider what happens in another portion of this population which happens to practice self-fertilization for one generation. Insofar as these self-fertilizing individuals are concerned, since they themselves already show X% homozygosis, their offspring will also have X% for this reason. But, if they show Z% heterozygosis, their offspring will have only $\frac{1}{2}$Z% heterozygosis, and will show a total homozygosis of X + $\frac{1}{2}$Z%. In other words, each generation of self-fertilization makes half of all heterozygous genes homozygous, and the effect of self-fertilization, in a normally random mating population, is to increase the random mating rate of homozygosis by $\frac{1}{2}$ of the rate of heterozygosis.

By how much is homozygosity increased in *brother-sister* (*sib*) *matings*? The chance that a particular gene in the male sib's father is present in the male sib is $\frac{1}{2}$, and the chance that the male sib's child will receive this is $\frac{1}{2}$. The chance for the occurrence of both events is $\frac{1}{4}$. The chance that the female sib receives and transmits this same gene to her child is also $\frac{1}{4}$. The chance that the child of the sib mating will receive two of this same allele is $\frac{1}{4} \times \frac{1}{4}$, or $\frac{1}{16}$, which is its chance of being homozygous for this gene. Since the child would have an equal chance to become a homozygote for the other allele in his grandfather and for each of the two alleles in his grandmother, this gives him $4 \times \frac{1}{16}$, or a 25% chance of homozygosis. In other words, sib matings will cause $\frac{1}{4}$ of heterozygous genes to become homozygous. As discussed above, this chance of homozygosis is additional to the chance of homozygosis which obtains for genes in the randomly mating portion of the population and which also obtains for sib matings.

Matings between individuals who have one parent in common are called *half-sib matings*. In this case, the frequency that a given allele in the common parent will pass to the male half-sib is $\frac{1}{2}$, and the frequency an offspring of this sib will receive this allele is ½. The frequency of both events occurring is, therefore, ¼. The frequency is also ¼ for these events to occur through the female half-sib, so that the frequency of a given allele becoming homozygous from a half-sib mating is ¼ × ¼, or ⅟₁₆. Since the other allele in the common parent could, in this way, also become homozygous ⅟₁₆ of the time, the combined chance of homozygosity for half-sib matings is ⅛. So, ⅛ of heterozygous genes become homozygous due to this type of inbreeding.

The amount by which heterozygosity is reduced because of inbreeding is called the *inbreeding coefficient*, F. In the case of *cousin marriage*, F is ⅟₁₆. The values of F for more complicated pedigrees can also be worked out.

We have seen that all forms of inbreeding increase homozygosity. Let us now calculate the consequence of cousin marriage upon the frequency of phenylketonuria. The frequency of heterozygotes per 10,000 people is 198 (see p. 231). Cousin marriage would reduce heterozygosity by ⅟₁₆, or 12 individuals, of which six would be normal (*AA*) and six affected (*aa*). Since random mating would produce one affected individual per 10,000, cousin marriages would bring the total number of affected homozygotes in this population to seven (six from inbreeding, plus one from random breeding). Accordingly, there

is a sevenfold greater chance for phenylketonuric children from cousin marriages as from marriages between unrelated parents.

An additional example can be given, of the increased risk of defect as a consequence of cousin marriages. In a Japanese population (Figure 27–3), congenital malformations, stillbirths, and infant deaths are 24–48 per cent higher in cousin marriages than when parents are unrelated. Since defects such as these are known to be due, in some cases, to recessive genes in homozygous condition, these data support the view that homozygosis resulting from inbreeding can produce detrimental results. The fact that inbreeding produces homozygosis, and that homozygosis can lead to the appearance of defects, does not automatically mean that inbreeding is disadvantageous under all circumstances. For, while many individuals become homozygous for detrimental genes as a result of inbreeding, just as many become homozygous for the normal alleles. The success of self-fertilizing species is testimony to the advantage of homozygosity at least in these species.

In populations that normally cross-fertilize, however, inbreeding usually results in a loss of vigor. This loss of vigor is directly connected to homozygosis. In what way is it theoretically possible to explain the adaptive superiority of heterozygotes, which is usually known as *heterosis* or *hybrid vigor*?

FIGURE 27–3. *Increased risk of genetic defect with cousin marriages.* (*Data from Hiroshima and Nagasaki.*)

	Frequency from Unrelated Parents	Increase in Frequency with Cousin Marriage	Per cent Increase
CONGENITAL MALFORMATION	.011	.005	48
STILLBIRTHS	.025	.006	24
INFANT DEATHS	.023	.008	34

Consider the three genotypic alternatives, AA, AA', $A'A'$ relative to their phenotypic effects. If A is completely dominant to A', and $A'A'$ is less vigorous than AA and AA', homozygosis resultant from breeding of AA' will clearly lead to detriment. This remains true even if A is incompletely dominant to A' or shows no dominance to it. In all these cases, the heterozygote is superior to one of the homozygotes. The second possibility remains, however, that the heterozygote, AA', may be of greater adaptive value than either homozygote. Suppose, to illustrate this, that A is pleiotropic and has a relatively very adaptive effect with respect to trait M, but a relatively less adaptive effect with respect to trait N, while its mutant allele has the reverse effect, namely, being relatively less adaptive for M, and relatively more adaptive for N. The heterozygote would, in the event of no dominance, be superior to either homozygote. Heterosis can be produced, therefore, if the heterozygote is superior to either one homozygote or both homozygotes.

The first type of heterotic effect can be demonstrated by crossing two pure lines homozygous for different detrimental recessives ($AA\ bb\ CC\ dd\ EE \times aa\ bb\ CC\ DD\ EE$). The F_1 ($Aa\ bb\ CC\ Dd\ EE$) will be uniform yet more vigorous (having four different normal alleles) than either parent (each of which had only three different normal alleles) because the dominant alleles hide the detrimental effects of the recessive alleles.

The second type of heterotic effect can be illustrated in human beings. As mentioned in Chapter 10, homozygotes for the gene for sickle cell anemia ($A'A'$) usually die from anemia before adolescence. AA individuals are of normal blood type, while AA' individuals are either normal or have a slight anemia. In certain countries, the frequency of A' in the gene pool follows expectation for a recessive lethal gene. In other countries, however, A' is more frequent than would be expected. How is this difference explained? It turns out that the heterozygote AA' is more resistant than the AA homozygote to certain kinds of malaria. Of course, in nonmalarial countries, A' confers no antimalarial advantage and so the fitness of the heterozygote $(1 - s)$ is lower than that of the normal homozygote (1), while the $A'A'$ individual has a fitness of 0. As expected, therefore, sickle cell anemia is rare or absent in most of the world where certain forms of malaria are absent.

On the other hand, in certain malarial countries, even though heterozygotes may be slightly anemic, the advantage of being resistant to malaria produces a greater overall fitness than does the AA genotype. Here the fitness of the heterozygote, AA', is 1 and that of the normal homozygote, AA, is $1 - s_1$. Mutant homozygotes, $A'A'$, have a fitness of $1 - s_2$, where s_2 equals 1, since all $A'A'$ die (even should $A'A'$ be extremely resistant to malaria). What natural selection does in this case is to maintain both A and A' in the gene pool, A' having a frequency equal to $\dfrac{s_1}{s_1 + s_2}$. This fraction can be read "the advantage of A' (as shown by the advantage of AA' over AA) divided by the total disadvantage of A and A'." You see, then, that when the heterozygote is more adaptive than either homozygote, showing heterosis in this way, natural selection will maintain a gene in the gene pool even though it is lethal when homozygous.

It should be noted that while we have discussed heterosis in terms of the phenotypic effects of the members of a pair of alleles, this does not mean that the unit of heterotic action is always a single pair of genes. Since we have already seen, in Chapters 7 and 8, that different pairs of genes interact in various ways in producing phenotypes, it would be no surprise to find that heterosis occurs as the result of the effect of certain combinations of nonalleles and alleles.

It has been found, in D. pseudoobscura,

FIGURE 27–4. *The variability of normal corn is being pointed out by* JAMES F. CROW. (*Photographed in 1959 by The Calvin Company.*)

that natural populations contain certain paracentric inversions. When laboratory populations are initiated, containing some individuals with the normal chromosome arrangement and others with a particular one of these inversions, in some cases, the population comes to contain only normal chromosomes after a number of generations has passed. In such cases, the inversion chromosome behaves like a detrimental gene which provides no advantage when heterozygous, and is eliminated from the gene pool. When other particular inversions are tested this way, however, an equilibrium is reached in which the normal and inverted chromosomes are both retained in the gene pool. In these cases, the inversion heterozygote is adaptively superior to either homozygote, showing heterosis, just as does the gene for sickling in malarial countries. It is not easy to de-

cide the genetic basis for heterosis in such cases, however, since hybrid vigor could be due to the genes gained or lost at the time the inversion was initially produced, or it could be due to position effect, or to individual genes or groups of genes contained within the inverted region. (It should be recalled that individuals with paracentric inversions are not at a reproductive disadvantage in *Drosophila*. Should a heterotic system exist or develop in paracentric inversion heterozygotes, based upon the action of several genes contained within the inverted region, this heterotic arrangement would tend to remain intact in the heterozygote, because of the failure of single crossovers within the inverted region to enter the haploid egg nucleus.)

Finally, it would be appropriate to describe briefly how hybrid vigor has been applied to agriculture, since it has been estimated that the use of hybrid corn alone has already enriched society by a billion dollars. You might ask: What is wrong with normal corn? The answer is that it is too variable in quality and vigor (Figure 27–4). The variability can be decreased by inbreeding, but unfortunately this also results in loss of vigor or other desirable traits. The way to overcome this impasse is first to obtain inbred lines, which are uniform because they are homozygous and which carry different desirable dominant genes (yet are also homozygous for different undesirable recessive genes). If different inbred lines are crossed, the F_1 will be multiply heterozygous, uniform, and more vigorous than either parental inbred line.

Accordingly, hybrids can be made between two selected inbred lines. But while these F_1 plants are vigorous and uniform, they come from seeds produced on ears grown on one of the less vigorous inbred lines. For this reason such seeds are not sufficiently abundant to make it economical to use them in raising crops of corn. This difficulty is overcome in practice (Figure 27–5) by first making two different single cross hybrids by crossing four selected inbred lines two by two. Then the two hybrids are crossed. Seeds produced by this *double cross* are plentiful, since they are formed on a vigorous single cross hybrid plant, and can be sold inexpensively to farmers for planting. Breeding procedures resulting in hybrid vigor are applied to many plants and animals; heterosis is of great economic importance.

SUMMARY AND CONCLUSIONS

Two of the factors which decide the fate of a mutant in the gene pool are mutation and selection. For equal mutation rates, the lower the reproductive potential the mutant causes, the lower is the frequency of the mutant in the gene pool. Specific examples of rare mutants are described which lower reproductive fitness by being dominant lethal, dominant detrimental, recessive lethal, and recessive detrimental.

Nonrandom breeding, by assortive mating or inbreeding, increases the rate of homozygosis. The per-generation rate of reduction in heterozygosity due to inbreeding is ½ for self-fertilization, ¼ for sib matings, ⅛ for half-sib matings, and ¹⁄₁₆ for cousin matings. Homozygosis in normally cross-fertilizing individuals leads to loss of vigor, while heterozygosis is accompanied by heterosis, or hybrid vigor.

Heterosis is the phenotypic result of gene interaction, and occurs because the heterozygote either serves to mask different detrimental recessives which are homozygous in the parents, or is adaptively superior to both types of homozygote. Heterosis is of great economic importance.

REFERENCES

Allison, A. C., "Sickle Cells and Evolution," Scient. Amer., 195:87–94, 1956.

Crow, J. F., *Genetics Notes*, 4th Ed., Minneapolis, Burgess, 1960.

Dobzhansky, Th., *Evolution, Genetics and Man*, New York, John Wiley & Sons, 1955.

Dobzhansky, Th., *Genetics and the Origin of Species*, 3rd Ed., New York, Columbia University Press, 1951.

Gowen, J. W. (Ed.), *Heterosis*, Ames, Iowa, Iowa State College Press, 1952.

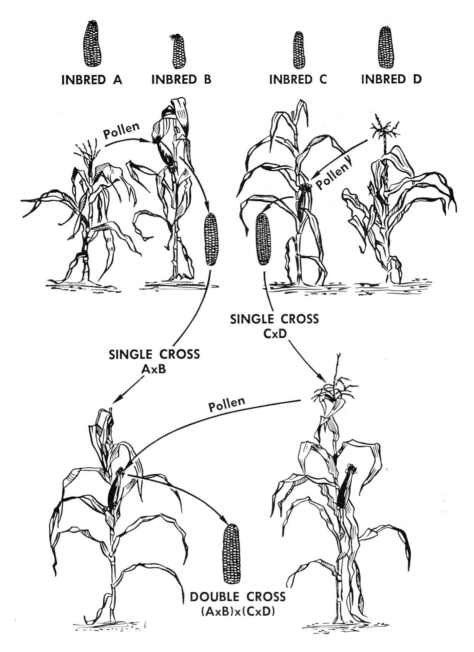

INBRED A   INBRED B   INBRED C   INBRED D

Pollen

Pollen

SINGLE CROSS
CxD

SINGLE CROSS
AxB

Pollen

DOUBLE CROSS
(AxB)x(CxD)

FIGURE 27–5. *The production of commercial hybrid corn by the "double cross" breeding procedure.*

QUESTIONS FOR DISCUSSION

27.1. In each of the following cases, explain whether the rate with which a particular allele mutates is of primary importance in shifting its frequency in the population, when this gene:

        a. is a dominant lethal in early developmental stages.
        b. is a recessive lethal.
        c. expresses itself phenotypically only after the reproductive period of the individual.
        d. is very rare.
        e. occurs in small cross-fertilizing populations.

27.2. Can the adaptive value of the same gene differ:

        a. in haploids and diploids?
        b. in males and females?
        c. in two diploid cells of the same organism?

Explain your decision in each case.

27.3. Other things being equal, what would happen to the frequency in the gene pool, of a dominant mutant whose selection coefficient changed from 1 to $\frac{1}{4}$? What would happen in this respect if the mutant was completely recessive?

27.4. If persons carrying detrimental mutants fail to marry, these particular genes are removed from the gene pool. Under what conditions is the failure to marry likely to reduce appreciably the frequency of detrimental mutants in the gene pool?

27.5. Are inbreeding and assortive mating mutually exclusive departures from random mating (*panmixis*)? Explain.

27.6. Explain why the inbreeding coefficient, F, is $\frac{1}{16}$ for cousin marriages.

27.7. Suppose the frequencies of *A* and *a* are .3 and .7, respectively, in a population obeying the Hardy-Weinberg rule and in which mating is at random.

        a. What per cent of the population is composed of homozygotes with respect to these genes?
        b. What would be your answer to a. after one generation in which hybrids could mate only with hybrids?
        c. What effect would the conditions in b. have upon the composition of the gene pool?

27.8. Discuss, from a genetic standpoint, the advantages and disadvantages of cousin marriages in man.

27.9. In Thailand, heterozygotes for a mutant gene that results in the formation of hemoglobin E are more frequent in the population than would be expected if the Hardy-Weinberg equilibrium obtained. How can you explain this?

FIGURE 28–1.
Chromosomal complement of D. pseudoobscura.

Chapter **28**

MUTATIONAL LOADS AND THEIR CONSEQUENCES TO POPULATIONS

ROSOPHILA PSEUDOOBSCURA is a fruit fly commonly found in northern Mexico and western United States. When collected in the wild almost all individuals are alike phenotypically, except for the sex differences, appearing "wild-type" or normal. We cannot accept such a phenotypic uniformity as evidence for genotypic uniformity, however, since we already know of the possibility that a wild-type population may appear uniform yet contain concealed genetic variability in the form of isoalleles or recessive mutants having a point mutational origin. In fact, we have already indicated the existence in natural populations of *Drosophila* of isoalleles (Chapter 9), of pericentric inversions and reciprocal translocations (Chapter 21), and of paracentric inversions (Chapter 27). What we would like to have is an estimate of the total amount of genetic variability present in a natural population. This can be studied using *D. pseudoobscura*.[1]

D. pseudoobscura has five pairs of chromosomes, composed of the usual X and Y sex chromosomes, three pairs of large rod-shaped autosomes (II, III, IV), and a dotlike pair of autosomes (V) (Figure 28–1). There are a number of laboratory strains of this species whose chromosomes are marked by various mutants of point and rearrangement type. It is possible, therefore, to perform a series of crosses between laboratory strains

[1] Based upon work of Th. Dobzhansky and collaborators.

and flies collected in the wild which yield information on the presence of mutants in the wild-type flies. In practice, autosomes II, III, and IV of wild-type flies were individually made homozygous to detect the presence of recessive mutants (cf. Figure 9–4) that are *lethal* (causing death of all individuals before adulthood), or *semilethal* (causing more than 90 and less than 100 per cent mortality before adulthood), or *subvital* (causing significantly less than normal but greater than 10 per cent survival to adulthood), or sterile to females (*female sterile*) or sterile to males (*male sterile*).

The results of such a study are summarized in Figure 28–2. About 25% of all autosomes tested this way carried a recessive lethal or semilethal mutant. Recessive subvital mutants were found in about 40% of III chromosomes tested, and in more than 90% of tested II's and IV's, while mutants causing sterility were present in 4–14% of tested chromosomes. The natural population clearly carries a tremendous load of detrimental mutants.

How is this load of mutants distributed in the fly population? Consider first one pair of the autosomes tested. Each member has a 25% chance of carrying a lethal or semilethal, and a 75% chance of being free of such a mutant. The chance that both members of a pair of chromosomes will carry a lethal or semilethal is $(0.25)^2$, or 6.25%. You cannot tell from the data presented whether the lethals and semilethals found in

239

FIGURE 28–2. *Genetic load in natural populations of* D. pseudoobscura. (*After Th. Dobzhansky.*)

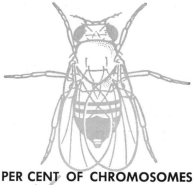

MUTANT TYPE	PER CENT OF CHROMOSOMES		
	II	III	IV
Lethal or Semilethal	25	25	26
Subvital	93	41	95
Female Sterile	11	14	4
Male Sterile	8	11	12

a particular pair of autosomes are allelic (in which case nearly 6% of zygotes in nature would fail to become adults because of homozygosity for the mutants), or whether the mutants involve different loci (in which case 6.25% of zygotes would be dihybrid for linked mutants of this kind), or whether some combination of these two alternatives obtains. In any case, the chance that both members of a given chromosome pair would be free of lethals or semilethals would be $(0.75)^2$, or 56%.

What portion of the population would carry no lethal or semilethal on either member of autosomes II, III, and IV? This is calculated to be $(0.75)^2 \times (0.75)^2 \times (0.75)^2$, or about 17%. If we consider the fact that the X and V chromosomes can also carry such mutants, the frequency of lethal-semilethal-free individuals in nature is still lower. When, now, the subvital mutants (which are an even more frequent class of mutant) and also sterility mutants are considered, it becomes clear that very few, if any, flies in natural populations are free of a load of detrimental mutants.

What is the mutant load in man? We have already discussed the fact that the vast majority of mutants are detrimental in homozygous condition (Chapter 24). Death rate data are available for a population in rural France in the last century which include fetal death, and all childhood and very early adult deaths. What we want to compare is the death rate of offspring from unrelated parents with that found from cousin marriages.[2] The death rate of progeny from unrelated parents is .12, while it is .25 from cousin marriages. We shall not be concerned here with establishing the genetic or nongenetic cause of death in the normal outcrossed human population. It can be assumed, however, that the excess mortality of .13 (.25 − .12) has a genetic basis in the excess homozygosity which is consequent to cousin marriage. This is a reasonable assumption in the absence of any other known nongenetic factor which would tend to cause more or fewer offspring to die from marriages between cousins than from marriages between unrelated parents. (These data would have a nongenetic bias, if, for example, it was a custom — which it is not — that all children from cousin marriages are purposely starved.)

Apparently, then, 13% more offspring died because their parents were cousins than would have died normally. What is the total amount of recessive lethal effect present in the population in heterozygous condition? This can be calculated as follows. Recall (from Chapter 27) that, of all heterozygous genes, an extra $\frac{1}{16}$ become homozygous in offspring of cousin marriages. Half of the $\frac{1}{16}$, or $\frac{1}{32}$, must have become homozygous for the normal genes and half of $\frac{1}{16}$, or $\frac{1}{32}$, for their abnormal alleles. So, to estimate the total heterozygous content of mutants which would kill if they were homozygous, it is necessary to multiply .13 by 32. The resultant value of about 4 represents a 400% chance that the ordinary individual carried in heterozygous condition a genetic load of detrimental mutants which would be lethal if homozygous. In other words, on the average, each person carried four *lethal equivalents* in heterozygous condition, or, four times the amount of detriment it would

take to kill if the genes involved were made homozygous.

This analysis does not reveal how many genes are involved in the production of the four lethal equivalents. In some individuals these might be due to the presence in heterozygous condition of 4 recessive lethals, or 8 mutants having 50% viability, or 16 mutants with 25% viability, etc., or any combination of detrimental mutants whose total is four lethal equivalents. It should be realized that, since the last century, improvements in the environment (in housing, nutrition, and medical care) make it most likely that the effect of these same mutants in present-day society would be expressed by somewhat less than four lethal equivalents. Similarly, in the light of such progress, the detrimental effects of these mutants in heterozygous condition would be expected to be somewhat less at present than they were a century ago. Accordingly, in the last century, a hypothetical homozygous combination which, because of variable penetrance and expressivity, produced no detectable effect 25% of the time, detrimental effect (but not lethality prior to maturity) 15% of the time, and lethality before maturity 60% of the time, might at the present time have the respective values of 50%, 10%, 40%. In the earlier period this combination would have produced .6 of a lethal equivalent and at present .4. Notice also that the detriment which is not lethal before maturity would also be reduced, changing from 15% to 10%, or, speaking in terms of *detrimental equivalents*, what was .15 would now be .10. It is clear that the genes responsible for lethal equivalents and for detrimental equivalents must be the same, at least in part.

It is equally clear that present-day man also carries a load of mutants. Some of those transmitted to him arose in his parents (probably two of each five zygotes carry a newly arisen mutant, as mentioned on p. 200), and others arose in his more remote an-

[2] Based upon an analysis of N. E. Morton, J. F. Crow, and H. J. Muller.

cestry. It has been calculated[3] that, on the average, each of us is heterozygous for what is probably a minimum of about eight mutant genes received in these ways. What happens to this load of mutants in successive generations?

In order to predict, in a general way, the fate of the "usual" mutant in the population, it is necessary for us to determine the phenotypic effect of the "usual" mutant. Since the typical mutant is detrimental, at least to some degree, when homozygous, the homozygous condition tends to eliminate the mutant from the gene pool. But we have seen in Chapter 27 that there are two opposite effects possible for mutants when heterozygous — either the heterozygote is superior to both homozygotes (as is found for the gene for sickling in malarial countries), or the heterozygote is somewhat inferior to the nonmutant homozygote (as is true for most heterozygotes for point recessive lethals). In the former case, the heterotic effect would tend to increase the frequency of the mutant, so that both the normal and mutant variants would be retained in the population at equilibrium. Such a population, which normally retained in its gene pool more than one genic (or chromosomal) alternative, would, therefore, exhibit *balanced polymorphism.* In the case where the heterozygote shows detriment, the heterozygous condition would increase the rate at which the mutant was eliminated from the gene pool.

Experimental evidence in *Drosophila*[4] and a statistical analysis of data for man[5] support the view that the great majority of point mutants are detrimental when heterozygous. We shall, therefore, consider that the usual mutant is not heterotic when heterozygous, but is detrimental to a degree that is some-

---

[3] By H. J. Muller and by H. Slatis.
[4] Based upon work of H. J. Muller and coworkers, C. Stern and coworkers, J. F. Crow and coworkers, I. H. Herskowitz and R. C. Baumiller, and others.
[5] Based upon an analysis by N. E. Morton.

what less than it would be when homozygous. How is such a mutant gene eliminated from the population? It need not be eliminated by producing the death of an individual, although it is sometimes removed this way. A more general way to express the removal of a mutant gene from the gene pool is by *genetic death*, the failure to produce descendants carrying the mutant. Thus, all the genes in an individual, whether they be normal or mutant, suffer genetic death if that individual fails to produce children. Since mutants are stable, they are removed from the gene pool only by genetic death, or, rarely, by mutation of the mutant. A person carrying a dominant lethal like retinoblastoma suffers genetic death (as well as physical death). In this case, the mutant gene is eliminated from the population the generation in which it arises by mutation; it shows, therefore, only one generation of *persistence*. The dominant mutant for achondroplasia produces an average reproductive potential of .2 as compared to normal and will persist for five generations, on the average, before suffering genetic death. This means that each generation, in a population maintaining approximately the same size in successive generations, the achondroplastic individual has an 80% chance of not transmitting the mutant. So, when this mutant arises, sometimes it will fail to be transmitted the very first generation, at other times it will suffer genetic death the fifth generation, and at still other times at the tenth. But, on the average, the mutant will persist five generations before being lost. You realize that even though genetic drift and migration can cause fluctuations in the frequency of the mutant, the principle of persistence will still obtain.

Consider the fate in the population of a rare recessive lethal gene like that involved in producing juvenile amaurotic idiocy. Each time that homozygosis for this gene occurs, it results in genetic death, and two mutant genes are eliminated from the gene pool. But consider the fate of the heterozygotes who are 600 times more frequent (Chapter 27), and carry 300 times as many of these genes as do the homozygotes. Since it is generally true that heterozygotes for a recessive lethal suffer genetic death about four per cent of the time (see p. 211), approximately .04 × 600, or 24, heterozygous people would suffer genetic death, involving the removal of 48 genes, of which 24 would be the recessive lethal allele. Accordingly, 12 times as many of these particular recessive lethal genes suffer genetic death in the heterozygote than in the homozygote, even though the reduction in reproductive potential in a group of the former type of individuals is only $\frac{1}{25}$ of what it is in a group of the latter type.

It is apparent that the rarer a mutant is, the smaller will be the proportion of all genetic deaths it causes in homozygotes, and the larger the proportion that it causes in heterozygotes. For rare mutants, then, natural selection removes mutant genes primarily via the genetic death of heterozygotes, the small amount of detriment when heterozygous being more important from the population or gene pool standpoint than the greater detrimental effect when homozygous. However, each mutant is harmful to the population to the same degree, in terms of its effect on reproductive potential, in that each is eventually the cause of a genetic death, at which time it is removed from the gene pool. Thus, hypoploidy which acts as a dominant lethal persists only one generation before it causes a genetic death. A point mutation which produces a reproductive disadvantage of only $\frac{1}{10}\%$ will persist, on the average, 1000 generations, at which time it will be the cause of genetic death.

As a matter of fact, speaking not in terms of biological fitness, but in terms of the total amount of suffering to which a human population is subject, point mutants with the smallest heterozygous detriment are the most harmful type of mutant. Consider, on one hand, the gross chromosomal abnormality which kills *in utero*. This destroys a life early, so that the individual involved has not suffered very long timewise. In this case, also, the parents may suffer relatively little, for such deaths may occur so early as to result in abortions which pass unnoticed. Consider, on the other hand, the effect of heterozygous point mutants in individuals who are past the reproductive age. These people already have or have not suffered genetic death, but continue, nevertheless, to be subjected to the previously produced, and newly produced, small phenotypic detriment of heterozygosity which adds to their aches, pains, and disease susceptibility. In this respect, then, the mutant with a smaller effect on reproductive potential causes more suffering than one with a larger effect, for the longer the persistence, the more damage that is done in postreproductive life.

You might at first suppose that the amount of gene-caused human suffering can be reduced through the practice of medicine. This is true, in terms of the individual being treated. For there is no doubt that the individual who is diabetic for genetic reasons, and who is given insulin, is better off than he would be without this medicine. But remember that this medicine does not cure the genetic defect. Moreover, the medicine, by increasing the diabetic's reproductive potential, serves to increase the persistence of the mutants involved, so that the genetic death which must eventually occur to remove the mutant is only postponed to a later generation, each additional generation requiring the same medication. It would be true that the total amount of human suffering also would be reduced, until the time of genetic extinction of the mutant, if in fact the medicine completely normalized the genetic defect. But to do this would require that the medicine replace the primary product(s) of the defective gene with that of the normal, in order to normalize all of the pleiotropic effects of the mutant. However, insofar as most, if not all, current medicines act later than this in the pedigree of causes (Chapter 10), they serve to alleviate some detrimental effects, but not others, and in this way cause an increase in the totality of human suffering by increasing persistence. This situation will persist until genetics and medicine have advanced somewhat further than they have at present.

In view of the foregoing you will agree that it is primarily the euploid or nearly euploid mutants which persist in the gene pool, and it must be these which are primarily responsible for changes in its composition during the course of evolution. By far the most common, and hence most important, class of mutants of this type, is the point mutant.

You may have noticed, in Chapter 27, that it was only suggested that mutations provide the raw materials for biological evolution. Our hesitance in specifying that evolution is the natural outcome of changes in gene pools was based upon the observation presented earlier that the great majority of mutants, including point mutants, are harmful in homozygous or hemizygous condition. In the present Chapter and in Chapter 24, we have indicated that most mutants are also detrimental when heterozygous. Under these circumstances how can mutation provide the more adaptive genotypes so necessary for evolution to take place as a result of changes in the gene pool? This dilemma is resolved in the light of two facts. It is true, in a given genotype under a given set of environmental conditions, that the great majority of point mutants are detrimental, and that perhaps only one point mutant in a thousand increases the reproductive potential of its carrier ever so slightly. Yet, provided the mutation rate is not too large and provided there is sufficient genetic

recombination, these rare beneficial mutants offer the population the opportunity to become better adapted. The second point is that mutants which lower biological fitness under one set of environmental conditions may be more advantageous than the normal genes under different environmental circumstances. So, for example, a mutant like vestigial wings in *Drosophila* is clearly inferior to its normal genetic alternative in an environment where flight ability is advantageous, but this mutant might be advantageous for *Drosophila* living on a small island where flight is not only unnecessary but harmful, where insects that fly can be lost by being blown out to sea. As a second example of this, we can mention the fact that several decades ago the environment was DDT-free, and mutants which conferred immunity to DDT were doubtless less adaptive than the normal genetic alternatives present. But once DDT was introduced into the insect environment, such mutants, even if they were detrimental in other respects, provided a tremendous over-all reproductive advantage over their alternatives, so that they became established in the population as the new wild-type genes. Still other examples could be cited involving microorganisms, where mutants occur that confer resistance to antibiotics; in an antibiotic-free environment these mutants would be less adaptive than the genes normally present.

It becomes clear, then, that mutation provides the opportunity for a population to become better adapted to its present set of environmental circumstances. It also provides the raw materials needed to extend the population's range to different environments, which already exist in some other territory or which will arise through change in the environment of its present territory. A population that is already very well adapted to its environment is appreciably harmed by the occurrence of mutation. But the environments in different territories differ, and the environment in a given territory will eventually change, so that a nonmutating population that is successful at one time will normally eventually face extinction in the future. Mutation, therefore, is the price paid by a population for future adaptiveness in the same or a different environment. We can now appreciate that mutation and selection, together with genetic drift and migration, represent the principal factors responsible for the origin of more adaptive genotypes. We can also appreciate better the advantage that genetic recombination provides in speeding up the production of adaptive genotypes, and the importance of the genetic regulation of mutability.

In view of what has already been presented, it is not at all difficult to predict the consequences of increasing the mutation rate in human beings. There can be no doubt that the exposure of human populations, to manmade penetrating radiations and certain reactive chemical substances, is increasing his mutation rate. Manmade, as well as spontaneous, mutations can occur in either the somatic line or the germ line. Somatic mutations are, of course, restricted to the person in which they occur. The earlier the mutation occurs in a person's life history, the larger will be the sector of somatic tissue to which the mutated cell gives rise.

Suppose a mutagen causes mutation in a certain percentage of all cells. If these mutant cells are in an adult they will usually be surrounded by nonmutant ones, of the same tissue, whose action would usually suffice to produce a near-normal effect. A smaller number of cells would be mutated in an embryo than in an adult. However, the mutant embryonic cells could later give rise to whole tissues or organs which would be defective, and in which no compensatory action of normal tissue would be possible. Furthermore, insofar as many mutants affect the rate of cell division, the earlier in development they occur, the more abnormal will be the size of the structure to be produced. It becomes understandable, then, even if developmental and postdevelopmental stages are equally mutable, that somatic mutations are more damaging to the individual, the earlier they occur in its development.

Almost all somatic damage is done by newly arisen mutants in heterozygous condition, since mutation involves loci which are usually nonmutant in the other genome. Although somatic mutants cannot be transmitted to the next generation, they can lower the reproductive potential of their carriers, and in this way affect the gene pool for the next generation.

Mutational damage to somatic cells depends upon whether or not the cell subsequently divides. Certain highly differentiated cells in the human body, like nerve cells, or the cells of the inner lining of the small intestine, do not divide. It is ordinarily difficult to detect mutations in such cells, since they have no progeny cells which can be classified as mutant and nonmutant. Such cells may be more or less mutable than cells which still retain the ability to divide, but in any case a variety of mutations can occur in them. These can include point mutations that inactivate genes or change the type of allele that is present, as well as structural rearrangements of all sizes. Nevertheless, the cell will remain euploid or nearly euploid because no cell division follows. Accordingly, phenotypic detriment to nondividing cells must be due almost entirely to point mutants in heterozygous condition and to position effect. (It is likely that position effect occurs in human beings.) Although the functioning of nondividing cells may be considerably impaired for these reasons, so that they may behave as though they were aging prematurely, their sudden and immediate death due to mutation is probably very rare.

The same mutations can occur in somatic

cells that divide as occur in nondividing cells, but in this case, aneuploidy can result following nuclear division (recall the discussion of aneuploidy in Chapters 18 and 19). In dividing cells, most of the phenotypic damage is the result of aneuploidy, and most of this is the consequence of single breakages that fail to restitute, at least for those mutation-inducing agents which are capable of breaking chromosomes. (It may be noted that all known agents that increase the point mutation rate also break chromosomes.)

We should not consider the preceding discussion of the somatic effects of mutation as a digression from the main aims of this Chapter, because such cells actually comprise a population which has been produced by asexual reproduction (cell division). Let us now consider, in a general way, the consequences of increasing the frequency of mutations in the human germ line. The earlier that mutation occurs in the germ line, the greater will be the portion of all germ cells produced which carry the mutant. Of course, the upper limit of gametes carrying a particular induced mutant is usually 50 per cent. Consider the effect of exposing the gonads to manmade high-energy radiation (Figure 28–3). Before the exposure to manmade radiation, the load of mutants is presumably at equilibrium, the rate of origin of mutants equaling the rate of their loss via genetic death. Starting with the first generation to receive the additional radiation exposure, the mutant load increases each generation until a new equilibrium is reached. At that point the higher number

of genetic deaths will equal the higher number of new mutants. If at some still later generation, the extra radiation exposure ceased, the mutational load would decrease gradually (because of variations in persistence) via genetic deaths, until the old equilibrium were reached once again.

It has become very important to learn in detail the genetic effects of high-energy radiation to which human populations are being subjected either purposely or circumstantially. In order to make the best evaluation, we would like to know, among other things, the precise way in which the energy of various radiations is distributed in tissue, the exact amount of gonadal exposure to radiations of different types, the kinds and frequencies of the different types of mutation each of these radiations would produce in the different stages of gametogenesis in males and in females, the detriment of the induced mutants in hetero- and homozygous condition, the exact proportions of all mutants that are heterotic, and their amount of heterosis, as well as the persistence of these mutants. We certainly do not have, at present, as much information about any one of these factors as we would like to have, but available information along these lines can already give us approximate answers (see references at the end of this Chapter). In the discussion following, it should be realized, therefore, that all figures used may be in error by as much as a factor of two or more.

It has been a practice to discuss the germ line effect of radiation in terms of the amount

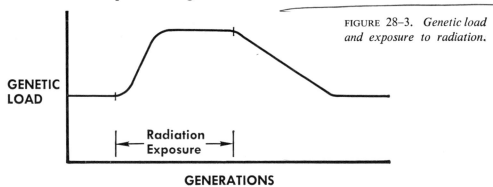

FIGURE 28–3. *Genetic load and exposure to radiation.*

of increase any particular exposure would produce in our spontaneous mutation rate. The general impression is held that we, as a species, are already adapted to the mutation rate ordinarily produced by nonmanmade mutagenic agents, and that if man causes this rate to double through his own activity, this will not pose a threat to his survival as a species! Accordingly, the question becomes, how much manmade radiation would be needed to produce as many mutations as occur normally? A United Nations' report calculated that about 30 rads (roughly equal to 30 r) would be sufficient to double the human spontaneous mutation rate. This is called the *doubling dose.* It is reckoned that in a population of one million people (which is the approximate size of the population in the St. Louis area), 1 rad delivered to the gonads or sex organs of each person would produce between 100 and 4,000 mutants which would be transmitted to future generations. This 1 rad of gonadal exposure for one generation would result in the birth of 100 to 4,000 people with new heterozygous mutants, the individuals showing the effects being spread out over the course of many generations. Only a part of the genetic deaths from these mutants would occur in the first generation, and these would not be evident when added to the number of genetic deaths consequent to spontaneous mutation. If the 1 rad gonadal exposure were repeated in every generation, eventually an equilibrium would be established, in which in each generation there would be 100 to 4,000 people per million showing the effects of radiation-induced mutants in the form of genetic death. However, since the kinds of phenotypic effects produced by the radiation-induced mutants would be the same as those from mutants which occur normally, one would not be able to recognize the particular people who were hurt by the radiation.

What part of our normal load of mutants comes from naturally occurring penetrating radiation? Since human beings receive about 5 rads in the course of a reproductive generation, that is in 30 years, it is possible that as little as $\frac{5}{30}$ of $\frac{1}{6}$ of our mutations are normally radiation-induced.

How much additional radiation are we exposed to in the course of medical treatment? It has been estimated that each person in the United States would receive, if medical use of radiation continued at its present level, a total dose to the sex cells of about 3 r per generation. Of course, while some people get no such amount of radiation, others get considerably more. But this average radiation dose to the germ cells from medical uses alone is 60% of the amount we receive spontaneously, and is raising our mutation rate about 10% above the spontaneous rate. With the increase, in the years to come, of the use of radiation for diagnosis and therapy, this amount of medical radiation might become greatly increased. Already, in a single year, radioactive materials were given in one million medical treatments.

How many germ-line mutations are being produced by the radiation associated with fallout following atomic explosions? This is not an easy question to answer. For some radiation could reach the gonads from the fallout on the ground, and other radiation could come from what is breathed in, or from what is included with the food. In the case of fallout taken in with food, the distribution of particular radioactive substances in the body will make a large difference in the amount of radiation reaching the sex cells. In this respect, three most important radioactive substances in fallout are cesium-137, strontium-90, and carbon-14. Because of its distribution, cesium-137 is expected to produce more gonadal radiation from ingested fallout than does strontium-90. This is so because cesium is distributed through the tissues more or less evenly, including the gonads, while strontium is preferentially localized in bone.

It should be noted that the period of time over which mutations are produced is different for these different radioactive chemicals. For relatively short-lived radioactive substances like strontium and cesium, the induction of new mutations would be restricted almost entirely to a few generations following the explosions that produced them. This may be compared with the distribution in time of the mutations produced by carbon-14. Carbon-14 has a half-life of 6,000 years. So, if the exposure were unchanged, even 200 generations from now there would be about half as many mutations produced, as there will be in the generation most mutated by the bombs already exploded. Accordingly, because of its abundance and long half-life, carbon-14, before it decays to nitrogen, has been calculated to deliver to the gonads 4 to 17 times as much radiation as cesium and strontium combined. This will produce proportionally more point mutations.

In the United States National Academy of Sciences — National Research Council report of 1956 (see References), the gonadal dose expected from fallout, if weapons of the same type continued to be tested at the same rate, was given as about 0.1 rad in the next 30 years. On the basis of the United Nations report, this would cause approximately 10 to 400 mutations per million people. How much modification does this figure now need to bring it up to date? Several considerations need to be taken into account. One is carbon-14, whose long half-life was not taken into account in that report. Another is the changed rate of testing, which was such that, according to the United States Atomic Energy Commission, the amount of fallout-producing radioactive material in the stratosphere was doubled by the numerous test explosions of nuclear weapons conducted by the U.S. and the U.S.S.R. in 1958 alone. Third, the unequal distribution of fallout in different parts of the world needs to be con-

sidered. Fourth, since fallout is descending faster than expected, less decay has taken place in the stratosphere. Finally, changes in the quality of bombs tested and the sites of the tests must also be taken into account before accurate estimates of germ-line mutational damage due to fallout may be obtained.

Each month brings more of the data required to estimate the fallout risk to the germ cells. Apparently, the possible damage has been underestimated. For, whereas the International Commission on Radiological Protection recommended a maximum permissible concentration of strontium-90 in food of 80 units in 1953, which was then adopted by various U.S. government agencies, in 1958 the Commission recommended this be lowered to 33 units, and the new value was recently employed as a guideline by the United States government.

There are several genetic problems, in addition to those already mentioned on page 246, which need to be solved, in order to estimate the effects of radiation upon future generations. It is necessary to determine the relative mutability, for various types of mutation, of a dose given in a concentrated, as opposed to a protracted, manner. It is also necessary to learn as accurately as possible, the doubling dose for spermatogonia (about 40 r in the mouse) and oocytes (probably less than 40 r in mouse and man), for it is in these stages that the human germ cells used to produce the next generation remain for the longest period of time. It may be suggested that the largest number of germ-line mutations may occur in the oocytes. Spermatogonia are constantly dividing, during which time mutants producing a detrimental effect may be selected against so that a considerable portion are lost prior to gamete formation. However, there is no parallel situation in the germ line of the human female. The human female is born with all, or almost all, her future gametes already in the oocyte stage. No further mitotic cell multiplication takes place in these cells, which remain relatively quiescent for decades before becoming ova. Not only is germinal selection against mutants via mitosis absent in women, but there is evidence suggesting that as oocytes age they become disproportionately sensitive to mutation (at least to nondisjunction that leads to the presence of extra whole chromosomes, *polysomy*, and probably to chromosome loss, also).

While there is no doubt, in principle, that exposure to radiation has produced point mutants in the somatic and germ lines of man, this has not been easy to demonstrate in practice, for two main reasons. The first is that the point mutants expected are not qualitatively different from those which would occur spontaneously, and the second is that the quantitative effect, although large in total, is, in any one generation, small enough to be masked by the general variability of human genotypes and environment. However, by means of the use of improved statistical methods, the evidence is becoming stronger and stronger that radiation has produced such genetic effects. On the other hand, there is clear proof that radiation can cause structural changes in human chromosomes. With the recent perfection of cytological methods for studying human chromosomes, and the evidence that aneusomy is a relatively frequent event in oocytes, it is likely that additional evidence will be forthcoming relative to the numbers and kinds of gross chromosomal mutations which different doses and kinds of radiation can induce in man.

In conclusion two more points need to be made. In our discussion of the genetic effects of low doses of radiation, we have recognized a danger which is not likely to be calamitous to the human gene pool. However, the very high dosages which are possible in a nuclear war could be disastrous. For if 500 r is given the whole body in a short period of time, the chances are 50% that the person will die in a few months. If a person survived this period, his life expectancy would be reduced by some years, probably because of somatic mutations, and children conceived after exposure would be handicapped by many detrimental mutants. It is even possible, but not probable, that we could receive enough radiation in a nuclear war to destroy the human species. Finally, it should be realized that we are being constantly exposed to manmade mutagenic chemicals. It is very probable that we are getting less germ-line mutagenic effect from chemicals than from radiation; on the other hand, however, it is possible that we are having more somatic mutants produced by chemical substances than by present radiation exposure.

SUMMARY AND CONCLUSIONS

Cross-fertilizing species carry a large load of mutants in heterozygous condition. The vast majority of these are detrimental when homozygous and, to a lesser extent, when heterozygous, although there are also some mutants that are heterotic. Other things being equal, all mutants are equally harmful in that all are eliminated from the population only via the genetic death of their carriers. For rare mutants, more detriment and more genetic deaths occur in heterozygotes than in homozygotes. Persistence of mutants in the population is inversely related to their effect upon reproductive potential. Mutants with the smallest detriment to reproductive potential cause the greatest total amount of human suffering. Mutation is the current price paid by a population for the possibility of having a greater reproductive potential in the same or a different environment in the future. So, despite the rarity, in a given environment, of mutants which increase reproductive potential, mutation provides the raw materials for evolution.

Natural and manmade penetrating radiations are doubtless causing mutations in our somatic and germ cells, increasing our load of detrimental mutants. This exposure, though detrimental, is most likely no threat to man's survival as a species at present, although it could be in the future, if it became large enough. Further research is needed to assess accurately the magnitude of the effect of manmade radiations and chemical substances upon his mutation rate and well-being.

REFERENCES

Auerbach, C., *Genetics in the Atomic Age*, Fair Lawn, N.J., Essential Books, 1956.

Background Material for the Development of Radiation Protection Standards, Report No. 1, Federal Radiation Council, U.S. Government Printing Office, Washington, D.C., 1960.

Chu, E. H. Y., Giles, N. H., and Passano, K., "Types and Frequencies of Human Chromosome Aberrations Induced by X-rays," Proc. Nat. Acad. Sci., U.S., 47:830–839, 1961.

Crow, J. F., "Ionizing Radiation and Evolution," Scient. Amer., 201:138–160, 1959.

Dobzhansky, Th., *Evolution, Genetics, and Man*, New York, John Wiley & Sons, 1955.

Herskowitz, I. H., "Birth Defects and Chromosome Changes," Nuclear Information, 3 (No. 2):1–2, 4, 1960.

Krieger, H., and Freire-Maia, N., "Estimate of the Load of Mutations in Homogeneous Populations from Data on Mixed Samples," Genetics, 46:1565–1566, 1961.

Morton, N. E., "The Mutational Load Due to Detrimental Genes in Man," Amer. J. Human Genet., 12:348–364, 1960.

Muller, H. J., "Mutational Prophylaxis," Bull. N.Y. Acad. Med., 2nd Ser., 24:447–469, 1948.

Muller, H. J., "Radiation Damage to the Genetic Material," Amer. Scientist, 38:33–59, 126, 399–425, 1950.

Report of the United Nations Scientific Committee on the Effects of Atomic Radiation, New York: General Assembly Official Records: 13th Session, Suppl. 17 (A/3838), Chaps. 5–6, Annexes G–I, 1958.

Selected Materials on Radiation Protection Criteria and Standards: Their Basis and Use, Joint Committee on Atomic Energy, Congress of the United States, U.S. Government Printing Office, Washington, D.C., 1960.

The Biological Effects of Atomic Radiation. Summary Reports, National Academy of Sciences — National Research Council, Washington, D.C., 1956 and 1960. (See Reports of the Genetics Committee.)

QUESTIONS FOR DISCUSSION

28.1. Do you suppose that the mutations which occur in man serve a useful function? Why?

28.2. Compare the fate of a mutational load in asexually reproducing populations that are haploid, diploid, and autotetraploid.

28.3. Discuss the effect upon the gene pool of mutants restricted to the somatic line.

28.4. Can the gene that comprises part of a detrimental equivalent also comprise part of a lethal equivalent? Explain.

28.5. Give examples of polymorphism, and of balanced polymorphism in the genetics of man.

28.6. What is the relation between phenotypic detriment, genetic death, and genetic persistence?

28.7. Discuss the relative importance, to the individual and to the population, of point mutants and gross structural changes in chromosomes.

28.8. What is the difference, in terms of mutation, between a maximum permissible dose and a doubling dose of ionizing radiation? Is any dose of any radiation safe from a mutational standpoint? Explain.

28.9. Compare the genetic composition of the mutational load caused by fallout, medical uses of radiation, and atomic reactor accidents.

28.10. Do you believe it is essential that the general public become acquainted with the genetic effects of radiation? Why?

28.11. What are some of the beneficial uses of radiation? Are any of these based upon the genetic effects of the radiation? If so, give one or more examples.

28.12. One of the components of fallout is radioactive I-131, which has a half-life of about a week. Discuss the genetic effects expected in the somatic and germ lines of persons exposed to fallout.

Chapter 29

RACES AND
THE ORIGIN OF SPECIES

IN cross-fertilizing species, different individuals in a population are heterozygous for different genes (see Chapter 28). This is true even though the gene pool is at equilibrium with the factors which cause shifts in gene frequency — namely, mutation, selection, drift, and migration. In other words, in reaching genetic equilibrium, all the members of cross-fertilizing populations do not eventually become homozygotes, nor do they all become heterozygotes. Such populations, therefore, do not become genetically either pure or uniform with the passage of time.

While any given population is polymorphic for some genes, this does not mean that it is necessarily polymorphic with regard to a particular gene. So, for example, Indians in South America are all of O blood type, being homozygous (ii) in this respect, but they have a polymorphic pool with respect to other genes. Moreover, an allele like I^B, for example, may be rare or absent in one population, as is true in certain North American Indians, while it may be relatively frequent in the gene pool of another population, as in central Asia. Thus, populations located in different parts of the world may differ both in the types and frequencies of alleles which they carry in their gene pools. For many purposes it is desirable to identify a population with certain gene pool characteristics as a *race*.

In certain studies the investigator may wish to define races only in terms of the distribution of the I^B gene for ABO blood type. It would then be perfectly reasonable and valid to define as different races, populations that do or do not contain I^B in their gene pool. On this classification, there would be only two races of man, the South American Indian (without I^B) and all other people (with I^B in their gene pool).

In another study, however, it may be desirable to define races on the basis of the prevalence of i and I^B in the population. The distribution of these genes in the gene pool has been studied extensively in populations all over the world. The results show that in western Europe, Iceland, Ireland, and parts of Spain, three fourths of the gene pool is i. However, as one proceeds eastward from these regions, this frequency decreases. The opposite tendency is true for I^B. In fact, in a world map, I^B is most frequent in central Asia and some populations in India, and becomes less and less frequent as one proceeds away from this center. Since the change in frequency of I^B is also a gradual one, it is not possible to draw lines on the map which would separate people into groups with sharply different gene frequencies. So, where these lines are drawn, and how many are drawn, are arbitrary matters, as a consequence of which, more or fewer races will be defined.

Not only are the genes for ABO blood groups useful in characterizing races, but so are other blood traits whose genetic basis is understood. It is actually valid, in defining races, to utilize differences in any trait so long as these are based upon genetic differences. So, for example, one can consider certain genetic differences in color of hair, eyes, and skin, and differences in stature and head shape, in delimiting races. Our knowledge of genetics should caution us, however, that the use of phenotypic criteria only may be quite unsatisfactory for classifying races. For the environment itself can cause phenotypic differences (see Chapter 1), and the same phenotypic result may be produced by different genotypes because of gene interaction in dominance and epistasis (see Chapter 7).

It should be reemphasized that the number of races recognized is a matter of convenience. For some purposes it may be adequate to separate mankind into only two races, while for others, as many as two hundred have been recognized. Most anthropologists usually recognize about half a dozen basic races, or define about thirty, when finer details of some populations are to be considered. Regardless of the number of races defined, however, each is best characterized in terms of the genes it contains. Since the people in a population are either A, B, AB, or O in blood type, and there are no intermediates, there is no average genotype for ABO blood group. Nor is there an average genotype for any other polymorphic gene. Because there is no average genotype for a population, a race must be defined in terms of the relative frequency of alleles contained in its gene pool, and since there is no average genotype for a race, there is also no average phenotype. You see, therefore, the invalidity of trying to picture a typical (average) member of any race.

A knowledge of the distribution of genes for ABO blood types in different populations the world over provides important information to geneticists, anthropologists, and other scientists. To what can the different distributions be attributed? Since people do not choose their marriage partners on the basis of their ABO blood type, and since there does not seem to be any pleiotropic effect which makes the possessor of one blood type sexually more attractive than another, we may conclude that mating is at random with respect to ABO genotype. There is some evidence, however, that in other respects not all ABO genotypes have the same biological fitness. It is possible

that differential mutation can also explain part of the differences in distribution. But, the greatest shift in ABO gene frequencies in different populations in the past few thousand years has probably been the result of genetic drift and migration. In fact, the paths of past migrations have been traced, utilizing the gradual changes in the frequencies of ABO and other blood group genes in neighboring populations.

It has already been mentioned (p. 235) that different paracentric inversions are found in natural populations of *D. pseudoobscura*. Even so, all of these flies found in nature are very similar phenotypically, even though they differ with respect to their chromosomal arrangements. This fly is common in the southwestern part of the United States (Figure 29–1), and different populations located there have been sampled to detect the relative frequency of these inversions.[1] It is found that California populations are rich in the inversion types called Standard and Arrowhead. Eastward, in nearby Arizona and New Mexico, the populations contain very few Standard chromosomes and have the Arrowhead arrangement almost entirely. Finally, in still more easterly Texas, there are no Standard, some Arrowhead; most chromosomes are of Pikes Peak type.

The shift in the frequency and type of inversions in different geographic regions cannot be explained as the result of differential mutation, since the spontaneous rate at which inversions arise is extremely low. Moreover, there is no reason to believe that the gene flow among these populations has changed appreciably in the recent past, so that migration rates have probably had a relatively small influence upon genotypic frequencies; nor is there any reason to attribute to genetic drift a major role in causing the differences in inversion frequency

[1] Based upon work of Th. Dobzhansky and collaborators.

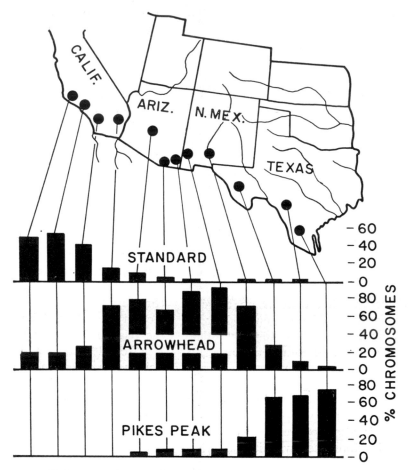

FIGURE 29–1. *Distribution of inversion types in* D. pseudoobscura *collected in the Southwestern United States.* (*After Th. Dobzhansky and C. Epling.*)

in the different areas. By a process of elimination, therefore, we conclude that the primary reason for these population differences lies in the different adaptive values which these different inversion types confer in different territories. In support of this view are laboratory tests which demonstrate that, despite the lack of any obvious morphological effects, these inversions have such different physiological effects that each type is different from the others in being more adapted to certain experimental environments than it is to others. It is reasonably certain,

therefore, that in nature, too, these different gene arrangements are adaptive, the differences among the three types of populations, which we may define as three different races, being the result of natural selection.

Similar results have been obtained with three California races of the cinquefoil plant species, *Potentilla glandulosa*, which live at sea level, mid-elevation, and the alpine zone, respectively. The sea level race is killed when grown in the alpine environment. The alpine race grown at lower elevations proves less resistant to rust fungi than the lower elevation races. By means of such experiments it was shown that each race is adapted to the conditions of its habitat.

In different parts of the territory occupied by a species, there are different inorganic and organic (including organisms) environments. It is clear, from what we have just described, that no single genotype would be equally well adapted to all the different environments encountered within this territory. One way in which a cross-fertilizing species may, as a whole, attain maximal biological fitness is for it to remain genetically polymorphic and to become differentiated into geographical populations or races which differ from each other genetically.

In all of the examples discussed so far, the different races of cross-fertilizing species have occupied geographically separate territories, and are said to be *allopatric*. Sometimes, however, different races may be *sympatric*, that is, they may be found in the same territory. In the absence of geographical separation, what factors operate to keep sympatric races from hybridizing to become one race? We can look for the answer to this from studies of the fate of races, originally allopatric, which have become sympatric. Man offers one example of this kind of change. Several thousand years ago, mankind was differentiated into a number of allopatric races. Since then, the development of civilization, and improved methods of travel, have made such races sympatric in part. But gene exchange in the now-sympatric races may be prevented by social and economic forces, so that some of these races may retain their identity. Domesticated plants and animals offer another example of what may happen when allopatric races become sympatric. Consider the case in dogs. Many different breeds, or races, which were originally allopatric, may now all be found living in the same city. Yet these now-sympatric races do not exchange genes with sufficient frequency to form the single

breed, or race, called mongrel, because their reproduction is controlled by man. It should be realized that, under other circumstances, allopatric races, which become sympatric, may form a single polymorphic race via crossbreeding.

A species of cross-fertilizing organisms usually consists of a number of races adapted to the different environments in which they are found. All these races are kept in genetic continuity by interracial breeding and hybrid race types, so that the species, as a whole, has a single gene pool within which no portion is completely isolated from any other. How does one species differ from another? Let us restrict our attention to cross-fertilizing species. We shall require that two groups of organisms be genetically discontinuous from each other in order to be considered different species. (This means that each species has, in effect, a gene pool which is so isolated from the gene pool of another species, that neither the one nor the other can lose its identity via cross-breeding, or backcrossing subsequent to cross-breeding.) In addition, the gene pools of different species must be isolated from each other for genetic, and not merely environmental, reasons.

New species have arisen during the course of past evolution, and since evolution continues today, new species are forming at present also. By what mechanisms do new species of cross-fertilizing individuals arise? The mechanism considered most common is the production of two or more species from a single species. How could this come about?

Suppose different portions of the same species become somewhat independent of each other reproductively, that is, they form different populations, and, while there is some interbreeding, most of the breeding is intrapopulation. In the course of time, the two populations may diverge genetically so that each is adapted to its own territory. We might now want to call these two populations different races of the same species.

These two races may continue to become more and more different in their gene pools because of mutation, natural selection of genotypes which further increase adaptiveness, and genetic drift. As this differentiation process continues, the genes which make the two races adaptive in their own territories may, via their pleiotropic effects, make matings between the two races still less likely to occur, or may cause the hybrids of such matings to be less adaptive than the members of either parent race. The greater the degree of reproductive isolation, which is an accidental or incidental by-product of the different genotypes which are adaptive in the two territories of the two races, the greater would be the selective advantage of other mutants which further increase the reproductive isolation between the two races. If the two races continued to diverge genetically in this way, they would eventually form separate and different gene pools, at which time they would have changed from two races of the same species to two different species. Note that speciation is an irreversible process, for once a gene pool has reached the species level, it can never lose its identity via crossbreeding with another species.

In this generalized account of how speciation usually occurs, races have acted as incipient species. But, you must also recall that, under other circumstances, what are two races may also often become a single race. Thus, for example, while several thousand years ago different allopatric populations of human beings were definitely different races which might have formed different species had the same conditions of life continued, some of these races have subsequently merged into one race because of civilization and migration.

What are the principal means by which races are known to become reproductively isolated from each other? The *barriers* leading to complete reproductive isolation include the following:

1. *Geographical.* Races may become separated by water, ice, mountains, wind, earthquakes, and volcanic activity.
2. *Ecological.* The habitat of the two races may be different or may become more different than it was originally, because of changes in temperature, humidity, sunlight, food, predators, and parasites.
3. *Seasonal.* In adapting to seasonal changes, one race may become fertile at a different time than the other, even if their territories overlap, or if the races are sympatric.
4. *Sexual or ethological.* The races may show preferences for intrarace mating. (In domesticated forms this preference may be decided upon by man.)
5. *Morphological.* The sex organs of the two races may be incompatible to various degrees.
6. *Physiological.* The sex cells of one race may fail to fertilize those of the other, so that the hybrid zygote is not formed at all, or is formed infrequently.
7. *Hybrid inviability.* Even when hybrid zygotes are formed, their development may be abnormal, so that they fail to complete development.
8. *Hybrid sterility.* Finally, even if hybrids complete development and even if they are hardy, they may be sterile.

Environmental differences in geography, ecology, or season which act to separate races do not automatically produce genotypic differences among them. They do furnish, however, the environmental variations which provide a means of selecting genotypes which are adaptive, i.e., which have the greatest reproductive potential under the different conditions. Of course, mutation must occur to provide the raw materials for this selection of more adapted genotypes, and since no single genotype is equally well adapted to all conditions, the races will come to contain different genotypes. Completion of reproductive isolation may be accomplished by the remaining barriers listed.

Reproductive isolation may be due genetically to either genic action or chromosomal behavior, or both. Thus, the many genes, by which the two incipient species differ, may produce seasonal, sexual, morphological, and physiological barriers, as well as hybrid inviability. Although hybrid inviability is due to developmental disharmony consequent upon the presence of two genetically different genomes in each cell, hybrid sterility may be due, also, to an additional factor. The two races may have become quite different with respect to the arrangement of their genes, by means of structural changes within and between chromosomes, so that during meiosis, synapsis between the two different genomes is irregular. Failure of proper pairing will mean that the segregation process will be abnormal and the products of meiosis aneuploid. You should recall that aneuploidy in pollen is lethal, while aneuploid gametes in animals usually produce dominant lethality of the zygotes they form at fertilization.

Are morphological differences a good indication of species differences? It would seem likely that the more divergent two forms are morphologically, the more likely they are to differ physiologically, and also the more likely that these differences derive from very different gene pools which are isolated from each other. We would certainly expect, simply from a comparison of horse and mouse morphology, that these are different species. However, when the two groups being compared are more closely related in descent, it is found that morphology is not well correlated with reproductive isolation. Thus, for example, European cattle and the Tibetan yak are quite different in appearance and are usually placed in different genera. Yet these two can be crossed, and in Tibet, many cattle have yaklike traits. On

the other hand, consider *D. persimilis* and *D. pseudoobscura*. These two species were once considered races of the same species, and are so similar morphologically that one can differentiate between their genitalia only if very careful measurements are made. Nevertheless, these two species have completely isolated gene pools in nature, even where their territories overlap. Such morphologically similar species are called *sibling species*, and have originated from different races of a single species in relatively recent times. Sibling species have been found in other *Drosophila*, mosquitoes, and other insects, and have been found in plants, among the tarweeds of the aster family, and in the blue wild rye.

D. pseudoobscura and *D. persimilis* illustrate two other principles relative to species formation. Their study demonstrates that any particular reproductive barrier usually has a multigenic and/or a multichromosomal basis, and that any two species are separated not by one, but by a number of reproductive barriers. Each of the barriers involved is incomplete, but all together they result in complete reproductive isolation, so that there is no stream of genes between the two gene pools in nature. In the particular case of these two sibling species, the known barriers include the fact that *pseudoobscura* lives in drier and warmer habitats, and that females accept the mating advances of males of their own species more often than they do of males of the other. *Pseudoobscura* usually mates in the evening, *persimilis* in the morning; when interspecific hybrids are formed, they are relatively inviable, or, when viable, mostly sterile.

In the formation of new species from races, the nature and origin of the reproductively isolating mechanisms involved shows that valid species do not originate by a single or simple mutation, but arise as the result of many different, independently occurring genetic changes. Moreover, we have seen

that the genetic changes which lead to speciation are not accomplished merely by the accumulation of more mutants of the kinds
which distinguish races. What is required
for speciation are mutants with special effects, effects which contribute to reproductive
isolation. Populations usually must be
physically separated while reproductive barriers are being built up, otherwise hybridization would break down these barriers. There
is also experimental evidence, in support of
the hypothesis described earlier, that natural
selection, acting both directly and indirectly,
will itself further the accumulation of genetic
factors promoting reproductive isolation between races.

We have discussed, so far, how one species
can give rise to two or more species, via races
which serve as incipient species. Note that
in defining a species, it was necessary to say
that it had an isolated gene pool, that is, a

gene pool closed to individuals of some
other alternative condition (species). There
is one possible type of species formation
which would be unrecognized by this cri-
terion, since the alternative state would no
longer exist. It is conceivable, for example,
that a species composed of a single population would gradually undergo numerous
changes in its gene pool during the course of
many generations. At the end of this time
should we call the new population the same
species, or should we give it a new species
name? It is likely that, in some cases, had
some of the members of the original population been miraculously preserved, the old
form would be found reproductively isolated
from the new. In this event we would be
dealing with the formation of a new species
whose origin was dependent upon the extinction of an old one. The occurrence of
this type of speciation will become a valid
subject of study, once man learns how to
preserve sample genotypes indefinitely.

Not only may new cross-fertilizing species
originate from a single species or its races,
but many have arisen as the consequence of
hybridization between two or more different
species. What we are dealing with here are
the *consequences of interspecific hybridization.* We already know that if interspecific
hybrids are formed, they pose no threat to
the isolation of the gene pools of their parental species. The question we are asking is:

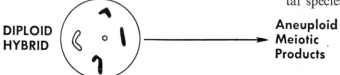

PARENT SPECIES

2n = 4   2n = 6

DIPLOID HYBRID   **Aneuploid Meiotic Products**

FIGURE 29–2. *Interspecific hybridization leading to new species formation via amphiploidy.*

AMPHIPLOID   **Euploid (n) Meiotic Products**

By what mechanisms can interspecific hybrids form successful, sexually reproducing populations that have their own closed gene pools? There are several methods by which interspecific hybrids, of plants particularly, may be converted into stable intermediate types that are isolated from their parental species. The first method involves *amphiploidy* (Figure 29–2).

Suppose one species has 2n = 4 and another 2n = 6. The F_1 hybrid between them will have five chromosomes. Even if the hybrid survives, it may be sterile because the chromosomes are all nonhomologous and none has a partner at meiosis. As a result, meiosis would proceed as if the organism were a haploid; the gametes usually produced would not contain a single set of the five chromosomes, but would be aneuploid. If, however, the chromosomes in such an F_1 hybrid are somehow doubled, artificially by the drug colchicine, or by some spontaneous agent, then the chromosome number in that individual or sector would be 2n = 10, or n = 5, and since each chromosome would now be paired, the chromosomes would behave normally in meiosis and produce euploid gametes. The progeny would be fertile, phenotypically more or less intermediate to, and isolated from, both parental species.

It has been estimated that 20–25% of the present species of flowering plants have originated as interspecific hybrids whose chromosomes have become doubled in number (being therefore "doubled hybrids" or amphiploids). Moreover, as many or more species have originated in this way in the past, and then later diverged to form different genera. Amphiploidy has been involved in the origin of cotton in the New World. In the present century, new species of goatsbeard have arisen in nature via amphiploidy. Amphiploidy also can be produced artificially. Thus, it has been possible for man to cross radish (2n = 18) with cabbage (2n = 18) (Figure 29–3). This produces an F_1 hybrid with 18 unpaired chromosomes at meiosis. If, however, the hybrid's chromosomes become doubled, an amphiploid is produced with 2n = 36 chromosomes (containing 9 pairs each from radish and cabbage). This amphiploid is fertile, genetically isolated from both radish and cabbage — and constitutes a new species.

The breeding success of the amphiploid is greater, the more different are the chromosomes of the two species which originally provided haploid genomes to the F_1 hybrid. For if each chromosome in F_1 is different, then, after becoming doubled, each will have just one partner at meiosis and segregation will be normal. It is not surprising, therefore, that when the two species hybridizing are very similar chromosomally, an amphiploid of them produces trivalents and quadrivalents at meiosis, which lead to abnormal segregation and sterility.

While amphiploidy is not successful for hybrids between very similar species, there is a second way such interspecific hybrids may become stabilized as a new species. If the two hybridizing species are very similar chromosomally, they could have the same haploid number, and the F_1 hybrid could have all these chromosomes synapse in pairs at meiosis. Segregation, independent segregation, and crossing over could yield progeny of the *hybrid whose recombinations may become stabilized* in nature, yet isolated from either parental species. Consider certain species in the larkspur genus, *Delphinium*. *D. gypsophilum* is morphologically intermediate between *D. recurvatum* and *D. hesperium*. All three species have 2n = 16. It is possible to cross the "parent" species, *recurvatum* and *hesperium*, and obtain an F_1 hybrid. If this F_1 hybrid is crossed to *gypsophilum*, offspring are obtained which are more regular and more fertile than those which would be produced by backcrossing this F_1 hybrid to either parent species.

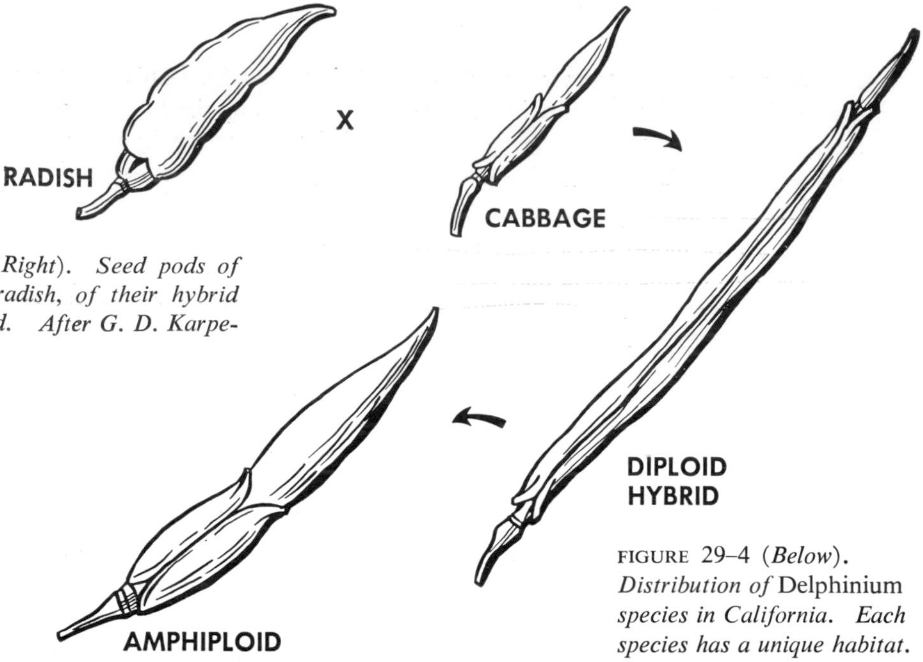

RADISH X CABBAGE

FIGURE 29–3 (*Right*). *Seed pods of cabbage and radish, of their hybrid and amphiploid. After G. D. Karpechenko.*)

DIPLOID HYBRID

AMPHIPLOID

FIGURE 29–4 (*Below*). *Distribution of* Delphinium *species in California. Each species has a unique habitat.*

Similarly, crosses of *gypsophilum* with either of its parent species are not as regular or fertile as are those made between it and the hybrid of the parent species. This comprises good evidence that *gypsophilum* arose as the hybrid between *recurvatum* and *hesperium*. Figure 29–4 shows the distribution of these species in California.

A third way in which interspecific hybrids can become stabilized as new species is by *introgression*. In this process, a new type arises after the interspecific hybrid backcrosses with one of the parental types. The backcross recombinant types favored by natural selection may contain some genetic components from both species. These recombinants may be true breeding and may eventually become a new species.

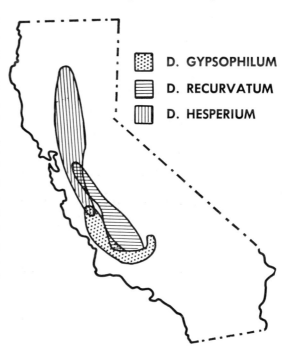

D. GYPSOPHILUM

D. RECURVATUM

D. HESPERIUM

SUMMARY AND CONCLUSIONS

The races within a cross-fertilizing species are characterized by the content of their gene pools. Each of the different races is adapted to the territory in which it lives. The races involved may be sympatric or allopatric. Races become species by the accumulation of genetic differences whose end effect is genetic discontinuity — i.e., the formation of isolated gene pools. The reproductive barriers separating any two gene pools are usually of several different types, each of which is incomplete, each of which has a polygenic and/or a poly-chromosomal basis, and need not be well correlated with morphological differences.

It is generally recognized that most cross-fertilizing species arose from the further differentiation of races. It is possible, however, that a new species may arise also by the gradual change of one species, as a whole, into another species.

Two (or more) species may give rise to a new one following interspecific hybridization. The interspecific hybrid may form a new species by means of amphiploidy, by selection of recombinants among its progeny, or by selection of individuals produced following introgression.

REFERENCES

Dobzhansky, Th., *Genetics and the Origin of Species*, 3rd Ed., New York, Columbia University Press, 1951.

Dobzhansky, Th., *Evolution, Genetics, and Man*, New York, John Wiley & Sons, 1955.

Dodson, E. O., *Evolution: Process and Product* (Rev. Ed.), New York, Rinehart, 1960.

Dunn, L. C., and Dobzhansky, Th., *Heredity, Race, and Society*, 3rd Ed., New York, New Amer. Lib. of World Lit., 1957.

Merrill, D. J., *Evolution and Genetics*, New York, Holt, Rinehart and Winston, 1962.

Stebbins, G. L., *Variation and Evolution in Plants*, New York, Columbia University Press, 1950.

QUESTIONS FOR DISCUSSION

29.1. Discuss the validity of the concept of a pure race.

29.2. What presumptions need be made in order to use the frequencies of ABO blood types to trace the course of past migration?

29.3. Under what future circumstances would you expect the number of races of human beings to decrease? to increase?

29.4. Can the definition we have used for a species be applied to forms reproducing only asexually? Why?

29.5. Differentiate between genic sterility and chromosomal sterility. Invent an example of each type.

29.6. Discuss the hypothesis that a new species can result from the occurrence of a single mutational event.

29.7. Is geographical isolation a prerequisite for the formation of a new species? Explain.

29.8. What is the relative importance of mutation and genetic recombination in species formation?

29.9. Is a species a natural biological entity, or is it, like a race, defined to suit man's convenience?

29.10. Does the statement, "We are all members of the human race," make biological sense? Why?

29.11. Suppose intelligent life, phenotypically indistinguishable from man, arrived on earth. Would intermarriage with earth people be likely to produce fertile offspring? Why?

29.12. Invent circumstances under which the present single species of man would evolve into two or more species.

Chapter **30**

DEVELOPMENTAL GENETICS

WHEN we are dealing with mutations other than point mutations, the genetic alternatives can often be recognized cytologically by modifications produced in chromosomal appearance. In the case of point mutation, however, we are restricted to a study of the phenotypic consequences of the change in genotype. In fact, we may usually note the presence of a mutant (of any type) by its phenotypic effects, that is, by its effects on the characteristics of an individual. Since the characteristics determined by gene action are themselves not inherited, the question is, how are these traits produced? What happens between the time the zygote is formed and the time the trait appears? Development. We are interested, therefore, in the ways in which development is influenced by different genotypes, or in what we may call *developmental genetics.*

You realize, of course, that regardless of the importance of a trait produced by a gene, we cannot learn anything about the role of the gene in the production of the trait, unless there is some genetic alternative which produces a change phenotypically. We would never learn of the existence or of the role in development of a gene, if its presence, absence, or alternative forms produced no difference in phenotype. Whenever two different genetic constitutions produce two different effects on the phenotype, it should also be realized that what is recognized is not the total phenotypic effect of one genotype and how this effect has been changed by

another genotype; what is seen is only the change in development which has been made by the change in genotype.

Let us invent an example that will illustrate both these points. Suppose a particular gene actually is responsible for the production of an entire protein composed of a chain of a hundred amino acids. So long as no genetic alternative is known which produces a change in this protein, there is no way of knowing whether this protein is the result of a specific gene's activity, or is entirely the result of the action of the total genotype together with the environment. But, suppose a mutant occurs which substitutes one amino acid in this protein for another, and that this phenotypic change is detectable. From this result we could conclude only that the normal gene places one amino acid and the mutant gene another amino acid in this protein molecule. Note again that we would have learned not the total effect of the gene, but just the difference between the phenotypic results of the two genetic alternatives.

Under ordinary circumstances, when mutants present at fertilization in multicellular plant and animal forms are detected, it is because they produce some visible change in morphology. This is usually a macroscopic phenotypic change, identified a considerable time after the organism starts its development. Two questions arise in this connection. What is the genetic basis for the mutant involved? The answer to this can be obtained by utilizing the principles and methods already discussed in previous Chapters. How does the mutant change normal development to produce the new morphological result? The answer to the latter question deals with learning how phenotypes (of any type) come into being via gene action, and is the subject of *phenogenetics,* a study which is of broader scope than developmental genetics.

Let us see what genetic and phenogenetic information can be obtained from studying one particular case. A novel phenotype

262

FIGURE 30–1. *Normal (right) and Creeper (left) roosters. (Courtesy of L. C. Dunn; reprinted by permission of McGraw-Hill Book Co., Inc., from* Study Guide and Workbook for Genetics *by I. H. Herskowitz. Copyright, 1960.)*

appeared in the domestic fowl in which the legs were shortened so as to give the impression that the bird was creeping. This abnormal "Creeper" phenotype and the normal phenotype[1] can be seen in the roosters at the left and right, respectively, of Figure 30–1.

The genetic study of this phenotype gave the following results. Reciprocal crosses of Creeper by normal gave a 1 : 1 ratio of Creeper : normal chicks. Creepers crossed to Creepers gave, in the adult stage, 775 : 388 as Creeper : normal, a result which can be considered an excellent fit to a 2 : 1 ratio. It is reasonable to suppose, therefore, that Creeper is heterozygous for a single pair of segregating genes, in which the *Creeper* gene, Cp, is dominant to its normal allele, $+$. The 2 : 1 ratio is taken to indicate that the mutant homozygote $Cp\,Cp$ is lethal (as is the case, see p. 65, for the mutant homozygote when yellow mice are crossed together). The view that Cp acts as a recessive lethal received support from a comparison of the survival rate of embryos from normal parents with that of embryos both of whose parents were Creeper. It was found that about 25% of

[1] Studied by W. Landauer, by V. Hamburger, by D. Rudnick, and by L. C. Dunn.

the embryos which would have survived in the former case died on or before the third day of incubation in the latter case.

What is the developmental, phenogenetic connection between $Cp\,Cp$ which acts as a recessive lethal, $Cp\,+$ which produces Creeper, and $+\,+$ which produces normal? Although $Cp\,Cp$ usually dies at about the third day of incubation, on rare occasions it may survive 19 days, or about until the time of hatching from the shell. Such a rare Creeper homozygote is shown at the left of Figure 30–2 (the comparable normal individual is at the right) and possesses the following syndrome of malformations: The eyes are split, are smaller than normal, and have no eyelids. The head is misshapen and the body is smaller. The skeleton is not ossified and, as seen on top of the black paper used as background in the Figure, only the digits of the limbs are well formed.

A study of $Cp\,+$ development shows, at seven days of incubation, that the leg buds are shorter than in normal embryos. This morphological manifestation of Cp action must be based upon events occurring earlier in development, for at 48 hours of incubation (Figure 30–3), a $Cp\,+$ embryo (left) is smaller,

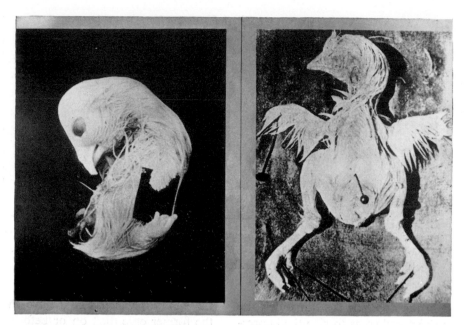

FIGURE 30–2.   *Normal (right) and Creeper (left) homozygote at about 19 days of development.   (Courtesy of L. C. Dunn; reprinted by permission of McGraw-Hill Book Co., Inc., from* Study Guide and Workbook for Genetics *by I. H. Herskowitz. Copyright, 1960.)*

FIGURE 30–3.   *Normal (right) and Creeper (left) heterozygote embryos at about 48 hours of development.   (Courtesy of L. C. Dunn; reprinted by permission of McGraw-Hill Book Co., Inc., from* Study Guide and Workbook for Genetics *by I. H. Herskowitz.   Copyright, 1960.)*

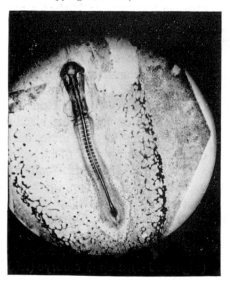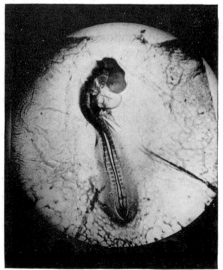

less developed, and does not have the head flexure already present in a $+ +$ embryo (right). In fact, differences like this can be seen even 12 hours earlier, i.e., at 36 hours of incubation.

In both the homozygote and heterozygote for *Cp*, the differentiation of cartilage has been interfered with. The *Cp* $+$ individual has the disease called *chondrodystrophy* (or *achondroplasia*) (see p. 230), the *Cp Cp* individual has the cartilage disease called *phokomelia*. Both diseases had been recognized more than a hundred years ago as occurring in human families; cases were found in which both parents were chondrodystrophic and some phokomelic children appeared, whose fingers protruded from the shoulders and whose toes came from a deficient hind limb. The condition observed in these latter individuals can be attributed to the presence of a mutant gene (like the *Cp* gene in fowl) in double dose, that is, when homozygous.

It was already mentioned that at 36 hours of incubation, *Cp* $+$ individuals are developing more slowly than $+ +$ individuals. Beginning about that time, the tissue for the hind limb buds would normally be growing very rapidly, while other tissues were growing more slowly. Let us suppose that some of the effect of *Cp* in single and double dose is to cause a generalized slowing-down of growth. In this event, the structures most affected by the slowdown would be those growing most rapidly at the time. The observed effects of one or two *Cp* genes on the hind limbs and on the long bones of both fore and hind limbs follow expectation from a slowdown in growth rate which starts at about this particular time in development.

It should not be concluded, however, that the tissue for hind limb is completely passive to *Cp* action, and that its sole response is to slowdown in growth rate. It is possible, by means of transplantation experiments, to study the developmental fate of prospective hind limb tissue. If such tissue from a normal chick embryo is transplanted to a more forward position in another normal chick embryo, it grows out as a normal limb. If, however, the prospective hind limb tissue is taken from a homozygous Creeper embryo and is transplanted to a more forward position in a normal chick embryo, it grows out as a Creeper type leg. This demonstrates that, even at a very early stage, before there is any hind limb as such, presumptive limb tissue from Creeper is already permanently determined by the Creeper genotype to develop as Creeper limb.

It also should not be presumed that all abnormal tissues found in homozygous Creepers have been determined at an early stage in development, so that they possess only the Creeper alternative. It was mentioned that *Cp Cp* individuals have small, split eyes. The early eye *anlage* (*imaginal disc*) from a normal embryo can be transplanted to an abnormal position in a normal embryo. In this position it grows into an eye just like that of homozygous Creeper. But an eye anlage from a *Cp Cp* embryo, transplanted to the eye-forming region of a normal embryo, grows into a normal eye. We may conclude, therefore, that the abnormal Creeper eye is due, not to some intrinsic differentiation factor in eye tissue, but to some kind of abnormality in its surroundings. It may be supposed that in the Creeper homozygote the eye is probably undergoing a kind of starvation due to the bad circulation the genotype produces. This is supported by two lines of evidence. First, most prospective tissues of *Cp Cp* placed on a complete culture medium *in vitro* grow quite normally, although heart tissue grows less well than normal heart tissue does. Secondly, when limb rudiments from normal embryos are grown *in vitro* in a nutritionally dilute culture medium, they develop many of the characteristics of the *Cp Cp* limbs.

The study of Creeper fowl demonstrates that the pleiotropic effects of this mutant found at the completion of development are due to gene-directed changes originating much earlier in development. In fact, we can infer, from the developmental fate of prospective limbs in Creeper embryos, that there are changes produced by a genotype which may precede any morphological changes. We can presume that what the Creeper gene does is to modify the physiology of the individual in such a way that general growth is slowed down, and the prospective fate of certain tissues is fixed, so that the morphological changes later noted are a direct consequence of these changes. The gene-caused physiological changes may be attributed, in turn, to changes in cellular *metabolism* (which deals with the biochemical activities associated with cells).

We have already seen that genetically determined metabolic changes taking place within certain cells (to produce an abnormal nutritional environment) may affect the functioning of other cells (the differentiation of eye tissue). Let us consider two groups of studies with mice to see if we can learn more about the genetic control of effects produced external to the cell in which the gene acts. One group of investigations [2] involves a comparative study of normal and dwarf mice. These dwarf mice have all of their body parts reduced in size to the same degree, so they are proportionally dwarfed, due to the presence of an apparently completely recessive gene in homozygous condition. During development both dwarf and normal mice grow equally fast, at first. Then, the dwarf suddenly stops growing and never reaches sexual maturity. A microscopic study of the anterior pituitary gland shows that the gland is very much smaller in the dwarf than it is in the normal mouse. Moreover, certain large cells, normally present, are absent in dwarf pituitaries, and it is these cells which apparently secrete growth hormone. That this is

a case of genetically produced *pituitary dwarfism* is supported by the following type of experiment. Pairs of dwarf litter mates, about 30 days old, are used. Each day, for 30 days, one mouse of a pair is injected with extracts of pituitary glands from dwarf mice (Figure 30–4, B), while the other mouse is injected in a comparable way with extracts of pituitary glands from normal mice (Figure 30–4, A). During this period of treatment, the former mouse remains essentially dwarf, while the latter grows until it is virtually normal. Here, then, we are dealing with a chemical messenger, pituitary hormone, which regulates growth in general, and whose presence is dependent upon a single pair of genes.

The second group of studies is concerned with mouse tails. While the normal $(+ +)$ mouse has a long tail, there is one strain in which a shortened tail (*Brachyury, or Brachy*) occurs.[3] Brachy crossed to Brachy produces $\frac{2}{3}$ Brachy : $\frac{1}{3}$ normal offspring, suggesting that a gene *Brachy* (T) is dominant for short-tailness and recessive for lethality. Brachy mice should be, therefore, $T +$. When the embryology was studied of offspring produced following the mating of Brachys with each other $(T +$ by $T +)$, about 25% of the embryos were normal $(+ +)$, about 50% showed tail degeneration at 11 days of development $(T +)$, and about 25% of the embryos $(T T)$ were monsters (Figure 30–5). These monsters had posterior limb buds misdirected dorsally and zigzag neural tubes; moreover, they had no notochord. Since their whole posterior part was not developed, they could not form a placental connection and died between 10 and 11 days of development.

Consider further the $T T$ individual, whose somites in the posterior part of the body are grossly abnormal. It is known, from other embryological work, that proper somite formation is dependent upon the presence of

[2] Based upon work of G. D. Snell, of P. E. Smith and E. C. MacDowell, and of T. Francis.

[3] Based upon work of L. C. Dunn, P. Chesley, and D. Bennett.

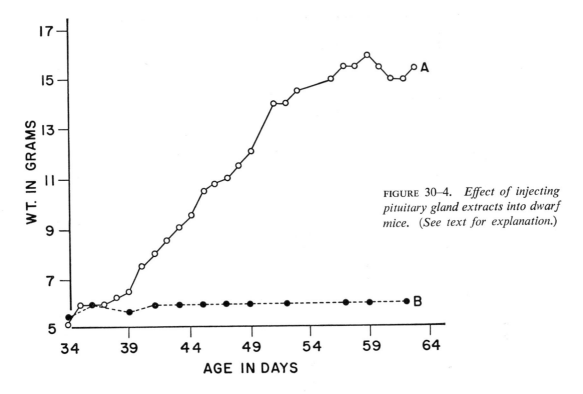

FIGURE 30–4. *Effect of injecting pituitary gland extracts into dwarf mice. (See text for explanation.)*

presumptive, that is, future, notochordal tissue. When normal presumptive notochord is present, the mesoderm surrounding it is induced to form cartilage and vertebral segments. It would seem reasonable to attribute the failure of cartilage and vertebrae formation in *T T* individuals to the failure of presumptive notochord (which has lost the ability to develop into notochord) to induce the differentiation of mesoderm. Is this, in fact, the nature of the change, in *T T* individuals, in the inductive relationship between these two adjacent tissues? This question can be studied using tissue cultures. A control experiment shows that it is possible to explant presumptive notochordal tissue, from a normal individual, which has wrapped around it mesodermal tissue, from the same or another normal individual, and to obtain the development of cartilage and vertebral segments. Surprisingly enough, however, the

mesoderm from normal embryos will develop into cartilage and vertebral segments when surrounding presumptive notochord from young *T T* embryos. Moreover, mesoderm from *T T* embryos does not form cartilage or vertebrae when surrounding presumptive notochord from normal embryos. We must conclude, then, contrary to expectation, that in the case of *T T* the normal inductive relationship has been disturbed in an unexpected way, the mesoderm being no longer able to respond to the normal inductive stimuli of presumptive notochord.

We have already seen how genetic change may influence or direct development of multicellular organisms by means of modifying (1) the relative growth rates of parts (Creeper limbs) and (2) the over-all growth rate (pituitary dwarfism). We have also found that genetic changes can act upon differentiation at a distance by means of (1) a general change

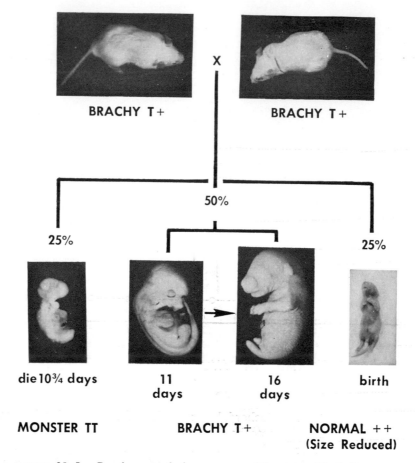

FIGURE 30–5. *Brachyury in the house mouse.* (*Courtesy of L. C. Dunn; re-printed by permission of McGraw-Hill Book Co., Inc., from* Study Guide and Workbook for Genetics *by I. H. Herskowitz.   Copyright, 1960.*)

in metabolism (starvation of the Creeper eye) or by means of (2) specific chemical messengers (mouse pituitary hormone).   Tissues, being acted upon at a distance, can have their competence changed for genetic reasons (homozygous Creeper limbs).   It was also found that adjacent tissues, which interact as induction systems, can have their differentiation modified by changes in their response to inducing agents (nonresponsiveness of mesoderm to presumptive notochord in homozygous Brachy), and, although no example of this was described, probably, also, by changes in inducing capacity.   It should be realized, however, even though differentiation during the development of higher multicellular organisms involves intercellular interactions of all the types mentioned, that some cellular traits are produced solely through the intracellular action of the genotype.   This is clear, for example, from the phenotypic effect of mutants induced during embryology which may be detrimental or lethal to the cells containing them, and from traits, as in *Drosophila*, showing phenotypic mosaicism in direct correspondence with genotypic mosaicism.

SUMMARY AND CONCLUSIONS

Phenogenetics, the study of how genetically determined phenotypes come into being, can be investigated for morphological traits. In this case, phenogenetics starts out as a study of the developmental genetics of morphology. Such studies reveal that the final morphological outcome, which is usually a pleiotropic one, is based upon earlier morphological changes which are in turn preceded by physiological changes occurring still earlier in development. The developmental genetics of morphological features thus becomes explicable in terms of gene-caused physiological changes, or by means of the study of physiological genetics.

The latter studies reveal that the physiological effect of the genotype is sometimes intracellular and sometimes intercellular. The action certain cells have on cells located elsewhere may involve a general or localized control of growth rates and differentiation. This action may occur nearby, via induction, or it may take place at a distance, by means of a general nutritive effect, or by hormones (or nerve impulse or muscular contraction). It is also found that the reacting tissue may have its competence to respond to these influences changed for genetic reasons.

Comprehension of physiological genetics must, in turn, involve an understanding of how genes influence metabolism, and since metabolism involves the study of physical and chemical reactions, phenogenetics must ultimately be described in biophysical and biochemical terms. You may recall, from Chapter 10, that this was the path taken (morphology to physiology to biochemistry) in the phenogenetic study of the gene for sickle cell anemia.

REFERENCES

Beutler, E., Yeh, M., and Fairbanks, V. F., "The Normal Human Female as a Mosaic of X-Chromosome Activity; Studies Using the Gene for G-6-PD-Deficiency as a Marker," Proc. Nat. Acad. Sci., U.S., 48:9–16, 1962.

Gluecksohn-Waelsch, S., "Physiological Genetics of the Mouse," Adv. in Genet., 4:2–49, 1951.

Goldschmidt, R. B., *Theoretical Genetics*, Berkeley, University of California Press, 1955.

Hadorn, E., *Developmental Genetics and Lethal Factors*, New York, John Wiley & Sons, 1961.

Landauer, W., "On the Chemical Production of Developmental Abnormalities," J. Cell Comp. Physiol., 43 (Suppl.):261–305, 1954.

Waddington, C. H., *Organizers and Genes*, Cambridge University Press, 1947.

Wright, S., "The Physiology of the Gene," Physiol. Rev., 41:487–527, 1941.

RICHARD BENEDICT GOLDSCHMIDT (*1878–1958*). (*By permission of Genetics, Inc., vol. 45, p. 1, 1960.*)

QUESTIONS FOR DISCUSSION

30.1. In what way does the study of genes help us understand normal embryonic development?

30.2. If most somatic cells have the same genetic content, why do different cells differentiate in different ways?

30.3. In what ways can genes regulate embryonic development?

30.4. Do the studies of Creeper, of Brachy, or of pituitary dwarfism in mice offer any support for the view that most, if not all, genes have a single primary effect?

30.5. What is the relationship between phenogenetics, developmental genetics, physiological genetics, and biochemical genetics?

30.6. Discuss the comparative importance of genes that act earlier, as compared with those which act later, in development.

30.7. Do you suppose that all genes act at all times in all cells of the body? Why?

30.8. "This Chapter tells more about development than it does about genes." Do you agree? Why?

Chapter *31

BIOCHEMICAL GENETICS (I)

IT WAS stated earlier (p. 16) that the nucleus is known to be very active chemically. While this conclusion can be justified by abundant evidence, let us consider one particular line of support at this time. It is possible [1] to remove the zygotic nucleus of a fertilized frog egg by microsurgery. The enucleated cell, so produced, cannot perform normally the functions of maintenance, growth, cell division, and differentiation, and eventually undergoes degeneration because of the failure of normal *metabolism* — the normal chemical reactions necessary to carry on such functions. That the metabolic failure is attributable to the loss of the nucleus, rather than being an effect of the operation, can be proven by the fact that zygotes undergoing similar operations without being enucleated subsequently show normal behavior. Most important, moreover, is the fact that the same or a similar nucleus can be replaced in a second operation, which is then followed by normal zygotic activity. We may conclude, therefore, that the nucleus is essential for normal metabolism, that is, for the cell's normal chemical activity, which has as its consequences cell maintenance, growth, multiplication, and differentiation.

Let us make the simplest assumption, namely, that the nuclear components which are essential for normal metabolism are the genes in the chromosomes. Let us presume also, as the simplest explanation, that all of the features of metabolism which are unique

to cells are the direct or indirect consequence of genic action. On this basis, then, all aspects of the phenotype having a genetic origin are founded upon the biochemical effects of genes. We would predict, because of the presence of numerous chemical substances in a cell, that one gene-initiated biochemical reaction would usually lead to others, which in turn would lead to still others, to form a kind of tree, whose successive branchings represent successive chemical reactions. Since all the branches would have been affected by the initial gene-caused biochemical change, one should find many different chemical, and/or physiological, and/or morphological consequences of it in the fully developed cell or individual. It would not be surprising to find, therefore, that a given genetic change has many different effects upon the phenotype, and that most, if not all, mutants have *manifold or pleiotropic effects* (see Chapters 10 and 30). It would also be expected, when these pleiotropic effects are traced back toward their origin, that the many different end effects would be found to be the consequence of fewer earlier-produced effects. Moreover, in tracing this pedigree of causes back toward its genic origin, we would also expect the more primary causes to be based upon metabolic changes, changes sometimes identifiable with modifications of particular chemical substances (such as hemoglobin in Chapter 10, or pituitary hormone in Chapter 30).

With this orientation in mind, let us attempt a study of the biochemical basis of gene action, an area of investigation which we can label *biochemical genetics*. Where shall we look for information regarding the biochemical basis of gene action? It might be fruitful to study a trait like eye color, which itself is describable in terms of chemical substances, pigments, for there might be, in this case, a relatively short series of steps to trace back before arriving at, or near, the primary gene-caused biochemical changes.

[1] Based upon work of R. Briggs and J. T. King.

271

You may recall (p. 53) that the dull-red eye color of wild-type *Drosophila* is due to the presence of both brown and red pigments. There are a large number of allelic and nonallelic point mutants that change eye color. Homozygotes for the mutant *brown*, *bw*, which are otherwise genetically wild-type, have brown eyes because they cannot make the red pigment. On the other hand, mutant individuals pure for *vermilion*, *v*, or for *cinnabar*, *cn*, cannot make the brown pigment, and so, even though otherwise genetically wild-type, have bright red eye color. Of course, flies pure for *bw*, and either *v* or *cn*, have white eyes, since they cannot make either the red or the brown pigments.

A series of investigations was initiated [2] to determine the effect that transplantation of prospective eye tissue has upon the type of eye color it later shows. The larva of *Dro-*

[2] By G. W. Beadle and B. Ephrussi.

FIGURE 31–1. *Results of transplanting eye anlage between* Drosophila *larvae.*

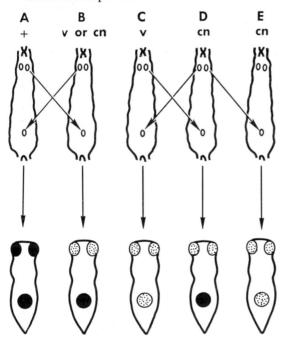

sophila contains prospective compound eye tissue in the form of *anlagen*, or *imaginal discs*. It became feasible to transplant an eye anlage from one larva into the body cavity of another and have development continue to completion. When the adult emerged from the pupal case, its own eye color and, after being dug out, the eye color of the implant, could be scored. It was found that if an implant was genetically the same as the host, all eyes developed the expected color (Figure 31–1, E). Moreover, the eye anlage of most mutants, when transplanted into wild-type larvae, developed the mutant eye color, even though the host eyes were wild-type. In these cases, therefore, the implant developed autonomously, and the host provided nothing which modified the development of the mutant phenotype in this respect.

There were two exceptions, however. If either *v* or *cn* discs (from homozygotes for *v* or *cn*) were transplanted into a wild-type host (B into A in the Figure), they developed into eyes with the dull-red color of the wild-type. In these cases, then, the wild-type host supplied something which the transplanted anlage needed to develop brown pigment. It was shown that what the wild-type host contributed was a diffusible substance. This substance itself was not brown pigment, but could be utilized metabolically by the implant to synthesize brown pigment.

It is a reasonable presumption, therefore, that *cn* and *v* are defective in the production of some substance which is present in wild-type, and which is essential for the subsequent formation of brown pigment.

Three kinds of explanations are possible for the two exceptional transplantation results. First, *cn* and *v* may be defective in the same way and fail to produce the same chemical precursor of brown pigment. If this is so, then reciprocal transplants of eye anlage between cn and v larvae should produce only the mutant (bright red) eye color. But, it is also possible that the *cn* and *v* mutants are defective in different ways. In this event, a second explanation can be based upon the possibility that the biochemical effects of the two different mutants are produced independently of each other. This can be visualized in the following way. Suppose that brown pigment has as two of its precursors a v^+ *substance* produced by the v^+ gene and a cn^+ *substance* produced by the cn^+ gene. If these substances are produced independently of each other, then a $v/v\ cn^+/cn^+$ larva should produce only cn^+ substance, and a $v^+/v^+\ cn/cn$ larva only v^+ substance. Reciprocal eye anlage transplants between these two larvae should produce wild-type eye color in the implants, if both precursors are diffusible, since whichever of the two precursors is missing in the implant will be furnished by its host.

Thirdly and finally, the two precursors of brown pigment may be different but related to, or dependent upon, each other in their production. The amount of relation or dependency between the two precursors might be of several kinds, and of almost any degree — ranging from almost complete independence to complete dependency. Dependency would be complete and unambiguous if the formation of one precursor had to precede the formation of the other precursor. Suppose, to make this example specific, that the hypothesized cn^+ substance is synthesized from the hypothesized v^+ substance. This means that v^+ substance is a precursor of cn^+ substance. In this particular case, what

should be the result of implanting a v anlage in a cn host? The host $(v^+/v^+\ cn/cn)$ manufactures v^+ substance (which the implant, $v/v\ cn^+/cn^+$ cannot make); the implant can convert this into cn^+ substance which, in turn, can be converted to brown pigment. This pigment together with red would make the implant eye wild-type. What is the result expected from the reciprocal transplant of a cn anlage in a v larva? Since the implanted cn disc $(v^+/v^+\ cn/cn)$ lacks the ability to make cn^+ substance, and does not receive this from the v host $(v/v\ cn^+/cn^+)$, no brown pigment should be formed and the transplant should form a bright red eye color.

When the reciprocal transplantations actually were made (D into C, and C into D in Figure 31–1) the specific results last hypothesized were obtained; that is, a cn disc in a v host remains cinnabar, while a v disc in a cn host becomes wild-type. Such results also rule out the first two types of explanations presented. What we are presumably dealing with is a chain of chemical reactions (Figure 31–2A) involving a minimum of four chemical substances: a precursor (1) which through the action of gene v^+ is converted to v^+ substance (2) which is converted by gene cn^+ into cn^+ substance (3), which is in turn converted to brown pigment (4). Note that v blocks the chemical pathway to brown pigment at an earlier stage than does cn. The transplantation results further support the concept that the chemical intermediates, formed prior to

FIGURE 31–2. *Chain of chemical reactions involved in the formation of brown eye pigment in* Drosophila.

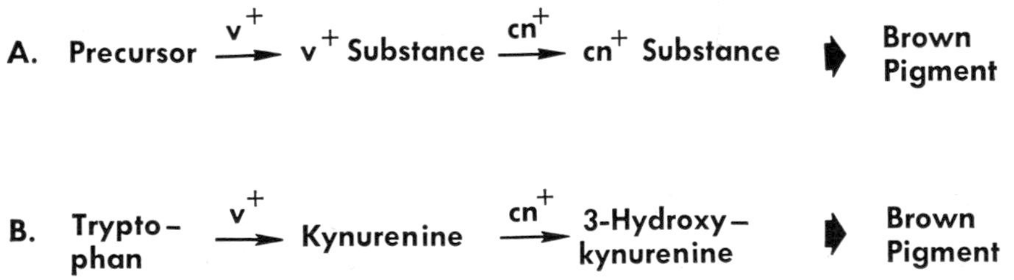

A. **Precursor** $\xrightarrow{v^+}$ v^+ **Substance** $\xrightarrow{cn^+}$ cn^+ **Substance** ▶ **Brown Pigment**

B. **Trypto- phan** $\xrightarrow{v^+}$ **Kynurenine** $\xrightarrow{cn^+}$ **3-Hydroxy- kynurenine** ▶ **Brown Pigment**

a blocked reaction, accumulate (as v^+ substance accumulates in a cinnabar larva), and can be used by a mutant that cannot form these intermediates (as does a v disc implanted in a cn host).

Subsequent work has confirmed these hypotheses and has elucidated the specific chemical nature of some of the substances involved; these are indicated in the appropriate position in Figure 31–2B. It was found, for example, that the v^+ substance is kynurenine, and that the cn^+ substance is 3-hydroxykynurenine. Note that the v and cn genes apparently block adjacent reactions in a sequence of reactions. You may ask next, by what mechanism do these mutant genes block these chemical reactions, or, conversely, by what means do the normal genes v^+ and cn^+ accomplish the chemical conversions into kynurenine and 3-hydroxykynurenine, respectively.

Kynurenine is converted to 3-hydroxykynurenine by the addition of a hydroxyl (OH) group. We can imagine two general ways that cn^+ could accomplish this. One might involve the manufacture by cn^+ of a unique, not otherwise produced, hydroxyl-containing substance capable of reacting with kynurenine to produce its chemical conversion. The other mechanism would presume that kynurenine and this hydroxyl-containing compound normally are both present in the same cell but react together in the desired way either not at all or with negligible frequency in the absence of cn^+. In this case, the presence of cn^+ would serve to expedite the chemical reaction, so it occurs with the required frequency and speed.

There are two unique features of cells known to be involved in expediting (or hindering) chemical reactions, features which are absent from nonliving mixtures of chemical substances. One of these involves the organization of certain cell components into structures (*intracellular organelles*) whose parts have specific physical relationships to each other. It is possible that different genotypes produce structural changes in the organelles so that a chemical reaction which could take place in one genotype is physically impossible in another genotype, because the reactants are spatially separated, and vice versa. The second unique feature for the regulation of metabolism in living material (*protoplasm*) is the occurrence of *enzymes*, organic catalysts which speed up chemical reactions between other chemical substances. It is also possible, then, that one genotype may have less, or none, of an enzyme produced by another genotype. Since many enzymes are known to be located in, or to comprise part of, organelles, it should be realized that a genetic change might result in a change in both structure and enzyme simultaneously. It is also possible that the manufacture of a unique substance, which may be of a nonenzyme nature, might affect cell structure and/or enzyme formation. In fact, it is possible that a change in any one of these three kinds of effects could automatically involve the others.

Can we eliminate any of these three explanations for gene action in the case of v^+ and cn^+? Even though kynurenine is diffusible between one cell and another, and therefore within a cell also, we cannot eliminate a purely spatial change in the structure of some organelle as the primary effect of the cn mutant. Moreover, it is also possible that cn fails to manufacture some unique hydroxyl-containing substance to combine with kynurenine, or that it fails to produce the specific enzyme required to couple already present hydroxyl to kynurenine.

Let us discuss next the biochemical genetics of certain traits in human beings, in the hope that we may be able to obtain more evidence concerning the mechanism whereby genes act to direct the chemical activities of protoplasm. There is a rare condition in man characterized by the fact that, beginning at birth, the urine, though normal in color when passed, soon darkens on contact with air and turns from light to dark brown and finally to black. This characteristic persists throughout the life of the individual. Affected persons are not otherwise greatly inconvenienced, although in middle or old age there is a greater tendency to develop arthritis. Older affected individuals may also show a bluish discoloration of their nose, ears, and knuckles, so that cartilage, tendons, and even bones can develop this pigment.

Family, pedigree, and population studies reveal (1) that normal parents may have affected children of either sex, (2) several siblings from normal parents may be affected, (3) affected children appear with a much higher incidence when their normal parents are related than when they are unrelated. In view of these results, and the fact that the blackening of the urine is expressed fully or not expressed at all, it can be concluded that affected individuals are homozygous for a single pair of autosomally linked genes.

The blackening is known to be due to the oxidation of a substance present in urine called *alcapton*, or *homogentisic acid*, whose chemical description is *2,5-dihydroxyphenylacetic acid* (cf. Figure 21–3). The disease is called *alcaptonuria*,[3] and affected individuals are *alcaptonurics*. It should be noted also that several pedigrees have been found in which apparently the same phenotype is attributable to the action of a single dominant gene. It is not surprising that the same biochemical phenotype can be produced by two different genotypes, for we have already found this to be true in the failure of brown pigment formation in *Drosophila*. Since dominant alcaptonuria has not been studied extensively biochemically, we shall confine our attention henceforth to the recessive form of this disease.

Alcaptonuria is clearly an *inborn error of metabolism*, and results in the daily excretion

[3] The account following is based upon the work of A. E. Garrod and subsequent investigators.

of several grams of alcapton. A study of the biochemistry of alcaptonurics shows that no other substance, among numerous others tested for, appears in abnormal quantities in the urine or blood, and that the reducing properties of the urine can be attributed entirely to the alcapton it contains. From these results it would seem that we have traced the pedigree of causes back to, or very close to, the primary effect of the gene. The question we may ask is whether the abnormal gene manufactures alcapton, or affects organelles, or modifies enzymes.

If alcapton is a substance produced by the abnormal gene, it should be absent in homozygotes for the normal allele. Now, when alcaptonurics are fed five grams of alcapton, approximately this additional amount is excreted in the urine. But when normal individuals are fed the same quantity of alcapton, no alcapton is found in the urine. If, however, normal individuals are fed eight grams of alcapton, some alcapton is found in the urine. We can conclude from this that normal people have the ability to metabolize alcapton to another form which does not become pigmented upon exposure to air, but that this ability has been lost, apparently completely, by alcaptonurics. So, the abnormal gene does not produce its effect by forming alcapton as a unique substance. Apparently alcapton is a normal product of metabolism which does not accumulate in normal individuals because it is further metabolized rapidly, but which does accumulate in alcaptonurics because of an organelle or enzymatic defect. Clear evidence has been obtained that it is an enzyme which has been changed in the abnormal genotype. For it has been found that the blood of alcaptonurics is deficient in an enzyme, normally present, which catalyzes the conversion of alcapton by oxidation to a noncolor-producing substance, and this enzyme, homogentisate oxidase, is in fact missing in the liver of the alcaptonuric.

If alcapton is not produced by the gene for alcaptonuria, but is a normal metabolic intermediate, it may have chemical precursors. If such a chemical precursor is added to the diet of alcaptonurics, it should be converted to alcapton which should be excreted in increased amounts. When alcaptonurics are fed an excess of glucose, the amount of alcapton found is unchanged, indicating that glucose is not a precursor of alcapton. But, if p-OH phenylpyruvic acid, or if either of the amino acids tyrosine or phenylalanine is increased in the diet of alcaptonurics, their excretion of alcapton is increased almost correspondingly. Accordingly, it can be postulated that there is a series of chemical precursors of alcapton (Figure 31–3). In the scheme illustrated, phenylalanine is nor-

FIGURE 31–3. *Sequence of chemical substances involved in the formation and metabolism of alcapton. 4 = homogentisate oxidase, 5 = isomerase, 6 = hydrolase.*

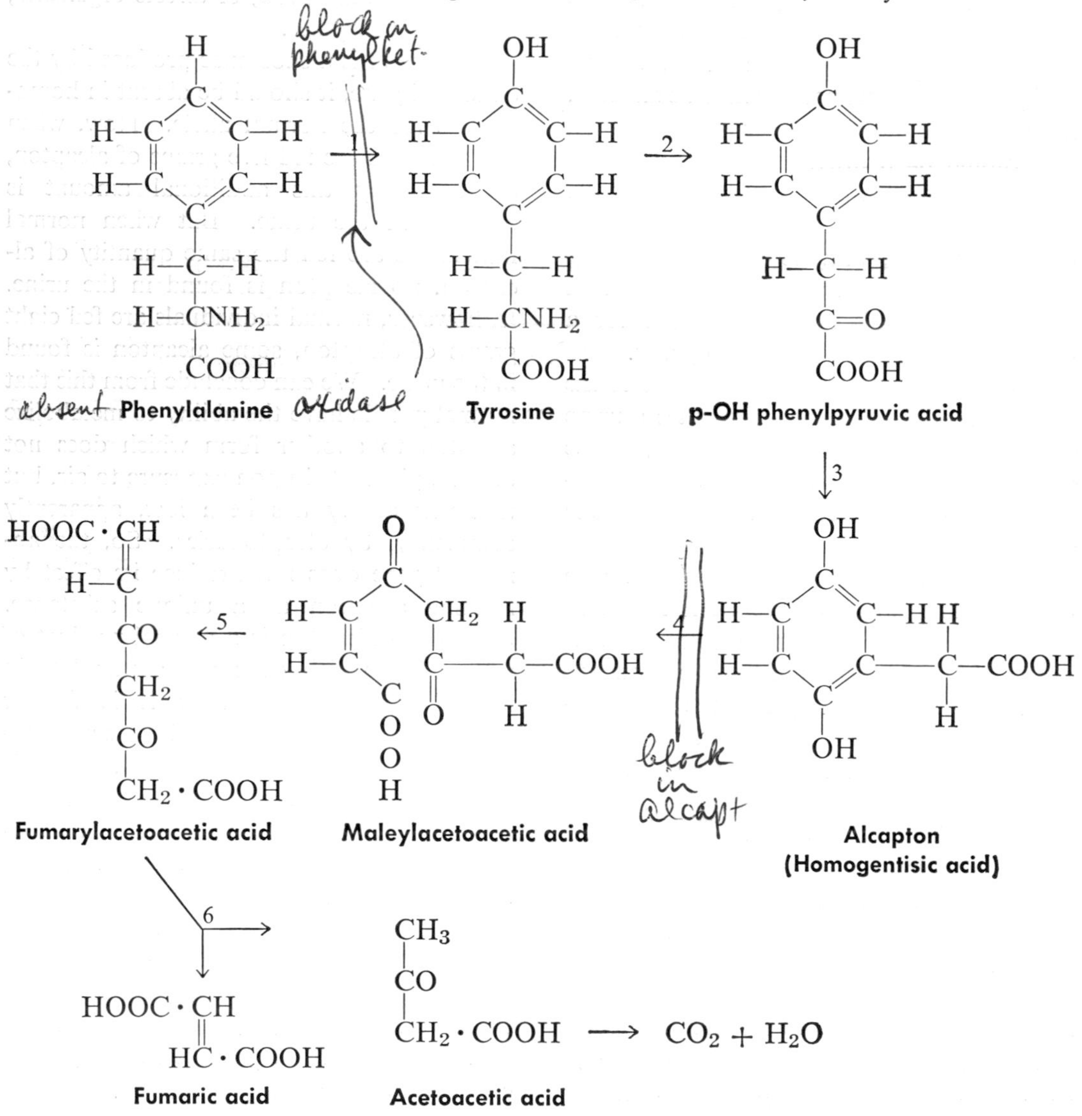

mally converted to tyrosine by the addition of an oxygen to the top carbon; tyrosine is normally converted to p-OH phenylpyruvic acid by replacing the amine (NH_2) group by an oxygen; p-OH phenylpyruvic acid is converted, by still other chemical reactions, to alcapton. Alcapton is normally converted to acetoacetic acid, by a process which involves the splitting-open of the benzene ring; it is the first step in this conversion which fails in alcaptonurics. This hypothesized pathway from phenylalanine via alcapton to acetoacetic acid has been confirmed in subsequent work, as the result of which six enzymatically catalyzed steps have been identified.

It should be realized, however, that tyrosine, which is an essential component of protein, can also partake in biochemical pathways other than the one that leads to alcapton (Figure 31-3). It has been found, for example, that tyrosine is part of the pathway of chemical reactions leading to melanin formation. So, tyrosine, by a different chemical pathway, is also a precursor of melanin. Albinism (lack or absence of melanin) could be caused genetically by the defective production of an enzyme necessary for the conversion of tyrosine to melanin.

In another disease, which is due to a single rare recessive gene, affected individuals are feebleminded, or of lower than normal mental ability, and have other phenotypic changes, including light pigmentation. This pleiotropism has been directly correlated with the presence of phenylpyruvic acid, which is toxic, in the urine of affected individuals. It has been shown that the normal conversion of phenylalanine to tyrosine fails to occur in affected individuals, and instead, the amine in phenylalanine is replaced by an oxygen (thus forming a keto group), so that phenylpyruvic acid is produced (Figure 31-4). Diseased persons are therefore *phenylpyruvics or phenylketonurics* (see Chapter 27). The disease, *phenylketonuria*, can be partially

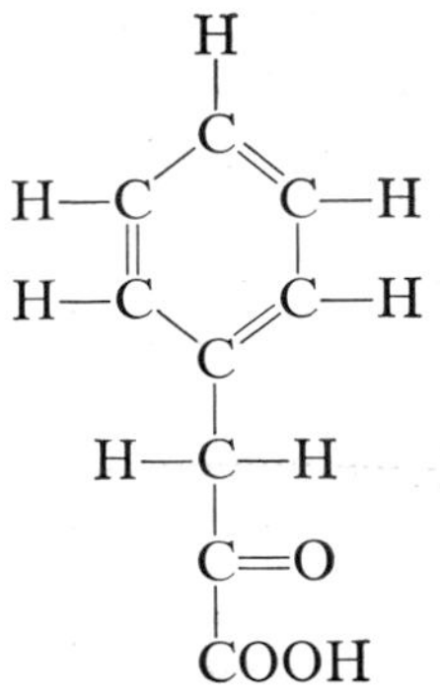

FIGURE 31–4. *Formula for phenylpyruvic acid.*

alleviated, or circumvented, if dietary phenylalanine is reduced to an amount that is enough for protein synthesis (for the presence of this amino acid is also essential in our proteins), but not enough so that any appreciable amount is converted to phenylpyruvic acid. Note that since tyrosine is also needed for human protein, this substance must also be included in sufficient quantity in the diet of phenylketonurics. Finally, it should be noted that a parahydroxylase enzyme that converts phenylalanine to tyrosine and is normally present in the liver has been found missing, or defective, in phenylketonurics. What is meant when an enzyme is said to be missing? This may mean either the total absence of the enzyme molecule, or else its presence in such a modified form that the molecule has lost the ability to perform its characteristic catalysis.

These studies of metabolic defects have been of great service in identifying the places where genes act to direct metabolic processes. They also permit the determination of precursors of a genetically defected step, and aid in the final elucidation of chains of biochemical reactions, and of metabolic pathways. For example, substance X is proven a precursor of substance Y, if mutant 1 cannot form Y but accumulates X, and if mutant 2 cannot form Y unless X is supplied (Figure 31-5). But biochemical genetics is of especial interest in another respect. We have seen, in the cases most thoroughly investigated, that

FIGURE 31–5.
Determination of precursors using mutant genes.
A accumulates X but makes no Y.
B makes no X but will make Y if X is supplied.
C is the normal pathway.

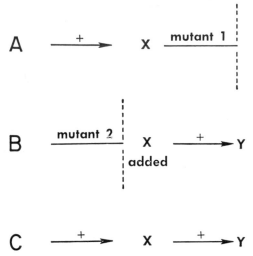

it has been possible to trace the pedigree of causes back to a point at which only one effect of the gene can be detected. This was true, for example, in the case of alcaptonuria. It is still possible (though improbable) that further study of this case would reveal that the gene for alcaptonuria, besides producing an effect upon the particular enzyme that metabolizes alcapton, has another effect which has no determinable relation to the enzyme effect. Such a finding would suggest that this gene acts upon the phenotype in more than one primary way.

In most of the book up to this point, we have employed the phenotypic effects produced by genetic differences to reveal the nature of the genetic material. Nevertheless, the properties of segments of the genetic material were described not in terms of phenotypic effects, but in terms of recombination and mutation. In this Chapter and certain preceding ones (particularly those Chapters not marked by asterisks), we were concerned more with the nature and consequences of the phenotypic effects produced by the genetic

material than we were with discovering the recombinational and mutational properties of this material. What have we learned about the way that the genetic material produces its phenotypic effects? We could cite abundant evidence that the genetic material does not act upon the phenotype as one single indivisible unit, but acts as though it is segmented into a number of units, or genes, each of which has a specific phenotypic effect. (Such units or genes for phenotypic effect were revealed because mutation made changes in genes, these different genes underwent recombination, and served, in some way, to produce different phenotypic effects.)

The simplest hypothesis is that the genetic unit of phenotypic effect is identical to the genetic unit of recombination, for in all our previous discussion the recombinational gene seemed to be identical with the phenotypically functional gene. But, it must be emphasized, because these two views of a gene are revealed through the use of different operational procedures, that the gene as a unit of phenotypic effect, the functional gene, could be larger than, identical to, or smaller than the recombinational gene. (We have already noted, on p. 199, the possibility that the segment of the genetic material defined by the recombinational gene may not be identical with the material affected when a single recombinational gene undergoes mutation.)

Our study of the genetic material revealed that it contains several different sized units of genetic recombination, including the genome, chromosome, and chromosome segment. The term *gene* came to be used to refer to the smallest unit of the genetic material capable of undergoing recombination. The study of the genetic material also showed there were different sized units of mutation — the genome, chromosome, and chromosome segment. It should now be apparent that we ought to embark upon a study to determine the smallest unit of the genetic material capable of producing a phenotypic effect. This, too, can be called a gene. Now that we have genes which are to be defined by at least two different operations, it becomes inconvenient for the reader to have to decide from context, each time the term *gene* is used, whether the gene referred to is defined by recombination or by phenotypic effect. Accordingly, let us give these two genetic units specific names, even though we have no evidence so far that they differ in their material basis. We can define *a recon as the smallest unit of the genetic material which is capable of recombination,* and *a cistron as the smallest unit of the genetic material capable of producing a phenotypic effect.* When the less specific, nonoperational, term *gene* is used, henceforth, it will refer to the smallest unit of the genetic material as identified by these, and especially other, operations.

Note that the recon, or cistron, is not defined in terms of properties which are beyond experimental test (see p. xi). For example, although the recon is part of the genetic material, we do not endow it with assumed or established properties of the total genetic material. Moreover, the recon is not the smallest unit of the genetic material capable of self-replication, of mutation, or of phenotypic influence. Notice also that there is no restriction as to the lower limit for the size of the recon or the cistron.

The study of biochemical genetics in the present Chapter (and also in Chapter 10) leads us to make the simplest hypothesis, namely, that a cistron produces only a single primary phenotypic effect, and that all its pleiotropic effects are consequent to this single activity. We can call this hypothesis a *one cistron-one primary phenotypic effect* relationship. If this hypothesis can be further tested and supported, we may be able to use the information gained in reverse, so to speak, to learn more about the size or scope of the genetic material required to produce a single primary effect. This would give us information regarding the nature of a cistron. But you should realize that the kind of information we obtain about the cistron will depend upon what we consider to be primary and what we identify as a phenotypic effect.

SUMMARY AND CONCLUSIONS

While the genes detected by recombination and by phenotypic effect are related to each other, their material basis need not be identical. The recon and cistron are defined, respectively, as the smallest unit of the genetic material capable of recombination, and of phenotypic effect.

The biochemical activities necessary for the existence of protoplasm are controlled by the nucleus, presumably by the cistrons it contains. These chemical reactions occur in sequences that form often-branched metabolic pathways leading to the chemical, physical, physiological, developmental, and morphological aspects of the phenotype. As a consequence of this branching, most, if not all, cistrons have pleiotropic effects.

The phenotypic differences produced by alternative cistrons can be traced by a pedigree of causes back toward the cistron. Such studies demonstrate that cistrons produce their effects at the metabolic level. It is reasoned that such action could involve the structural components of protoplasm (organelles) or particular chemical substances, including enzymes specifically, although none of these effects need exclude any of the others.

The study of inborn errors of metabolism in man demonstrates that cistrons control various steps in biochemical sequences, through their influence upon enzymes. At least in these particular cases, the effect on enzymes can be supposed to be the primary and only consequence of the action of a segment of the genetic material.

In view of the experimental results, a one cistron-one primary effect relationship is hypothesized.

REFERENCES

Bearn, A. G., "The Chemistry of Hereditary Disease," Scient. Amer., 195:126–136, 1956.

Ephrussi, B., "Chemistry of 'Eye Color Hormones' of Drosophila," Quart. Rev. Biol., 17:327–338, 1942.

Harris, H., *Human Biochemical Genetics*, Cambridge University Press, 310 pp., 1959.

Hsia, D. Y.–Y., *Inborn Errors of Metabolism*, Chicago, The Year Book Publishers, 1959.

Wagner, R. P., and Mitchell, H. K., *Genetics and Metabolism*, New York, John Wiley & Sons, 1955.

HARRIET EPHRUSSI-TAYLOR (*see p. 341*), BORIS EPHRUSSI, *and* LEO SZILARD (*see p. 336*) *at Cold Spring Harbor, N.Y. in 1951. (Courtesy of the Long Island Biological Association.)*

QUESTIONS FOR DISCUSSION

31.1. List five diseases in human beings that are caused by inborn errors of metabolism.

31.2. In what respect can an inborn error of metabolism be cured?

31.3. Do all mutations produce inborn errors of metabolism? Explain.

31.4. What evidence can you present that cistrons control different steps of a bio-synthetic sequence of reactions?

31.5. Has our study of recons and recon mutation been dependent upon the concept of a cistron? Explain.

31.6. Do you suppose that proof of the one cistron-one primary effect hypothesis would reveal anything regarding the chemical properties of a gene? Explain.

31.7. From which of these areas of investigation would you expect to obtain the most information regarding the cistron — morphology, physiology, biochemistry? Why?

31.8. Do you think that the concept of the cistron has any consequences for the practice of medicine? Explain.

31.9. In what way is our study of the cistron related to, or dependent upon, mutation and recons?

31.10. Discuss the evidence relative to the diffusibility of v^+ substance and cn^+ substance.

Chapter *32

BIOCHEMICAL GENETICS (II)

IT HAS been hypothesized that the cistron has a single, primary effect on the phenotype. This hypothesis is of value insofar as it provides motivation for studies aimed at determining whether a given segment of genetic substance has, in fact, a single, primary action. We found, in the last Chapter, that investigations of specific genes, causing inborn errors of metabolism, gave support to this view. There is an additional implication of the one cistron-one primary effect hypothesis. If we knew the nature of such a primary effect it should always prove to be the product of one cistron. It may be possible to subject this prediction to test also. In order to do so it will be necessary to decide which particular aspects of the phenotype are primary products of cistronic action.

We have already discussed, in the previous Chapter, cases where the primary effect of a mutant cistron is upon the capacity of an enzyme to catalyze a particular reaction. Since different enzymes catalyze different reactions, each is said to show specificity of action. The mutants referred to resulted in a change in enzyme specificity. Let us presume that the specificities of all enzymes found in protoplasm are the result of the primary action of cistrons. If this is so, then it ought to be possible to study any particular enzyme and find that its specificity can be changed for genetic reasons. Let us proceed to study this hypothesis experimentally as a specific, if limited, test of the more general concept, one primary effect-one cistron.

We have already described the use of *Neurospora* as material for studies of genetic recombination (beginning p. 121). Certain characteristics of *Neurospora* also make the organism very favorable material for biochemical studies. *Neurospora* can manufacture all of the components it needs for existence and reproduction from a very simple, basic, food medium. This basic medium may consist solely of water, an array of inorganic salts, including sources of nitrogen, phosphorus, sulfur, and various essential trace elements, a carbon and energy source such as cane sugar, and a single vitamin, biotin. From these raw materials it can synthesize some 20 different amino acids, all essential vitamins (but biotin), compounds like purines and pyrimidines, and everything else it needs for its total activity. According to the hypothesis under consideration, it should be possible to induce mutations in cistrons, which should then fail to correctly specify enzymes, so that various chemical syntheses should become blocked.

Previous work has established that the last step in the synthesis of *vitamin B$_1$*, or *thiamin*, is normally accomplished by the enzymatic combination of a particular thiazole with a particular pyrimidine. If enzymes owe their specificities to cistrons, it should be possible to induce a mutation in the cistron that normally specifies this B$_1$-forming enzyme. If the mutant no longer specifies active B$_1$-forming enzyme, no B$_1$ will be made. Then, since B$_1$ is required for growth, the mutant mold will require B$_1$ in its diet in order to grow.

What is done [1] is to obtain haploid spores (produced asexually by the haploid organism grown from an ascospore) and treat them with a mutagenic agent (like X rays or ultraviolet light). The treated spores are then grown on the basic medium which has been supplemented with vitamin B$_1$. Under these circumstances the spores that grow will in-

[1] Based upon work of G. W. Beadle and E. L. Tatum.

clude those which can still make B_1 themselves, and those which can no longer make it, but which obtain B_1 from the culture medium. Once the spores have grown sufficiently, a portion of each of the haploid growths can be placed on the basic, minimal medium, which contains no B_1. Those samples that continue to grow when transplanted to minimal medium are presumably nonmutant, in respect that they can perform all the biochemical steps leading to B_1 production; those samples that fail to grow presumably carry mutants involving failure to make B_1. Those failing to grow might be mutants which lack a precursor of B_1, a precursor whose presence as such is not essential for growth, but which is essential for subsequent B_1 synthesis. Any mutant of this type can be eliminated from further consideration if it grows on minimal medium supplemented with the particular thiazole and pyrimidine which are the immediate precursors of vitamin B_1. (All other imaginable nutritional factors except B_1 itself may also be added, but they would have no effect on the decision being made.) The residue of cultures, which grow on medium containing B_1 but not on medium containing the immediate precursors of B_1, are clearly defective for the enzyme that catalyzes the last step in B_1 synthesis.

Each of the haploid strains remaining is then crossed to a haploid strain normal for B_1 synthesis, and each diploid hybrid is studied separately as follows. After the hybrid undergoes meiosis (refer to pp. 121–124), a sac containing eight haploid ascospores is produced. Each of the eight spores is removed and grown on B_1-supplemented minimal medium. If the haploid strain being tested is indeed B_1-deficient because of a mutant, a subsequent transplant of each of the eight haploid cultures to B_1-free minimal medium will produce exactly four that can grow and exactly four that cannot. Note that because all four products of meiosis are recovered and tested, each in duplicate, the 4 : 4 ratio

is purely mechanical and is not subject to errors of sampling, as it would be if a random sample of spores were taken from a large pooled lot made up by mixing the spores from many sacs. When the experiment was performed, mutants were found. These had changed the specificity of the enzyme studied, as expected on our hypothesis.

If, for a given mutant, a number of spore sacs are tested as described, it is also possible to map the location of the mutant relative to the centromere of the chromosome in which it is located. The way in which this is determined is illustrated in Figure 32–1, which shows only the single pair of chromosomes involved. If, as shown in the left portion of the Figure, no chiasma occurs between the loci of the mutant and the centromere, segregation of normal ($+$) and mutant (*th*) recons will occur at the first meiotic division, and, because the last two divisions in the ascus are tandem to the first, the eight ascospores will be in the relative order

$$+ + + + \ th\ th\ th\ th.$$

If, however, a single chiasma does occur between the mutant and the centromere, as shown in the right portion of the Figure, segregation will occur in the second meiotic division, and the ascospores will be in the relative order

$$+ + \ th\ th\ + + \ th\ th.$$

If a record is kept of the order of the spores in each ascus, then these two segregation arrangements can be identified when the spore genotypes are determined later. If 20% of all sacs showed second division segregation (two $+$ spores alternating with two *th* spores), then 20% of the meiotic divisions had a chiasma between the mutant and the centromere. This, you remember, means that the mutant is located 10 map units from the centromere.

When a number of separately occurring point mutants, defective in the enzyme catalyzing the last step in B_1 synthesis, were local-

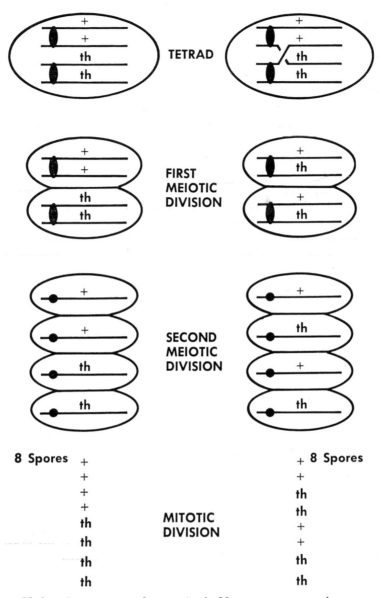

FIGURE 32–1. *Arrangement of spores in the* Neurospora *ascus when segregation occurs at the first meiotic division (left) and at the second meiotic division (right), as determined by the absence and presence, respectively, of a chiasma between the segregating genes and the centromere.*

ized this way, they were all found to be on the same chromosome and appeared to be the same distance from the centromere. This suggests that the specificity of a particular enzyme is the result of the action of a particular cistron.

For the efficient detection of biochemical mutants in *Neurospora*, certain modifications are made in the procedure already outlined. Potentially mutant spores are grown on a medium supplemented with all substances which might conceivably be involved in biochemical mutation. Growing cultures are then transferred to basic (minimal) medium containing no additions, where failure to grow indicates a mutant culture which has lost the ability to synthesize some component added to the basic medium. The specific ability lost is determined by testing for growth in basic medium supplemented in turn with the individual enriching components of the complete medium. Techniques have been developed also to selectively eliminate non-mutant strains. Thus, spores given an opportunity to grow on minimal medium can be subjected either to filtration, which separates the larger (growing) nonmutant cultures from the smaller (nongrowing) mutant ones, or to an antibiotic which kills actively growing cultures, but which has less or no effect on nongrowing ones. In this way, the sample later tested for mutants can be mutant-enriched. It is even possible to find mutants for unknown growth factors by supplementing the culture medium with extracts of normal strains of *Neurospora* which contain various substances, both known and unknown, that are needed by the mold. The same mutants requiring unknown growth factors can then be used in the specific bioassays needed for the isolation and identification of such substances.

Such improvements in the techniques for detecting biochemical mutants in *Neurospora* expedited additional tests of the enzyme-cistron relationship. Two additional examples will be described briefly. The first study deals with the final step in the synthesis of the amino acid tryptophan, which involves the catalyzed union of indol and the 3-carbon amino acid serine by the enzyme *tryptophan synthetase*. First, separately occurring tryptophan-requiring point mutants were obtained; of these, the only ones tested were those that proved to be blocked in the final synthetic step and were lacking full tryptophan synthetase activity. Of 25 mutants qualifying, all proved to be located on the same chromosome at about the same locus. The second example involved the final step in the synthesis of adenine which is catalyzed by the enzyme *adenylosuccinase* which splits succinic acid off adenylosuccinic acid to leave adenine. Of 137 independently occurring point mutations with little or no adenylosuccinase activity, again, all were on a particular chromosome at about the same locus. The cistrons acting to specify tryptophan synthetase and adenylosuccinase are different, each having completely separate locations in the genome.

These results, and similar ones for other enzymes in *Neurospora*, offer strong support for the hypothesis that the specificity of all enzymes is under cistronic control. Moreover, different enzymes are specified by different cistrons. The fact is observed that the addition of B_1, tryptophan, or adenine to the diet of mutants defective in the enzymes directly responsible for their respective syntheses makes the mold completely, or almost completely, normal. This is good evidence that the cistrons involved have only one function to perform, which is to determine the specificity of one enzyme. If a cistron had more than one primary effect, surmounting one defect nutritionally would not be expected to produce normality or near-normality in all cases. From the results so far described, we might also be tempted to conclude that the total specificity of an enzyme is the result of the primary action of a single cistron, because in all these cases the enzymatic defect was found to be due to a defect in one specific localized area of the genetic map. We can call this the *one enzyme-one cistron hypothesis.*

All enzymes are protein, at least in part, and the specificity of an enzyme is known to be due to its protein content. Proteins are composed of amino acids (Figure 32–2) strung together in chains to form polypeptides, so that the specificity of an enzyme must be attributed to the number and kinds

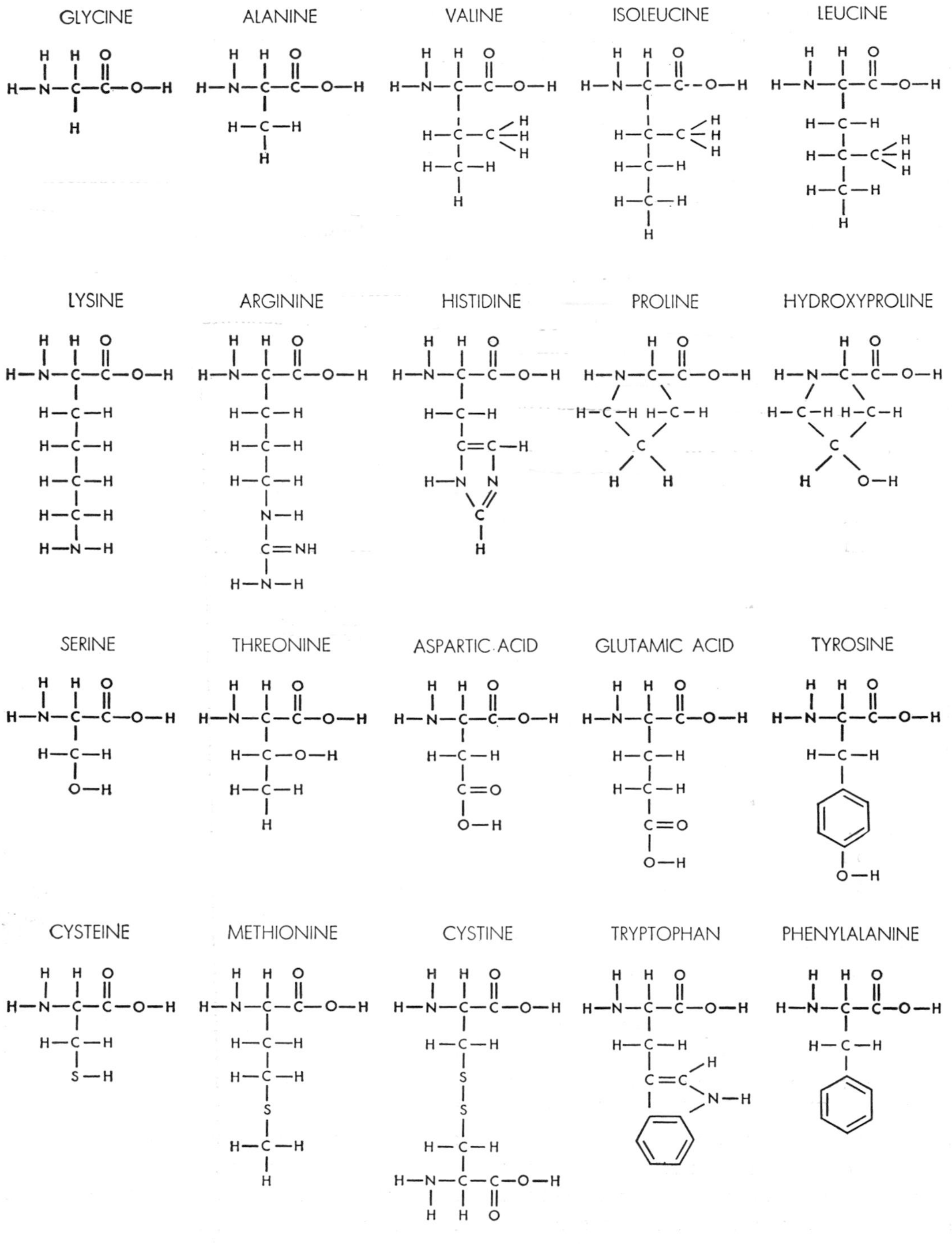

FIGURE 32–2. *The twenty types of common amino acids.*

of amino acids it contains, their order in the polypeptide, the number of polypeptide chains, the way in which the parts of a polypeptide chain are arranged relative to each other, and the way in which the different polypeptide chains in a protein are arranged relative to each other.

It has been possible to study, in some detail, the enzyme tryptophan synthetase that is found in the bacterium *Escherichia coli.* This enzyme can be treated *in vitro* so that it dissociates into two proteins, i.e., two polypeptide chains. By itself, neither of these chains has the usual enzymatic activity. But these two proteins can be reassociated, whereupon the normal enzymatic property is restored. Clearly, then, both portions need to be united in order to have this specific enzymatic action, so that part of the enzyme's specificity must be due to the joining of these two polypeptides. (You might suppose that this part of the specificity is due to the primary action of a single cistron.) But this must be only a portion of the total specificity of this enzyme. Another portion of it must reside in the nature of the polypeptide chains, which when joined make not just any enzyme, but tryptophan synthetase in particular. The fact that the two chains are so easily dissociable and reassociable indicates that these chains do not have a complex physical relationship when joined together, and suggests that each chain might be specified independently. In this case two distinct cistrons would be involved, each one specifying one polypeptide chain.

A number of bacterial mutants were obtained which lacked tryptophan synthetase activity.[2] Some of these defected one polypeptide chain and others defected the second. A genetic study showed that all the mutants defecting one chain were recombinationally separable from those defecting the other, although adjacent areas of the genetic map were involved. In this case, then, we have

[2] Based upon the work of C. Yanofsky.

the choice of considering the two adjacent areas either as a single cistron, or as two separate cistrons. Because the detailed specificity of this enzyme seems to depend upon what each of these two genetic areas does individually, we shall consider that two cistrons are involved. On this alternative, each cistron completely specifies a polypeptide chain, and the union of the two chains comprising tryptophan synthetase may somehow be connected with the fact that the two cistrons involved are adjacent.

How do these results, and our interpretation of them, affect our general hypothesis of one primary effect-one cistron? The answer is that the general hypothesis is not at all affected. However, the specific hypothesis to test it, one enzyme-one cistron, should be made more comprehensive and be stated as *one polypeptide-one cistron.* This means that the total specificity of a polypeptide chain is determined by one cistron. According to the general hypothesis, the primary effect which a cistron has would be, at least in some cases, the complete specification of a polypeptide.

Not all proteins are enzymes. If the hypothesis one polypeptide-one cistron is correct, we should predict that each polypeptide chain in all proteins is completely specified by the primary and solitary action of a single cistron. Consider now certain results obtained by studying the protein *hemoglobin.*[3] Human hemoglobin has a molecular weight of 66,700. In the horse, and probably in man, too, the molecule is spheroidal in shape, and its dimensions are $55 \times 55 \times 70$ A (Angstrom units). It is composed of two half-molecules which are usually exact duplicates of each other. In each half-molecule there are two different polypeptide chains, called α and β, each containing about 150 amino acids. The chains coil to form what are termed right-handed helices, and different

[3] Based upon the work of V. M. Ingram, L. Pauling, H. A. Itano, H. Lehrmann, J. V. Neel, M. F. Perutz, and others.

chains are coiled about each other in a regular way. Each chain has an iron-containing heme group fitting into a pocket on the outer surface of the coil it makes. In the whole hemoglobin molecule, therefore, there are four heme groups, one for each of the two α and two β chains, and a total of about 600 amino acids. Henceforth, we shall be concerned with the protein, or globin, part of this molecule, since the heme groups are not involved in the variations to be considered.

It has been possible to partially digest the globin portion of the molecule with trypsin, an enzyme which splits a polypeptide at every place where either of the amino acids lysine or arginine is present. This produces some 28 smaller polypeptides, or peptides, in duplicate (since there are two chains of each type), plus an undigested core that makes up about 25% of the globin. The 28 peptides can be separated from each other by their differential migration on filter paper when the digest containing them is subjected to an electrical field and various solvents. The result is that there are separate spots or "fingerprints" for each of the peptides on the filter paper (Figure 32–3). Each peptide (fingerprint) is given a different number, and can be further analyzed as to its amino acid content. Peptide 4, for example, normally contains eight amino acids in the following sequence:

Val-His-Leu-Thr-Pro-*Glu*-Glu-Lys . . . .[4]

There is also evidence that the valine is an end amino acid in the β chain. This sequence is found in normal adult hemoglobin, called *hemoglobin A*. The core of globin can be digested with chymotrypsin and fingerprints obtained of its peptides.

Persons heterozygous for the *recon for sickling* have the "sickle cell trait," which is readily detected when their red blood corpuscles are exposed to an oxygen tension very much lower than normal, while persons

[4] Valine, histidine, leucine, threonine, proline, glutamic acid, glutamic acid, lysine.

homozygous for this mutant have "sickle cell anemia," and their red cells will sickle even when the oxygen tension is not so drastically reduced. The hemoglobin of such people has been fingerprinted and analyzed as to amino acid content. The mutant homozygote has hemoglobin apparently identical with hemoglobin A, with the proven exception that the sixth amino acid in peptide 4 has valine substituted for glutamic acid (the particular amino acid italicized in the previously given sequence) (Figure 32–3). The heterozygote produces both this type of abnormal hemoglobin, called *hemoglobin S*, and hemoglobin A. Previous study of the pleiotropism of the recon for sickling (see Chapter 10) showed that all its phenotypic effects are traceable through a pedigree of causes to this single amino acid substitution in the β chain. This is excellent evidence that a change in the specification of a single polypeptide has been produced as a result of the change in the primary action of a cistron whose nature had been changed previously by mutation.

Another mutant is known that is located on the same chromosome as the recon for sickling and is probably an allele of it. This produces *hemoglobin C* which differs from hemoglobin A by replacing the same glutamic acid in the β chain, this time by lysine.

Still another genetic change produces another hemoglobin, *hemoglobin G*. The amino acids in all the trypsin-produced peptides are the same as in hemoglobin A, except that the seventh one from the end in peptide 4 is glycine instead of glutamic acid. In this case, then, the amino acid sequence in peptide 4 is:

Val-His-Leu-Thr-Pro-Glu-*Gly*-Lys . . . .

Here, then, an amino acid in a different position is changed in the β chains. In *hemoglobin E*, a glutamic acid, normally found in peptide 26, is replaced by lysine, and it is likely that this is the only change in the whole molecule. Peptide 26 is also part of the β chain.

While we have seen that there are mutants

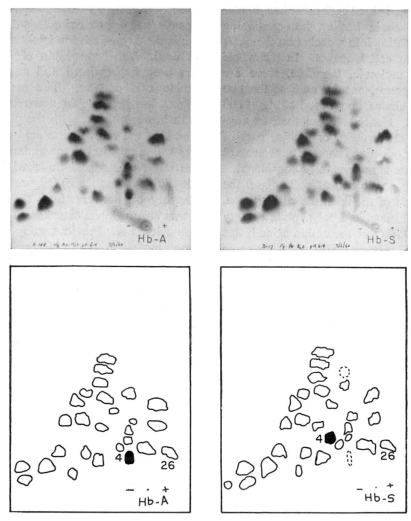

FIGURE 32–3. *The "fingerprints" of hemoglobin obtained following trypsin treatment.* (*Courtesy of V. M. Ingram, from C. Baglioni, Biochim. Biophys. Acta, 48:392-396, 1961.*)

which cause a single amino acid located in different positions in the β chain to be replaced by other single amino acids, the detailed genetic basis for the different mutants is not known as precisely, although in some cases the mutants are believed to be different alleles of the same recon. The available evidence is consistent with the view that all these mutants are at least on the same chromosome.

Still other kinds of hemoglobin have been found in which the amino acid sequence in the α chain has been modified. This is true for *hemoglobin I* (in which a change occurs in peptide 23), and for *hemoglobin "Hopkins-2."*

A person homozygous for hemoglobin A has a molecule describable as $\alpha_2^A \beta_2^A$ (see Figure 32-4), one homozygous for the recon for sickling can be described $\alpha_2^A \beta_2^S$, and one homozygous for the production of hemoglobin I can be written $\alpha_2^I \beta_2^A$. *Hemoglobin H* is produced by persons homozygous for the recon for *thalassemia* (see p. 36); this type of hemoglobin has four β chains of A type (instead of two being α chains), so that it can be written β_4^A. Such homozygous persons also produce some hemoglobin A. It is also known that fetal hemoglobin, *hemoglobin F*, has two α chains like those in adult hemoglobin A; the other two chains are different from β and probably from α also, and are called γ chains, so that hemoglobin F is $\alpha_2^A \gamma_2^F$. Finally, it is known that homozygotes for the sickling recon can make hemoglobin F which is apparently normal, $\alpha_2^A \gamma_2^F$, so that a change in the β chains has no effect on the γ chains.

The results with the recon for sickling prove that the synthesis of the nonenzymatic protein globin is cistron-directed in a primary way. What we would like to decide is whether one or more cistrons are involved. There are several lines of evidence which point to an independent specification of α and β chains:

1. Mutations that change the specifications of the β chain (producing hemoglobins S, C, E, G) produce no change in the α chain.
2. Mutations that change the α chain (producing hemoglobins I, Hopkins-2) produce no change in the β chain.

Further evidence consistent with the independent specification of α and β chains comes from the study of individuals who possess both Hopkins-2 and S hemoglobins. Such individuals are known who have had one parent like themselves and the other of normal blood type (hemoglobin A). However, these individuals also have siblings who have Hopkins-2 but not S hemoglobin, and those who have the reverse. Accordingly, these Hopkins-2 + S persons cannot be monohybrid but must be dihybrid, for the abnormal hemoglobins occur both separately and together in different siblings. Moreover, the number of siblings who must be recombinant

is so large as to preclude the two mutant recons being linked very close together. We may write the genotype of these dihybrids as $m^{Ho-2} \, m^A \, n^S \, n^A$. Since the two recons are not very close together, they may be in different cistrons.

It has been shown that the two α and the two β chains in a given globin molecule are identical, even in heterozygotes. If the Hopkins-2 + S individuals are dihybrid for recons in different cistrons, it would seem reasonable that the two α chains specified by m^{Ho-2} (that is, α_2^{Ho-2}), or by $m^A(\alpha_2^A)$, would be produced independently of the two β chains specified by $n^S(\beta_2^S)$, or by $n^A(\beta_2^A)$. If so, then either product of the two different

FIGURE 32–4. *Normal hemoglobin and some abnormal types due to mutation.*

TYPE	CHAINS	SPECIFIC NAME	
Hgb A	$\alpha_2^A \;\; \beta_2^A$	Adult	Normal
Hgb F	$\alpha_2^A \;\; \gamma_2^F$	Fetal	
Hgb S	$\alpha_2^A \;\; \beta_2^S$	Sickle cell	
Hgb C	$\alpha_2^A \;\; \beta_2^C$		
Hgb G	$\alpha_2^A \;\; \beta_2^G$		
Hgb E	$\alpha_2^A \;\; \beta_2^E$		
Hgb I	$\alpha_2^I \;\; \beta_2^A$		
Hgb Ho-2	$\alpha_2^{Ho-2} \;\; \beta_2^A$	Hopkins No. 2	
Hgb H	β_4^A	Thalassemia	

α-specifying cistrons might be found joined to either of the two different products of the β-specifying cistrons. In this event, the dihybrid under discussion would prove to have all four of the following types of globin: $\alpha_2^{Ho-2}\beta_2^S$, $\alpha_2^{Ho-2}\beta_2^A$, $\alpha_2^A\beta_2^S$, $\alpha_2^A\beta_2^A$. This has been found to be the case (see References at end of Chapter).

The results, showing that sickle cell heterozygotes make normal γ chains and defective β chains, suggest that three different cistrons are involved — one making α chains, one β, and one γ. What working relationship might these three cistrons have? Subsequent to birth, the cistron that makes γ chains normally has its action turned off, so to speak, and that for β chains is turned on. In the case of thalassemia major, the γ cistron is turned off, and the β turned on, as in normal people, but the α cistron often fails to be turned on; when the α cistron is turned on, hemoglobin A is produced, and when it is not, hemoglobin H (β_4^A) is produced. (One might expect the t. major fetus to have γ_4^F and $\alpha_2^A\gamma_2^F$ hemoglobin since the β chains are not being produced. One would also expect that an adult with hemoglobin I, $\alpha_2^I\beta_2^A$, would also produce abnormal fetal hemoglobin of type $\alpha_2^I\gamma_2^F$.)

All results support the view that each different polypeptide chain is specified by a single but different cistron. However, because of the rarity of heterozygotes, for mutants in different cistrons specifying hemoglobin, and the paucity of linkage data in man, it is difficult to obtain precise data on the relative positions of the different cistrons. For the same reasons, it is difficult to study the allelism of hemoglobin mutants affecting the same chain, which presumably involve defects in the same cistron. What kind of study would we like to be able to make in this respect?

Heterozygotes for two mutants in the same cistron would usually have received one mutant from each parent. If the cistron was identical to, or smaller than, the recon, the genotype could be written $\dfrac{m_1}{m_2}$, the mutants would always segregate (barring mutation, including nondisjunction), and all gametes would receive either m_1 or m_2 but never both or neither. This kind of result would prove the mutants were reconically allelic (see Chapter 22). If, however, the cistron was larger than a recon, being composed of a number of recons, the mutations involved would sometimes have been in two different recons of a cistron. In this case the heterozygote hypothesized would be reconically dihybrid, $\dfrac{m_1 +}{+ m_2}$, and crossing over would, on rare occasions, give rise to gametes of $m_1 m_2$ type and of $++$ type. (To obtain evidence for intracistron recombination one would prefer to test individuals who are heterozygous for both hemoglobins S and E, say, rather than those that are heterozygous for S and G. For the latter might involve adjacent recons between which crossing over might be very rare, and one might fail to obtain the crossover and conclude incorrectly that these mutants were reconic alleles. One would certainly not choose heterozygotes for S and C hemoglobins for this purpose, for it is likely that these are, in fact, reconic alleles.)

As indicated, the lack of appropriate numbers of heterozygotes for mutants in the same cistron has thus far prevented us from making this test in man. This question can be investigated in *Neurospora*, however, which is a more suitable organism than is man for crossover studies. It was already mentioned that a large number of independently occurring point mutations, defecting adenylosuccinase, had been localized to the same region of a chromosome. We would like to know whether this enzyme contains only a single, very long polypeptide (which would be specified by one cistron), several polypeptides (which would be specified by several cistrons in the same general area of the chromosome), or many polypeptides.

Evidence has been obtained that this enzyme is dissociable into two portions. This behavior is reminiscent of that of tryptophan synthetase, and suggests that two polypeptides, and hence two cistrons, are involved in specifying this enzyme.

It is possible, by crossing two mutant individuals, to obtain progeny that are hybrid for separately arisen point mutants defecting adenylosuccinase. If these mutants are reconic alleles, and reverse mutations to adenine independence are recognized and discounted, the haploid ascospores produced by the hybrid will all still require adenine in the diet in order to grow. But, if the mutants involve different recons, then crossovers may be produced which have normal adenylosuccinase activity (see Figure 32–5).

Large numbers of ascospores need to be screened to detect these recombinants, for these are expected to be rare. But this can be done simply by placing the ascospores on minimal medium and scoring the number that form growing cultures. Of all tested spores, the percentage that grow, times two, equals the crossover percentage, or map distance, between the defective recons. When 20 or so independently occurring point mutants were crossed together in various combinations, it was found that a small number did not show recombination, indicating that they are mutant in the same recon. But a large number of these mutants proved, by showing recombination, to involve different, non-allelic recons, and the map distances obtained between them were consistent with the hypothesis that they are located in a linear array. Moreover, their arrangement was found to be continuous with that of recons in different cistrons in the same chromosome. These results suggest that there are more recons involved in the specification of adenylosuccinase than there are cistrons. Accordingly, *it is hypothesized that a cistron is composed of a number of linearly arranged recons.*

FIGURE 32–5. *Normal (adenylosuccinase-specifying) cistron resulting from crossing over within two mutant (adenylosuccinase-defective) cistrons.*

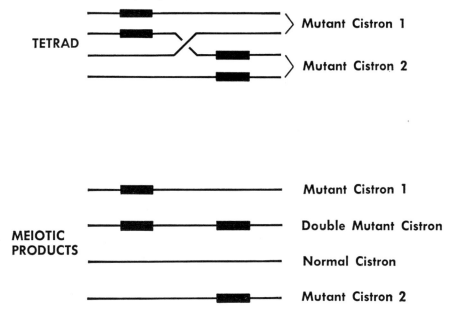

SUMMARY AND CONCLUSIONS

The general hypothesis "one cistron-one primary effect" states that a cistron produces only one primary effect and that any primary effect is the result of the action of a single cistron.

The specific hypothesis, one enzyme-one cistron, proposed as a test of the general hypothesis, was found to be essentially correct. However, its modification was necessitated by studies of the biochemical genetics of tryptophan synthetase and hemoglobin. These studies required that the specific hypothesis be made more general, so that it is stated as "one polypeptide-one cistron," and means that each polypeptide is specified completely by the primary action of a single cistron.

It is concluded that one way a cistron can act in a primary way is to specify the amino acid content of a polypeptide.

It is hypothesized that a cistron is composed of a number of linearly arranged recons.

about 500 — 1000 nucl. pairs

REFERENCES

Beadle, G. W., and Tatum, E. L., "Genetic Control of Biochemical Reactions in Neurospora," Proc. Nat. Acad. Sci., U.S., 27:499–506, 1941; reprinted in *Classic Papers in Genetics*, Peters, J. A. (Ed.), Englewood Cliffs, N.J., Prentice-Hall, 1959, pp. 166–173.

Harris, H., *Human Biochemical Genetics*, Cambridge University Press, 310 pp., 1959.

Hsia, D. Y.–Y., *Inborn Errors of Metabolism*, Chicago, Year Book Publishers, 1959.

Ingram, V. M., "How Do Genes Act?" Scient. Amer., 198:68–74, 1958.

Itano, H. A., and Robinson, E. A., "Genetic Control of α- and β-Chains of Hemoglobin," Proc. Nat. Acad. Sci., U.S., 46:1492–1501, 1960.

Yanofsky, C., and Crawford, I. P., "The Effects of Deletions, Point Mutations, Reversions and Suppressor Mutations on the Two Components of the Tryptophan Synthetase of Escherichia Coli," Proc. Nat. Acad. Sci., U.S., 45:1016–1026, 1959; reprinted in *Papers on Bacterial Genetics*, Adelberg, E. A. (Ed.), Boston, Little, Brown, 1960, pp. 384–394.

See Supplement IV and the first portion of Supplement V.

QUESTIONS FOR DISCUSSION

32.1. What significance can you give to the fact that it is a glutamic acid in hemoglobin A which is replaced by another amino acid (valine, lysine, or glycine) in hemoglobins S, C, G, and E?

32.2. What are the disadvantages of human beings as material for the investigation of the cistron?

32.3. Can crossing over occur within a gene? Explain.

32.4. Is the hypothesis, one cistron-one primary function, equivalent to the hypothesis, one polypeptide-one cistron? Why?

32.5. What evidence can you give for rejecting the hypothesis that a cistron is equivalent to a single recon?

32.6. Would you expect that a chemical substance, specified in a primary way by a cistron, would be composed of linearly arranged parts? Why?

32.7. Can you apply the term *cistron* to the one or more recons that determine whether glutamic acid or lysine shall be located at a particular place in hemoglobin? Why?

32.8. What things do genes actually do? Has your answer any bearing upon the concept of a cistron? Explain.

32.9. Under what circumstances is it proper to use the term *allele* to describe cistronic alternatives rather than reconic alternatives?

Chapter *33

CHEMICAL NATURE OF GENES

WHILE many of the preceding Chapters dealt with defining the genetic material in terms of its capacity to recombine, to mutate, and to act by performing a single primary function, no mention was made of the possibility of studying the chemical nature of the genetic material. Our attention is now drawn to the nature of the genetic material as revealed by studies utilizing the operation of chemical analysis. Let us use the knowledge we already have to decide which of the cell's chemical components are, and which are not, suitable candidates for genetic material. Since we know that the nucleus contains genetic material in its chromosomes, any chemical substance which is located exclusively in the cytoplasm can be eliminated from consideration as the chemical basis for nuclear genetic material. In view of the fact that the properties which we know the genetic material possesses are complex, we should expect the genetic substance to be of suitable complexity chemically. On this basis, we can eliminate from consideration all inorganic compounds (compounds not containing carbon), since such compounds do not provide evidence of being suitably versatile in their chemical reactions. Elimination of inorganic compounds as genetic material, on this basis, is particularly reasonable with respect to those inorganic components which are present in greater abundance in the cytoplasm than in the nucleus.

We have already noted (p. 274) that the unique feature of protoplasm is the speed and orderliness of its chemical activities. This we have attributed to the presence of proteins, in the form of enzymes and cellular structures. We have found, in Chapters 31 and 32, that the primary action of some cistrons is to specify the amino acids in a polypeptide chain. This would require that cistrons be capable of providing at least 20 different kinds of meanings or specifications (one for each of the 20 different kinds of amino acids found in protein), and suggests that intra- or intercistronic arrangement is somehow capable of manifesting the same degree of complexity as is exhibited by the polypeptide chain this arrangement specifies. It is entirely reasonable, therefore, to entertain the idea that the genetic material is itself protein, in which case it would clearly possess the correct amount of complexity.

If the gene is protein in nature, we would expect to find protein in the chromosomes. Moreover, we might hope to find that the chromosomes contain a unique type of protein, one not found in the cytoplasm. Chemical analyses of nuclei and chromosomes fulfill these expectations in the form of the protein *histone*. Histone is a complex basic protein that is found only in chromosomes. However, while it is found in the chromosomes of many organisms, it is not found in all chromosomes. Thus, for example, though it is present in the somatic nuclei of fish, it is replaced in the sperm of trout, salmon, sturgeon, and herring by a basic protein, *protamine*, of simpler composition.

Assume protamine is genetic material. If the protamine in fish sperm is replaced by histone, in the somatic cells produced mitotically after fertilization, then the genetic specifications or information must be transferred from protamine to histone, which in turn is capable of acting as genetic material. In these organisms, then, the same genetic specifications would have to be carried in two chemical forms, protamine and histone. There is nothing in our previous knowledge to prevent us from

293

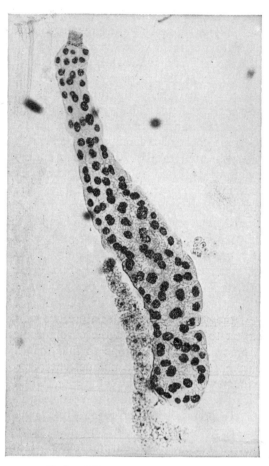

FIGURE 33–1. *Whole mount of a larval salivary gland of* Drosophila. *DNA stain is restricted to the nuclei. (Courtesy of J. Schultz.)*

cal which could serve as a candidate for the genetic material.

There are other proteins found in chromosomes. Unfortunately, the quantity of these proteins changes according to the type and rate of metabolic activities performed by the cell. There is, therefore, no simple one-to-one relationship between their quantity and gene quantity. Accordingly, as in the protamine-histone case, additional hypotheses would be required in order to explain genetic behavior. We may conclude that despite the initial attractiveness of the hypothesis that the genetic material is proteinaceous, the types and amounts of nuclear protein actually found do not offer any clear support for this view.

There does remain another chemical substance found in chromosomes, which is routinely absent in the cytoplasm (Figure 33–1). This is a type of nucleic acid called *deoxyribonucleic acid* or *DNA*, which is found combined with basic proteins like protamine and histone, by means of a chemical linkage whose nature is not completely understood, to form *deoxyribonucleoproteins*. Before discussing DNA as a candidate for being genetic material, let us first proceed to study the chemical composition of this material as it is found in chromosomes.

Chemical Composition of DNA

When DNA from chromosomes is analyzed chemically, it is found to contain organic ring compounds of which nitrogen is an integral part. The basic N-containing ring is six-membered like *benzene*, C_6H_6. Figure 33–2a shows the complete structural arrangement of benzene. Figure 33–2a' abbreviates this, by omitting the carbon atoms in the ring, and Figure 33–2a'' also eliminates showing the hydrogen atoms attached to ring carbon atoms. The basic N-containing ring in DNA is called a *pyrimidine*. This has N substituted for the CH group at position 1, as well as at position 3, in benzene (Figure 33–2b).

accepting the view that the chemistry of the genetic substance might change in this way. We merely require, if there are alternative chemical compositions for the genetic material, that these be capable of performing a variety of activities in accordance with the principles already established. Nevertheless, the hypothesis that protamine and histone are both genetic material, in the same organism, is complicated, at least in the respect that it requires two chemical substances to account for a single genotype. It would be more satisfactory, because of its economy of assumptions, to discover a single nuclear chemi-

Figure 33–2b′ and Figure 33–2b″ show successive abbreviations of this formula, corresponding to those used for benzene.

The N found in DNA is also found in a derivative of the basic pyrimidine ring, called a *purine*, which is composed of a pyrimidine ring, minus the H atoms at positions 4 and 5, to which is joined an imidazole ring (5-membered), so that the carbons at these positions are shared by both rings (as shown in

Figure 33–2c, and the shorthand forms in c′ and c″). Henceforth, the most abbreviated structural representation will be used for pyrimidines and purines. All pyrimidines and purines act chemically as bases.

Figure 33–3 includes various types of pyrimidines, the names of those found in DNA being underlined. Note that all the derivatives of pyrimidine shown have an oxygen added at position 2 to replace the H which is

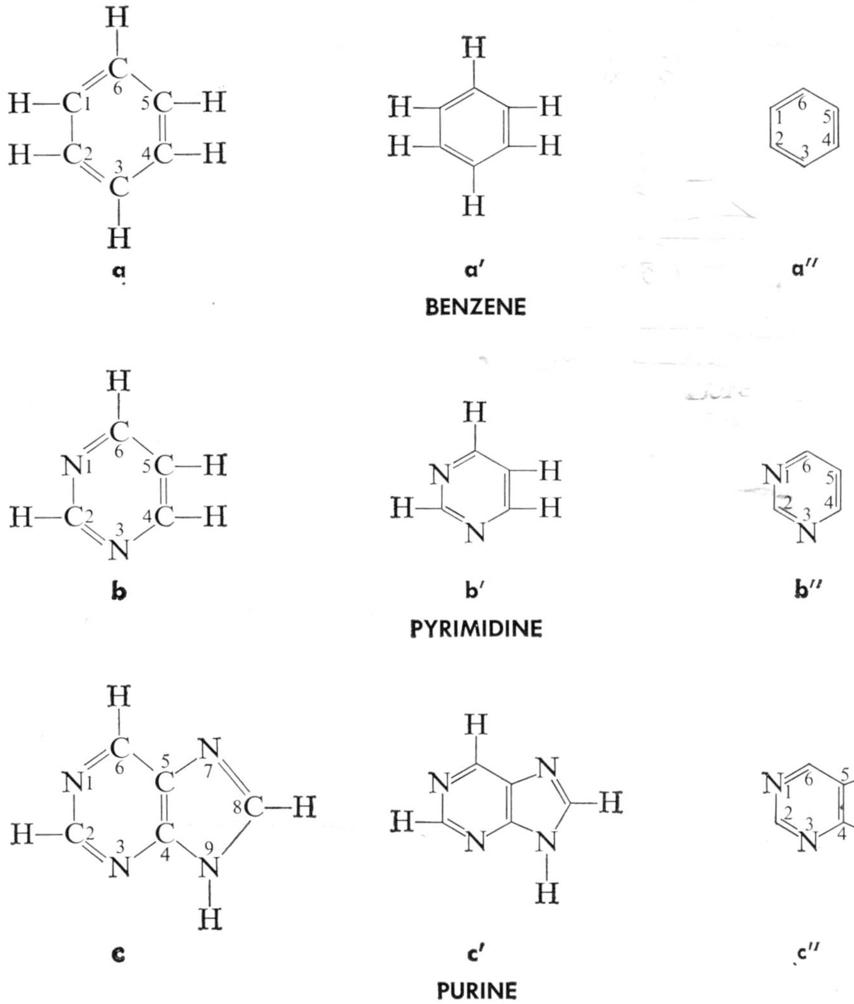

FIGURE 33–2.   *Relationship between certain ring compounds.*

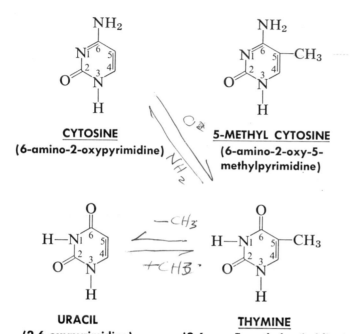

FIGURE 33–3. *Pyrimidines. Names of pyrimidines found in DNA are underlined.*

relocated at position 3. This O is shown in the keto form ($O=C\diagdown^{R}_{R}$, where R represents an atom or group other than H). One of the two pyrimidine derivatives most commonly found in DNA is *cytosine*. Cytosine differs from pyrimidine by having also an amino group (NH_2) substituted for the H attached to the C at position 6. Accordingly, cytosine can also be called 6-amino-2-oxypyrimidine. (Substitution, in cytosine, of CH_3 for the H attached at position 5 produces *5-methyl cytosine*, a DNA pyrimidine found in appreciable amounts in wheat germ, and in trace amounts in mammals, fish, and insects. Another pyrimidine, found only in the DNA of certain viruses that attack bacteria, has a

hydroxymethyl group (CH_2OH) replacing the H at position 5 of cytosine, and is therefore called *5-hydroxymethyl cytosine*.)

The other most frequently occurring pyrimidine in DNA is *thymine*. Thymine is unique in having a keto group replacing the H attached to the C at position 6, and has also replaced the H at position 5 by a methyl group. So thymine can be called 2,6-oxy-5-methylpyrimidine. Note that the differences between pyrimidines lie primarily in the variation in the groups present at the 5 and 6 positions in the ring.

Figure 33–4 shows the structural formulae for various purines, the names of those found in DNA being underlined. One of the two purines which commonly occur in DNA is *adenine*. Adenine differs from the basic

FIGURE 33–4. *Purines. Names of purines found in DNA are underlined.*

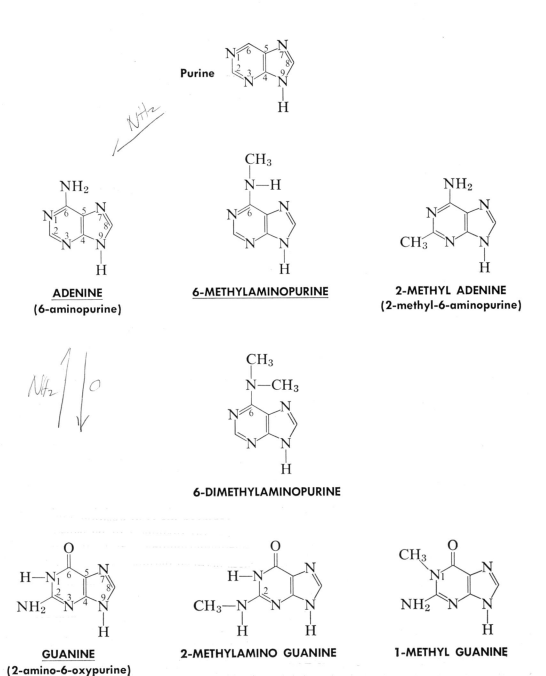

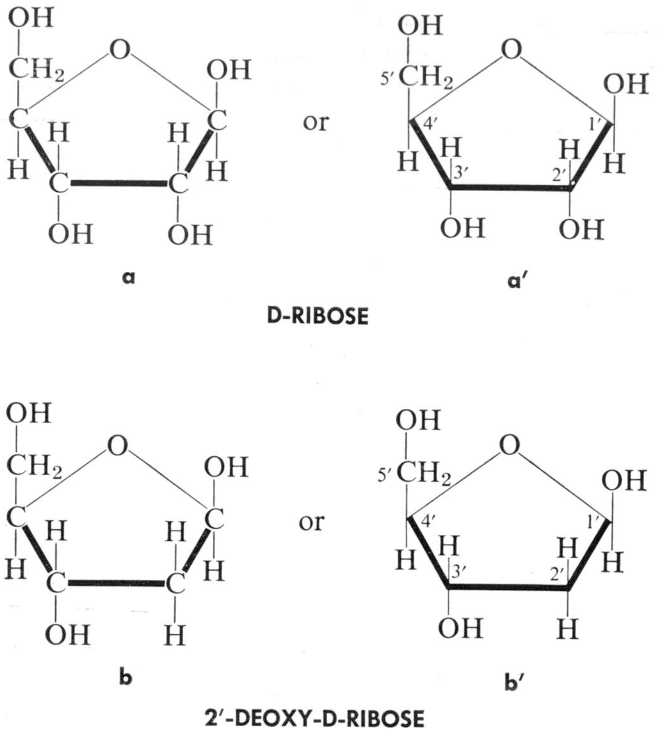

FIGURE 33–5. *Pentose sugars found in nucleic acids.*

formula of purine by having an NH_2 group in place of H at position 6, so that this compound can be identified also as 6-aminopurine. (A purine similar to adenine, having a CH_3 substitution on the NH_2 group at position 6, has been found in limited amounts in DNA, and is called, appropriately, *6-methylaminopurine*.)

The other purine most frequent in DNA is *guanine* (Figure 33–4). Guanine has an NH_2 group at position 2 and an O in keto form at position 6, so it can be called also 2-amino-6-oxypurine. Note that differences among purines lie largely in the groups attached at the 2 and 6 positions of the double ring.

D-ribose is a sugar (Figure 33–5a) containing five carbons, being, therefore, a pentose sugar, of which four C are joined with an O to form a five-membered ring. Figure 33–5a'

employs the convention, used hereafter, of not showing the carbons in the ring. DNA contains a pentose sugar modified from the D-ribose structure by the absence of an oxygen at position 2', so that this sugar is named *2'-deoxy-D-ribose*, and is often called *2-deoxyribose*, or *deoxyribose* (Figure 33–5b and b').

Each organic N-containing purine or pyrimidine base in DNA is normally joined to a deoxyribose sugar to form the combination called a *deoxyriboside*. The four main deoxyribosides in DNA are those for cytosine, called *deoxycytidine*, for thymine, called (deoxy)*thymidine*, for adenine, called *deoxyadenosine*, and for guanine, called *deoxyguanosine*. The structure for these is shown in Figure 33–6. Note that the deoxyribose sugar always joins to these bases at its 1' position, the linkage being at position 3 of pyrimidines and at position 9 in the case of purines.

In DNA, a phosphate group (PO₄) is always joined to a deoxyriboside forming a *deoxyribonucleotide*. The phosphate is attached either at position 3′ or at 5′ of the sugar, as shown in a generalized form in Figure 33–7. This is shown specifically for the deoxyribonucleotides containing the pyrimidine cytosine and the purine adenine in Figure 33–8. The deoxyriboside 5′-mono-

phosphates of cytosine, thymine, adenine, and guanine are called, respectively, *deoxycytidylic acid*, *thymidylic acid*, *deoxyadenylic acid*, and *deoxyguanylic acid.* In summary, then, the basic unit of DNA is the deoxyribonucleotide which is composed of a phosphate joined to a deoxyriboside, which, in turn, is composed of a deoxyribose sugar joined to an organic base. These bases are either pyrimidines (most commonly cytosine and thymine) or purines (most commonly adenine and guanine).

FIGURE 33–6.   *Common deoxyribosides.*

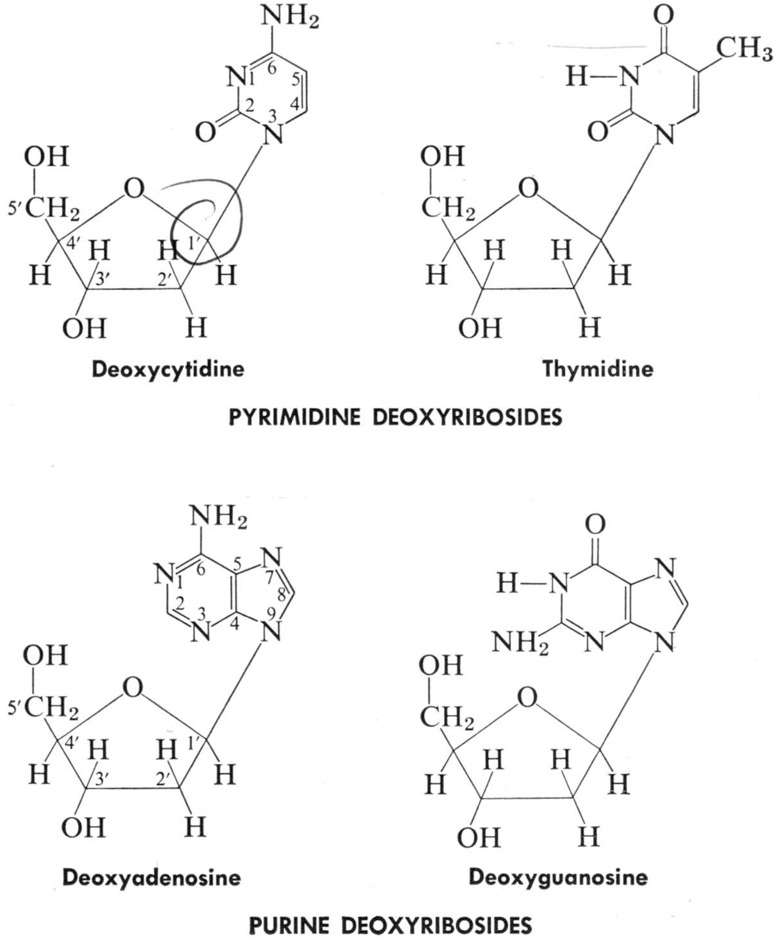

Deoxycytidine **Thymidine**

PYRIMIDINE DEOXYRIBOSIDES

Deoxyadenosine **Deoxyguanosine**

PURINE DEOXYRIBOSIDES

FIGURE 33–7.   *Deoxyribonucleotides.*

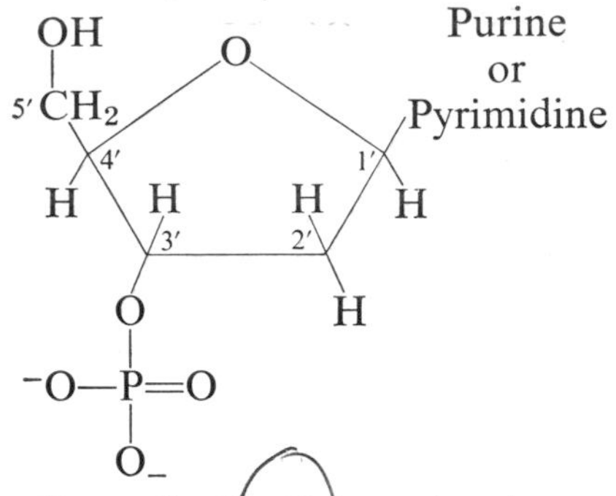

Deoxyriboside 3'-monophosphate

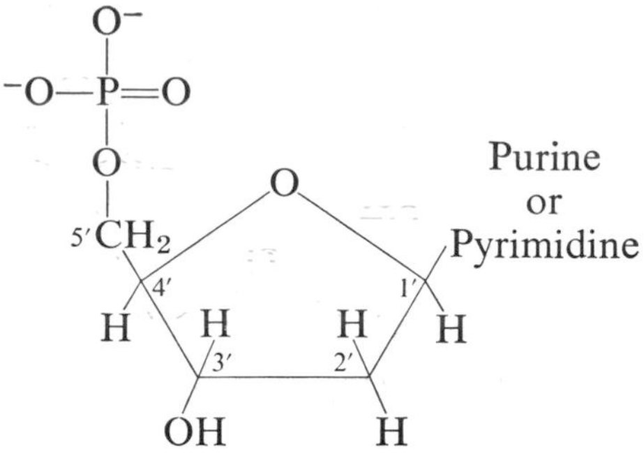

Deoxyriboside 5'-monophosphate

Most of the DNA analyzed does not occur in single deoxyribonucleotide units, but is found to be composed of *polydeoxyribonucleotides*, chains in which the individual deoxyribonucleotides comprise the links. The way these links are joined can be understood by examining the two deoxyriboside 5'-monophosphates at the right of Figure 33–8. These two compounds can become linked together if the topmost O of the bottom compound replaces the OH at position 3' of the sugar in the top compound. This reaction would be the equivalent of adding a phosphate to position 3' of the pentose in the top compound. The occurrence of such a reaction has already been mentioned, and is illustrated in the two molecules at the left of Figure 33–8. Since deoxyriboside 5'-monophosphates are capable of joining to each other by means of a phosphate linkage at 3', single unbranched chains of polydeoxyribonucleotides of great length are produced. Figure 33–9 shows a portion of such a chain. Note here that the polydeoxyribonucleotide is a linear, unbranched, molecule, whose backbone is made up of sugar-phosphate linkages, and whose linearity is independent of the particular bases present at any point. This means that the structure of the chain is uninfluenced by the

sequences of bases, which are therefore in indeterminate, or unspecified, array. Notice, moreover, that this *polymer* (a molecule composed of a number of identical units) of deoxyribonucleotides does not read the same in both directions. In the direction indicated by the arrows the sugar linkages to phosphates are 3'5', 3'5', etc., while in the opposite direction they read 5'3', 5'3', etc. Because of this, the polymerized DNA molecule is said to be *polarized*.

There are two main methods of determining the amount of DNA present in the nucleus. One method is *histochemical* and employs whole tissues for the chemical extraction and measurement of DNA. In such work, one may perform the chemical analyses using masses of nuclei from which the surrounding protoplasm has been largely removed by special treatment. As a result of such studies, one can determine the average amount of DNA per nucleus.

The second main method is a *cytochemical* one, by which the DNA content of individual nuclei, or chromosomes, or of chromosomal parts, is determined. This procedure makes use of the fact that DNA is the only substance in the cell which is stained when certain procedures are followed. The *Feulgen-Rossen-*

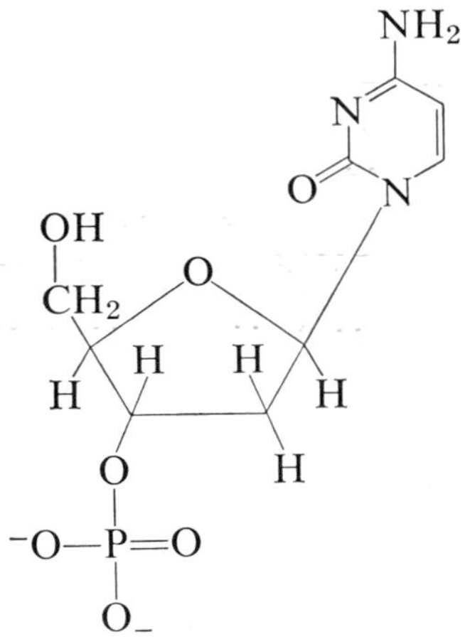

NH₂

OH
CH₂   O

H   H   H
H   H
O   H
⁻O—P=O
O₋

Deoxycytidine 3′-monophosphate

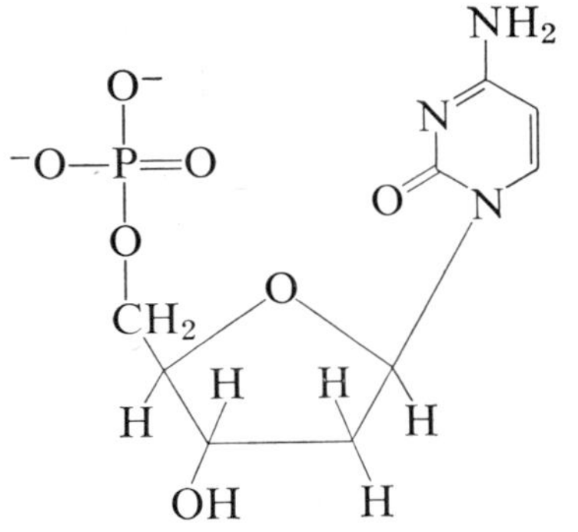

O⁻
⁻O—P=O
O
CH₂   O

H   H   H
H   H
OH   H

Deoxycytidine 5′-monophosphate
or
Deoxycytidylic acid

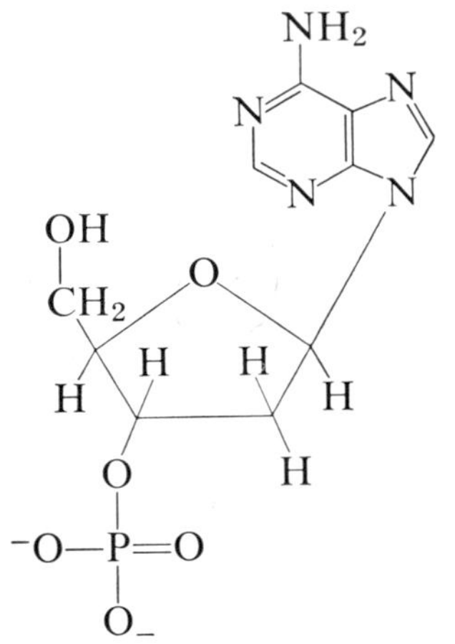

NH₂

OH
CH₂   O

H   H   H
H   H
O   H
⁻O—P=O
O₋

Deoxyadenosine 3′-monophosphate

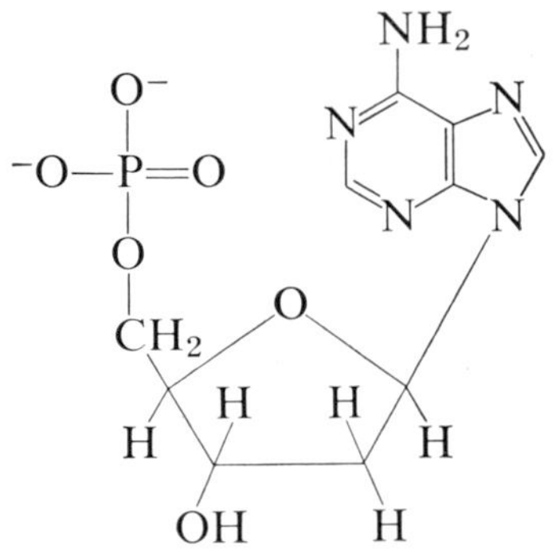

O⁻
⁻O—P=O
O
CH₂   O

H   H   H
H   H
OH   H

Deoxyadenosine 5′-monophosphate
or
Deoxyadenylic acid

FIGURE 33–8. *Specific deoxyribonucleotides.*

beck technique stains DNA purple (see p. 19), while the *methyl green method* causes it to stain green. Not only are these stains, when applied properly, specific for DNA, but the amount of staining is directly proportional to the amount of DNA present. A given amount of stain retained in the nucleus will make a known quantitative change in the amount of different wave lengths of light it transmits, and this measurement can then be used to calculate the amount of DNA present. When, under the *micro*scope, such a stained nucleus has different, appropriate, wave lengths of light in the visible *spectrum* sent through it, it is possible to determine, from changes in the density of its *photo*graphs, a *measure*ment of its DNA content. From the portions of words italicized you can understand why this procedure is called *microspectrophotometry.*

A different application of microspectro-photometry makes use of the fact that DNA is highly absorbent of ultraviolet light of wave lengths near 2600 A. When other substances, which absorb ultraviolet of these wave lengths, are removed, by enzymatic or other treatments, the quantity of DNA can be measured by its absorbence of these wave lengths. As one test of the validity of the

FIGURE 33–9. *Polydeoxyribonucleotide.*

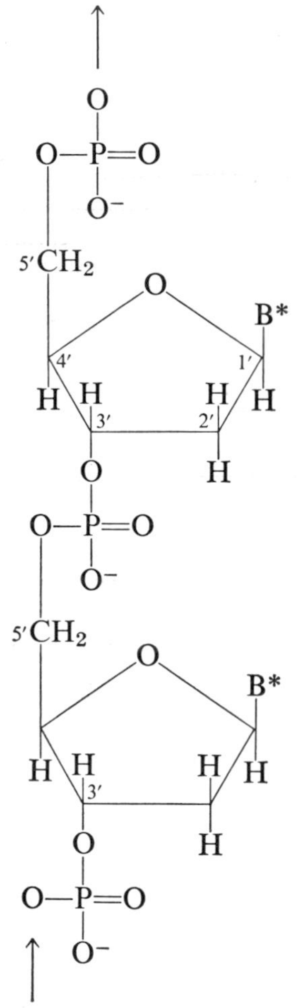

* Pyrimidine or purine base of appropriate type (usually cytosine, thymine, adenine or guanine).

absorbency, one can remove the DNA from the chromosome by the use of enzymes, *deoxyribonucleases*, or *DNAases*, which break up the long DNA chains so that the pieces can be washed out of the nuclei, leaving no DNA in the chromosome. Such treatment produces the expected loss of absorbency.

Having digressed to study the chemical content and quantitative measurement of chromosomal DNA, let us list some results which bear upon a possible association of chromosomal DNA with the genetic material in the nucleus:

1. The amount of DNA increases during the metabolic stage until it is approximately double the amount present at the beginning of this stage. Mitosis partitions the DNA approximately equally among the two telophasic nuclei. Accordingly, all diploid nuclei of an individual have just about the same DNA content when first formed after mitosis.

2. The amount of DNA in a haploid gamete is approximately half that found in a newly formed diploid metabolic nucleus of the same individual. Fertilization, which restores the diploid chromosome condition, restores the DNA content characteristic of the diploid cell.

3. Cells which have extra sets of chromosomes, being therefore polyploid, have a proportional increase in DNA content.

4. Different cells in a tissue, like those in the salivary gland of larval *Drosophila*, may show different degrees of polyteny in their chromosomes. The DNA content of these different nuclei is found to be proportional to the degree of polyteny.

5. The capacity of different wave lengths of ultraviolet light to induce mutations, in fungi, corn, *Drosophila*, and other organisms, is paralleled by the capacity of DNA to absorb these wave lengths. In other words, the mutational efficiency of ultraviolet light parallels the absorption curve of ultraviolet by DNA.

6. Through the use of labeled atoms, tagged because they are radioactive or have an abnormal weight, it is found that parts of many cellular components are constantly being replaced. In these cases, then, there is an atomic turnover even though no addition is being made to the total amount of substance demonstrating the turnover. DNA is unusual in that it shows little, if any, turnover.

7. DNA is a long, linear, unbranched polymer, as would be expected if it represents a string of recons. Each deoxyribonucleotide is bipolar, in the respect that it typically can join only to two other deoxyribonucleotides via its 3' and 5' sugar linkages to phosphate, as would be expected if each deoxyribonucleotide was the equivalent of a nonterminal recon (cf. p. 197).

We have discussed briefly the location of DNA, the amount and behavior of DNA before, during, and at the conclusion of mitosis (1), meiosis and fertilization (2), the quantity of DNA in polyploid (3) and polytene (4) chromosomes, the relation of ultraviolet light mutability to DNA absorbence (5), and the constancy or stability with which DNA maintains its integrity at the molecular level (6). In all these respects, the observations are consistent with the view that DNA either is the genetic material or is intimately associated with the genetic material. Furthermore, the linear arrangement of recons has a parallel in the linear arrangement of deoxyribonucleotides in the DNA polymer (7).

Chemical Composition of RNA

Besides DNA, there is another type of nucleic acid found in the nucleus. This is called *ribonucleic acid, or RNA.* RNA is normally found in combination with protein in the form of *ribonucleoprotein.* Because the RNA content of chromosomes varies within and among diploid cells of the same organism, according to the metabolic activity of the cell, it can be concluded that RNA is unlikely to be the chemical basis of genes in typical (DNA-containing) chromosomes. Nevertheless, let us take this opportunity to discuss the chemical composition of RNA, noting in particular how it compares with DNA.

Chromosomal RNA, like DNA, is a long, unbranched polymer of a basic unit called a *ribonucleotide.* The ribonucleotide is like the deoxyribonucleotide in being a combination of a base + sugar + phosphate; one way in which it differs is that the sugar is *D-ribose* (Figure 33–5). Another difference is found in the pyrimidine bases which it may contain. The two pyrimidines commonly found in RNA are cytosine (also common in DNA) and *uracil* (2,6-oxypyrimidine; not found in DNA). Uracil's structure is shown in Figure 33–3. The two purines commonly found in DNA, adenine and guanine, are also common in ribonucleotides. In RNA, the base + sugar combination is called a *riboside.* Ribonucleotides are joined together by phosphates joined both at the 3' and 5' positions of the sugar, just as in DNA, so that Figure 33–9 would equally well represent a polyribonucleotide if an O was added at each 2' position (making each sugar D-ribose), and if uracil was substituted for thymine as one of the bases usually included. It should be noted, finally, that RNA also absorbs ultraviolet light of 2600 A, but can be removed from the chromosome by treatment with *ribonucleases,* or *RNAases.*

In summary, we can say that the chromosomes contain two nucleic acids, DNA and RNA. These normally occur in combination with protein to form *nucleoproteins* (deoxyribonucleoprotein and ribonucleoprotein, respectively), in which these acids occur as *polynucleotides* (polydeoxyribonucleotides and polyribonucleotides, respectively), each of which is built of (mono-) *nucleotides* (deoxy- and ribonucleotides, respectively), composed of phosphates joined at 5' of *nucleo-*

sides (deoxyribo- and ribosides, respectively), composed of a *pentose sugar* (2'-deoxy-D-ribose and D-ribose, respectively), joined to a pyrimidine (usually cytosine or thymine and cytosine or uracil, respectively) or to a purine (usually adenine or guanine). Some of this terminology is summarized in tabular form in Figure 33–10.

Although the RNA in chromosomes does not possess either the proper quantitative variation or constancy we would expect of ordinary chromosomal genes, it does possess the same linear organization as DNA, as would be expected for linearly arranged recons. Suffice it to say at this point that certain *viruses* (influenza, poliomyelitis and other encephalitic viruses, viruses like tobacco mosaic virus which attack plants, and even a virus attacking bacteria)[1] possess genetic properties, but do not contain DNA. These viruses are composed primarily of ribo-

[1] See T. Loeb and N. D. Zinder (1961).

nucleoprotein. Since DNA rather than protein is favored as being the genetic chemical under typical chromosomal conditions, it is reasonable to entertain the view that it is RNA rather than the protein which is the chemical basis of genetic specification in these particular viruses.

What we will attempt to do, in subsequent Chapters, is to present additional evidence that tests the view that DNA typically (and RNA in special cases) either is the genetic material or is intimately associated with it. Clearly we are seeking ultimately to determine the chemical units of the genetic material which may correspond to the cistron and the recon, and the chemical basis for the mutation of single genes. In view of the likelihood that the cistron contains more than a single recon, it should be realized that the chemical units, which correspond to the cistron and recon, are expected to be different, at least quantitatively.

FIGURE 33–10.   *Terminology for nucleic acids and their components.*

NUCLEIC ACID	COMMON PYRIMIDINE (PY) or PURINE (PU) BASE	PENTOSE SUGAR	NUCLEOSIDE	(MONO-) NUCLEOTIDE with PO_4 at 5'
		2'-deoxy-D-ribose	deoxyriboside	deoxyribonucleotide
DNA	Cytosine PY		Deoxycytidine	Deoxycytidylic acid
	Thymine PY		Thymidine	Thymidylic acid
	Adenine PU		Deoxyadenosine	Deoxyadenylic acid
	Guanine PU		Deoxyguanosine	Deoxyguanylic acid
		D-ribose	riboside	ribonucleotide
RNA	Cytosine PY		Cytidine	5' Cytidylic acid
	Uracil PY		Uridine	5' Uridylic acid
	Adenine PU		Adenosine	5' Adenylic acid
	Guanine PU		Guanosine	5' Guanylic acid

SUMMARY AND CONCLUSIONS

When restricted to substances unique to the nucleus, the search for chemical substances which are genic, or intimately connected with the recombination, mutation, and function of genetic material, led to a consideration of protein as a possible candidate. The evidence available does not support protein as having such a primary role.

In view of the localization of DNA, its quantity and distribution in mitosis, meiosis, fertilization, and polyploid and polytene chromosomes, the parallelism between DNA absorption and the mutability of ultraviolet light, the molecular integrity of DNA as revealed by turnover studies, and its long, linear, unbranched arrangement, it is hypothesized that DNA is the genetic material in chromosomes or is at least intimately associated with the genetic material therein. It is also hypothesized that RNA may assume the genetic role of DNA in certain DNA-free viruses.

Accordingly, some details of the chemical nature of RNA and DNA were presented.

This Chapter initiates our attempt to discover the chemical units of the genetic material corresponding to the recon and cistron, and the chemical basis for single gene mutation.

REFERENCES

Chargaff, E., and Davidson, J. N. (Eds.), *The Nucleic Acids*, 2 Vols., New York, Academic Press, 1955.

Loeb, T., and Zinder, N. D., "A Bacteriophage Containing RNA," Proc. Nat. Acad. Sci., U.S., 47:282–289, 1961.

Potter, V. R., *Nucleic Acid Outlines*, Vol. 1, Minneapolis, Burgess Publ. Co., 1960.

QUESTIONS FOR DISCUSSION

33.1. Do you think it is simpler to postulate that DNA rather than protein is genetic material? Why?

33.2. What is the chemical distinction between:

        a. a mononucleotide and a polynucleotide?
        b. a nucleotide and a nucleoside?
        c. a pyrimidine and a purine?
        d. a ribose and a deoxyribose sugar?

33.3. Draw the detailed chemical structure of a polyribonucleotide having the base sequence adenine, uracil, guanine, cytosine.

33.4. Express thymine as a derivative of uracil. What part of the term *deoxythymidine* is superfluous? Why?

33.5. What evidence can you provide, from your own knowledge, to support the view that viruses possess genic properties?

33.6. How would you proceed to measure the absorbency of ultraviolet light by chromosomal DNA? chromosomal RNA?

33.7. Do you believe that the evidence so far presented provides conclusive proof that DNA is genetic material in chromosomes? Why?

33.8. What is your opinion of the hypothesis that DNA is the chemical basis for recons, but that protein is the chemical basis for cistrons?

33.9. Is DNA complex enough to serve as the chemical basis of cistrons? Explain.

33.10. Do you think the term *chemon* could be defined usefully? Justify your opinion.

*Chapter *34*

ORGANIZATION, REPLICATION, AND TYPES OF DNA *IN VIVO*

INDIRECT evidence, consistent with the view that DNA can serve as the chemical basis of chromosomal genetic material, was presented in the last Chapter. That Chapter described what may be called *the primary structure of DNA*, as being a single, long, unbranched, polarized chain of nucleotides. In accord with the view that the DNA polymer is genetic, we would expect it to be linearly differentiated so that different portions of it could represent different units of genetic material. This differentiation cannot be attributed to either the deoxyribose sugar or the phosphate, since one of each is present in every nucleotide. Differences in genetic information along the length of the DNA strand must be due, therefore, to the bases present. Since species differ by numerous point mutations, we would expect to find differences in the DNA's of different species.

Histochemical analyses have been made of the organic bases in DNA extracted from various species. Considering the total amount of the bases in an extract as 100%, Figure 34–1 gives the percentages of this found as *adenine* (A), *thymine* (T), *guanine* (G), and *cytosine* (C). Note that there is considerable variation in base content, ranging from organisms relatively rich in A and T and poor in C and G (sea urchin), to those showing the reverse, where A and T are considerably less abundant than C and G (tubercle bacillus). These results demonstrate that the relative amounts of the four bases are different in

306

the DNA's from radically different species.

Can these data tell us whether a shift in the sequence of bases also could produce differences in the properties of the genetic material? That different orders of the same bases may also be involved, in specifying different genetic units, is suggested by the fact that the chicken, salmon, and locust, which must be very different genetically, all have very similar base ratios. One might suggest as an alternative explanation that these species are molecular polyploids, differing only in the number of the same types of DNA molecules which they possess. This possibility can be eliminated from serious consideration in the light of our knowledge of the limited contribution which chromosomal polyploidy has made to evolution, at least in the animal kingdom (Chapters 18, 29).

So long as histochemical analyses are made, of the total DNA of cells having a high DNA content, approximately the same base ratios would be expected to be obtained from different members of a single species. This has proven true. Moreover, as expected, the same base ratios have been found in different normal and neoplastic tissues of the same and different human beings. Nevertheless, it is expected that a genome would contain many molecules of DNA which differ from each other in base sequence and content.

The variation, found in different species, in the ratio $A + T/G + C$ (which is about .4 for the tubercle bacillus and is about 1.8 in the sea urchin), is understandable in terms of our chemical knowledge, since the DNA strand imposes no limitation upon which base may be present, or how often it may appear along the length of the fiber. There is, however, a remarkable equality in the amount of A and the amount of T in the DNA within a species, and also an equivalence in the amounts of G and C (refer to Figure 34–1). Since, in each species, $A = T$, and $G = C$, it is also apparent that $A + G = T + C$, or, in other words, the total number of DNA

	ADENINE	THYMINE	GUANINE	CYSTOSINE
Man (sperm)	31.0	31.5	19.1	18.4
Chicken	28.8	29.2	20.5	21.5
Salmon	29.7	29.1	20.8	20.4
Locust	29.3	29.3	20.5	20.7
Sea urchin	32.8	32.1	17.7	17.7
Yeast	31.7	32.6	18.8	17.4
Tuberculosis bacillus	15.1	14.6	34.9	35.4
Escherichia coli	26.1	23.9	24.9	25.1
Vaccinia virus	29.5	29.9	20.6	20.3
E. coli bacteriophage T_2	32.6	32.6	18.2	16.6

FIGURE 34–1.   *Base composition of DNA from various organisms.*

purines always equals the total number of DNA pyrimidines. While this regularity is common to all the chromosomal DNA's listed, there is nothing in the nature of the primary structure of DNA which would help explain it. However, the fact that the primary structure of DNA is the same in all these organisms suggests that these regularities may be connected with some additional, general, structural characteristic of chromosomal DNA.

An understanding of the basis for the A = T and G = C relationships may come from studies of an entirely different kind. It has been known for a long time that a beam of X rays is bent or refracted when it passes through material. If the material through which the rays pass is completely heterogeneous in structure, no regularity is found in the way in which the emergent beam is refracted. But, if the material is composed of macromolecular units and/or molecular subunits, which are spatially arranged in a regular manner, then the emergent beam will form what is called an *X-ray diffraction pattern*. Moreover, a particular X-ray pattern can be used to identify units and subunits that are repeated at regular intervals of space. Thus, it has been found that each nucleotide in a DNA chain occupies a length of 3.4 A along the chain, and that this repetition is detectable by the characteristic X-ray diffraction pattern it produces.

X-ray diffraction patterns have been obtained for DNA from a variety of species. In some cases the DNA was not removed from the nucleus, in other cases it was removed from the nucleus and separated from protein as well. In all cases, provided the DNA was suitably hydrated, essentially the same patterns attributable to DNA were found (see Figure 34-2). A study of these

FIGURE 34–2. *X ray diffraction photographs of suitably hydrated fibers of DNA, showing the so-called B configuration. A. Pattern obtained using the sodium salt of DNA. B. Pattern obtained using the lithium salt of DNA. This pattern permits a most thorough analysis of DNA. (Courtesy of Biophysics Research Unit, Medical Research Council, King's College, London.)*

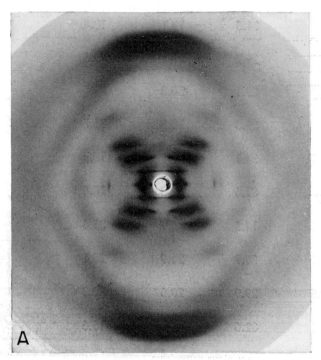

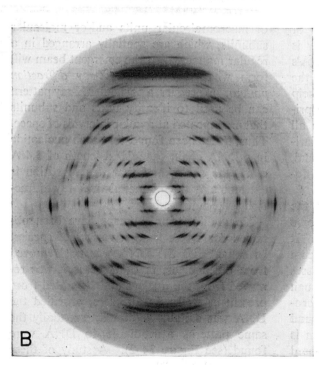

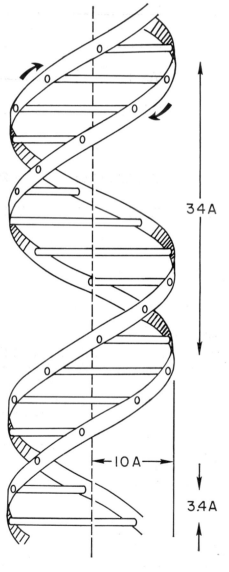

FIGURE 34–3. *The Watson-Crick double-stranded helix configuration of DNA.*

common patterns showed, besides the 3.4 A repetition, other repeat units which would be explained only if *DNA usually does not occur as a single strand.* (On the other hand, X-ray diffraction studies show that RNA is usually single stranded.) Here, then, was a clear demonstration that there is a *secondary structure to DNA* which was hitherto unexpected, and there was every reason to believe this was the organization normally found in the chromosome. The simplest explanation consistent with the diffraction results was proposed by J. D. Watson and F. H. C. Crick (see the 1953a reference to them at the end of this Chapter). They hypothesized that DNA is normally two-stranded (see Figure 34–3). Each strand is a polynucleotide, and the two strands are coiled around each other in such a manner that they cannot be separated unless the ends are permitted to revolve. This kind of coiling is *plectonemic* (as is found in the strands of a rope) and can be contrasted with *paranemic coiling* in which two coils can be separated without their ends revolving (just as two bedsprings pushed together can be separated).

The Watson-Crick model for the secondary organization of DNA macromolecules involves a double helix in which each strand is *coiled right-handedly* (i.e., *clockwise*). This is the same direction of coil as is found in the secondary structure of polypeptides (see p. 286). The model shows the pentose and phosphate backbone of each strand on the outside of the spiral, while the relatively flat bases which project into the center lie perpendicular to the long axis of the fiber. The backbone completes a turn each 34 A. Since each nucleotide occupies 3.4 A along the length of a strand, there are 10 nucleotides per complete turn and each nucleotide has a pitch of 36° relative to the long axis (so that 10 nucleotides complete the 360° required for a complete turn).

The two helices are held together by chemical bonds between bases on different strands. It has been found that the two strands can form a regular double helix, whose diameter is uniformly 20 A, only if the bases on different strands join in pairs, each of which is composed of one pyrimidine and one purine. Two pyrimidines together (being single rings) would be too short to bridge the gap between backbones, while two purines (being double rings) would take up too much space. Moreover, the pyrimidine-purine pairing must be either between C and G or between T and A, for only in this way is the maximum number of stabilizing bondages between them produced. The type of stabilizing bond holding the members of a base pair together is called a *hydrogen bond* or "*H bond.*" The base pairs, with their H bonds shown as dotted lines, are diagrammed in Figure 34–4. (All these diagrams really should be at a 36° tilt from the horizontal.) The top half of the Figure shows the C-G (and G-C) arrangements. Note, in the C-G pair, that cytosine has been turned over (from left to right) relative to the way it was diagrammed in Figure 33–3. Three H bonds are formed. Two occur between NH_2 and O (the 6—NH_2 of C with the 6—O of G; the 2—O of C with the 2—NH_2 of G), and one occurs between the 1—N of C and the 1—NH of G. The G:C pair is identical to C:G, as shown, except that, in this case, the base turned over is guanine.

The bottom half of Figure 34–4 shows the other type of base pair (T:A or A:T, in which T and A, respectively, have been turned over relative to the way they were shown in Figures 33–3 and 33–4). In this pair only two H bonds are formed, one between the 6—O of T and the 6—NH_2 of A, and the other between the 1—NH of T and the 1—N of A. Although the H bond is a weak electrostatic bond (requiring only about 5 kcal of energy to break the H bond in N—H . . . O, whereas a regular C—C bond would require 50–100 kcal for breakage), there

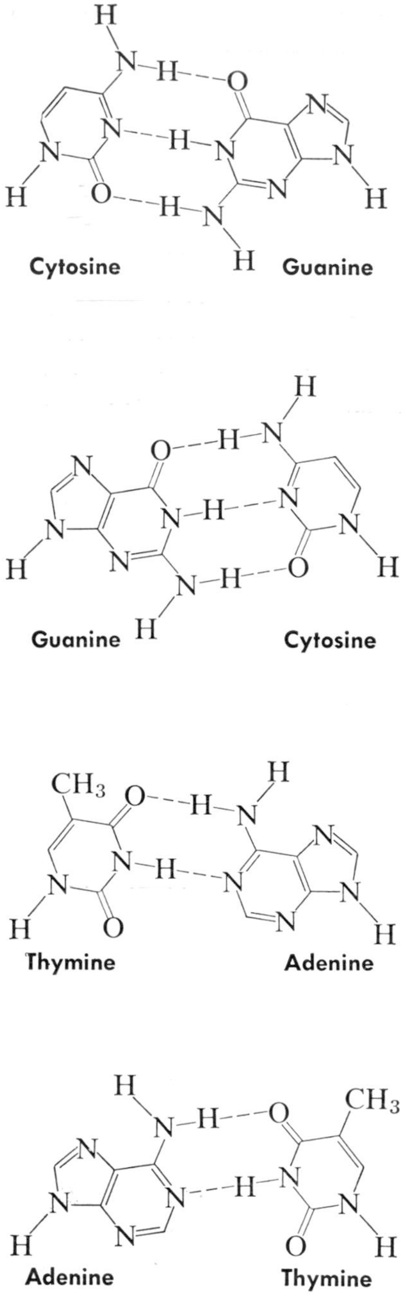

FIGURE 34–4.
Base pairs formed between single DNA chains.

are so many of them along a long double helix that the entire structure is fairly rigid and paracrystalline even when moderately hydrated.

You will recall that the double helix configuration of DNA does not dictate the sequence of bases along the length of a chain. But you will also remember that the sizes of, and the H bonds in, the pyrimidines and purines did dictate that A in one chain can pair only with T in the other chain, and C with G, in order to form a double helix of constant diameter whose strands are held together by the maximum number of H bonds. Since A and T always go together, as do C and G, the equivalences A = T and C = G, found when DNA is analyzed chemically, become meaningful as being the direct consequence of the secondary structure of DNA. In fact, the chemical equivalences provide the first independent test of the Watson-Crick model, which was constructed initially on the basis of other considerations.

Recall that in order to maximally H-bond a purine and a pyrimidine, it was necessary to represent one of the two as being turned over, so that the number 1 atoms of both face each other. This has an important consequence for the orientation of the two chains relative to each other, as is illustrated by means of Figure 34–5. The bases in the chain at the right all face the accustomed way, while those in the left chain are all turned over. In order that each base join to its sugar in the same way, the sugars must be arranged as shown. Notice, in proceeding downward from the top of the right chain, that the PO_4 linkages to sugar read $3'5'$, $3'5'$, etc. But, when read the same way, the left chain is $5'3'$, $5'3'$, etc., so that the member chains in a double helix run in opposite directions, as indicated by the arrows.

The X-ray diffraction results, which led to the double helix hypothesis, do not tell us that all DNA in chromosomes is two-stranded, or that a double strand is never

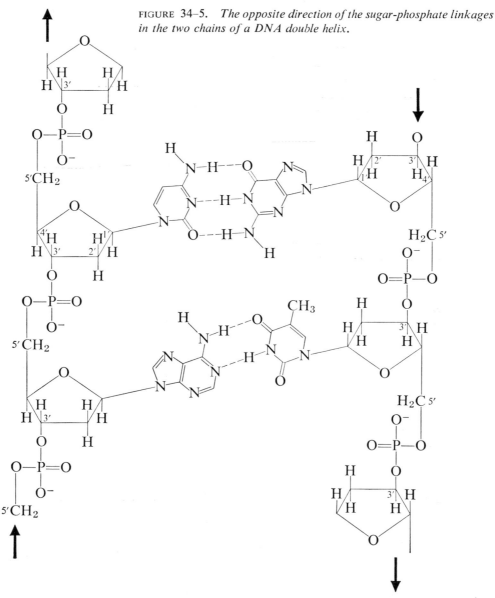

FIGURE 34–5. *The opposite direction of the sugar-phosphate linkages in the two chains of a DNA double helix.*

single-stranded at certain places or at certain times. Such data merely prove that a very appreciable part of the chromosomal DNA, in the wide variety of organisms studied, is not single-stranded. The content and organization of DNA in viruses attacking bacteria have also been studied by chemical analysis and by X-ray diffraction. In the varieties T_2 and T_7, for example, the data are entirely consistent with the DNA's being present in the Watson-Crick double helix configuration. In two other smaller varieties, however, called ϕX174 and S13, the DNA is definitely single-stranded.

Whenever the DNA is in the double helix configuration we can consider one strand to be the complement of the other, so that if we know the sequence of bases in one strand we can specify exactly the composition of the other strand. Thus, if one strand had the base sequence ATTCGAC, the other strand would have to contain TAAGCTG in the corresponding regions.

If DNA is genetic material, we should expect it to be capable of being replicated just as precisely as is the genetic material. Since the sequence on one chain is complementary to the sequence on the other, this immediately suggests a simple way that the double helix might replicate itself.[1] What we would require is that the two chains first separate, after which each chain would build its complement. This can be called the *chain separation hypothesis of DNA replication*. This can be visualized as occurring by having each strand serve as a *mold* or *template*. We know that complex surfaces (like statues) can be copied exactly by making a mold, which can be used in turn to make a second mold. The second mold is then an exact copy of the original configuration. In the present case *the two complementary strands of DNA can be viewed as molds, or templates, for each other*. Either strand could act as a mold on which the complementary strand could be synthesized. Figure 34–6 shows one possible sequence of events. At the top of this Figure, the two strands start to come apart. At the center the two single chains exist in the presence of single nucleotides or their precursors. When the complementary free nucleotide approaches the single chain, its base would be H-bonded. Then, after several nucleotides have bonded to the single chain, perhaps an enzyme would link them to start the new complementary chain. The bottom shows sections of the complementary chains whose synthesis is already completed.

It is possible to design an experiment[2] which tests, simultaneously, the hypotheses

both for the double helix structure of DNA and for its replication by chain separation. You remember that every pyrimidine or purine base, usually found in DNA, contains two or four N atoms, respectively. These atoms normally are what we can call *light nitrogen* (*N-14*). It ought to be possible to grow bacteria in a culture medium whose only nitrogen is in the form of a heavier isotope, N-15, which we can call *heavy nitrogen*. If so, after a number of generations have passed, almost all of the DNA present will have been synthesized utilizing heavy nitrogen. Suppose also that it has been possible to synchronize the multiplication of the bacteria containing heavy DNA. What would you expect to happen if these bacteria are quickly washed with, and then placed in, culture medium containing only light nitrogen, and are permitted to continue their synchronous multiplication? The DNA should replicate each time the bacteria undergo cell division. During the first replication of DNA the two chains containing heavy N should separate, and each should synthesize a complementary chain containing only light nitrogen. Thus, after one DNA replication, the density of the DNA molecules should be exactly intermediate between completely light and completely heavy DNA.

To test whether or not this expectation is actually observed, the DNA is extracted from "all-heavy" bacteria and also from "all-light" bacteria. These extracts, serving as controls, are ultracentrifuged, first separately, and then together, in a fluid medium of appropriate density (containing cesium chloride). After about 20 hours, the position of the DNA in the medium can be detected by its absorbence of ultraviolet light of 2600 A wave length. Two separate bands of DNA are found in the medium, corresponding to the all-heavy and all-light DNA. When DNA is extracted at various time intervals, after the originally all-heavy bacteria have been placed in the all-light nitrogen medium, the DNA band in the

---

[1] Based upon the hypothesis of J. D. Watson and F. H. C. Crick (1953b,c).
[2] Based upon the experiments of M. Meselson and F. W. Stahl.

ultracentrifuge tube is observed to move from the all-heavy DNA position to a position exactly intermediate between the all-heavy and all-light positions (Figure 34–7). This is exactly what is expected if the DNA is "hybrid" in density after one replication.

What would you expect to find after one additional DNA replication? In this replication the two chains of the hybrid DNA should separate, and light complementary chains should be made by both the light and heavy single chains. So, after a second replication half of the double-chain DNA molecules should be all-light and half should be intermediate between all-light and all-heavy (that is, they should be hybrid). And, in fact, in the samples of DNA taken at later intervals, the single band at the intermediate position

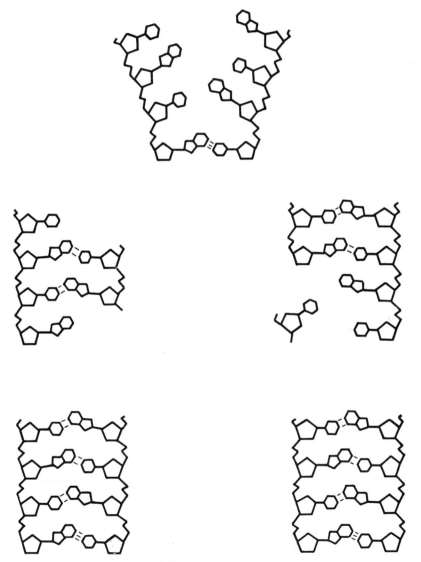

FIGURE 34–6. *Diagrammatic representation of the hypothesis of DNA replication after chain separation.*

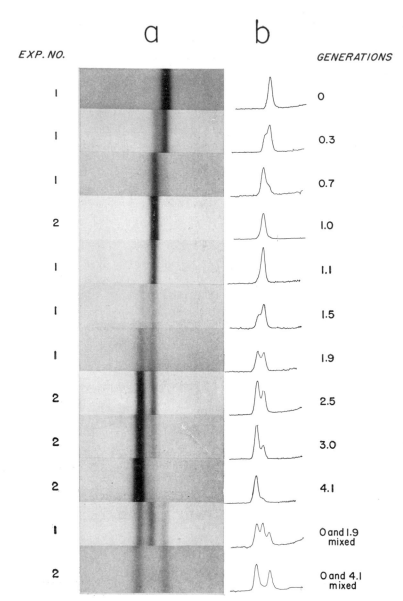

FIGURE 34–7. *Test of the "replication after chain separation" hypothesis, using the technique of density gradient centrifugation. DNA was extracted from all-heavy (N-15-labeled) bacteria grown for different generation times on all-light (N-14-containing) medium. The extracts were subjected to ultracentrifugation to position the DNA in the centrifuge tube according to its density. (Density increases to the right of the figure.) DNA absorption of ultraviolet light is indicated by the bands in different photographs under* a *and the height of the peaks in the corresponding densitometer tracings under* b. *The rightmost band in the bottom two frames and the band in the top frame represent all-heavy DNA. The leftmost band, seen clearly in all generation times after 1.5 generations, represents all-light DNA. The only other clear band is between the all-heavy and all-light ones. This is the only band present after 1.0 generations, and represents DNA which is hybrid in density. Note that at 1.9 generations, half the DNA is all-light and half is hybrid in density (see row showing 0 and 1.9 mixed). (Courtesy of M. Meselson and F. W. Stahl, Proc. Nat. Acad. Sci., U.S., 44:675. 1958.)*

in the ultracentrifuge tube is found to become two bands, one at the hybrid position and one at the all-light position. It should be noted, moreover, that the time required for the change from all-heavy to all-hybrid molecules, or for the change from all-hybrid to half all-light and half hybrid molecules, is approximately the interval occupied by a bacterial generation.

Although these results are consistent with the hypothesis of replication of double-strand DNA by chain separation, they do not automatically exclude other possible explanations. It might be claimed, for instance, that the double helix grows, not by separation of chains followed by the synthesis of complementary ones, but by the addition of new double chain material to the ends of the original double chain. One can test this alternative explanation in two ways.

If the all-heavy molecules grew by adding light material to their ends, they should be composed linearly of double chains that are successively light, heavy, and light. Then it should be possible to fragment the macromolecules by sonic vibrations into smaller segments, some of which should be all-heavy and others all-light. This should be detectable in the ultracentrifuge tube by some DNA assuming the all-light and all-heavy positions. This does not happen. The DNA remains in essentially the same hybrid position whether or not it is fragmented sonically.

A second test of the view, that synthesis is at the ends of the double chains, is made possible by the following fact. If double-stranded DNA is heated to an appropriate temperature (near 98° C), the H bonds are broken and the complementary strands separate. (Double-stranded DNA's with high $A + T/G + C$ ratios become single-stranded at lower heats than do those with low ratios. This is expected since high-ratio DNA is richer than low-ratio DNA in A–T, each pair of which has one less H bond than a C–G pair, so that less energy is needed to break the

smaller total of H bonds present in the former than in the latter.) If the appropriately heated mixture is cooled quickly, the chains remain single. That this heat denaturation followed by quick cooling produces single strands from double helices can be confirmed by the loss of that part of the DNA X-ray diffraction pattern which denotes polystrandedness. The change to single-strandedness is also accompanied by an increase of as much as 40% in the absorbence of ultraviolet light of 2600 A. The second test of endwise DNA synthesis involves converting all-light and all-heavy DNA to the single-stranded condition and locating the positions of the two types of single strands in the ultracentrifuge tube. Then "hybrid" DNA is made single-stranded and ultracentrifuged. This preparation shows only two major components, one located at the all-light single-strand position and the other at the all-heavy single-strand position. This result also is inconsistent with the hypothesis under test. Not only do the two tests eliminate the view that appreciable endwise synthesis of DNA occurs in bacterial DNA, but they offer additional support for the hypothesis of replication after chain separation.

Experiments like those done with bacteria have been performed, with similar results, using the unicellular plant, *Chlamydomonas*, and other higher organisms, including man. The general agreement in the results of all these experiments furnishes conclusive, or at least almost conclusive, evidence of the correctness of the Watson-Crick hypotheses for the double helix configuration of DNA in the chromosomes, and for DNA replication after chain separation.

The work we have just discussed shows clearly that the great proportion of chromosomal DNA exists in double helix configuration, and replicates by chain separation once a generation, as would be expected were this substance genetic material. We can ask now whether all the DNA found in chromosomes

SEGMENT   CHROMOSOME   B

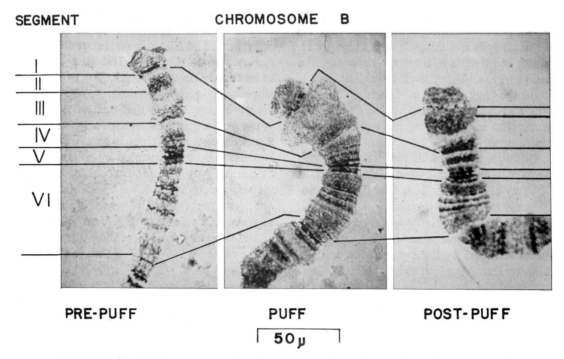

I
II
III
IV
V

VI

PRE-PUFF   PUFF   POST-PUFF

⌐ 50 µ ⌐

FIGURE 34–8. *Puffing and unpuffing in a region of a salivary gland chromosome of* Rhyncosciara. *(Courtesy of G. Rudkin.)*

behaves the same way in this and in other respects. It can be inferred (from page 19) that the synthesis of DNA occurs during the metabolic stage. Not only does the synthesis sometimes require a period of several hours for completion (so that some genes replicate, or are replicated, before others), but it has been shown that the DNA in *heterochromatin* (p. 181) is synthesized at a different time (sometimes later) than DNA in *euchromatin* (p. 181), even when the synthesis of both is traced in the same chromosome. This has been found both in animal and plant organisms.

Besides different portions of chromosomal DNA being synthesized at different times, there is also evidence that DNA is synthesized in disproportionate amounts by certain regions of polytene chromosomes. In the salivary gland cells of *Rhyncosciara* larvae, there is, for example, a disproportionate in-

crease in the manufacture of DNA in regions of the polytene chromosomes that temporarily puff out (Figure 34–8). Different chromosome regions puff and unpuff at specific times in the life history of the salivary gland cell. Moreover, in the polytene chromosomes found in other tissues of this larva, a given chromosome region will puff and unpuff at different stages of larval development.

Such results suggest that the disproportionate synthesis of DNA is concerned with developmental changes and differentiation. That such disproportionately synthesized DNA, or other DNA, may leave the nucleus to produce an effect in the cytoplasm is supported by various evidences. In a number of organisms (for example, the fungus gnat, *Sciara*), some chromosomes are regularly eliminated from the nuclei of cells destined to differentiate in particular ways; the possible extrusion of Feulgen-Rossenbeck staining material from the nucleus has been described in *Artemia* oocytes; extrusions of DNA from the nuclei of ovarian cells of an insect have been reported, and this DNA has been associated with the transference of nutritive substances to the developing eggs. Finally, the high DNA content in the salivary gland cells of *Helix* progressively decreases as the secretion product is manufactured.

In almost all of the cases where chromosomal DNA is produced in excess, either by proportionate or disproportionate replication, it occurs in cells which themselves do not give rise to future cell generations. Thus, dipteran cells containing polytene chromosomes do not divide again, and *Artemia* oocytes that extrude DNA die. While we may conclude that DNA is sometimes released to the cytoplasm to perform certain functions, we have no data from the studies mentioned which indicate that this material shows any of the other known or assumed properties (replication, mutation, recombination) of genetic material once it has left the chromosome. Accordingly, whether or not this material is genetic remains an open question.

It should be realized that the DNA which leaves the nucleus might serve an extranuclear function which is quite different from that which DNA performs as a nuclear cistron. For example, nucleus-derived, cytoplasmically located, DNA may serve as raw material for future synthesis of nuclear DNA. This may be the fate of the DNA contained in the nonfertilizing sperm which degenerate in the cytoplasm of insect eggs fertilized by *polyspermy* (in which more than one sperm enters the egg although only one fertilizes). The DNA in the nurse cells of *Drosophila* is reported to enter the cytoplasm of the developing oocyte, presumably to perform this function even before maturation. It has been reported also that extracted DNA is phagocytosed by fibroblasts and white blood cells *in vivo*, and that phagocytosis of extracted DNA by mammalian cells in tissue cultures is followed by the appearance of this DNA in the nucleus. We should note again that these cases furnish no evidence that such DNA has any of the characteristics we have described for genetic material. Moreover, with the exception of the special case of chromosome elimination, we do not know if there is a flow of DNA from the nuclei of more typical cells — those that subsequently undergo cell division. Nevertheless, it is clear from the preceding discussion that all the DNA which occurs in a nucleus may not always remain there to perform the usual functions we would expect from nuclear genetic material. In this respect, then, there are *two kinds of DNA, one that is conserved* as a part of the chromosome, which remains our candidate for nuclear genetic material, *and one that is not conserved*, and which may or may not be genetic material.

SUMMARY AND CONCLUSIONS

DNA *in vivo* usually exists in the Watson-Crick double helix configuration and usually replicates, after the chains separate, by the formation of complementary chains.

In certain viruses, φX174 and S13, the DNA is single-stranded.

From the standpoint of behavior there are two kinds of DNA. One type is conserved as a regular part of the chromosome and is presumably genetic. The other type is not conserved, is nucleus-derived, and may be found in the cytoplasm and/or the nucleus. The examples mentioned offer no clear evidence that nonconserved DNA has genetic properties.

REFERENCES

Bensch, K. G., and King, D. W., "Incorporation of Heterologous Deoxyribonucleic Acid into Mammalian Cells," Science, 133:381–382, 1961.

Crick, F. H. C., "Nucleic Acids," Scient. Amer., 197:188–200, 1957.

Meselson, M., and Stahl, F. W., "The Replication of DNA in *Escherichia Coli*," Proc. Nat. Acad. Sci., U.S., 44:671–682, 1958.

Sueoka, N., "Mitotic Replication of Deoxyribonucleic Acid in *Chlamydomonas Reinhardi*," Proc. Nat. Acad. Sci., U.S., 46:83–90, 1960.

Watson, J. D., and Crick, F. H. C., "Molecular Structure of Nucleic Acids. A Structure for Deoxyribose Nucleic Acid," Nature, London, 171:737–738, 1953a; reprinted in *Classic Papers in Genetics*, Peters, J. A. (Ed.), Englewood Cliffs, N.J., Prentice-Hall, 1959, pp. 241–243.

Watson, J. D., and Crick, F. H. C., "Genetical Implications of the Structure of Deoxyribonucleic Acid," Nature, London, 171:964–969, 1953b; reprinted in *Papers on Bacterial Genetics*, Adelberg, E. A. (Ed.), Boston, Little, Brown, 1960, pp. 125–130.

Watson, J. D., and Crick, F. H. C., "The Structure of DNA," Cold Spring Harbor Symposia on Quantitative Biology, 18:123–131, 1953c; reprinted in *Papers on Bacterial Viruses*, Stent, G. S. (Ed.), Boston, Little, Brown, 1960, pp. 193–208.

JAMES D. WATSON *in 1959.* (*Photographed by The Calvin Company.*) (*Photograph of* F. H. C. CRICK *is unavailable.*)

QUESTIONS FOR DISCUSSION

34.1. Can you draw any conclusions from the observation that most of the multicellular organisms studied are richer in A + T than C + G?

34.2. Why is it expected, among the DNA molecules contained in a genome, that many would differ in base sequence and content?

34.3. How many different base pairs normally occur in a double helix of DNA? What are these?

34.4. If a coil is right-handed when looked at from one end, is it also right-handed when seen from the other end?

34.5. What would you have expected to see in the ultracentrifuge tube following sonic treatment of DNA (p. 315), or following the conversion of DNA to its single-stranded condition (p. 315), if synthesis occurred at the ends of the double DNA helix?

34.6. What evidence can you give that heating double helix DNA causes the chains to separate?

34.7. When is DNA single-stranded?

34.8. A double helix of DNA has a base sequence ATTAGCA on one strand. Can you make an inversion after breaking the backbone at two places on this single strand? Explain. Can you make an inversion if the backbone of the complementary chain is also broken at exactly the same two levels? Explain.

34.9. Given two double helices whose backbones are broken at the places indicated by periods.

ATCG.GCAT   AT.TAG

TAGC.CGTA   TA.ATC

Draw the base sequences which may occur following reciprocal translocation between double helices.

NH₂ structure diagram (ATP chemical structure shown in figure)

Chapter 35

REPLICATION OF DNA
IN VITRO

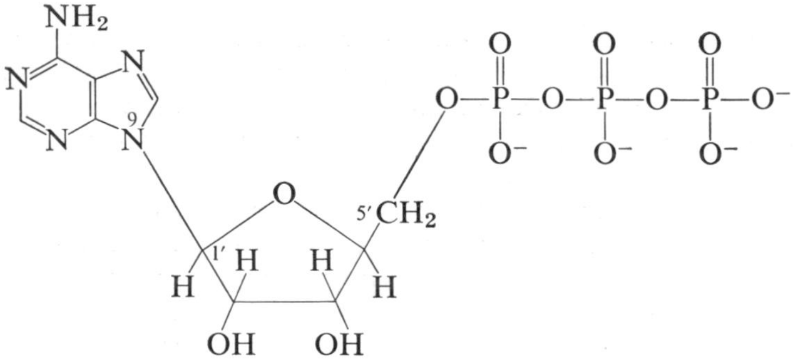

FIGURE 35–1.
Adenosine 5'-triphosphate (ATP) (ARPPP).

SELF-REPLICATION was assumed, on p. 9, to be a characteristic of the genetic material. In view of the indirect evidence that the DNA normally conserved in chromosomes is genetic material, we are particularly interested in learning more about the double helix of DNA and how it accomplishes its replication after chain separation. Although we can accept the evidence (in Chapter 34) as being fairly conclusive that complementary chains are synthesized after chain separation, no evidence was presented bearing on the mechanism by which this replication is accomplished. Figure 34–6 and the discussion on page 312 only postulate a mechanism, which includes an enzyme that joins the nucleotides together so as to complete the new complementary strand.

Since the linear combination of nucleotides doubtless requires energy, we should consider the source from which this energy might be derived. There is abundant evidence that considerable chemical energy is contained in the ribonucleotide *adenosine triphosphate* *(ATP)* which is a riboside 5'-triphosphate (Figure 35–1). ATP is known to react with (1) nicotinamide mononucleotide (a *ribonucleotide*, or *ribotide*) to produce a combination of the two, with the resultant elimination of two phosphates as *inorganic pyrophosphate* (Figure 35–2a), and (2) flavin mononucleotide to produce a dinucleotide plus inorganic pyrophosphate (Figure 35–2b). Evidence that it is ATP which contributes the pyrophosphate, by losing its two terminal

phosphates, is obtained from the reaction of ATP with certain acids (Figure 35–2c). Since ATP supplies the energy for many chemical reactions in the cell, it is reasonable to suppose that it may also supply the energy to join the separate *deoxyribonucleotides (deoxyribotides)* into a DNA strand during replication.

In view of the fact that DNA can be removed from the nucleus, and can be separated from protein, and still retain what appears to be the main characteristics which it had before it was removed (i.e., it presumably retains the properties it had in the living cell), we can hope to study DNA synthesis under nonliving conditions. What should we extract from cells in order to study DNA synthesis *in vitro*? Initially, we ought to make use of all the apparatus that the cell normally provides for this function. On the chain separation view, DNA is needed to serve as a template for new DNA synthesis, so our extract should contain the DNA of the cell. We should add ATP to the extract as a source of the energy required for the synthesis; we can also add magnesium ions, in the form of $MgCl_2$, for this serves to activate many enzymes, including perhaps one which might be required for DNA chain formation.

How will we be able to tell whether DNA was synthesized in the extract? Any crude extract from cells might be expected to contain DNAases which might depolymerize or otherwise degrade DNA as fast or faster than

320

any synthetic process which may be taking place. The problem of identifying DNA synthesis in the absence of a net increase in DNA quantity can be solved by preparing the deoxyriboside thymidine, which has radioactive C^{14} incorporated in its pyrimidine, and adding this substrate to the extract. If any radioactively labeled thymidine is incorporated into the DNA of the extract, it probably would do so by a synthetic reaction, since, you recall, there is little incorporation into DNA except during synthesis.

Finally, we ought to obtain our extract from cells that are growing and dividing rapidly, so that they are likely to contain a maximum amount of apparatus for DNA synthesis, which is being used at full capacity. In line with this reasoning and after such preparation,[1] an experiment was performed

[1] The preceding and following account is based primarily upon work by A. Kornberg and his associates.

with an extract of the bacterium *Escherichia coli.* After a suitable time interval (about 30 minutes) during which extract, radioactive thymidine, ATP, and Mg ions were incubated at an appropriate pH, the pH was then made suitably acidic, under which condition DNA is precipitated but *deoxyribonucleosides (deoxyribosides)* remain soluble. The acid precipitate was washed many times until it was certain that the DNA precipitate was not contaminated by adsorbed deoxyribosides. The precipitate was then examined and found to be only slightly radioactive (50 counts as compared with the 5 million counts present in the added thymidine substrate)! In fact, the amount of thymidine incorporated was so small that it would have been 10,000 times too small to be detected by ordinary chemical analysis. Nevertheless, this radioactivity was doubtless due to thymidine which had been incorporated into the DNA, as could be

a. ARPPP + NRP ⇄ ARPPRN + PP

ADENOSINE   NICOTINAMIDE   DIPHOSPHOPYRIDINE
TRIPHOSPHATE   MONONUCLEOTIDE   NUCLEOTIDE
(ATP)

b. ARPPP + FRP ⇄ ARPPRF + PP

FLAVIN   FLAVIN ADENINE
MONONUCLEOTIDE   DINUCLEOTIDE

c. ARPPP + RCH$_2$COOH⇄ARPOCCH$_2$R+PP
$$\overset{\|}{O}$$

A = Adenine
R = Ribose
N = Nicotinamide
F = Flavin
P P = Inorganic Pyrophosphate

FIGURE 35–2.
Reactions involving ATP.

shown by its release from the precipitated DNA when this was treated with DNAase.

Although this result is not impressive quantitatively, it furnished C^{14}-thymidine, incorporated into acid-precipitable, DNAase-sensitive material; the amount formed, of this labeled material, could be used as an assay of the effect of changes in the experimental procedure. Let us see how this led to a change in the procedure and to a better understanding of the nature of the reaction.

Derivatives of adenosine are commonly formed from reactions involving ATP; derivatives of uridine, cytidine, and guanosine likewise involve their respective triphosphates and the liberation of inorganic pyrophosphate. Such facts lead us to conclude that the basic building block, in the formation of diribotides or polyribotides, is the riboside 5′-phosphate, when activated in the form of the riboside 5′-triphosphate. It is a reasonable hypothesis, therefore, to suppose that the active building block of polydeoxyribotides is the deoxyriboside 5′-triphosphate.

If this is so, the ATP added to the extract of the *in vitro* experiments might be functioning to convert deoxyribosides to the 5′-triphosphate condition (making specifically C^{14}-thymidine 5′-triphosphate). This view was supported when DNA synthesis was obtained *in vitro* using labeled thymidine 5′-triphosphate (T*PPP), instead of labeled thymidine (T*) + ATP (ARPPP).

In order to learn more about the ingredients essential for DNA synthesis, the initial extract, obtained from the sonic treatment of bacteria, was fractionated and its protein concentrated. This was accompanied by about a 4,000-fold increase in synthetic activity. From this and other evidence, it became clear that the presence of a protein catalyst, or enzyme, was essential for the synthetic reaction to proceed.

Once the enzyme was concentrated, it was possible to obtain a large net increase (final amount minus initial amount) in DNA.

However, such a net increase was obtained only if the 5′-triphosphates of all four deoxyribosides commonly found in DNA were added to in the incubation mixture. Deoxyriboside 5′-*di*phosphates were not active, nor were *ribo*side 5′-triphosphates. The other requirements, for net increase in DNA amount, were the presence of already formed DNA of high molecular weight, Mg ions, and the enzyme-containing protein. The already formed, high molecular weight DNA, which serves as a primer for the reaction, may come from a plant, animal, bacterial, or viral source. Similar DNA synthesizing extracts can be prepared from other bacteria and various animal tissues.

Using *E. coli* preparations, it is possible to obtain an *extended synthesis of DNA* which produces 20 or more times as much DNA as was present at the start (that is, than there was primer). In this case, therefore, 95% or more of the DNA present at the end must have been synthesized from the triphosphates added as substrate. The extended synthetic reaction proceeds until the supply of one of the four triphosphates is exhausted, and releases one inorganic pyrophosphate for each deoxyribotide incorporated into DNA.

While there is no extended synthesis of DNA, if only one of the deoxyriboside 5′-triphosphates is added as substrate, there is some incorporation of this nucleotide into the DNA chain in what is called a *limited reaction*. By what mechanism does the nucleotide add on to the DNA chain? Suppose the only triphosphate added to the substrate was deoxycytidine 5′-triphosphate, whose innermost phosphate carried radioactive P^{32} (*d*CP*PP). The two possible ways the DNA chain might lengthen are shown at the left and right of Figure 35–3. The DNA chain which is present as primer is indicated there by being enclosed in brackets. The primer chain can be considered to have a *nucleotide end* (top) (to which pyrophosphate, P–P, is shown added in the diagram to the right), and a *nucleoside end* (bottom). (It is possible to remove a nucleoside by a single break at the 5′ position at the nucleoside end but requires the removal of a nucleotide at the nucleotide end.) The diagram at the left of the Figure shows the dCP* adding on to the nucleoside end, by the formation of a 3′ linkage between P* and the sugar at the end of the chain, with P–P being split off the dCP*PP. The diagram at the right shows dCP*PP being added to the nucleotide end of the chain by linkage to the 5′ position of the end nucleotide which supplies the pyrophosphate that splits off. In brief, the DNA chain might be lengthened by having a nucleotide add on at either the 3′ position of the nucleoside end or at the 5′ position of the nucleotide end.

It is possible to distinguish between these two alternatives in the following way. The product of a limited reaction is treated first with DNAase from micrococci in order to enhance the action of another enzyme, *spleen phosphodiesterase*, which is also added. The latter enzyme degrades DNA by breaking the chain at position 5′, so that deoxyriboside 3′-monophosphates are produced. This position of breakage is indicated by the arrows in Figure 35–3. If the chain grows according to the diagram at the right of the Figure, radioactive P^{32} would be expected to be found in phosphate attached to deoxycytidine. Also, P* should not be found as part of the 3′-deoxyribotides of A, T, or G. If, on the other hand, attachment is at the 3′ position at the nucleoside end of the chain, then, as

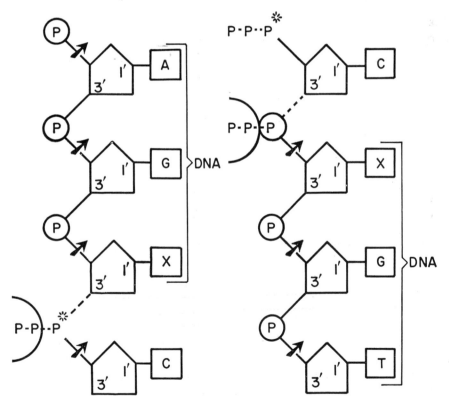

FIGURE 35–3. *Growth of a DNA chain at its nucleoside end (left) and nucleotide end (right). Arrows show position of degradation by micrococcal DNAase plus splenic phosphodiesterase.*

can be seen in the diagram at the left of the Figure, P* should not occur in inorganic phosphates but should sometimes appear in other deoxyriboside 3'-monophosphates besides the one containing C. When the experiment was performed, the latter result was obtained. Not only was P* absent from inorganic phosphate, but it was found frequently in all four kinds of deoxyriboside 3'-monophosphates.

An additional test of the view that the DNA chain grows at its 3' position is furnished by treatment of the limited product by a different enzyme, _snake venom diesterase_. This enzyme digests DNA by breaking the bond between the phosphate and sugar at the 3' position, starting at the nucleoside end of the chain and proceeding toward the nucleotide end. In this way, the DNA is gradually digested into deoxyriboside 5'-phosphates as indicated by the arrows in Figure 35–4. When the limited product was treated this way, it was found, as expected, that almost all the radioactivity had been removed from the chain, even though only a very small portion of the DNA had been digested. Other results show clearly that the product of a limited reaction is DNA, which has one or very few deoxyribotides added to the nucleoside end of the chain. Still other evidence supports the view that the 3' point of lengthwise linkage is the same when net DNA is greatly increased as it is when the limited reaction occurs.

The fact that lengthening of a DNA chain can occur _in vitro_, when any of the four common deoxyribosides happen to be at the nucleoside terminus, is consistent with our knowledge of the nondependence of DNA primary structure upon base sequence. Is there any other evidence that the DNA synthesized _in vitro_ has the characteristics of DNA synthesized _in vivo_? Let us summarize some of the physical properties of samples of DNA composed of 90% or more of the product synthesized _in vitro_. Such samples have physical characteristics that are similar to

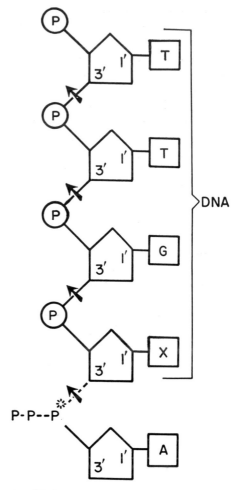

FIGURE 35–4. _Degradation of DNA (arrows) by snake venom diesterase._

that of DNA isolated from calf thymus, insofar as sedimentation rate and viscosity are concerned. From such characteristics a molecular weight of about 6 million was calculated, and it was inferred that the product was not usually single-stranded. In support of the latter inference was the finding that the macromolecular structure of the _in vitro_ product was destroyed when heated for 10 minutes at 100°C, as expected if this treatment produced single chains which collapsed to form compact, randomly coiled structures. Like thymus DNA, the enzymatic product shows the same type of increase in ultraviolet absorption following digestion with pancreatic DNAase.

If the *in vitro* synthesis occurs in the same way as it does *in vivo*, one might expect that single-stranded DNA would serve as a better primer than does double-stranded DNA. Thus, we might expect the single-stranded DNA, isolated from the virus φX174, to be capable of acting as primer. In fact, such material is excellent primer, and heat-treated DNA is better primer than unheated DNA. Moreover, the preparations containing the most active *"synthesizing"* enzyme, which can be called a *polymerase*, will not work with double-stranded primer DNA unless this is first heated or treated with DNAase. Finally, the products of such syntheses behave as though they are primarily two-stranded.

In view of these results we may conclude that the physical characteristics of the DNA synthesized *in vitro* and *in vivo* are indistinguishable. Synthesis clearly involves single chains which produce double chains probably held together by H bonds.

We can also study the detailed chemical and physico-chemical characteristics of the *in vitro* synthesis of DNA. If single chains produce double chains by forming complementary structures, then the capacity to form a complementary chain should depend upon the presence of purine and pyrimidine bases in the substrate which can form appropriate H bonds with the bases in the primer. Figure 35-5 shows some pyrimidine and purine bases that do not naturally occur in DNA as well as the four principal types that do. The unnatural bases include uracil and 5-bromo uracil (both of which might be expected to have the same H-bonding capacities as thymine), 5-methyl cytosine and 5-bromo cytosine (both of which might be expected to have the same H-bonding capacities as cytosine), and hypoxanthine (which has two of the three sites for H-bonding found in guanine).

If an A in the single-strand primer dictates its complement, by specifying that the complementary base provide the proper sites for H-bonding A, then we would expect that uracil, or 5-bromo uracil, could be substituted for the thymine in thymidine 5'-triphosphate.

When substrate containing deoxyuridine 5'-triphosphate (or 5-bromo deoxyuridine 5'-triphosphate), *d*CPPP, *d*APPP, and *d*GPPP were employed, DNA synthesis was supported. Similarly, 5-methyl cytosine and 5-bromo cytosine could substitute for cytosine. On the other hand, the substitution of hypoxanthine for guanine did not support DNA synthesis as well as did the other substitutions mentioned. This would be expected, on the hypothesis under test, since the former has one fewer site for H-bonding than the latter. Moreover, as expected, neither uracil nor 5-bromo uracil would substitute for C, A, or G in *d*CPPP, *d*APPP, or *d*GPPP, respectively. Both 5-methyl and 5-bromo cytosine replace cytosine specifically. Finally, hypoxanthine replaces only guanine. Although hypoxanthine has the same H-bonding groups as thymine, it does not replace thymine, probably because the A-hypoxanthine pair, being composed of two purines, takes up too much space to fit the regular double helix configuration. These results support the hypothesis that normally the *in vitro* synthesis of DNA is dependent upon the formation of complementary purine-pyrimidine pairs — A with T, and C with G — just as is the case *in vivo*.

It is also possible to analyze chemically the DNA synthesized *in vitro* from the usual four deoxyriboside 5'-triphosphates. The analysis shows that in the *in vitro* synthesized DNA, A = T and C = G, just as they do in natural DNA, even though the relative concentration of the four triphosphates in the substrate was distorted widely. Not only do total pyrimidines = total purines in "synthetic" DNA, as described, whether a moderate or a large amount is synthesized, but the particular A + T/G + C ratio found

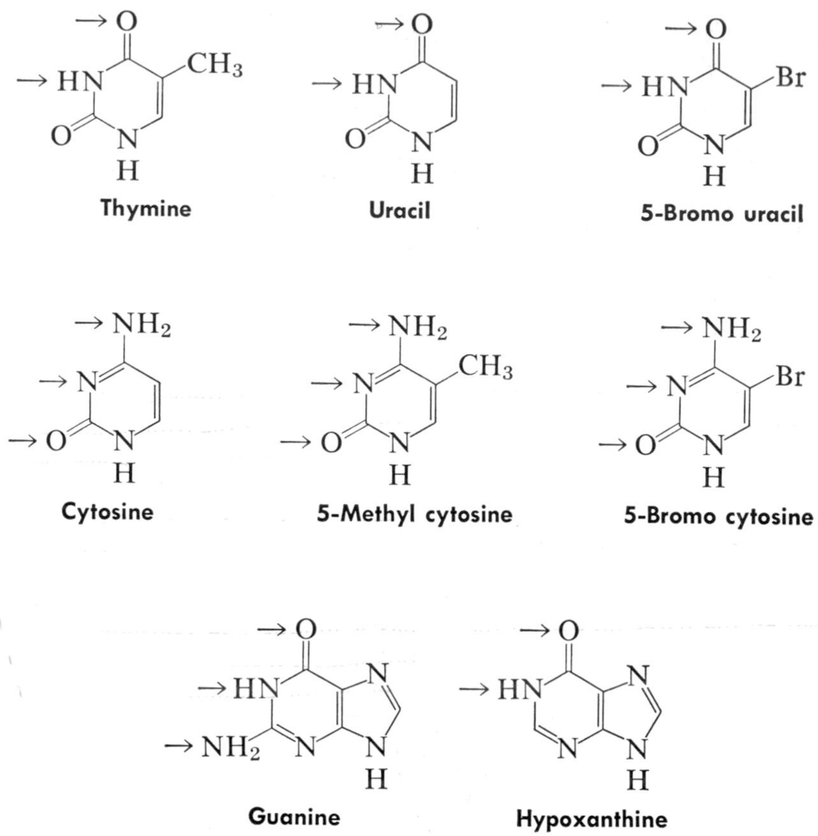

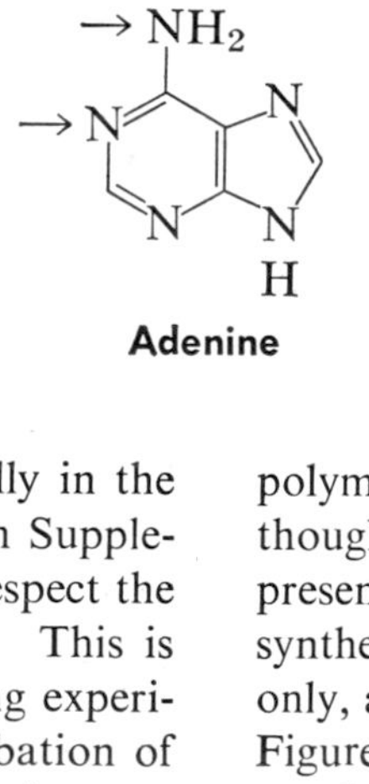

FIGURE 35–5. *Unnatural and common natural bases utilized in* in vitro *synthesis of DNA. Arrows point to groups capable of typical H-bonding.*

in the primer is reproduced faithfully in the synthesized product (see Figure 8 in Supplement VI). In other words, in this respect the product is a replica of the primer. This is illustrated strikingly by the following experiment. After a long period of incubation of all the usual components except primer, a linear deoxyribotide polymer composed only of A and T is formed spontaneously. If this polymer is then used as the primer, even though all four usual triphosphates are present in the substrate, there is an extensive synthesis of material which contains A and T only, and has no trace of C and G (see again Figure 8 in Supplement VI).

It has been mentioned that for each nucleotide added to the end of the DNA chain an inorganic pyrophosphate is liberated. It has been observed that when PP is added to the usual synthesizing complex in great excess (about 100 times the concentration of the triphosphates), the synthetic reaction is inhibited by about 50%. This suggests the reversibility of DNA synthesis *in vitro*.

It was also mentioned earlier that, in a limited reaction, *d*CP*(PP) could add onto a chain terminating in all four types of nucleotides (*d*CP, TP, *d*AP, and *d*GP). This should not be assumed to mean that *d*CP* joins linearly to each nucleotide with equal frequency, or that any nucleotide joins to all others with equal frequency. Other results indicate that the limited reaction does not add nucleotides to the end at random; this reaction probably involves the repair of the shorter strand of a double helix, the particular nucleotide added being specified in the usual way by the bases present in the longer strand.

What is the linear arrangement of nucleotides in the DNA synthesized in an extended reaction? We have noted (p. 306) that, if DNA is genetic material, different linear segments of it may represent different genes. If so, the differences among genes would lie in the sequence of the organic bases they contain. Considering only the four usual deoxyribotides, how many different sequences of two nucleotides are possible? The first nucleotide may be one of four, and so may the second, so that there are 4 × 4, or 16, different possible linear arrangements in dinucleotides. The orders of dinucleotides can be determined experimentally as follows. One of the four triphosphates added as substrate is labeled with P^{32} in the innermost phosphate, the other three are not. Extended synthesis is permitted, during which the P* attaches to the 3′ of the sugar of the nucleotide which is its linear neighbor (refer to the left part of Figure 35–3 and Figure 9 in Supplement VI). This linear neighbor can be identified by digesting the synthesized product with micrococcal DNAase and splenic

phosphodiesterase. You recall that the latter produces deoxyriboside 3′-monophosphates by breaking the chain at 5′. Consequently the labeled phosphate (P*) will be found joined at the 3′ position of the deoxyriboside just anterior to the one with which it entered the DNA strand. The digest is then analyzed to see how frequently P* is part of *d*A 3′-P*, T 3′-P*, *d*C 3′-P*, and *d*G 3′-P*. If the P* was originally in *d*AP*PP, this would tell the relative linear frequencies of AA, AT, AC, and AG. If this procedure is carried out three more times, each time labeling a different one of the triphosphates, the relative frequency of all 16 sequences can be determined.

The results of such studies show that all 16 sequences are produced by each type of natural primer, although each primer type has a unique and reproducible pattern, not predictable from its base composition. Moreover, if, for example, TG is a common linear sequence, so is CA, while if AG is rare, so is CT. This can be explained by the fact that both strands of a double helix are synthesized in an extended reaction, and that the two chains run in opposite directions. Thus, if TG is the dinucleotide sequence found in one strand, the dinucleotide sequence in the complementary strand would be CA.

All the physical and chemical characteristics of DNA synthesis in an extended reaction, including the requirement of all four deoxyriboside 5′-triphosphates and of DNA primer, are consistent with the view that this is a biological process. This means that the synthesis is performed *in vitro* in essentially the same manner as in the living cell, and produces essentially the same product. It should be emphasized that there are two, perhaps separate, processes involved in the biological replication of DNA. One process results in the side-by-side arrangement of complementary base pairs by means of H-bonding, the other produces the linear attachment of nucleotides by the establishment of the 3' phosphate to sugar linkages.

Finally, special attention should be drawn to the polymerizing enzyme essential for the extended biological synthesis of DNA. Previously known enzymes are specific in the respect that they act upon one or a few particular substrates which are usually modified in the same way. Recall (p. 287), for example, that trypsin breaks peptide bonds only at places in a polypeptide chain where lysine or arginine are present. The DNA synthesizing enzyme, DNA polymerase, is unique in that it takes directions from a template; in lengthening a strand it adds the particular component of the substrate which is of the proper size and which will form the correct hydrogen bonds with the base on the single strand acting as template.

SUMMARY AND CONCLUSIONS

DNA can be synthesized *in vitro*. Extended synthesis requires pre-existing single-stranded DNA, the 5' triphosphates of deoxyadenosine, of deoxycytidine, of deoxyguanosine, and of thymidine, Mg ions, and a polymerizing enzyme. In making the product the polymerase takes directions from pre-existing single-stranded DNA.

Study of the physical and chemical properties of the synthesized product reveals that it closely resembles natural DNA and possesses the primary and secondary structure of DNA as elucidated by Watson and Crick. This DNA synthesis is considered to be a biological process.

These results may also be considered as offering further support for the Watson-Crick structure of chromosomal DNA and for its replication after chain separation through the formation of complementary strands.

REFERENCES

Trautner, T. A., Swartz, M. N., and Kornberg, A., "Enzymatic Synthesis of Deoxyribonucleic Acid, X. Influence of Bromouracil Substitutions on Replication," Proc. Nat. Acad. Sci., U.S., 48:449–455, 1962.

See Supplement VI. A list of references can be found at the end of Dr. Kornberg's Nobel Prize lecture.

QUESTIONS FOR DISCUSSION

35.1. Has this Chapter dealt with genetics? Explain.

35.2. Which single experiment described in this Chapter would you consider to be the most important? Why?

35.3. Differentiate between the action of splenic phosphodiesterase and snake venom diesterase.

35.4. What are the requirements for the *in vitro* synthesis of DNA to proceed as a limited reaction? To proceed extensively?

35.5. What differences exist between DNA chain formation *in vitro* in the absence and presence of primer DNA?

35.6. List the evidences that the synthesis of DNA *in vitro* represents a biological process.

35.7. Does DNA polymerase from *E. coli* take directions only from *E. coli* DNA? Explain.

35.8. Does chain separation occur during an extended synthesis of DNA *in vitro*? Explain.

35.9. Of what significance is the nearest nucleotide neighbor analysis?

Chapter *36

BACTERIA: CLONES
AND MUTATION

YOU MAY have noticed that our present understanding of the mechanisms involved in the biological replication of DNA *in vivo* (Chapter 34) and *in vitro* (Chapter 35) has been very significantly advanced by means of experiments with bacteria. Such studies used the DNA as well as the DNA polymerase of these organisms. The presumption was made, in evaluating that work, that the bacterial DNA employed was typical "chromosomal" DNA. Though microscopic examination of bacteria reveals a nuclear body, it has not been possible, so far, to clearly delineate any chromosome structure within it. Nevertheless, the DNA within the bacterial nucleus is similar to typical chromosomal DNA in (1) basic chemical content, (2) primary and secondary organization, (3) mechanism of synthesis, and (4) conservation. We are, therefore, justified in considering bacterial DNA as being primarily chromosomal DNA.

Since bacteria contain chromosomal DNA, we would expect them also to contain chromosomal genes, in accord with the hypothesis, for which much indirect support has already been presented, that DNA is genetic material. How suitable are bacteria as experimental material for the study of mutation? In the case of a particular bacterium, *Escherichia coli*, microscopic observation reveals that each cell contains one to four nuclei, usually two or four (Figure 36–1). Although the nature of the morphological

329

mechanism of nuclear division is still controversial, the exact replication of DNA occurs at each nuclear division, and it may be concluded the daughter nuclei are genetically identical, just as they are following typical mitosis. After nuclear replication the bacterium divides to produce daughter bacteria. This means of increasing bacterial cell number is called *vegetative reproduction*, and is an asexual process. *We shall make the assumption, until such time as experimental evidence to the contrary may be presented, that genetic recombination cannot occur within or between bacterial cells.* In the absence of genetic recombination we shall, of course, be unable to study the recon. (It should be recalled that in Chapter 2, p. 8, the choice was made to study the properties of the genetic material as revealed from a study of sexually reproducing, cross-fertilizing species. That pathway led to our present concept of the recon based upon the recombinations which the genetic material undergoes consequent to segregation, independent segregation, crossing over, and fertilization.)

Starting with a single bacterium, continuous vegetative reproduction results in the production of a population of cells called a *clone*. Since a clone is a population of individuals all derived from a single cell by asexual reproduction, all clonal members are genetically identical, barring mutation. If mutation occurs during clonal growth, the mutant will be transmitted to all the progeny of the mutant cell. This would produce a genetically mosaic clone, whose proportion of mutant individuals would vary depending upon the time the mutation occurred and the relative reproductive potential of mutant and nonmutant cells. You may recall (p. 245) that except for meiosis, its products, and fertilization, all cells of a sexually reproducing organism are also clonal in origin, so that multicellular organisms can also be mosaic for a mutant. Let us consider the characteristics of bacteria and their clones which

def

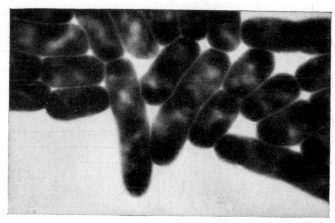

A

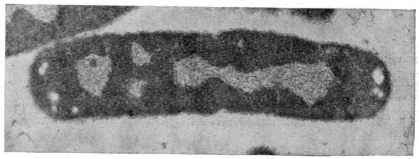

B

FIGURE 36–1. *Electron microscope photographs of* Escherichia coli. *A. Whole cells in which nuclear bodies are revealed as less dense areas. Original magnification 3000X, present magnification about 12,000X. (Courtesy of E. Kellenberger.) B. Thin section showing nuclear bodies and the fine DNA-containing fibers within them. Original magnification 10,000X. Present magnification about 15,000X (Courtesy of W. H. G. Schreil.)*

may be of significance for a study of mutation.

One great advantage in the use of bacteria for mutation studies derives from the ease and speed with which large populations can be obtained. For example, under appropriate culture conditions, *E. coli* divides about once each half hour. Under such conditions, one cell will produce a clone containing about 10 billion (10^{10}) individuals after the 30 successive generations that take place in a period of 15 hours. Starting with a single cell, one can calculate the number of *E. coli* produced after n generations (or t hours) by the expression 2^n (or 2^{2t}) (Figure 36–2). Of course, space is no problem in working with bacteria since 10^{10} individuals can be grown readily in liquid broth in an ordinary test tube.

The advantage of small size becomes a handicap, however, when it comes to detecting phenotypic changes in bacteria due to mutation. Mutants that change the morphology of bacteria must be detected by examining individuals microscopically. Unfortunately, the single bacterium shows few clear-cut morphological variations. These involve such traits as size, shape, and the presence or absence of flagella, so that the detection of mutants by examining individual bacteria is seriously limited to those which affect particular morphological traits to a measurable degree.

After a suspected mutant is found under the microscope, it is essential to isolate it and determine, from the members of the clone it produces, whether or not the new trait appears in the offspring, that is, was caused by a mutant. There are several methods by which an individual bacterium may be isolated. This can be done directly by the tedious, but exact, procedure of removing a single bacterium from a culture with the aid of a micromanipulator and placing it in fresh culture medium. Single bacteria can also be obtained by two, less exact, but quicker, indirect methods. If the bacteria are growing in a liquid medium, it is possible to dilute the culture sufficiently so that a sample contains relatively few individuals. When this sample is poured onto the surface of a petri dish containing nutrient agar, the individual cells will be located on the agar at random, usually so spaced that the visible clone each produces will be discrete (Figure 36–3). It is also possible to take a small amount of a broth culture and spread the bacteria in the sample in the following way. A small amount of the culture is picked up by a sterile innoculating loop and streaked across the surface of fresh agar (Figure 36–4). At some places on the agar single bacteria will have been deposited far enough apart so that they give rise to separate colonies. Which of these methods is actually used depends upon the precision required to obtain the isolation of a particular bacterium or bacterial type.

The study of the individual bacterium is

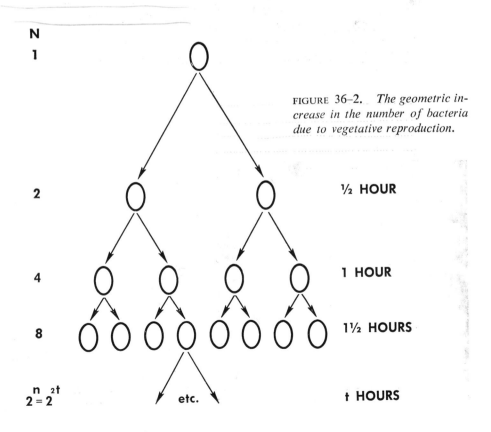

N
1

2   ½ HOUR

4   1 HOUR

8   1½ HOURS

$2^n = 2^{2t}$ etc.   t HOURS

FIGURE 36–2. *The geometric increase in the number of bacteria due to vegetative reproduction.*

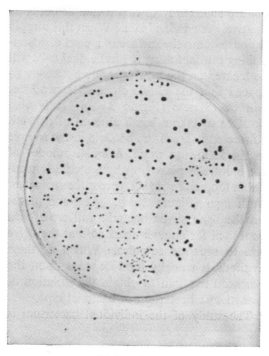

FIGURE 36–3. *Discrete clones, growing on agar nutrient in a petri dish, obtained by plating a dilute culture of bacteria.*

FIGURE 36–4. *Separate bacterial clones obtained by the streaking method. (Courtesy of N. E. Melechen.)*

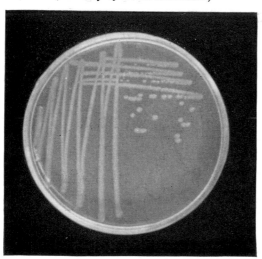

restricted to morphological variation, since it is not yet feasible or possible to make physiological and biochemical studies on such a microscopic scale. We can, however, make use of the fact that, barring mutation, clones are composed of genetically identical individuals. Genetically different clones may show phenotypic differences in the size, shape, and color of the colonies formed on agar. Genetically different clones may also respond differently to various dyes, drugs, and viruses. Therefore, we can establish the genotype of a single bacterium from the phenotype it produces as a clone, and we have already indicated a number of clonal traits useful for this purpose.

E. coli, for example, is an easily cultured organism. This is so because it can grow and reproduce on a simple, chemically defined food medium. Strains which grow on such a basic, minimal medium may be considered to be *prototrophic*, or wild-type, being capable of synthesizing the numerous metabolic components of the cell not supplied in the medium. In this respect prototrophs of *E. coli* or other bacteria are identical to wild-type *Neurospora* which also grows on a minimal medium (Chapter 32, pp. 281–282). It is no surprise, then, that in bacteria, just as in *Neurospora*, the richest source of mutants comes from the study of the biochemical variations which occur in different clones, particularly those involving changes in nutritional requirements. And, in fact, numerous mutants have been obtained, arising either spontaneously, or after treatment with physical or chemical mutagens, which, in order to grow and reproduce, require the addition of one or more of a variety of chemical substances to the basic medium. Thus, for example, one strain of *E. coli* requires the addition of the amino acid threonine to the minimal medium in order to grow, while another strain requires the amino acid methionine. Such nutritionally dependent strains, which need a supplement to the basic food medium in order to grow, are said to be *auxotrophic*.

It is known that the vast majority of the mutants produced following treatment with a mutagenic agent have nonadaptive or detrimental phenotypic effects (Chapter 24). Moreover, the detriment of these mutants is clearly not dependent upon the continued presence in the environment of the mutagen which induced them. It is also true that many of the rare mutants that increase adaptability are beneficial in the absence of the mutagen which induced them. However, on rare occasions a mutagen (like X rays) produces a mutant which has an adaptive advantage in the presence of the mutagen (resistance to the genetic or nongenetic detrimental effects of X rays). Was this adaptive mutant produced fortuitously, or was it a genetic response specifically elicited by the mutagen? The same question can be raised about adaptive mutants occurring spontaneously. Are these, by some mechanism, an adaptive genetic response to some unidentified factor present in the environment (so that we say the mutant arose for no known reason, and is, therefore, "spontaneous")? What we are asking is whether there is or is not a type of mutant which occurs specifically because it provides adaptiveness to some factor in the environment.

This general problem can be illustrated with a particular example. There is a strain of *E. coli* that has, apparently, never been exposed to streptomycin. If such a strain is plated onto agar containing this drug almost all the individuals cannot grow and do not form colonies. These individuals are called *streptomycin-sensitive*. However, in one particular strain, about one bacterium in 10 million does grow to form a colony composed of *streptomycin-resistant* individuals, the basis for this resistance clearly being transmissible and adaptive. Was the adaptive resistant mutant produced in response to the streptomycin exposure, so that the streptomycin acted as a directive mutagenic agent? Or,

do streptomycin-resistant mutants occur in the absence of streptomycin, spontaneously, so that the streptomycin acts only as a selective agent to reveal the prior occurrence (or nonoccurrence) of resistant mutants? Or, are both explanations true? We can restate the problem more generally and ask whether mutants, adapted to a treatment, arose only after treatment (being postadapted), or had already been present before treatment (being preadapted), or both.

It becomes clear that an unambiguous decision cannot be made so long as it is necessary to treat the individuals scored, with the factor being tested — streptomycin, in the particular example under discussion. For, under these conditions, one cannot decide whether the resistant mutant had a post- or preadaptive origin. This difficulty can be circumvented in the following way. If streptomycin-resistant mutants are preadaptive, they should occur in the absence of the drug, and give rise to clones, all of whose members should be resistant. It should be noted again that the mutation to streptomycin-resistance is a very rare event, whatever its mechanism of origin. Accordingly, what we need to do is to grow about 10 million clones on streptomycin-free agar medium and sample each one for streptomycin-resistance, by placing each sample on streptomycin. If this is done, at least part of one sample will be resistant to the drug. If the resistance is due to a preadapted mutant, one will be able to return to the particular original clone (itself never exposed to streptomycin) and repeatedly obtain other samples which test as resistant. If, on the other hand, the mutant is postadaptive, return to the original clone will provide additional samples which show no greater chance of furnishing resistants than have additional samples taken from different clones.

There are three clone-sampling procedures one may use for testing the pre- or post-adaptiveness of mutants. The first method starts with a single (presumably) streptomycin-sensitive clone grown in liquid medium which is plated on agar to produce a large number of separate colonies. A sample of each colony is then taken and streaked across agar which has a strip containing streptomycin. All clones will grow on the agar, except in the streptomycin region. But if enough clones are tested, one will be found to grow there also (Figure 36–5). If streptomycin-resistant mutations are postadaptive in origin, the growth found on the streptomycin should be sharply discontinuous, since the members of the clone streaked across the streptomycin were originally sensitives, and only rarely would more than one of these bacteria be expected to respond to streptomycin by post-adaptive mutation. Moreover, return to the original clone would furnish other samples which would succeed in growing on strepto-mycin only rarely, and then only to the same limited degree as did the first positive sample. If, on the other hand, the mutation is pre-adaptive, the growth across the streptomycin should be just about as continuous as one would find after the drug was streaked with a pure clone of resistant bacteria, or a mixture of bacteria rich in resistant individuals. The demonstration that the parental clone represented a spontaneous, preadaptive, strepto-mycin-resistant mutant would be completed, if other samples of that clone also grew readily when streaked across this drug.

FIGURE 36–5. *Streptomycin-sensitive and strepto-mycin-resistant* E. coli *as determined by streaking individual clones.*

BAND OF STREPTOMYCIN

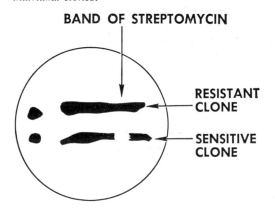

RESISTANT CLONE

SENSITIVE CLONE

In view of the rarity in this strain of mutation from streptomycin-sensitivity to resistance (1 per 10^7 cells), the labor involved is so prohibitive that this clone-sampling technique is impractical for testing the pre- or postadaptive nature of streptomycin-resistant mutants. (Nevertheless, this method has numerous uses in other genetic studies of bacteria.)

The second method which can be used to sample clones involves *replica plating*.[1] One starts the procedure, as before, with a single clone which has been spread on streptomycin-free agar in a petri dish. After the plate is incubated, there may be as many as a thousand separate colonies. A sample of almost every colony can be obtained simultaneously by pressing this master plate on the top of a sheet of velvet whose fibers pick up 10–30% of each colony. The velvet is then used to plant a corresponding pattern of growth on a series of additional plates. The first copy is made on drug-free medium also, whereas the second and later copies are made with plates containing streptomycin. (Of course, preliminary control tests show that the velvet makes a number of very good replicas of the master plate — Figure 36–6 shows one replica — and that both streptomycin-resistant and sensitive clones are replicable this way.) On the second and later replicas, only streptomycin-resistant bacteria will grow into colonies. If the postadaptive view is correct, a colony that grows in the presence of streptomycin on one replica will not show any greater likelihood of growing on other replicas, made from the master plate at the same time or subsequently, than will a colony located in a different position. In other words, the positions of the resistant colonies on different replicas should be at random to each other. If the mutants are preadaptive, however, there should be a very good likelihood that all replicas will be resistant in the same position

[1] Based upon work of J. Lederberg and E. M. Lederberg.

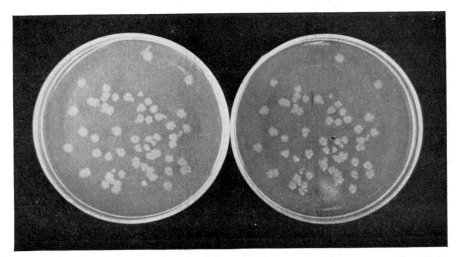

FIGURE 36–6. *Separate colonies replica-plated (right) from a master plate (left). (Courtesy of N. E. Melechen.)*

(although there may be some exceptions due to the failure of the velvet to place a portion of the same colony on every replica plate). Of course, one should also readily find resistant bacteria on the master plate in the corresponding position. Despite the fact that this clone-sampling technique is advantageous for many other purposes, it is still too laborious for testing the pre- or postadaptation hypothesis, since to be reasonably sure of finding one clonal mutant to streptomycin-resistance would require making replicas of about 10 thousand plates.

It is possible to circumvent this difficulty by using a third method for clone-sampling, which involves replica-plating contiguous colonies. A billion or so bacteria can be plated on drug-free agar. These will form small clones so closely spaced as to show continuous growth (Figure 36–7A). Nevertheless, a replica of this growth can be made on streptomycin agar. The replica will show growth whenever there are drug-resistant mutants (Figure 36–7B, C, D). One can then return to the corresponding site on the master plate and obtain samples to be tested for resistance to the drug. If such a sample is much richer in resistant mutants than a

sample from a site on the master plate randomly chosen from those not mutant on the replica, the preadaptive view is proved; if not, the postadaptive view is. This experiment has been performed and the results prove that most mutants are clearly preadaptive (Figure 36–7). Moreover, other experiments show conclusively, in the case

FIGURE 36–7. *Replica-plating continuous colonies for the detection of mutants to streptomycin-resistance. (After J. Lederberg and E. M. Lederberg.)*

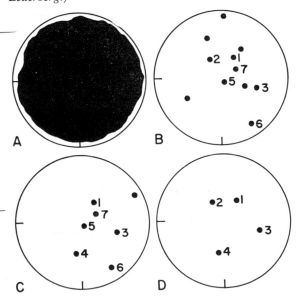

of streptomycin, that all mutants resistant to the drug are preadaptive — that is, this drug does not induce resistant mutants. The same results were obtained with the drug chloramphenicol, so that we may extrapolate from such results and conclude that generally all resistant mutants on drug plates arise spontaneously prior to exposure to the drug.

Large numbers of bacteria can be tested for mutations with ease. For example, a billion drug-sensitive individuals can be plated on agar containing the drug, and the number of resistant mutant clones readily detected by counting the colonies formed. Or, similarly, the number of mutants to prototrophy can be scored, by plating auxotrophs on agar lacking the nutrient required for their growth, and counting the number of colonies formed. In order to give information in terms of a rate of mutation, however, it is necessary to state the number of mutants that occur per unit event. In multicellular organisms, mutation rate is usually expressed in terms of mutations per cell, individual, or generation. This definition can be applied to bacteria, also. Thus, the mutation rate, from streptomycin-sensitivity to resistance in one particular strain of *E. coli* (other than the one used beginning on p. 333) is one per billion bacteria, the lowest mutation rate so far measured in any organism.

It is sometimes desirable to express mutation rates in terms of mutations per unit time. This could have been done, for example, in describing the increase in mutations obtained by means of aging *Drosophila* spermatids or sperm (Chapter 23, p. 201). In the case of bacteria, it is possible to vary considerably the length of time required to complete a generation. For generation times between 37 minutes and 2 hours, the shorter the generation time, the larger the mutation rate *per hour*. When generation time is lengthened to occupy from 2 to 12 hours, the rate of mutations *per hour* is constant — each hour of delay increasing the number of mu-

tants by the same amount. (Thus, in this 2–12 hour range, there is an increase in the number of mutations that occur per generation.) Finally, even when the generation time is extended to infinity (when nondividing cells, provided with a source of energy, are studied), some mutations are found to take place.

It becomes apparent, therefore, that it is best to define *mutation rate* as the chance of a mutation per cell (or individual) per unit time. When, however, each of the division cycles or generations requires the same length of time (as would be true for bacteria under optimal environmental conditions), time is usually measured in terms of generations.

What causes the spontaneous mutation rate in bacteria? We have already discussed how the spontaneous mutation rate is influenced by naturally occurring physical mutagens, like ultraviolet light or ionizing radiations (Chapter 21), and possibly by naturally occurring chemical mutagens (Chapter 23). We also know that there is some genetic control of mutability (Chapter 25). We may be able to learn more about these or other factors influencing the spontaneous mutation rate after considering the results of certain experiments with *E. coli*.

In the studies of the effect of generation length on spontaneous mutation rate, mutations from sensitivity to resistance to infection by virus were investigated.[2] In some experiments virus T5 and in others virus T6 were used (a mutant resistant to one of these viruses is still sensitive to the other). Generation time was lengthened by limiting the amount of one of the nutrients required by the bacteria for growth. The nutrient medium was simple and contained lactate, ammonium, chloride, and magnesium sulfate. Since the *E. coli* employed was a mutant requiring supplementary tryptophan in order to grow, this substance was also added to the medium.

[2] Based upon work of A. Novick and L. Szilard (1951).

Significant differences in mutation rate were observed when different components of the nutrient medium were made the limiting factor for growth. The highest rate was obtained when tryptophan was the growth-controlling factor and the lowest rate was obtained when lactate was the growth-controlling factor.

The fact that limiting different nutrients has a significant effect upon spontaneous mutation rate is a clear indication that this rate depends upon the physiological or biochemical state of the organism. This view is supported by the effect of temperature changes upon the spontaneous mutation rate (see p. 200). This also suggests that if chemical substances are added to a culture of *E. coli* growing in a medium with one essential nutrient limited in supply, a pronounced mutagenic action might be obtained. A number of substances were chosen to be tested (some of which were already known to be mutagenic in other organisms) and were used in concentrations that produced no appreciable killing of bacteria.

One group of substances tested for capacity to induce mutations to T5 resistance, when nutrition was tryptophan-limited, was purines and purine derivatives. Many were mutagenic. The most mutagenic was caffeine; theophylline was nearly as effective; azaguanine was mutagenic, and so also, to a lesser degree, was adenine itself. In contrast, no pyrimidines or their derivatives were mutagenic under the same conditions.

It was also found [3] in this system that if purine ribosides, like adenosine or guanosine, were added to the medium containing any one of several purine mutagens, that there was complete suppression of the mutagenic activity. Thus, for example, adenosine completely suppresses the mutagenicity of adenine or caffeine. The purine nucleosides were clearly acting as *antimutagens*, just as anoxia or catalase are antimutagens so far as chromosomal breakage (p. 179) or point muta-

[3] A. Novick (1956); see reference at end of Chapter.

tions (p. 201) produced by X rays are concerned, and were not acting as selective agents against induced mutants. On the other hand, pyrimidine ribosides, deoxyadenosine, and deoxyguanosine were either not at all antimutagenic to purines and their derivatives, or much less efficient than the purine ribosides. None of the purine ribosides had any antimutagenic effect on ultraviolet or gamma radiation treatments.

Theophylline is mutagenic, as mentioned, under aerobic conditions. But under anaerobic conditions theophylline is not mutagenic. One need not be satisfied just to call anaerobiosis antimutagenic, for it has been found that adenosine is present in significant concentrations in bacteria growing anaerobically but is not present in detectable quantities in bacteria growing aerobically. Apparently, under anaerobic conditions, adenosine is a normally present antimutagen that acts against the effect of purines added in the medium. It should be noted that the ultraviolet induced mutation rate is unaffected by anaerobiosis, and gamma radiation is less effective only because of the reduction in oxygen; this is consistent with the finding, already mentioned, that added adenosine has no antimutagenic effect on either mutagen.

One may ask whether the spontaneous mutation rate itself is reduced by the presence of purine ribosides in the medium. It was found that adenosine and guanosine, but not the pyrimidine ribosides uridine and cytidine, suppress the spontaneous mutation rate. With adenosine in the medium, the spontaneous rate could be reduced to about one third its original value. Moreover, the spontaneous rate is lower under anaerobic than aerobic conditions, as would be expected from the metabolic production of adenosine. Finally, it may be noted that all the purine mutagens increase the mutation rate to T5 resistance more than to T6 resistance, while the reverse is true for ultraviolet and gamma radiation.

From these results it seems reasonable to

distinguish two kinds of mutagens, a purine type and a radiation type, which produce two different kinds of mutations. In considering the basis of the spontaneous mutation rate, it can be postulated that, under the experimental conditions described, about two thirds of it is produced by the action of some purine type of substance produced spontaneously during the normal metabolism of the cell. It may seem surprising that only purines, their analogs, and purine nucleosides were found to affect the mutation rate. Perhaps this is related to the particular mutations studied, namely resistance to T5 and T6. It may be that these mutations happen to depend more upon changes in purines than upon changes in pyrimidines, and that other mutations may prove to be relatively pyrimidine-sensitive and purine-insensitive.

While it is not clear how the purines and their nucleosides accomplish these mutagenic and antimutagenic effects, and how these effects are related to the changes in mutation rate with generation length, two general conclusions are warranted. First, these experiments prove that a considerable portion of the spontaneous mutation rate is the normal consequence of the cell's biochemical activity in producing mutagens and antimutagens. Second, these experiments demonstrate a connection between mutation rate and nucleic acid metabolism. While the mutation rate was directly connected only with purines and their nucleosides, it is not unreasonable to suppose that there is also an indirect connection with DNA and its precursors. This supposition is supported by the fact that thymine, which is a component of DNA and not RNA, is mutagenic when withheld from bacteria requiring it.

SUMMARY AND CONCLUSIONS

Bacterial clones provide excellent experimental material for the study of the mutation process and its rate. Mutants occur spontaneously, independently of the factors to which they may be adaptive.

A considerable portion of the spontaneous mutation rate is based upon the intracellular production of mutagens and antimutagens. For this reason, spontaneous mutation is in many respects an incident of the normal metabolism of the cell, in which nucleic acids are specifically implicated.

REFERENCES

Lederberg, J., and Lederberg, E. M., "Replica Plating and Indirect Selection of Bacterial Mutants," J. Bact., 63:399–406, 1952; reprinted in *Papers on Bacterial Genetics*, Adelberg, E. A. (Ed.), Boston, Little, Brown, 1960, pp. 24–31.

Novick, A., "Mutagens and Antimutagens," Brookhaven Symposia on Biology, 8:201–215, 1956; reprinted in *Papers on Bacterial Genetics*, Adelberg, E. A. (Ed.), Boston, Little, Brown, 1960, pp. 74–90.

Novick, A., and Szilard, L., "Experiments on Spontaneous and Chemically Induced Mutations of Bacteria Growing in the Chemostat," Cold Spring Harbor Sympos. Quant. Biol., 16:337–343, 1951; reprinted in *Papers on Bacterial Genetics*, Adelberg, E. A. (Ed.), Boston, Little, Brown, 1960, pp. 47–57.

QUESTIONS FOR DISCUSSION

36.1. Which single characteristic of bacteria provides the greatest advantage for genetic studies? Why?

36.2. Has any evidence been presented, in previous Chapters, that spontaneous mutations are preadaptive? If so, state where.

36.3. Suppose 1000 streptomycin-free test tubes are each inoculated with one bacterium of a streptomycin-sensitive clone. Growth is permitted until there are about one billion bacteria present in each tube. The contents of each tube are then plated on streptomycin-containing agar.

What kind of result would you expect if mutations to streptomycin-resistance were postadaptive in origin? Preadaptive in origin? Could you distinguish between these two alternatives from the results expected? How?

36.4. Is it valid to conclude, from our discussion of drug-resistant mutants, that no drugs are mutagenic? Explain.

36.5 On the assumption that all members of a clone are identical, genetically and physiologically, has there been any opportunity for sexual processes to influence the results of any of the experiments described in the present Chapter? Explain.

36.6. Discuss the causes of the "spontaneous" mutation rate.

36.7. Does this Chapter offer any new evidence that the genotype regulates its own mutability? Explain.

36.8. What, if any, new information does the present Chapter provide you with regard to the genetic or chemical basis of mutation?

JOSHUA LEDERBERG *and* ESTHER MARILYN LEDERBERG *about 1951. (Courtesy of The Long Island Biological Association.)*

Chapter 37

BACTERIA: RECOMBINATION

(I. Transformation and Strand Recombination *in Vitro*)

IT HAS been known for some time that *Pneumococcus* (*Diplococcus pneumoniae*) occurs in several types which may be characterized by their clonal phenotype. One type, S, produces a smooth colony, and this trait is directly connected with the fact that the bacterium possesses a capsule of polysaccharide material. Another type of colony is rough, R, due to bacteria which lack this polysaccharide capsule. There are, moreover, several types of S colonies, which can be distinguished from one another because they differ antigenically, and different antisera can be obtained which specifically cause the clumping of each different type of S. Antiserum can also be produced that will clump R cells, which can also occur in several different antigenic types.

When a large number of R cells is placed in nutrient broth containing anti-R serum [1] and growth continues, clumps of agglutinated R cells settle to the bottom of the test tube, leaving the supernatant fluid clear. If this supernate is plated on nutrient agar, any bacteria still present form typical R colonies, so that any mutation which would cause R to form S must occur so rarely as to be undetected using this particular technique.

When the same experiment is performed, with the exception that heat-killed (65° C for 30 minutes) S cells are also added to the nutri-

[1] The following account is based upon experiments of F. Griffith, of M. H. Dawson and R. H. P. Sia, and of O. T. Avery, C. M. MacLeod, and M. McCarty (1944).

340

ent broth, plating of the supernate shows that numerous clones of S type appear on the agar! This S phenotype is stable and is clearly the result of a transmissible change. We conclude, therefore, that the heat-killed S cells are acting as a mutagen in the genetic transformation of R to S cells. What is most surprising is the fact that the type of S mutant produced is always identical to that of the heat-killed bacteria acting as mutagen. We are apparently dealing with a unique situation in which the mutagen acts specifically to produce mutations in only one predictable direction (to one S type), rather than in several directions (to two or more S types).

In order to determine the chemical nature of the mutagen involved, the transforming capacity of different fractions of the heat-killed S bacteria was tested. Fractions containing only the polysaccharide coat, or protein, or RNA, were completely inactive. Only the fraction containing DNA had transforming capacity. The purest DNA extracts retained the full transforming capacity, even though they could have contained less than .02% protein, and even after having been treated with protein-denaturing agents or proteolytic enzymes. Chemical analyses and serological, electrophoretic, ultracentrifuge, and spectroscopic tests also indicated that this active DNA showed no detectable contamination by protein, unbound lipid, or polysaccharide. RNAase had no effect on the transforming capacity of this purified DNA fraction. On the other hand, the transforming factor was completely destroyed by DNAase. The last result shows that transformation is not produced by exposure to nucleotides or nucleosides of D-ribose type, singly or in small groups.

Transforming DNA has the double-stranded configuration of chromosomal DNA, as revealed from its X-ray diffraction pattern. The fact that pure DNA can be used to transform means that no contact need be made between the cell acting as DNA donor and the one acting as recipient. Moreover, it was shown that transformation does not involve the mediation of a virus. Therefore, *beyond any reasonable scientific doubt, it must be DNA itself and alone which is the transforming agent.*

Other work showed that transformation can occur in either direction (that is A → A′ and A′ → A) and that bacteria can become transformed with respect to any chromosomal gene they possess. A′ cells can be transformed to A″ type which, in turn, provide large quantities of A″-DNA capable of transforming other A′ cells to A″. So, *the DNA of transformed bacteria can be extracted in turn to provide greatly increased amounts of the same transforming principle.* One transforming principle (A′) can transform bacteria having any one of several alternative phenotypes (e.g., A or A″). If the A′-DNA, from bacteria transformed from A to A′, is used to transform bacteria of a third genotype (A″), the only transformations produced are those involving the genes of the immediate donor (i.e., only A′ and no A transformants are found). This demonstrates that transformations are not transmissible changes involving a simple addition of particular genetic material to the genotype, but entail the loss of host genetic material at the same time that the new genetic material is acquired. Thus, *the genetic change in transformation is of a replacement type.*

How does transforming DNA accomplish this replacement? It is possible [2] to trace the fate of transforming DNA by labeling its phosphate groups with radioactive P^{32}. At various times after exposure to this labeled DNA, one portion of the treated bacteria is killed and analyzed with respect to the presence of P^{32} in its DNA, while another portion is tested to determine whether it has been transformed. Only after bacteria have been exposed to the DNA extract for a suitable period of time is the labeled DNA found in the extract containing the host's chromosomal DNA. Moreover, *the frequency with which the host cell is transformed is directly proportional to the amount of labeled DNA so incorporated.*

The results mentioned in the last two paragraphs indicate that the transformer DNA actually enters the bacterium and replaces a segment of the host's chromosomal DNA,[3] after which the newly introduced material replicates as a normal part of the chromosome. Since it is DNA which alone carries the genetic information for transformation, we conclude that *transformation provides direct and conclusive evidence that DNA is genetic material.* Accordingly, *chromosomal DNA contains the chemical units of the genetic material.* All other transformation studies support this conclusion.

We should now reexamine the assumption, made earlier in this Chapter, that transformation involves mutation. The first results on transformation seemed to involve novel, rare changes in the genetic material, and were hence called mutations (see p. 137). We now know that transformation involves replacement of one segment of genetic material by another. No new type of genetic material appears; there is only a shuffling of already existent genes. Thus, no novel genes are produced by transformation. Moreover, genetic transformation has been found not only in *Pneumococcus*, but in *Hemophilis, Xanthomonas, Salmonella, Bacillus, Neisseria*, and *Escherichia* and other organisms as well. In the case of *Neisseria*, DNA is regularly liberated into the slime layer by autolyzing cells which are found in aging cultures. Such DNA is effective in transformation, as is the DNA obtained from penicillin-sensitive pneumococci lysed after treatment with penicillin. Not only is transformation widespread, but a given type may occur with frequencies as

---

[2] Based upon work of L. S. Lerman and L. J. Tolmach (1957).

[3] See H. Ephrussi-Taylor (1951) for specific evidence for the latter observation.

high as 25%. Such results demonstrate that transformation is not rare. In view of the possibility that transformation may be a routine process, it is best not to consider it as mutation. Accordingly, *transformation*, like segregation, independent segregation, crossing over, and fertilization, is probably best considered as *a potential mechanism for normal genetic recombination*.

It is now believed that completion of the transformation process requires a series of discrete stages.

1. *Cell competence*. There are certain periods in cell division or in the growth of a culture during which transformation does not occur, whereas in other periods the cells are competent to react.

2. *Binding of the transformer*. When cells are in a competent stage, the transforming DNA is first transiently bound to the cell, and can be removed by several methods, including the action of added DNAase, before it is bound permanently.

3. *Penetration of transformer*. Permanently bound DNA is considered to have penetrated the recipient cell. If the transformer DNA has been fragmented sonically, so that the DNA particles have a molecular weight of less than 4×10^5, these do not penetrate. Only high molecular weight DNA penetrates. *Pneumococcus* contains about 6 million pairs of nucleotides per haploid nucleus, equivalent to about 200 molecules of about 10×10^6 molecular weight. It has been found that about 60–4800 molecules of such a molecular weight penetrate. It is clear, therefore, that a large amount of DNA (equal to a considerable portion of the donor genome) succeeds in penetration. This, plus the fact that smaller pieces of DNA cannot penetrate, recalls the circumstances under which DNA uptake occurs in tissue culture (see p. 317). In such cases, DNA enters by phagocytosis, which occurs only when the DNA adheres to a suitably large particle. Perhaps, in bacteria also, a mechanism of

penetration is involved in which the cell also takes an active part, and can do so only if the amount of DNA is sufficiently large. (It may be noted that the success of transformation is inversely related to the thickness of a polysaccharide coat, which probably acts as some kind of barrier to binding or penetration.)

Whatever the specific mechanism for penetration may be, it is known that there are a finite number of sites on the bacterial surface which act as receptors for DNA. Since nontransforming DNA, such as DNA from a widely separated genus, can also penetrate readily, receptor sites can be saturated by nontransforming DNA, after which transforming DNA cannot penetrate.

4. *Synapsis*. Alternatives of the same trait (for example, resistance and sensitivity to streptomycin, or auxotrophy and prototrophy for a particular nutrient) can be found in different species of bacteria. On the reasonable assumption that the same gene and its alternatives perform the same functions in different species, it ought to be possible to produce interspecific transformations. This has been accomplished, but, in any given case, interspecific transformation is usually less frequent than the intraspecific one. The fact that interspecific transformation takes place at all favors the idea that the transformed locus is normally part of the genotype of both species. The scarcity of interspecific transformations, therefore, is probably not due to the locus transformed; nor is it due to any failure of competence, or of binding or penetration of the foreign DNA. Moreover, the transformation rate is actually lower, and is not an artifact due to a delay in phenotypic expression which might occur in interspecific, but not in intraspecific, transformation.

We are led, therefore, to hypothesize that the capacity to transform, which already-penetrated DNA has, is dependent upon the nature of the genes adjacent to those whose transformation is under test. These neighbor genes can be visualized as influencing transformation by their effect upon synapsis between the transforming DNA and the corresponding region of the host's genetic material. In intraspecific transformation, the loci adjacent to the transformed ones are homologous in transformer and host, so that synapsis between the two segments may occur properly, whereas in interspecific transformation, these loci are likely to be nonhomologous (or act to prevent synapsis), and, therefore, may often fail to synapse.

5. *Integration.* Even if the hypothesized synapsis occurs properly between host and transformer DNA, some process has yet to occur by which the host gene, whose transformation is being followed, is lost from the chromosome, and the new locus becomes an integral part of it. Some understanding of the mechanism of this final stage in transformation may be gained from a study of the frequency of transformation. Different loci transform intraspecifically at different rates. Using genes that transform with suitably high frequencies, it has been possible to study the rate of *double transformations,* that is, the frequency with which bacteria are transformed with respect to two markers present in the donor DNA. In several cases (for example, penicillin- and streptomycin-resistance), the frequency of doubly transformed bacteria is somewhat less than the product of the frequencies for the single transformations. In these cases, this means that the transformer DNA carries the two loci either on separate particles, or else in widely separated positions on the same particle. On the other hand, the markers for streptomycin-resistance and mannitol-fermentation are transformed together with a frequency (.1%) which is about 17 times that expected from the product of the frequencies of the single transformations (.006%). This is taken to mean that these two genetic markers are located on the same transforming

particle, i.e., they are reasonably close together in the same bacterial chromosome.

How can we explain single and double transformations of closely linked loci? Because of fragmentation during extraction, a given penetrating DNA particle may not always have the same composition relative to the two markers; it may sometimes carry only one of these, and at other times carry both markers. We can test the effect, on single and double transformations, of reducing the particle size of penetrating DNA. On the present hypothesis, we would expect, when particle size is reduced by DNAase or sonic treatment, that sometimes the particles would be broken between the two markers, thereby reducing the relative frequency of the double transformation and increasing the relative frequencies of the single transformations. When the particle size is reduced, the over-all rate of transformation is lower, as expected. However, no change is found in the ratio of double to single transformations. This must mean that the two markers are so closely linked that they are separated only rarely when particles are fragmented. Accordingly, this may be taken to mean that the penetrating particles must usually carry both markers, or neither, and that the failure to obtain 100% double transformations from the former type must be due to the fact that only a small portion of such a penetrant, synapsing particle is integrated.

Integration of a portion of a synapsed particle may be visualized as occurring in two possible ways (Figure 37–1). One method could involve "breakage and exchange" of the kind that takes place in *chromosomal rearrangement* or *crossing over.* In this case (Figure 37–1A), "breaks" would have to occur on each side of the marker to be introduced, so that a "2-strand-double crossover" (refer to p. 133) is produced. While double crossovers within a short distance would be expected to be extremely rare between two homologous chromosomes of higher organ-

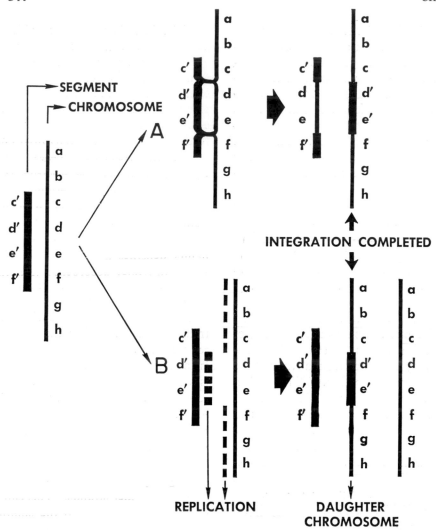

FIGURE 37–1. *Postulated mechanisms for the incorporation of a segment of genetic information into a host chromosome. A. Breakage method; B. Copy-choice method.*

isms, this may occur under special circumstances, and may be possible between the visibly less well-defined chromosome of bacteria and the shorter synapsed segment of transformer DNA.

The second method might involve what has been called *copy-choice* (Figure 37–1B). In this procedure, a daughter chromosome is formed by the alternate use of the normal chromosome and the transformer DNA as a template, so that when completed it is exactly

like the original chromosome except for a segment that was replicated using transformer DNA as a template. Although we cannot decide by which of these two mechanisms (or yet another) integration occurs, there is evidence that the process is fixed, so that it does or does not occur, within a single generation, and it is likely that the transformed marker is replicated beginning with the second division cycle.

It is clear that the portion of penetrant

DNA which is not integrated is also not conserved as chromosomal gene material. If integration occurs by copy-choice then the transforming segment is not conserved either; whereas if integration occurs by crossing over the chromosomal segment replaced is not conserved.

We have already mentioned that DNA from different sources and DNA particles of different sizes behave differently in various parts of the sequence leading to transformation. Several studies have been made of DNA *in vitro* which may shed light on the transformation process in particular, and upon genes in general. When DNA *in vitro* is exposed to dilute concentrations of DNAase, the results [4] indicate that single strands of the double helix are attacked first, and only later, when both strands have been attacked at reasonably proximal positions, is the molecule severed. Once severed, the smaller molecule penetrates poorly, you recall. However, even if only the single strand has been attacked, transformation rate declines. This effect is attributed to the failure of penetrant molecules to transform, because the transforming locus, or a locus necessary for synapsis or integration, has been inactivated.

We have already mentioned (refer to pp. 315, 325) that heating chromosomal DNA denatures it by causing strand separation. Under certain conditions, the single chain can fold so that a large number of complementary base pairs are formed between bases at different levels of the single chain. After pneumococcal DNA has been heated for 10 minutes at 100° C, all chains are single and all H bonds are broken.[5] If such a sample is cooled quickly under appropriate conditions, almost no double chains are formed, almost

all chains being single, with half the molecular weight of the original DNA. This is called *denatured DNA* (cf. p. 315). On the other hand, if such a sample is cooled slowly, double strands are produced, which are united by complementary base pairing over most of their length. This is called *renatured DNA*. Denatured and renatured DNA differ in several properties. These include their appearance under the electron microscope (renatured DNA looks very much like native DNA while denatured DNA is irregularly coiled with clustered regions), their density (renatured and native DNA have similar and lighter densities than denatured DNA), and their ultraviolet absorbency (renatured and native DNA have similar but lower absorbencies than denatured DNA).

Several factors affect renaturation. Renaturation is dependent upon the concentration of DNA in the slowly cooling mixture. When the concentration of single strands is high, so is the amount of renaturation, while slow cooling of single strands in low concentration does not produce any substantial recombination of strands. A second factor, influencing union between strands, is the effect of salt concentration. The negatively charged phosphate groups of single strands tend to prevent union with other strands. This can be overcome by adding KCl to the solution; this acts as a shield against the repulsion between phosphates. Accordingly, within a certain range, the more KCl that is present the greater is the amount of renaturation obtained by slow cooling of heated DNA. A third factor upon which strand recombination depends is the source of DNA. Assuming that the molecular weight of native DNA is approximately the same in all organisms, then a mammalian nucleus would have about a thousand times as many DNA molecules as a bacterial nucleus. Assume also, as is likely to be true, that the DNA molecules within a genome all differ in base sequence. Then, for a given concentration of denatured DNA,

[4] Of L. S. Lerman and L. J. Tolmach.
[5] The following account is based primarily on work reported by P. Doty, J. Marmur, J. Eigner, and G. Schildkraut (1960), and J. Marmur and D. Lane (1960).

there would be of the order of one thousand times fewer complementary chains present when the sample came from calf thymus than there would be in a sample that was obtained from *Pneumococcus*. It has been possible to show that when denatured DNA is heated to 80° C, a large amount of double strands is formed by the bacterial DNA but no detectable amount is produced by the calf thymus DNA. Therefore, what is important in renaturation is the concentration of complementary strands.

Another physical-chemical change may occur when DNA is heated *in vitro*. As already mentioned, native pneumococcal DNA has a molecular weight of about 10 million. When certain preparations of this native DNA are heated, the single chains obtained may have a molecular weight less than half this value. This can be explained, as the consequence of the presence of DNAase, as follows. Single chains are enzymatically severed by DNAase while still part of the double chain, as described previously, but the whole complex retains the double helix configuration. However, once the complementary chains are separated by heat denaturation, the fragments of each single chain fall apart.

It is also possible to make hybrid molecules by renaturing a mixture of N-14 and N-15 DNA from *E. coli*. These synthetic molecules can be identified by the position they assume in the ultracentrifuge tube (see discussion beginning p. 312). Such hybrid molecules are also formed between single DNA strands from different species, but only if the species are closely related genetically (as would be suggested if they showed interspecific transformation), and if they have similar base compositions.

Because of the occurrence of genetic recombination in bacteria via transformation, it is possible to test the biological activity of the various DNA's produced by strand separation and recombination. It is found, using *Pneumococcus*, that denatured DNA has very little transforming activity. (It is likely that this activity is due to the small amount of renaturation which could have taken place in the denatured solution.) On the other hand, the transforming ability of renatured DNA may be as much as 50% of that shown by an equivalent concentration of native DNA. Just as an increased concentration of DNA and a high ionic strength increase renaturation, so do they also increase transforming ability.

The transforming ability of various chemically hybrid molecules has been studied also. The pneumococci to be transformed were streptomycin-sensitive, and transformants were counted by the streptomycin-resistant colonies growing after these bacteria were plated on an agar medium containing streptomycin. The material to be tested for transforming ability was obtained as follows. A constant concentration of DNA, from streptomycin-resistant pneumococci, and a series of increasing concentrations of DNA, from streptomycin-sensitive pneumococci, were heat denatured together and then renatured together (by cooling slowly). The larger the amount of streptomycin-sensitive DNA in the mixture, the larger was the transformation rate to streptomycin resistance. This increase proves that the higher the concentration of streptomycin-sensitive DNA, the greater the number of renatured molecules capable of transformation.

It should also be noted that the addition, to cooling, denatured, streptomycin-resistant DNA, of *homologous DNA* (DNA from the same species, as from sensitive *Pneumococcus*) in the native (double-stranded) state, showed no increase in transformation ability over the rate obtained in its absence. Also, if, during the slow cooling, denatured *heterologous DNA* (DNA from radically different species, as from *Salmonella, Micrococcus, Streptococcus*, or calf thymus) is added, even in large quantities, there was also no increase in transforming activity over the control rate.

Was the increase in transformation rate, obtained in the presence of denatured, homologous DNA, due to the formation of hybrid molecules or did the excess denatured streptomycin-sensitive DNA merely cause an increase in unions between pairs of streptomycin-resistant single strands? The latter possibility cannot be the explanation, since, as mentioned previously, hybrid molecules can be formed between single strands even when these are derived from different (but related) species. It is clear, therefore, that hybrid molecules were produced, that these can transform, and that just as only one strand is required for the replication of DNA, *only one of the complementary strands is needed to carry all the information for cistronic action contained in the normal double helix.* (We would expect that the viruses φX174 and S13, cf. p. 311, also carry all their genetic information in a single DNA strand.)

Three additional observations should be made. First, strand separation is accomplished by heat in a matter of a few minutes or less. This is important since it suggests the direction further work may take in studying how this might occur with adequate rapidity *in vivo.* (It has been suggested that chain separation is normally produced enzymatically, through the activity of *ravelase*.) Strand recombination by slow cooling has as yet no known biological counterpart, although it might be a mechanism for genetic exchange between closely related DNA molecules. The second point is that the capacity to routinely separate and combine single strands should lead to a better understanding of transformation, in particular the mechanism of integration. Experiments along these lines and others would be greatly aided by the use of closely linked marker recons, one on each strand of the hybrid molecule. In fact, such studies have already been reported, in which double transformations have been obtained with a complex of strands containing different markers. Molecular hybrids may also be useful for comparing base sequences in closely related organisms even when genetic recombination between them cannot take place. The final point is that, *in bacteria, the recon can be identified as the smallest unit of DNA capable of being integrated or replaced in a host chromosome subjected to the transformation process.*

SUMMARY AND CONCLUSIONS

Contrary to the simplifying assumption made on page 329, genetic recombination occurs in bacteria by means of genetic transformation. This process involves a sequence of events in which competent cells permanently bind transiently-bound, large molecular weight particles of DNA. Once the DNA particle has penetrated, it apparently undergoes a synapsis-like process with a corresponding segment of the bacterial chromosome. Transformation is completed when a small segment of the DNA particle becomes integrated by replacing a similar segment of the recipient chromosome.

Transformation provides direct and conclusive evidence that chromosomal DNA is genetic material. In bacteria, the recon is the smallest unit of DNA involved in transformation.

Strand separation and recombination *in vitro* produces denatured and renatured DNA, respectively. Renatured DNA can transform, even when a hybrid molecule contains one normal and one mutant chain. This proves that all the information for cistronic action can be carried in one of the two strands of double helix DNA.

REFERENCES

Avery, O. T., MacLeod, C. M., and McCarty, M., "Studies on the Chemical Nature of the Substance Inducing Transformation of Pneumococcal Types," J. Exp. Med., 79:137–158, 1944; reprinted in *Papers on Bacterial Genetics*, Adelberg, E. A. (Ed.), Boston, Little, Brown, 1960, pp. 147–168, and in *Classic Papers in Genetics*, Peters, J. A. (Ed.), Englewood Cliffs, N.J., Prentice-Hall, 1959, pp. 173–192.

Doty, P., Marmur, J., Eigner, J., and Schildkraut, C., "Strand Separation and Specific Recombination in Deoxyribonucleic Acids: Physical Chemical Studies," Proc. Nat. Acad. Sci., U.S., 46:461–476, 1960.

Ephrussi-Taylor, H., "Genetic Aspects of Transformations of Pneumococci," Cold Spr. Harb. Sympos. Quant. Biol., 16:445–456, 1951.

Herriot, R. M., "Formation of Heterozygotes by Annealing a Mixture of Transforming DNAs," Proc. Nat. Acad. Sci., U.S., 47:146–153, 1961.

Hotchkiss, R. D., "Transfer of Penicillin Resistance in Pneumococci by the Desoxyribonucleate Derived from Resistant Cultures," Cold Spr. Harb. Sympos. Quant. Biol., 16:457–461, 1951; reprinted in *Papers on Bacterial Genetics*, Adelberg, E. A. (Ed.), Boston, Little, Brown, 1960, pp. 169–176.

Lerman, L. S., and Tolmach, L. J., "Genetic Transformation. I. Cellular Incorporation of DNA Accompanying Transformation in *Pneumococcus*," Biochim. et Biophys. Acta, 26:68–82, 1957; reprinted in *Papers on Bacterial Genetics*, Adelberg, E. A. (Ed.), Boston, Little, Brown, 1960, pp. 177–191.

Marmur, J., and Lane, D., "Strand Separation and Specific Recombination in Deoxyribonucleic Acids: Biological Studies," Proc. Nat. Acad. Sci., U.S., 46:453–461, 1960.

QUESTIONS FOR DISCUSSION

37.1. On what basis is transformation classified as a mechanism for genetic recombination rather than as a mutation? Do you agree with this interpretation? Why?

37.2. In view of the fact that native and renatured DNA are lighter in density than denatured DNA, was the experiment with denatured DNA, described on p. 315, performed correctly? Explain.

37.3. Devise an experiment to detect whether chain separation occurs during extensive *in vitro* synthesis of DNA.

37.4. Do the transformation results obtained with chemically-hybrid DNA prove that only a single DNA strand is required for cistronic action? Explain.

37.5. Do the studies on transformation offer any clues as to the ploidy of *Pneumococcus*? Explain.

37.6. What kinds of problems would you study, if you had a feasible method of studying the fate of individual cells exposed to transforming DNA?

37.7. What do studies of genetic transformation reveal regarding the genetic nature of conserved and nonconserved chromosomal DNA?

37.8. Redraw Figure 37–1, showing hypothetical base sequences in double-stranded DNA. Has your drawing any bearing on your answer to question 37.6? Explain.

37.9. How can you explain the fact mentioned on p. 343 that the frequency of double transformations is sometimes somewhat less than the product of the frequencies of the single transformations?

Chapter *38

BACTERIA: RECOMBINATION
(II. Conjugation)

I T WAS found in Chapter 37 that genetic recombination may occur in bacteria by means of genetic transformation. The transformation process has two unique features which had hitherto not been encountered. The first is that the donor DNA enters the recipient bacterium without the intervention of any other organism, as was demonstrated by the infectivity of naked DNA. Accordingly, although transformation involves the genetic material of two different cells it is not a typical sexual process, since it does not depend upon contact between donor and recipient cell. The second unique feature is that the integration process leading to genetic recombination occurs in the presence of a portion of the entire genome of the donor cell and the entire genome of the recipient, as a consequence of which only a small segment of the penetrant donor DNA replaces a small homologous segment of the recipient chromosome.

It would seem to be a reasonable hypothesis that any homologous DNA may integrate, by the same mechanism involved in transformation, provided it penetrates the cell. One can therefore institute a search for other means whereby DNA may be introduced into a recipient cell. The present Chapter deals with experiments designed to test whether or not DNA passes from one bacterium to another, when these are in contact.

The first experiment [1] can be designed as

[1] Based upon work of J. Lederberg and E. L. Tatum (1946).

349

follows. A prototrophic strain (K12) of *E. coli* is treated with a mutagen (like X rays or ultraviolet light) to obtain single mutants requiring different nutritional supplements in order to grow. The mutagenic treatment is repeated on the single, and then on the double mutant auxotrophs to obtain finally two lines, each different from the other by three nutritional mutants, all six mutants having arisen independently. One triple mutant strain is auxotrophic for threonine (T^-), leucine (L^-), and thiamin (B_1^-) while the other triple mutant is auxotrophic for biotin (B^-), phenylalanine (Pa^-), and cystine (C^-). The genotypes of these two lines can be given, respectively, as $T^-L^-B_1^-B^+Pa^+C^+$ and $T^+L^+B_1^+B^-Pa^-C^-$.

The pure lines are grown separately on complete liquid medium. Then about 10^8 bacteria from one line are plated onto agar containing complete medium, to form a lawn of continuous colonies. In the case of the $T^-L^-B_1^-$ line, three replica plates are made (see Figure 38–1), each one containing complete medium minus a different single nutrient (lacking T, L, and B_1, respectively). Occasionally, a replica has a clone growing on it, which can be shown to be due to mutation to prototrophy for the nutrient missing from the medium. However, such clonal growth is not found in the same corresponding position on all three replicas, or even on two replicas, with greater than chance frequency. The same results are obtained when the $B^-Pa^-C^-$ line is tested on appropriate replicas. We conclude, therefore, that on rare occasions single mutants to prototrophy for one nutrient do occur, but that double or triple mutants do not occur with detectable frequency.

Next, the same experiment is repeated, except that the two triple mutant strains are first mixed in the liquid medium before being plated on agar containing complete medium. In this case (Figure 38–2), six replicas are made with medium which is complete except in the following respects. Three lack B, Pa, and C besides T, or L, or B_1; the other three lack T, L, and B_1 besides B, or Pa, or C. Individuals of the $T^-L^-B_1^-$ strain cannot grow on the first three replicas mentioned because single required nutrients are missing, and cannot grow in the last three because all three are missing. Individuals of the $B_1^-Pa^-C^-$ strain cannot grow on the first three replicas because all three required nutrients are missing and cannot grow on the last three because one of these is absent. If the master plate contains a mutant to nutritional independence for one of the nutritionally dependent loci only one replica will show growth. For example, if on the master plate there was a T^+ mutant among the individuals of the $T^-L^-B_1^-$ strain, a clone will grow only on the replica lacking B, Pa, C, and T. Actually, about 100 different positions on the master plate show growth on the replicas. This is a very much larger

number than is detected in the six replicas that test spontaneous mutation rate when the two lines are plated separately. Some positions show growth only on one of the six replicas. However, there are many positions that show growth on two replicas; these must have gained nutritional independence at two loci. Finally, there are also many positions which grow on all six replicas, each representing the occurrence of complete prototrophs ($T^+L^+B_1^+B^+Pa^+C^+$). One can use the clones on the replicas, or return to the master plate, and demonstrate that these changes are transmissible and preadaptive. When tested, these clones prove to be pure, that is, the nutritional independence gained is not attributable to some kind of physical association between two or more different auxotrophs. The large number of clones growing on the replicas, plus the fact that many are complete prototrophs or are auxo-

FIGURE 38–1. *Use of replica-plating (shown diagrammatically) to detect spontaneous mutations in* E. coli. *Replica 1 detects one mutant to* T+, *replica 3 detects one mutant to* B_1+, *and replica 2′ detects one mutant to* Pa+.

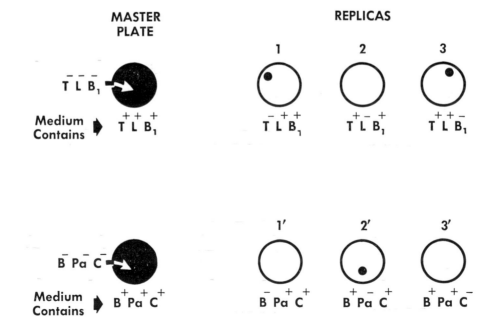

FIGURE 38–2. *Replica-plating (shown diagrammatically) to detect genetic recombination in E. coli. A completely prototrophic recombinant is found at 12 o'clock in all replicas. A recombinant for both* Pa *and* C *is found at 3 o'clock on replicas 5 and 6. Replica 1 has a clone growing at 9 o'clock which may be due either to recombination or to mutation to* T+.

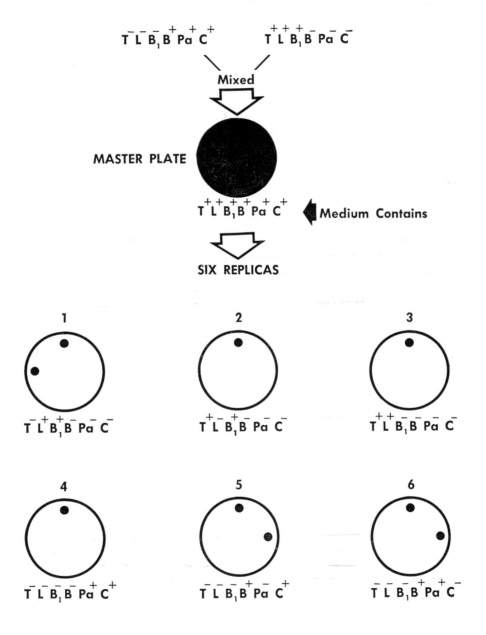

trophs for only one nutrient, is proof that these results are not due to spontaneous mutation. They must, therefore, be attributed to some type of genetic recombination.

Could the genetic recombination observed be the result of transformation? This possibility is unlikely since almost all transformations involve single loci. Recall that the frequency with which two loci are transformed in the same bacterium is much lower than that for single transformations, and is presumably dependent upon the close proximity of two loci on the bacterial chromosome. Yet, in the present experiment, double recombinants are common. In fact, certain recombinations for two loci occurred more frequently than did the recombination of these loci singly. Transformation would even less readily explain the large number of triple recombinants, the complete prototrophs.

Nevertheless, specific tests may be made to rule out transformation as an explanation. It is found that the number of prototrophs obtained by recombination is uninfluenced when DNAase is added to the mixing and plating media. No transforming activity is demonstrated when one culture is exposed to filtrates or autolysates of the other. Finally, a U-tube can be constructed with a filter of sintered glass separating the arms. Broth can be added and the two strains placed in different arms. The medium plus soluble substances and small particles (including viruses) can be flushed back and forth through the filter. Yet no recombinants are found in platings made from either arm. We may conclude, therefore, that the genetic recombination detected in *E. coli* is not due to transformation. It is also not dependent upon a virus. It can be shown, moreover, by plating a mixture of three lines of K12 differing in the mutants which they carry, that the large number of different recombinants obtained can all be explained as the result of recombination between any two lines; no individuals are obtained recombinant with respect to markers in all three lines. Apparently, *this type of genetic recombination depends upon actual cell-to-cell contact between pairs of bacteria, and therefore involves a sexual process.*

The frequency of sexual recombination in the first experiment is only about one per million cells (100 sites of recombination per 100 million bacteria placed on the master plate). The rarity of the event makes it fruitless, at this point in the investigation, to search microscopically for evidences of bacterial mating. (You should, however, recognize that the importance of a new phenomenon should not be judged by the frequency with which it occurs in experiments that first detect it. Recall, for example, that the initial quantity of DNA first synthesized *in vitro* was infinitesimal in comparison with the amount synthesized in later work, and that the rate of transformation observed initially was very much smaller than the 10–25% rate which can be obtained today with modified techniques.)

It should be noted that we have used a medium that selects certain recombinants for detection and not others. In the first experiment discussed, only recombinants possessing certain markers for nutritional independence were selected. These are called *selective markers*. Thus, while the prototroph $T^+L^+B_1^+B^+Pa^+C^+$ was detectable, it was not possible to test for the occurrence of the complementary polyauxotroph $T^-L^-B_1^-B^-Pa^-C^-$. Since no test has been made for the multiple auxotroph one could doubt its occurrence. It is entirely reasonable that the immediate result of mating is a zygote which contains a combination of part or all of the genotypes of the two parental cells. Although we have assumed that integration could take place if DNA passed from one cell in contact with another, that is, between two bacteria in *conjugation*, we have so far no evidence that it does. In other words, the possibility re-

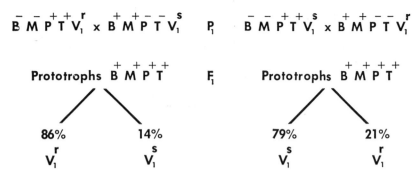

FIGURE 38–3. *Genetic recombinations, involving unselected markers, obtained in reversed crosses.*

mains, at least with respect to the genes showing recombination, that the recombinant may be diploid.

It is possible, however, to add markers that are not selected for or against when one is selecting for recombinant prototrophs. These are called *unselected markers*. *E. coli* is available in two genetic forms, one, $V_1{}^r$, is resistant to infection by the bacterial viruses T_1 and T_6 while the other, $V_1{}^s$, is sensitive to infection by these viruses, which cause the bacteria to lyse. Using the auxotrophic mutants P^- (proline-requiring) and M^- (methionine-requiring), it is possible to make the cross [2] $B^-M^-P^+T^+V_1{}^r \times B^+M^+P^-T^-V_1{}^s$ and select for the prototrophs $B^+M^+P^+T^+$.

A number of prototrophs were obtained. These were then tested for sensitivity to virus T_1. Because V_1 is an unselected marker both of its alternatives are testable. Eighty-six per cent of the prototrophs were typically resistant, $V_1{}^r$, and 14% typically sensitive, $V_1{}^s$ (Figure 38–3). Note that both of these alternatives are recombinant relative to some of the markers for prototrophy, and that the alternative present is typically expressed.

A diploid $V_1{}^rV_1{}^s$ would be either resistant, or sensitive, or intermediate in expression. The fact that both typical sensitivity and typical resistance to virus occurs proves that some recombinants contain only one representative of this locus. It is therefore

[2] See J. Lederberg (1947).

reasonable to extrapolate from this finding and say that only one alternative is present of any gene in a recombinant, which is the same as saying that all the genes in a nuclear body of *E. coli* are normally haploid. This means that conjugation produces a temporary (partial or complete) diploid condition which, following integration, results in haploid recombinants, just as is presumably the case in transformation. The haploid recombinants may also be called *segregants*.

When the reverse cross is made, $V_1{}^r$ entering with the $B^+M^+P^-T^-$ parent and $V_1{}^s$ with $B^-M^-P^+T^+$, the prototrophs show approximately the reversed percentages which are sensitive and resistant to T_1. In other words, the parent that provides P^+T^+ to the prototroph also contributes the V_1 locus which it contains about 80% of the time. The fact that there is an imbalance in the frequency of resistants and sensitives among prototrophs (i.e., their ratio is not 50% : 50%), which is reversed when the V_1 markers are reversed in the parent cells, is clear evidence that V_1 does not segregate (or integrate) independently of the markers with which it entered the zygote and which were subsequently integrated to form the haploid prototroph. Accordingly, V_1 must be linked to P T, segregating from these loci (or failing to be integrated in the same segment with them) about 20% of the time. On a linkage map, therefore, V_1 is about 20 recombination (segregation or integration) units from $P\ T$.

It is possible also to determine the linkage relationships between auxotrophic markers in the following way. The cross $T^+L^+B_1^-B^- \times T^-L^-B_1^+B^+$ is made on complete medium, plated on complete medium, and replica-plated four times on complete medium minus T, or L, or B_1, or B. Prototrophic recombinants grow on all four replicas, single auxotrophs grow on three, while double auxotrophs grow on two of the replicas. Since prototrophs are found to be more frequent than either $T^+L^-B_1^+B^+$ or $T^-L^+B_1^+B^+$, T and L are linked. A further analysis of the results, for other markers and from other experiments, reveals that all the genetic markers tested in *E. coli* are linked to each other, and can be placed on a map arranged in a linear order according to their recombination (segregation or integration) distances. This means, in all likelihood, that *E. coli* has a single chromosome.

Can zygotes actually be demonstrated? Since it would be almost impossible to find these microscopically, we must look for them genetically. Following mating, certain clones behave as though they are mosaic for a number of markers. When single cell isolates, made from such clones, are grown and tested, it is found [3] that their progeny may possess either of the parental genotypes of the original cross, or they may be recombinants between the two. Clearly, the isolated cells were derived from more or less persistent heterozygotes, individuals that are diploid for various markers. Thus, the segregants within a clone offer unambiguous proof that they were derived from a true zygote. We conclude, therefore, that the zygote produced following bacterial conjugation usually has only a temporary existence which terminates, after recombination, in the production of haploid progeny.

[3] By J. Lederberg and M. Zelle.

SUMMARY AND CONCLUSIONS

Genetic recombination occurs in *Escherichia coli* following the sexual process of conjugation. This organism normally has a haploid nuclear body, in which all tested genes belong to a single linear linkage group.

REFERENCES

Lederberg, J., "Gene Recombination and Linked Segregation in Escherichia Coli," Genetics, 32:505–525, 1947; reprinted in *Papers on Bacterial Genetics*, Adelberg, E. A. (Ed.), Boston, Little, Brown, 1960, pp. 247–267.

Lederberg, J., "Bacterial Reproduction," Harvey Lect., 53:69–82, 1959.

Lederberg, J., and Tatum, E. L., "Gene Recombination in Escherichia Coli," Nature, London, 158:558, 1946; reprinted in *Classic Papers in Genetics*, Peters, J. A. (Ed.), Englewood Cliffs, N.J., Prentice-Hall, 1959, pp. 192–194.

QUESTIONS FOR DISCUSSION

38.1. Criticize an attempt to prove the occurrence of genetic recombination by conjugation, by simply mixing two bacterial strains which are singly auxotrophic for different nutrients, and subsequently testing for prototrophs.

38.2. Why is it futile to search cytologically for bacteria in the process of conjugation?

38.3. Differentiate between, and give an example of:
    a. A selective and an unselected marker.
    b. A singly auxotrophic and a prototrophic bacterium.

38.4. In this Chapter, what is the evidence that the two auxotrophs which produced proto- trophic progeny did so because of conjugation rather than because of mutation, genetic transformation, or viral infection?

38.5. In what ways does genetic transformation differ from conjugation?

38.6. Invent suitable genotypes for parents, a zygote, and its clonal progeny, which would prove the existence of the zygote, from the genotypes of the members of the clone it produces.

38.7. Ignoring the centromere, draw all the different ways you can represent a chromosome whose recombination map is linear.

38.8. Do you think the Summary and Conclusions section for this Chapter is adequate? Why?

38.9. Do you suppose the discovery of sexuality in bacteria could have important implica- tions for the practice of medicine? Why?

38.10. What is meant by integration in genetics? Describe verbally the mechanisms by which it may occur.

38.11. List those features of crossing over which are difficult to explain on a copy-choice basis.

38.12. Discuss the genetic control of gene synthesis and gene degradation.

38.13. Criticize the statement, on p. 16, that reconic transmission can only occur between generations by means of a cellular bridge.

Chapter *39

BACTERIA: RECOMBINATION
(III. The Episome F)

ARE THE members of a pair of conjugating bacteria equivalent? In other words, does DNA from either one go into the other, so that both bacteria can act either as donor or recipient? Suppose two auxotrophically different, streptomycin-sensitive lines can normally conjugate and give recombinant progeny. If both lines are exposed to streptomycin before, but not after being mixed, none of the pretreated individuals can divide, and since all eventually die, no recombinant clones are formed. When one of the two parental lines is given such a pretreatment with streptomycin, it is found [1] that no recombinants are detected, whereas when the other parental line is pretreated prototrophic recombinants do occur. This demonstrates that the two parents are not equivalent. The former type of parent (giving no recombinants when pretreated) must always act as the DNA-receiving cell, which, after conjugation, normally becomes the zygote. So, when this parent is killed by streptomycin, it is impossible to obtain recombinant clones. The latter type of parent must always serve in conjugation as DNA donor, its death, after acting as donor, having no effect upon the zygote and subsequent recombination. The latter type which acts as genetic donor is called F^+ (for "fertility"), whereas the former type, which acts as genetic recipient, is called F^-; these types serve, so to speak, male and female functions, respectively. In bacterial conjugation, therefore, the genetic transfer

[1] Following the work of W. Hayes (1953).

356

which takes place is a one-way process.

The original wild-type strain of *E. coli* K12 is F^+, and in the period during which one of the auxotrophic lines was being prepared (cf. pp. 349–351), an F^- variant must have arisen. $F^+ \times F^-$ crosses are fertile; $F^- \times F^-$ crosses are sterile (show no recombination); $F^+ \times F^+$ crosses are fertile only because F^+ cells may on occasion spontaneously change to F^-. If one F^+ cell is placed in a culture of F^- cells, all the F^- cells are rapidly converted to F^+ type! The rapidity of the change from F^- to F^+ is such that the causative agent must multiply at least twice as fast as the typical cell (and, therefore, twice as fast as chromosomal DNA), sex conversion occurring with an efficiency about 10^5 times higher than that of recombination. Moreover, the new F^+ cells transmit this trait to their progeny. We conclude, that in *E. coli*, F^+ *male sexuality is an infectious phenomenon due to a factor or particle which we can call* F^1.

Several properties are known regarding F^1. It is transferred from male to female only upon contact, and it cannot be isolated as a cell-free particle retaining sex conversion potency (accordingly, it does not give evidence of being a typical virus). The matings that transfer F^1 are more frequent but less stable than matings involving chromosomal transfer. Exposure of F^+ individuals to the dye, acridine orange, inhibits the replication of F^1 so that F^+ cells are converted to F^-. However, this dye has no apparent effect on chromosomal genes. This fact, plus a division rate which is faster than that of the chromosome, is sufficient evidence for concluding that F^1 *is an extra-chromosomal particle*.

The F^1 particle modifies the cell harboring it, in several ways. Not only does F^1 make a cell a potential male, but it has several effects upon the cell surface. F^1 must change the cell surface of a male, so that a male cell can recognize, and react with, a female cell which it contacts; it must be the cause of some kind of bridge-formation between male and female cell, over which F¹ is passed to the F⁻ cell; it must also be the cause of the formation of a receptor, at the surface of the cell, for a virus that attacks males only.[2] Finally, the *low frequency of recombination, Lfr*, of chromosomal markers following the mating of F⁺ and F⁻ must also be a property attributable to F¹.

So far, we have found that *E. coli* has two mating types, F⁻ and F⁺ (Lfr). Another mating type arose from F⁺ cells. This type produces a *high frequency of recombination* of chromosomal genes, and is hence called *Hfr.* Since the fertility of Hfr cells is unaffected by pretreatment with streptomycin, Hfr cells are donors. Hfr can mate with F⁻ cells, and, with low fertility, with F⁺ (Lfr which have probably spontaneously reverted to F⁻). Crosses of Hfr × F⁻ produce 100–20,000 times as many recombinants as does the Lfr × F⁻ cross. Since the progeny of the Hfr × F⁻ are typically F⁻, and rarely Hfr, Hfr does not carry infective F¹ particles. However, Hfr can revert to Lfr strains which show all the characteristics of F⁺, including infective F¹. Since Hfr can only come from, and revert to, F⁺, it is concluded that *F¹ must be retained in masked or bound form in Hfr strains*, in which condition the presence of extrachromosomally located infective F¹ is prohibited.

The occurrence of Hfr strains makes a cytological search for conjugating pairs more likely to be successful. This is found to be the case. Figure 39–1 is an electron micrograph showing conjugation between an F⁻ cell and an Hfr cell. The Hfr cell has ultraviolet-killed bacterial virus particles (tadpole-shaped objects) adsorbed to its surface; the F⁻ cell does not since it is genetically resistant to this virus. The cytoplasmic bridge between the conjugants is obvious. When exconjugants of such visibly marked

pairs of Hfr and F⁻ cells are isolated by micromanipulation and cultured, only the clones from the F⁻ partner yield recombinants. We may note, in passing, that these findings conclude another demonstration, of numerous ones already cited, of the mutual aid genetics and cytology have provided in the advancement of both branches of investigation.

Using Lfr strains, it is commonly found that most of the unselected markers in recombinant progeny are those derived from the F⁻ parent. This can be explained either by the transfer of the entire genome of the male into the female followed by the integration of only a portion of it, or by the transfer of only a portion of the male genome and its integration in toto, or a combination of these two possibilities. Experiments can be designed to test one or more of these explanations.[3]

[3] The following discussion is based principally upon work of E. L. Wollman and F. Jacob (see references at end of this Chapter).

FIGURE 39–1. *Conjugation in* E. coli. (*Courtesy of T. F. Anderson.*)

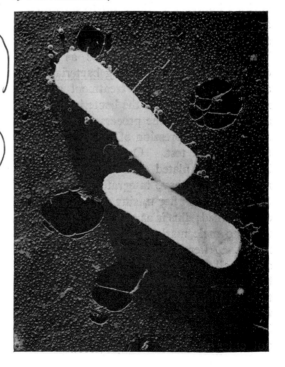

[2] See reference to T. Loeb and N. D. Zinder (1961) on p. 305.

MINUTES	RECOMBINANTS HAVING Hfr MARKERS
0	None
8	T
8½	T, L
9	T, L, Az
11	T, L, Az, T₁
18	T, L, Az, T₁, Lac
25	T, L, Az, T₁, Lac, Gal

FIGURE 39–2. *Recombinants obtained following artificial interruption of conjugation at various times after mixing F⁻ and Hfr strains. The Hfr strain has markers for T, L, Az, T₁, Lac, Gal. (After W. Hayes.)*

Particular strains of Hfr and F⁻, both marked with suitable genetic factors, are grown separately and then mixed in the proportion of 1 : 20, respectively, to assure rapid contact of all Hfr with F⁻ cells. At various intervals of time, up to 60 minutes after mixing, samples are withdrawn and subjected to a strong shearing force in a Waring Blendor. This serves as a very efficient means of separating bacteria in the act of conjugation, the treatment affecting neither the viability of the bacteria, nor their ability to undergo the process of recombination, nor the expression of the various genotypes under test. Once separated, the bacteria are plated and scored for male markers which have integrated. It is found that 0 minutes after mixing no recombinants are obtained; this is as expected, since at this time no male markers have yet been transferred. After 50 minutes of conjugation almost all the male markers that are going to be transferred have done so. However, the time at which different male markers enter the female cell varies widely within this time interval. For example, T and L markers do not enter until after about nine minutes of conjugation, while the *Gal* marker (for galactose) requires about 25 minutes of conjugation before it is transferred. T and L are known to be close together and widely separated from *Gal* in the recombination map of Lfr referred to earlier (p. 354). Accordingly, there is a definite relationship between time of transfer from Hfr to F⁻ and the location of the marker on the Hfr chromosome.

If different portions of the Hfr chromosome were entering the F⁻ cell at random times, the results mentioned would not be obtained. We conclude, therefore, that the Hfr chromosome is transferred in a preferential order, one particular end of the DNA string usually entering the F⁻ cell first, since the *loci that transfer do so in a regular linear procession* (Figure 39–2). Other experiments reveal that energy is required for the transfer process and that the entrance rate is uniform from the first part of the chromosome to be transferred, O (representing the "origin"), up to and including the locus of *Lac* (for lactose).

Whether or not they have received or lost a segment of an artificially ruptured chromosome, both the female and male cells survive, since *E. coli* is normally multinucleate. In fact, such breakages are found to occur spontaneously also. Because of spontaneous rupture, the spontaneous transfer of the Hfr chromosome is usually partial, so that a piece of variable size is injected into the recipient cell. The resultant zygote of an Hfr cross is, then, a partial diploid (as is true of a cell undergoing transformation), and can be called a *merozygote*, produced by a process of partial genetic exchange or *meromixis*. The last two new terms are applicable also in transformation.

While the frequency of recombination is low for all chromosomal genes in an Lfr strain, it is relatively very high for markers in Hfr nearest O, decreases as the distance of the markers from O increases, and is only .01–.001% for the markers most distal to O. It was mentioned that only rarely is an offspring of Hfr × F⁻ itself Hfr. This happens only in cases where there is evidence that the marker most distal to O has also been transferred. This suggests that the locus responsible for Hfr is located on the chromosome. Moreover, no chromosomal locus is found to be transferred after the Hfr locus. We conclude, therefore, that *Hfr is always located at the terminus of the chromosome which is in the process of being transferred.*

A fourth mating type is known,[4] derived from F⁺ cultures, which produces a *very high frequency* of recombination, and is appropriately called *Vhf*. In Vhf strains (all are male), recombination rates for the markers most distal to O occur with a frequency of 1–2%, a rate at least 100 times that found in Hfr strains. (Even so, less than about 1% of the progeny from mating Vhf and F⁻ are Vhf.) Three independently arisen Vhf strains are known. By means of artificial rupture experiments, the sequence of certain marker genes can be determined in each case. These sequences are shown in Figure 39–3,

[4] See A. L. Taylor and E. A. Adelberg (1960).

together with the frequency of recombinants per 100 Vhf cells in the mating mixture. What do these results show?

The different Vhf strains demonstrate that the markers held in common are in the same sequence. However, the O point is in a different position in each case! Accordingly, so is the position of the Vhf locus at the end of the linkage map. This suggests the following hypotheses.[5] *The linkage group of* E. coli *is normally circular; the location of the Vhf-causing factor can occasionally change; before chromosome transfer the linkage group is opened adjacent to the point of Vhf attachment, so that the Vhf locus is at the end oppo-*

[5] Following F. Jacob and E. L. Wollman.

FIGURE 39–3. *Recombination percentages for Vhf strains.* O = point of origin; — = untested. (After A. L. Taylor and E. A. Adelberg, 1960. See References.)

SELECTED MARKER	STRAIN		
	AB-311	AB-312	AB-313
his+	42	2.5	—
gal+	12	4	—
pro+	—	8	—
met+	4	22	—
mtl+	3.7	25	49
xyl+	2.8	26	43
mal+	1.5	40	32
ade+	—	—	15
try+	—	—	6
arg+	—	—	0.3

site the O point. The results obtained from the study of Hfr strains [6] confirm all these assumptions, including the occasional relocation of Hfr as a consequence of which a new O point and sequence of entry is determined. To what can we attribute the difference between Vhf and Hfr strains? One simple explanation is that these differ in the rate with which they cause spontaneous chromosome rupture during conjugation, Vhf having the lower rate.

There is a remarkable similarity between a Vhf or Hfr locus in the chromosome and its capacity to produce breakages in nearby regions, on the one hand, and certain cases already described on pp. 214–222 in corn (Activator and Dissociation, and Modulator), or referred to on pp. 222 and 223 in *Drosophila* (Segregation-Distorter), on the other hand. Suffice it to say, at this point, that these cases may provide another example of what at first appears to be a wide variety of apparently different and unique phenomena and which later proves to be due to minor variations in the expression of a more general, common event. In the light of results with higher organisms, it is reasonable that the positions of spontaneous rupture are merely places where the already opened *E. coli* chromosome is subsequently broken by the action of Hfr, and to a lesser degree Vhf, these breakages being more probable the closer the region is to the Hfr or Vhf locus. It may be noted that the results are not contrary to the view that once the chromosome is broken, Hfr (or Vhf) ceases to cause additional breakages in the now-free, other segment.

Since a frequently recombining male strain always has the same marker leading the others in transfer, we conclude that Hfr or Vhf can cause the ring chromosome to open at only one of the two regions immediately adjacent to it. The fact that the entry sequence is different in different strains (the chromosome of AB-312 enters in the reverse

[6] See A. L. Taylor and E. A. Adelberg (1961).

direction from that of AB-311 or AB-313, as can be seen from Figures 39–3 and 39–4) may be due to an inversion of Hfr or of Vhf in moving from one chromosomal position to another.

There is experimental evidence that the *E. coli* chromosome is composed of a single double-stranded DNA helix, although it is possible that there may be nonnucleic acid links between DNA molecules (each with a molecular weight of about 10×10^6, and about 16,000 nucleotides long). (The ordinary chromosome of higher organisms may be composed of one or of as many as 16 double strands of DNA; we do not yet know for certain how many DNA strands are present per chromatid.) Since the ring chromosome of *E. coli* is opened where F attaches, you may wonder if these two new ends are able to join in restitution. These two open ends must usually remain unjoined, otherwise one would not observe, in Vhf lines, the selective marker nearest O transported and integrated from as many as 49% of donor males (Figure 39–3).

The recombination frequencies observed after conjugation will depend, of course, upon the frequency of penetration of a marker plus the efficiency with which it becomes integrated. Interruption of mating experiments reveal the sequence of markers, regardless of the frequency (greater than 0) with which their integration occurs. Once the marker sequence is known, integration efficiency can be studied. For example, if matings are permitted to continue long enough so that just about all F⁻ cells are penetrated by the marker closest to O, the percentage of zygotes producing recombinants for that marker will indicate the efficiency of integration. Thus, if only about 20% of the recipient cells show integration of a marker near O, this locus has an integration efficiency of $\frac{1}{5}$. By essentially similar methods the integration efficiency for markers more distal to O can be determined. These are found to be of lower

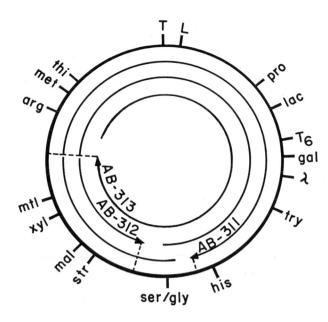

efficiency. Thus, the closer a gene is to O, the greater is its chance for integration.

In this connection it may be fruitful to recall the observation (cf. p. 345) that when one strand of a double helix of donor DNA is broken via DNAase activity, incorporation of donor DNA into the recipient DNA fraction is unaffected but transformation rate is drastically reduced. Accordingly, the fact that the farther a locus is from O, the lower

is its integration efficiency, may be a direct consequence of the action of an Hfr or Vhf locus which breaks one strand of double-helix DNA and not the other. In this event, such loci could be producing effects not only on chromosome rupture (by severing both strands of the DNA double chain at the same level), but also on integration (by breaking only one chain of the two at any given level).

In cases when penetration of a chromosome

FIGURE 39–5. *Genetic map of*
Escherichia coli *in which distances*
are expressed in minutes;
markers in parentheses are less
precisely mapped. (After A. L.
Taylor and E. A. Adelberg, 1960.
See references.)

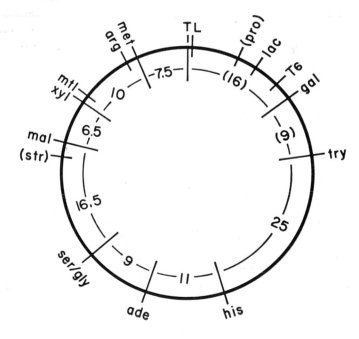

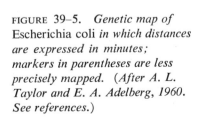

is stopped by Blendor treatment, we cannot decide whether the treatment breaks the chromosome, or the cytoplasmic bridge, or both. However, since conjugants, which have been visibly joined for two or more hours, may show only limited amounts of recombination, it is likely that a chromosomal defect, and not bridge rupture, is responsible for spontaneously halting transfer and/or integration.

Taking into account the changes in rate of penetration and in integration efficiency, it is possible to construct, from interruption experiments using Vhf or Hfr males, a genetic map of *E. coli* markers whose relative distances are expressed in minutes. This is shown in Figure 39–5. This map is essentially identical to the one derived from the relative frequencies of recombinants from Lfr × F⁻ crosses (p. 354).

Let us now return to a consideration of F⁺ (Lfr) strains. One can perform an interruption experiment to determine when the F¹ particle in Lfr males is transferred in mating. It is found that F¹ is first transferred about five minutes after mixing F⁺ and F⁻. This is several minutes earlier than any marker on the chromosome is transferred. Moreover, there is no linkage of F¹ with any marker on such a chromosomal segment. Accordingly, this is additional support for the extrachromosomal nature of F¹.

We have mentioned already that Hfr strains are always derived from F⁺ strains, as were the Vhf strains. We have also noted that Hfr strains may revert to F⁺. (So can Vhf.) We have taken this to mean that Hfr (and doubtless Vhf too) harbors a latent F¹ particle. Since the fertility of Hfr is unaffected by exposure to acridine orange, the latent F¹ particle cannot be located extrachromosomally, or it would disappear. Accordingly, the *latent F¹ particle in Hfr (or Vhf) must be located chromosomally*. Since F¹ is the only known factor essential for maleness, *the locus we have assigned to the Hfr and Vhf genes*

must be the locus of chromosomal F¹. Once F¹ enters the chromosome all remaining cytoplasmic F¹ particles are normally lost.

In the light of this information, what can we reason concerning what happens in F⁺ cells when, on rare occasions, they do transfer chromosomal material (so that, as a whole, the F⁺ clone gives a low frequency of recombination)? A number of hypotheses can be suggested, but we will consider a particular one. We can suppose that in order for chromosomal transfer to take place in F⁺ cells, an F¹ particle must attach to the chromosome, making it a typical Hfr chromosome. This can be tested as follows.[7] After mixing suitably marked F⁺ and F⁻, replica plates are made to show the places where recombination has taken place. A search can then be made for Hfr strains among cells growing on the master plate. Although new Hfr strains occur rarely, they are obtained much more frequently from positions on the master plate where recombination has taken place than where it has not. Moreover, it is often found that the Hfr strain obtained produces a high frequency of recombination of the same marker whose recombination on the replica aided in the detection of the Hfr strain. In other words, it seems valid to believe that before an F⁺ individual transfers chromosomal material, it first changes to a particular Hfr (or Vhf) condition. This Hfr produces the recombination detected on the replica, while its clonal members on the master plate yield the same type of Hfr. This interpretation also receives support from other experiments.

Some additional properties of F¹ may now be listed. F¹ is characterized by having a low affinity for the chromosome; it has no preferential site of attachment, and once it attaches, the extrachromosomal multiplication of F¹ ceases. A genetic variant is now known,[8] F², which has a high affinity for the chromosome (so that it frequently produces an Hfr

---

[7] Based upon work of F. Jacob and E. L. Wollman.
[8] See E. A. Adelberg and S. N. Burns (1960).

strain), and has a preferential site of attachment near *Lac* (lactose). However, the Hfr produced also carries F² particles in the cytoplasm.

Because of its replicability and genetic variability, the male fertility factor of *E. coli* must be considered to be composed of genetic material. F is probably neither lytic nor otherwise rapidly lethal to F⁻ cells. In view of this and the fact that it has a stable relationship with the F⁺ cell, it may be considered a normal cellular component, when present. Since it can exist and reproduce extrachromosomally, *F furnishes the first example so far presented of normal extrachromosomal genetic material.* When F, as an autonomous extrachromosomal agent, is lost, either spontaneously or after treatment with acridine orange, it represents genetic material that is not conserved for future generations.

F also has the capacity to assume a regular locus on a chromosome. When integrated into the chromosome, it behaves as an ordinary chromosomal locus. In regular vegetative reproduction, chromosomal F is transmitted to all progeny, that is, it is conserved. In conjugation, however, chromosomal F may not be conserved, since it is not transmitted to the zygote with appreciable frequency, except in the case of Vhf strains, and even when transmitted, it may fail to be integrated.

To the genetic elements restricted to the chromosome, the only type of gene discussed in detail until this Chapter, we can now add the male fertility factor, F, which may be present or absent from the cell, and, when present, may be autonomous extrachromosomally or integrated in the chromosome. To such genes which can participate in the cell facultatively, as extrachromosomal or as chromosomal elements, the name *episome* is given.[9]

[9] See F. Jacob and E. L. Wollman (1958).

SUMMARY AND CONCLUSIONS

In *E. coli*, there is only one female mating type, or genetic recipient (F⁻) but several male mating types, or genetic donors (F⁺, Hfr, Vhf). Male mating type depends upon the presence, location, and genotype of F.

F is an episome. When present extrachromosomally, F is infective. When located chromosomally, the ring chromosome of *E. coli* is opened near the locus of F. The end opposite the F locus proceeds first, in the linear transfer of part or sometimes all of the opened chromosome into the recipient conjugant.

REFERENCES

Adelberg, E. A., and Burns, S. N., "Genetic Variation in the Sex Factor of Escherichia Coli," J. Bact., 79:321–330, 1960; reprinted in *Papers on Bacterial Genetics*, Adelberg, E. A. (Ed.), Boston, Little, Brown, 1960, pp 353–362.

Hayes, W., "The Mechanism of Genetic Recombination in *Escherichia coli*," Cold Spr. Harb. Sympos. Quant. Biol., 18:75–93, 1953; reprinted in *Papers on Bacterial Genetics*, Adelberg, E. A. (Ed.), Boston, Little, Brown, 1960, pp. 268–299.

Hayes, W., and Clowes, R. C. (Eds.), *Microbial Genetics*, Cambridge, Cambridge University Press, 300 pp., 1960.

Jacob, F., and Wollman, E. L., "Episomes, Added Genetic Elements" (in French), C. R. Acad. Sci. (Paris), 247:154–156, 1958; translated and reprinted in *Papers on Bacterial Genetics*, Adelberg, E. A. (Ed.), Boston, Little, Brown, 1960, pp. 398–400.

Jacob, F., and Wollman, E. L., "Genetic and Physical Determinations of Chromosomal Segments in Escherichia Coli," Sympos. Soc. Exp. Biol., 12:75–92, 1958; reprinted in *Papers on Bacterial Genetics*, Adelberg, E. A. (Ed), Boston, Little, Brown, 1960, pp. 335–352.

Jacob, F., and Wollman, E. L., *Sexuality and the Genetics of Bacteria*, 374 pp., New York, Academic Press, 1961.

Taylor, A. L., and Adelberg, E. A., "Linkage Analysis with Very High Frequency Males of Escherichia Coli," Genetics, 45:1233–1243, 1960.

Taylor, A. L., and Adelberg, E. A., "Evidence for a Closed Linkage Group in Hfr Males of *Escherichia coli* K-12," Biochem. Biophys. Res. Commun., 5:400–404, 1961.

Wollman, E. L., Jacob, F., and Hayes, W., "Conjugation and Genetic Recombination in *Escherichia coli* K12," Cold Spr. Harb. Sympos. Quant. Biol., 21:141–162, 1956; reprinted in *Papers on Bacterial Genetics*, Adelberg, E. A. (Ed.), Boston, Little, Brown, 1960, pp. 300–334.

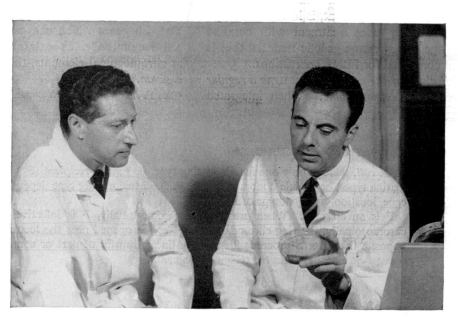

ELIE L. WOLLMAN (*left*) *and* FRANÇOIS JACOB (*right*) *in 1961*.

QUESTIONS FOR DISCUSSION

39.1. What events do you suppose occur between the time that donor DNA enters a female conjugant and the time of appearance of a segregant which is haploid for a segment of the donor DNA?

39.2. What is the evidence that F can integrate in a chromosome? That it can deintegrate?

39.3. What properties are attributable to F when this is integrated at a chromosomal locus?

39.4. Does the occurrence of spontaneous ruptures of the donor bacterial chromosome interfere with mapping the linear order of genes via artificial interruptions of mating? Explain.

39.5. Assume, correctly, that the decay of P^{32} incorporated into DNA can break the *E. coli* chromosome, and that this decay is temperature-independent. Devise an experiment to determine the gene order in this bacterium.

39.6. What kinds of evidence can you present that per nucleus of *E. coli* there is normally:

a. A single "chromosome"?
b. That this is a ring?

39.7. Give the genotypes of parents and recombinants, and the specific culture conditions you would employ in searching the progeny of $F^+ \times F^-$ crosses for Hfr lines.

39.8. Would you, in the light of our knowledge of episomes, revise the discussion on p. 198 regarding recon polarity? Why?

39.9. What relationships exist between episomes and genetic recombination?

Chapter *40*

BACTERIA: RECOMBINATION
(IV. Episomes and Nucleotide-Sharing)

Genetic recombination, by the sexual process of conjugation, is known to occur in bacteria like *Pseudomonas* and *Salmonella*, as well as *Escherichia*. In *Escherichia*, male sexuality is attributed to the presence of an F particle, the particular male type being determined by the location and genotype of F. We have found that bacterial conjugation leads to new combinations of either or both the chromosomal genes and the extrachromosomal, episomal, genes.

Let us consider the sequence of events involved in the genetic recombination of the F particles themselves. What happens when an Hfr or Vhf strain reverts to F+ (Lfr)? The F particle which is integrated into the Hfr or Vhf chromosome is somehow *deintegrated* or liberated from it, enters the cytoplasm, replicates, and is infectious thereafter. Subsequently, in some future generation, the F+ particle may reintegrate into a chromosome making it Hfr or Vhf. What would we expect to be the property of an F particle responsible for its integration into a chromosome? It is reasonable to require that the F particle be attracted to the chromosome. Could the cause of the attraction between F and chromosome be the same as that between a transforming segment of chromosome (or a piece of chromosome transmitted by conjugation) and the recipient chromosome? If so, the attraction aspect might be explained merely by supposing that the F particle is composed of DNA. But this assumption, alone, is not

366

sufficient to explain the integration of F, since in transformation the donor loci which integrate must be homologous to those replaced in the recipient cell (and this homology is probably also required for the integration of chromosome fragments introduced by conjugation). We would have to suppose, in addition, that an integrating F particle contains a piece of DNA homologous to a segment of DNA already present in the chromosome. What might be the source of the homologous segment F presumably contains? It might have been present "initially" or it might have been obtained on the last occasion that F deintegrated from the bacterial chromosome.

If a free F particle sometimes carries a particular segment of chromosomal DNA, which it obtained at the time of deintegration, one should be able to find free F particles which have an affinity for a given chromosome region when introduced into a normal F$^-$ strain. This is indeed the case for the F^2 particle (see p. 363), which has a high affinity for a particular locus near *Lac*. On the other hand, the fact that F^1 has a low affinity for the chromosome may mean that it has a smaller amount of chromosomal DNA attached to it than has F^2.

Using the F^2 particle as a particular example, it is possible to visualize several different genetic segments which might be liberated from the chromosome by deintegration. What may be liberated is the complete F^2 particle with, or without, normal chromosomal material still attached, or a defective F^2 particle with, or without, normal chromosomal material still attached. Liberated, defective F^2 particles may or may not be capable of replication. (By being defective or incomplete, we mean that such particles would have lost their F characteristics, and would be undetected phenotypically. If, in fact, deintegration produces defective F^2 particles that cannot replicate, these particles would be lost at some future time, furnishing an example of nonconserved chromosomal DNA.)

What would be the reciprocal product if a defective F² particle is deintegrated? In that event, the chromosome would retain a portion of the F² genotype as a "memory." Thus, just as complete or incomplete F² might carry a piece of chromosome which serves as "memory," a chromosome may retain a part of the F² genotype as "memory." Should a complete *F² with chromosomal memory* infect a normal F⁻ cell, it would be expected to integrate with relatively high frequency at a preferential position in the chromosome. And, reciprocally, should a *chromosome with F² memory* be exposed to complete F², the episome also would be expected to integrate with relatively high frequency at a preferential locus.

We have just expressed certain expectations, regarding the frequency and locus of F integration, on the basis of certain assumptions. Let us now see how experiments [1] (part of whose conclusions were already presented in the last Chapter) bear upon these expectations. An F⁺ strain (carrying F¹ extrachromosomally) gave rise to an Hfr strain, P4x, whose chromosome is transferred with the following orientation: O (origin or lead point)-*Pro-TL-Thi-*...-*Gal-Lac*-SF (place of attachment of the sex factor). P4x × F⁻ gives F⁻ progeny except for *Lac* recombinants which are in turn Hfr males, because of the close linkage of F¹ and *Lac*.

A new strain, P4x-1, derived from P4x, has the following characteristics: (1) From interrupted conjugations it is established that P4x-1 is identical to P4x with respect to order and times of entry of chromosomal markers. Thus, for example, both transfer *Pro* at about six minutes, *TL* at about 20 minutes, and *Lac* last. However, the frequency of recombination for *Pro* is reduced in P4x-1, being only

.3–.5% of donor cells as compared to 4.8% of donor cells for P4x. (2) Moreover, in interrupted conjugation experiments with P4x-1 many of the recombinants for *Pro* or *TL* behave as males. It is also found that the male factor in P4x-1 is linked neither to these loci nor to any other chromosomal marker showing recombination, and that, like free F¹, it enters the F⁻ cell about five minutes after conjugation begins. In brief, the results prove that the male sex factor in P4x-1 is located extrachromosomally.

This cytoplasmic sex factor is called F² because it shows certain differences from F¹ (cf. p. 362). Whereas F¹ can attach at any one of a number of different sites, giving Hfr and Vhf chromosomes which differ in O point position and in direction of transfer, F² attaches at a particular locus near *Lac* to give rise to an Hfr which always transfers its chromosomal loci in the same order and direction.

The fact that P4x-1 transfers its chromosome more frequently than does the typical F⁺ (F¹-containing) male may mean that the F² particle has a chance for integrating at its restricted locus near *Lac* which is greater than the total chance that F¹ has of integrating at any one of a number of different loci. On the other hand, P4x transfers more frequently than P4x-1. This suggests the possibility that F is already integrated in P4x, but is usually only paired with a homologous region in P4x-1, at which position it has the potentiality of being integrated. This suggested difference could explain the observation that P4x has no free F while P4x-1 has, repression of F reproduction cytoplasmically being a characteristic only of F when integrated into the chromosome. The experimental data are consistent with the view that, in P4x-1, integration of the F² particle takes place only after conjugation is initiated.

In those cases where F² is known to be transferred as an extrachromosomal particle to F⁻ cells, these cells are converted to males who transfer their chromosome relatively

---

[1] The preceding and following discussion is based largely upon the work of E. A. Adelberg and S. N. Burns (1960), and F. Jacob and E. A. Adelberg (1959).

frequently with the same marker sequence found for P4x and P4x-1. This demonstrates that an ordinary F⁻ cell carries a chromosome which has, near *Lac*, a segment of DNA which is homologous to a segment carried by F²; that is, F² has a chromosomal segment serving as memory for pairing and integration.

It is possible, also, by treatment with acridine orange, to eliminate the extrachromosomal F particles from the P4x-1 strain, converting it to F⁻. Such a strain will conjugate with males carrying either F¹ or F² extrachromosomally. In both cases the F⁻ strain can relatively frequently become a donor (male) which transfers its chromosome with the same orientation as does P4x and P4x-1. Clearly, then, the F⁻ chromosome derived from P4x-1 has retained near *Lac* a segment of F² as memory, the portion retained being one held in common by F¹ and F². This experiment shows, moreover, that so far as the F portion of the particle is concerned, F¹ and F² are not detectably different. Accordingly, we can think of F² as being an F¹ particle with a longer, particular piece of chromosome attached.

Since, thus far, the experimental results obtained support our expectations, let us continue our reasoning further. We have found evidence that F may carry chromosomal DNA which is apparently still capable of replicating in its new location. Let us suppose also that this chromosomal segment is still capable of performing its normal function. The fact that F¹ carries no phenotypic effect expected of a normal chromosomal locus was presumed to mean that its chromosomal piece is short. Suppose a cistron usually contains hundreds or thousands of linearly arranged deoxyribotides. F¹ might carry, say, four chromosomal nucleotides as memory. In that case, the piece of chromosome would contain only part of a cistron and could therefore produce only a portion of the product of the complete cistron. Since

an incomplete primary gene product would not be unique, F¹ would be scored in practice as producing no gene product for this cistron. Yet the shortness of its chromosomal piece would mean that there would be many places where F¹ would find a similar deoxyribotide sequence when placed alongside the chromosome in one direction or the other. This would explain the fact that F¹ can integrate at a number of loci, giving rise to Hfr or Vhf lines that transfer markers in opposite sequences.

The failure of F² to show a phenotypic effect for a normal chromosomal locus may be due either to the fact that its chromosomal piece, though longer than that of F¹, is still not long enough to include a cistron, or that it contains one or more, as yet unidentified, chromosomal cistrons. If the latter possibilities occur in fact, we should expect to find still different F¹ particles to which a known chromosomal marker is attached. This last expectation can be tested experimentally.

In studies of interrupted conjugation, using *Lac*⁻F⁻ cells and a *Lac*⁺ strain of Hfr where F¹ is known to be integrated very close to *Lac*⁺, rare recombinants are obtained which have received *Lac*⁺ too early. Certain of these recombinants have the following properties:

1. They have received only F¹ and *Lac*⁺.
2. They are unstable, and occasionally give rise to *Lac*⁻F⁻ individuals. Hence the original recombinant was a merozygote carrying both *Lac*⁺ and *Lac*⁻ alleles.
3. When crossed to *Lac*⁻F⁻ cells they simultaneously transfer F¹ and *Lac*⁺ together with 50% or higher frequency. This transfer starts at a time soon after conjugation begins, just as in the case of free F¹ (or F²), and is unlinked to other chromosomal markers. Thus, F¹-*Lac*⁺ behaves as a free single unit.
4. The recombinant transfers its chromosome in the same sequence as, but with a lower

as in leuk in cattle?
or in terato in CHD

frequency (⅒) than, the original Hfr line. This is exactly what is found in comparisons of P4x-1 with P4x.

5. The F¹-*Lac*⁺ element can be transmitted in a series of successive conjugations, each recipient possessing the properties of the original recombinant.

All these results are most simply explained by the deintegration, in the original Hfr strain, of an F¹ particle carrying a chromosomal piece bearing *Lac*⁺. The attached *Lac*⁺ piece is known, moreover, to contain three cistrons; these govern the synthesis of β-galactosidase, β-galactoside permease, and the repressor for this system, respectively. From subsequent integrations and deintegrations it is possible also to obtain F¹-*Lac*⁻ particles, and other particles differing in *Lac* and F¹ capacity. Finally, another Hfr, where F¹ is integrated close to *Pro*, has been found to produce an F¹-*Pro* particle having properties analogous to those of the F¹-*Lac* particle.

Since F¹ can integrate at a variety of loci, we can extrapolate from such results that as a consequence of deintegration, any one of a variety of normal chromosomal loci may become a part of the genotype of cytoplasmic F¹. When long enough, this memory piece of chromosome attached to F¹ will both replicate and produce its phenotypic effect. The evidence seems conclusive, then, that *chromosomal DNA need not be located in the chromosome in order to replicate or function.*

We see, therefore, that F¹ is involved in four types of genetic recombination. F¹ makes possible recombination between a chromosome segment of a donor and the chromosome of a recipient; F¹ can itself be added as a locus to the chromosome at a variety of positions, this being repressive of F¹ located extrachromosomally; F¹ can be removed from its chromosomal locus in toto (or in part) by deintegration; the deintegration that liberates F¹ can include also neighboring cistrons. The last event produces recombination of chromosomal genes between F¹ and the chromosome. There is, therefore, a two-directional gene flow between the extrachromosomal episome F and the chromosome.

So far, we have restricted our attention exclusively to the episome F in *Escherichia coli.* Evidence also has been obtained that *colicines* (certain substances [2] having the capacity to kill colon bacilli, i.e., having colicidal properties) are produced by a colicinogenic determinant which acts as an episome in *E. coli.* The colicinogenic determinant can leave its chromosomal locus, multiply autonomously extrachromosomally, and later integrate into the chromosome. [3] When extrachromosomal, the free episome can migrate actively, as F does, arriving in the F⁻ cell as early as 2½ minutes after conjugation is initiated.

Do episomes occur in organisms other than bacteria? It has already been suggested (refer to p. 360) that certain genetic elements in the chromosomes of corn and of *Drosophila* possess characteristics similar to those of episomes. [4] In this connection let us also consider the relationship between the centromere and *centrosome.* The centrosome is an organelle often found at each pole of a spindle, particularly in animal cells, and a granular structure called the *centriole* is sometimes seen within it. Similar granules can sometimes be seen within the centromere (Figure 40–1). The granules in both the centromere and centrosome stain the same (both doubtless containing DNA), and so does the material surrounding these granules. In the living cell, also, centromere and centrosome have a similar appearance. (The granules within the centromere are thickenings of the DNA thread which passes through the centromere and which is continuous with

[2] At least two colicines are lipocarbohydrate-protein complexes.
[3] See F. Jacob and E. L. Wollman (1958).
[4] See F. Jacob and E. L. Wollman (1961), p. 364.

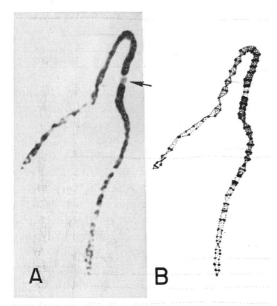

FIGURE 40–1. *The centromere and its granules in corn. (Courtesy of A. Lima de Faria, "Compound Structure of the Kinetochore in Maize," J. Hered., 49:299, 1958.)*

the DNA thread in the chromosome arms.) The morphological similarity of centromere and centrosome is paralleled by their similarity in behavior. Centromeres are sometimes attracted to each other and to the centrosomes. At anaphase, the centromeres migrate toward the centrosomes. The centrosome also has the capacity for movement, as demonstrated by its preanaphase movement and its behavior after a sperm has penetrated an egg.

From these facts some sort of kinship is suggested [5] between centrosome and centromere. This view is strikingly supported by an additional piece of evidence. It has been found,[6] during the meiosis of certain mollusc sperms, that certain chromosomes degenerate, as a result of which free, "naked" centromeres are produced. These now-free centromeres form a group with the centro-

some, and thereafter duplicate centrosomal behavior and appearance exactly. In effect, then, the freed centromeres become extra centrosomes. The preceding evidences suggest *the hypothesis that the centromere and centrosome represent alternative states of a presently or previously existing episome.* The change from one episomal state to the other would probably be influenced by the presence of a nuclear membrane, by various other genetic factors present in highly organized cells, as well as by mutations which have occurred in the episome when in its alternative states.

It is known that at the base of each cilium or flagellum is a granular body, the *kinetosome,* which is responsible for the motion of the organelle. There is excellent evidence that these kinetosomes are homologous to centrioles (or centrosomes). This suggests that kinetosomes are also episomes or episomal derivatives. It has been suggested [7] that the episome F functions like a centromere. Is it possible that the movements attributed to F and the centromere and centrosome have the same basis as the flagellar and ciliary movement produced by kinetosomes?

Let us speculate with regard to certain matters which may not, at first, seem to have any possible relation to episomes.[8] Heterochromatin (cf. p. 181) behaves cytologically and physiologically (phenotypically) less specifically than does euchromatin. Moreover, because portions of heterochromatin can be added or subtracted from the genotype without causing great phenotypic modification, it is reasonable to believe that the cistronic product of heterochromatin is not only unspecific, but is duplicated in successive heterochromatic segments. In view of the likelihood that the cistrons of heterochromatin produce an unspecific product, it is hypothesized that each has a short nucleo-

[5] Originally by C. D. Darlington, by F. Schrader, and by others.
[6] By A. W. Pollister and P. F. Pollister.

[7] Originally by R. C. Baumiller.
[8] See I. H. Herskowitz (1961). The reading of the remainder of this Chapter is optional.

tide sequence, since the complexity, and hence the specificity, of a cistron's product would be expected to be directly correlated with the number of nucleotides in the cistron.

It can also be hypothesized that most, if not all, of the heterochromatin in a cell is composed of a monotonous repetition of the same nucleotide pair, usually A-T. This view receives support from the following observations: (1) The sequence of A, T, C, G on a single strand of DNA is far from random; at least 70% of the bases are distributed so that three or more pyrimidines (and hence purines, too) occur in successive nucleotides; sequences of five successive T's have been identified; 4.9% of a tested DNA contains sequences of eight or more pyrimidines in succession; (2) a polymer of A-T alone may make up as much as 30% of certain crab sperm DNA; (3) the amount of thymine is increased in *Drosophila* cells carrying an extra, almost entirely heterochromatic, Y chromosome; (4) 5-bromo deoxyuridine, which is known to replace thymine in DNA, causes a high frequency of breaks near or in heterochromatic regions.

Suppose, to exemplify these suggestions, that all nucleotides in a particular stretch of heterochromatin have the same formula, A, and that three in succession (AAA) comprise a cistron. (We can ignore, at this time, the complementary chain composed of T's.) Since the number of successive A's is expected to be considerable, it is reasonable that a particular A may be used cistronically, sometimes with two A's to its right, and other times with two A's to its left. In other words, in heterochromatin, a nucleotide can be shared by adjacent cistrons. On the other hand, a typical, highly specific cistron in euchromatin would be expected to be composed of several hundred or a thousand linearly arranged nucleotides. Suppose a particular euchromatic cistron terminates in -TAA. If a break occurs between the -TA and A, and another occurs almost anywhere

in the heterochromatin, and cross-union of broken ends occurs, the euchromatic cistron will have its proper nucleotide sequence completed. But, since any three successive A's can serve as template for making heterochromatic product, there could be *nucleotide-sharing* between the now-adjacent euchromatic and heterochromatic cistrons. In this case, whenever the heterochromatic cistron was used to make product, no complete product would be formed from the euchromatic cistron. Thus, so long as the adjacent heterochromatic cistron made its product, the euchromatic cistron would be functionally suppressed, and would be scored as an amorph (see p. 210). If conditions changed, so that the euchromatic cistron was able to function as usual, the normal euchromatic phenotype would result. If the heterochromatic and euchromatic cistrons were functional alternately, no detectable phenotypic effect would be expected with regard to the heterochromatic product, but phenotypic mosaicism could result because of the intermittently produced euchromatic product. In these ways, suppressed or variegated phenotypic effects, which are known to be due to the placement of heterochromatin near euchromatin, may be explained. Such position effects (cf. Chapters 22 and 25) are frequent following structural changes in chromosomes of *Drosophila*. Some of these cases of phenotypic suppression involve genetic elements like *Segregation-Distorter* in *Drosophila* and *Dissociation* in corn, which are associated with heterochromatin, can also cause breakage, and can change their location in the genome. Since such factors resemble episomes, it may not be too far-fetched to study these and known episomes for the occurrence and possible consequences (phenotypic suppression, organelle movement, and chromosomal breakage) of nucleotide-sharing.

Many of the ideas relative to homologous organelles, nucleotide-sharing, and suppressive and variegated position effects discussed in the last portion of this Chapter are highly speculative. (Speculation in science is permitted, however, if it conforms to the facts known at the time, and if it leads to expectations subject to test in feasible experiments. When these rules are followed, and the speculation is identified as such, no permanent scientific damage ensues.) In the Chapters that follow you should keep these ideas in mind, and search for more information to test the correctness of part or all of the hypotheses presented.

SUMMARY AND CONCLUSIONS

The free episome F may carry chromosomal markers, and chromosomes may carry only a part of F. This results in a two-directional flow of genetic material between extrachromosomal F and the chromosome, which represents a new type of genetic recombination.

The chromosomal markers carried by free F are still capable of replication and of phenotypic function, having retained these genic characteristics though removed from the chromosome.

Colicines are the product of an episome. Episomes may exist in organisms more complex than bacteria. The characteristics of centrosomes, kinetosomes, and centromeres suggest that these show a present or past episomal relationship with each other. Elements like *Modulator* and *Dissociation* have some of the properties of episomes.

Speculation leads to the tentative concept that nucleotides may be shared by adjacent cistrons. This might lead to suppressed or variegated phenotypic effects, chromosomal breakage, and movement of cell organelles. The study of episomes and of episomal-like factors may provide a test of the occurrence and consequences of nucleotide-sharing.

REFERENCES

Adelberg, E. A., and Burns, S. N., "Genetic Variation in the Sex Factor of Escherichia Coli," J. Bact., 79:321–330, 1960; reprinted in *Papers on Bacterial Genetics*, Adelberg, E. A. (Ed.), Boston, Little, Brown, 1960, pp. 353–362.

Jacob, F., and Wollman, E. L., "Episomes, Added Genetic Elements" (in French), C. R. Acad. Sci. (Paris), 247:154–156, 1958; translated and reprinted in *Papers on Bacterial Genetics*, Adelberg, E. A. (Ed.), Boston, Little, Brown, 1960, pp. 398–400.

Herskowitz, I. H., "The Hypothesis of Nucleotide Sharing by Adjacent Functional Units of DNA," (Abstr.) Genetics, 46:870, 1961.

Pollister, A. W., and Pollister, P. F., "The Relation Between Centriole and Centromere in Atypical Spermatogenesis of Viviparid Snails," Ann. N.Y. Acad. Sci., 45:1–48, 1943.

Spencer, J. H., and Chargaff, E., "Pyrimidine Nucleotide Sequences in Deoxyribonucleic Acids," Biochim. Biophys. Acta, 51:209–211, 1961.

QUESTIONS FOR DISCUSSION

40.1. Answer question 39.9 on page 365.

40.2. Do all matings transfer F particles of one genotype or another?

40.3. Discuss the relationship between the transmission of free F particles and of a segment of the male chromosome.

40.4. Discuss the reality of a bacterial "chromosome" and its linear arrangement.

40.5. By what series of events can you explain the origin of strain P4x-1 from P4x?

40.6. Specify a particular Hfr strain of *E. coli* and tell how you would proceed to obtain an F-*Pro* (proline) particle.

40.7. What characteristics of *Dissociation* and *Modulator* resemble those of the episome F?

40.8. By what mechanisms for shuffling genes might nucleotide-sharing be initiated?

40.9. Discuss the possible role of nucleotide-sharing in integration, and in deintegrated episomes.

40.10. What do you think of the hypothesis that most, if not all, episomes or episomal derivatives are nucleotide-sharing, and that nucleotide-sharing is associated with motility?

40.11. How do you suppose episomes originate?

40.12. Have integrated episomes and episomal derivatives the general capacity to break chromosomes? Explain.

    Could nucleotide-sharing be associated with such a capacity? Explain.

40.13. Devise nucleotide sequences which would explain the differences between Bar, Ultrabar, and wild-type eye shape in *Drosophila*.

40.14. Devise nucleotide sequences which could be used to explain cis-trans position effects. List the assumptions you have made in such an explanation.

λ transduction in E. Coli
no transformation " " "

Chapter *41

BACTERIA: RECOMBINATION
(V. Transduction)

THE FOUR Chapters preceding this have dealt with the shuffling of genetic material in bacteria. In the cases discussed, the new genetic combinations typically involved the relocation of only a portion of a bacterial genome. While, in the case of conjugation, a segment of chromosomal DNA passes from donor to recipient bacterium through a cytoplasmic bridge formed by the activity of an F particle, no organismal assistance is necessary for the entrance of donor DNA in all of the cases of transformation previously discussed. It has been shown in the last two Chapters that the F particle itself undergoes recombination, not only because it is infectious, but because it can enter and leave the bacterial chromosome, i.e., because it is an episome. Moreover, because of the episomal cycle, F may acquire chromosomal memory and the chromosome may acquire F memory. Such new nucleotide combinations in turn foster further genetic recombinations which result in a flow of cistrons between F and chromosome.

It has been reasoned earlier (p. 349) that any homologous segment of DNA introduced into a bacterium has the potentiality of pairing with, and integrating into, a bacterial chromosome. Have we exhausted the mechanisms for introducing homologous DNA into bacteria? *Bacteriophages* or *phages* [1] are viruses that have the capacity to destroy bacteria. After these fasten onto the bacterium, all or part of the phage that is external

[1] The Greek letter ϕ, phi, is used to denote phage.

374

to the bacterium can be shaken off by the shearing action of a Blendor. Nevertheless, the course of the infection is unchanged by such treatment, that is, the virus still produces its characteristic effects on the bacterium. This can be taken to mean that the part of the virus essential for these effects actually enters the bacterial cytoplasm, and that what remains attached to the outside of the bacterium is dispensable in this regard. In view of this behavior by phage, two new ways for the entry of homologous DNA into a phage-infected cell can be envisaged. First, the virus might carry externally, adsorbed to its outer surface, a segment of DNA derived from its previous bacterial host. This piece may penetrate the new host at the same time that the essential part of the phage enters, the latter action providing a place of entry for the bacterial DNA.

The second mode of DNA entrance involves the internal contents of the phage which enter the bacterium. The part of the virus which enters the bacterium may contain DNA which possesses a nucleotide sequence also found in the bacterial chromosome. There are two possible origins for such homologous DNA. It might be (1) a segment of DNA, not normally a part of the virus, which originated in the previous host chromosome (in which case the phage may or may not be defective in its own DNA or RNA content), or (2) a segment of DNA that is normally found as a (continuous) part of the viral DNA.

With this introduction, let us examine the results of a series of experiments [2] employing the mouse typhoid organism, *Salmonella typhimurium*. This bacterium is a close relative of *E. coli*, and also can be cultured on a simple medium. A number of auxotrophic strains of *Salmonella* have been obtained, including one that requires methionine (M^-T^+) and another that requires threonine (M^+T^-).

[2] The following discussion is based upon the work of N. D. Zinder and J. Lederberg (1952).

When these two strains were mixed and then plated on medium lacking methionine and threonine, prototrophic colonies appeared in such large numbers that they could be explained entirely, or almost entirely, as being the result of genetic recombination, and not of mutation. Prototrophs also were obtained, if a liquid culture of the M^+T^- strain was centrifuged (to remove most of the bacteria), the supernate heated for 20 to 30 minutes (to kill any remaining bacteria), and the supernate added to the M^-T^+ strain. This demonstrates that no living M^+T^- donor cells are required in order to furnish the M^+ factor for the establishment of prototrophy. So, this is clearly not a case of genetic recombination involving conjugation. Moreover, the filtrate retained its full M^+ capacity after treatment with DNAase. Accordingly, this is not a case of genetic recombination via transformation. Since the M^+ factor could pass through filters that held back bacteria but not viruses, it can be called a *filterable agent* (FA).

It was also found that the M^+T^- strain harbored a phage. This virus, P22, is said to be *nonvirulent* or *temperate*, for only occasionally does it become virulent, at which time it replicates itself and then lyses or bursts the host cell to liberate as many as several hundred progeny phage. Accordingly, temperate phage does not cause conspicuous lysis. Since the M^+T^- strain of *Salmonella* carries P22 as a temperate virus and is potentially capable of having its cells lysed, it is said to be a *lysogenic* strain. Lysogeny also confers on the bacterium immunity to infection by identical or homologous phage. The M^-T^+ strain happens normally to lack P22, that is, it is a *nonlysogenic* or *sensitive* strain. When a sensitive strain is infected with temperate phage, a certain fraction of the cells lyse and liberate phage, but another fraction survives, becomes lysogenic, and gives rise to lysogenic progeny. Lysogenic bacteria can be lysed artificially and tested for phage. None is detected. Apparently, in cells that become lysogenic, the phage is converted to a new form, called *prophage*, which reproduces at the same rate as the host. When a lysogenic cell is to be lysed by viral action, prophage normally first rapidly replicates a number of times to produce infective phage which is liberated at the time of lysis.

A natural question to ask now is: What is the relationship between the filterable agent M^+ and the phage P22? The following facts were determined experimentally. Both FA M^+ and phage P22 (1) were unaffected by RNAase and DNAase, (2) showed the same inactivation pattern with temperature changes, (3) had the same susceptibility to an antiserum that blocks the attachment of phage to the bacterium, (4) attached to susceptible cells simultaneously, (5) had the same size and mass as determined by filtration and sedimentation tests, (6) appeared in the medium at the same time and in a constant ratio, and (7) retained this constant ratio even though various purification and concentration procedures were applied. It is evident from these results, therefore, that FA M^+ is phage-bound. Since the genetic material of *Salmonella* is known to be composed of DNA, so is the genetic factor M^+. Moreover, since fact (1) precludes the attachment of the M^+ genetic factor to the outer surface of the phage particle, the M^+ gene must be located in the interior of the virus.

Genetic transduction is the term we shall use to define the process of genetic recombination which is made possible when homologous DNA, contained within a virus particle, is sent into a recipient cell.

Is there any limitation to the genetic material which can be transduced by P22? P22 can be grown on bacteria which are genetically marked $M^+T^+X^+Y^-Z^-$, and the crop of phage produced, following this infection, can be harvested. Part of the harvested phage is then tested on suitable indicator strains (M^-, T^-, X^-, Y^-, Z^-) one at a time. The results show transduction of M^+, of T^+, and of X^+, but not of Y^+ or Z^+. Another part of the harvested phage is not tested yet but grown instead on another genetically marked strain, for example, $M^+T^-X^+Y^+Z^-$. The new crop of phage produced is harvested and then tested on the indicator strains already mentioned. It is found now that the new crop has lost T^+ transducing ability but has gained Y^+ transducing capacity. These results demonstrate that a phage filtrate has a range of markers for transduction which is exactly the range of the markers present in the bacteria on which the phage was last grown. In other words, the phage is passive with respect to the content of genes it transduces, and retains no transducing memory from hosts previous to the last. Since additional tests demonstrate that practically any locus in *Salmonella* is transduceable by P22, we may call this a case of *generalized transduction*. In generalized transduction a particular marker is transduced once for about each 10^6 infecting phage particles.

Although almost any chromosomal marker is transduceable by P22, what is the length or scope of the transduced DNA? P22 can be grown on $M^+T^+X^+$, harvested, and then grown on $M^-T^-X^-$. The latter bacteria are replica-plated on different media, of which one selects for M^+ recombinants, another selects for T^+, and a third selects for X^+. When the M^+ clones are further typed they are still T^-X^-. Similarly, T^+ clones are still M^-X^- and X^+ clones are still M^-T^-. This demonstrates that usually a single bacterial marker is transduced. In this respect, then, transduction is similar to transformation but is different from conjugation, where, especially in Vhf strains, large blocks of genes may be transmitted and integrated.

Several examples are known in *Salmonella*, however, in which several genetic markers are transduced together, in what may be called *linked transduction* or *cotransduction*. It was established, in other work, that the biological synthesis of the amino acid tryptophan is

part of a sequence of genetically determined reactions that proceeds from anthranilic acid to indol to tryptophan. Cotransductions were found [3] of genes controlling different steps of this biosynthetic sequence, indicating that these genes are closely linked to each other.

Histidine biosynthesis in *Salmonella* involves at least eight loci, of which four produce identifiable effects on the sequence of chemical reactions involved. Linked transductions have been found between two or more of these loci.[4] In fact, using the relative frequencies of different cotransductions and other evidences, it was possible to prove that all eight loci are continuous with each other and are arranged linearly (see Figure 46–1, page 422). The close linkage of cistrons controlling different parts of a biosynthetic sequence is not a universal phenomenon, however. But, when such close linkage does occur, it may be adaptive, in that a single mechanism may suffice to turn off or on the whole series of enzymatic reactions. (In this regard it may be suggested that nucleotide-sharing could provide a mechanism for turning chemical sequences on or off, depending upon which of the overlapping cistrons was functional on different occasions.) Cotransduction of closely linked markers is known to occur [5] also in *E. coli* infected with phage P1.

When, in a generalized transduction experiment, a prototroph is obtained by transducing an auxotroph, the new prototroph is stable and produces clones phenotypically identical to typical prototrophs. We may call this *complete transduction*. In this case, the introduced prototrophic gene must have integrated into the *Salmonella* chromosome in place of the recipient's auxotrophic gene. It was noticed, however, that in addition to the large colonies formed, each of which represented a complete transduction, there were

---

[3] By M. Demerec and coworkers.
[4] By M. Demerec, P. E. Hartman, and coworkers.
[5] From the work of E. Lennox.

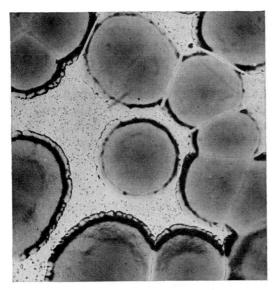

FIGURE 41–1. *Large and minute colonies of* Salmonella, *representing complete and abortive transductions, respectively. (Courtesy of P. E. Hartman.)*

about ten times as many minute colonies (see Figure 41–1). These minute colonies did not appear in platings of auxotrophic mutants on deficient medium. They were also not attributable to any interaction between auxotrophs and colonies of normal or transduced prototrophs located elsewhere on the plate. It was possible to show, in a variety of cases and by various methods,[6] that each minute colony contained but a single genetically prototrophic cell. Minute colony formation was demonstrated to have the following origin. The initial cell of the minute colony received through phage infection the segment of DNA containing the gene for prototrophy under test. However, this gene (1) failed to be integrated, (2) failed to replicate, (3) but retained its functional capacity to produce a phenotypic effect. As a consequence, a partial hybrid or *heterogenote* was produced in which the injected cistron for prototrophy was functional. Because prototrophic cis-

[6] By B. A. D. Stocker, J. Lederberg, N. D. Zinder, and by H. Ozeki (1956).

tronic product was made, the cell was able to grow and then divide. However, only one of the first two daughter cells received the extra chromosomal segment, or *exogenote*. The daughter cell without the exogenote was able to grow and divide only until the prototrophic cistronic product became too scarce; on the other hand, the heterogenotic daughter cell could continue to grow and divide, in turn producing only one heterogenotic daughter cell. In this way, a minute colony is produced which contains a single genetically prototrophic cell. This consequence, of the failure of complete transduction, is called *abortive transduction.*

Hypothetically, there are two possible fates for the exogenote in an abortive transduction. Eventually, the exogenote might either be lost (by mutation) or it might undergo integration to result in a complete transduction. The latter alternative has, so far, not been found to occur. Regardless of its ultimate fate, we can agree that the exogenote is cistronic in nature. Note that the exogenote is still considered to be a segment of genetic material, even though it does not self-replicate. But, remember, self-replication was an assumed characteristic of the total genetic material, and that no such capacity was required of a cistron when this was defined.

In most transduction studies, an excess of phage is used. In such experiments transduced cells are always found to have simultaneously become lysogenic. This means that the cell being transduced has received not only the exogenote segment but an apparently complete genome of a phage as well, the former resulting in genetic recombination, the latter in immunity and eventual lysis of some progeny (lysogeny). Is the phage particle whose contents enter the host cell and make it lysogenic, the same particle which introduces the exogenote? This need not be so, since the use of high concentrations or multiplicities of infecting phage means that the host could have been penetrated by the contents of two or more phage particles, one particle furnishing the exogenote and another causing lysogeny. Using different concentrations of phage, and low multiplicities especially, it was possible to prove that only one phage particle is needed per transduction. It was shown,[7] moreover, that a single phage which attacks a susceptible bacterium can produce only one of three mutually exclusive effects on its host, namely, death (by lysis some 60 minutes later), lysogeny, or transduction. A phage that produces generalized, complete or abortive, transduction is, therefore, defective with regard to its phage genotype and is subsequently unable to replicate, at least when it is the only phage of that type infecting the cell. What has happened is that a small chromosome segment of the last host bacterium must have replaced a particular segment of the phage genome whose presence is necessary for the subsequent lysis or lysogenization of a new host. We had already anticipated this possibility (p. 374). We cannot tell in the present case, however, whether the DNA of the exogenote is separate from, or attached to, the defective phage genome.

E. coli strain K-12 is normally lysogenic for the temperate phage *lambda* (λ), to which it is relatively insensitive. A mutant strain of *E. coli* was found which is sensitive to lambda, that is, which is nonlysogenic. Since the nonlysogenic strain exposed to lambda is often lysed, it can be used to test for the presence of lambda in a filtrate. Sometimes, the sensitive strain becomes lysogenized. This permits the study of the transducing capacity of lambda by using a lysogenic strain with different genetic markers from those of the sensitive, nonlysogenic, strain. The strains and procedure, then, are comparable to those used to study transduction by P22 in *Salmonella*. Lambda to be tested for transducing ability can be collected from the filtrate of the lysogenic strain. Lambda can

[7] By J. N. Adams and S. E. Luria.

also be harvested, in greater quantity, a few hours following a short treatment of lysogenics with ultraviolet light. Such *UV-induction* causes prophage to replicate progeny phage which lyse the cell. When the transduceability of various markers is tested, it is found that only a very limited range of markers can be carried by lambda. These are restricted to a cluster of loci, *Gal*, controlling galactose fermentation, loci which, from conjugation studies, are known to be very closely linked to each other. Lambda is therefore capable only of *restricted transduction.*

Lysis, and the consequent liberation of infective phage, can be induced by ultraviolet light, as mentioned. It is also found that when lysogenic Hfr conjugate with sensitive F−, a number of zygotes are induced to lyse and liberate infective phage. This method of inducing prophage to replicate and liberate infective phage by lysis, initiated by conjugation, is called *zygotic induction*. It is found, moreover, that zygotic induction occurs, with a given Hfr strain, only if about 26 minutes of conjugation takes place before it is interrupted. This suggests that the chromosome has a locus, *Lp* (or *ly*), with which prophage is physically associated. In a nonlysogenic cell there is no prophage attached to or associated with the *Lp* site, whereas in a lysogenic cell there is. Moreover, in crosses between nonlysogenic Hfr (*Lp* without prophage) and lysogenic F− cells (*Lp* with prophage), there is no zygotic induction, and the nonlysogenic trait (*Lp* without prophage) is transferred and segregates (cf. p. 353) among recombinants just as any other genetic marker. From these results and others, it is found that *Lp*, the locus for lambda prophage maintenance, is closely linked to the *Gal* loci which lambda may subsequently transduce (see Figure 39–4, page 361, where the locus under discussion is given as λ).

The original lambda-containing lysogenic

bacterium is stable and haploid with respect to the *Gal* "locus" and produces per 100 thousand lambda only about one *Gal*-carrying lambda. Such progeny phage are said to be capable of producing a *low frequency of transduction (LFT)*. About two thirds of the transduced cells from LFT phage form clones that are unstable with respect to *Gal*, i.e., that segregate out the *Gal* genotype of the recipient cell. In other words, a *Gal⁻* bacterium transduced with lambda carrying *Gal⁺* is usually an unstable heterogenote, being diploid and heterozygous for the *Gal* locus, occasionally segregating *Gal⁻* progeny. (It should be noted that the merozygote produced by lambda transduction differs from the merozygote produced by P22 in an abortive transduction. In the latter case the transduced segment is incapable of replication, whereas in the former case the transduced segment can replicate, so that clones of merozygotes may be produced.) When infective lambda is induced from a lysogenic individual merozygotic for *Gal*, the transducing lysate may contain 100 times as many phage carrying a *Gal* locus as does the lysate of haploids. Such a crop of phage is capable of what may be called a *high frequency of transduction (HFT)*. (There is a second difference between generalized and restricted transduction. In generalized transduction, transducing phage may be obtained from the lysate of nonlysogenic cells infected with free phage, whereas this is not so in the case of restricted transduction. Thus, in the case of restricted transduction, transducing phage are released only from lysogenic [haploid, or merozygotic] bacteria.)[8]

From the results obtained by employing different multiplicities and combinations of transducing lambda (harvested from lysogenic cells) and nontransducing lambda (harvested soon after nonlysogenic cells are infected), it has been possible to prove,[9] just as is true for generalized transduction, that transducing lambda is defective for a portion of the lambda genome. What happens is that the *Gal* loci being transduced probably replace a segment of the lambda genome. The transducing defective lambda particle (called λ*dg*) has retained certain phage properties and lost others. Thus, when only a single *Gal*-transducing particle is involved in an infection, the particle is still capable of eventually killing and lysing the cell. But it has lost the ability to replicate and produce infective phage progeny, so that the prophage it forms must be defective. Also, such a particle can only rarely lysogenize its host. This means the host is only rarely immune to further infection with lambda. Accordingly, a cell infected by such a defective lambda is still subject to infection by nontransducing phage, whose additional presence (1) makes the host lysogenic and (2) contributes a function which permits the defective prophage to multiply. At the time of lysis of such a doubly infected cell, infective phages of both nontransducing and transducing ability are liberated. This situation is similar to that already described in *Salmonella* which cannot be lysed or lysogenized if infected by a single transducing particle but which can demonstrate either of these characteristics if the host is also infected with one or more normal, nontransducing P22 phage particles.

Transformation is not known to occur in *E. coli*, probably due to some difficulty in DNA penetration. One would predict, however, if the DNA of a defective lambda were isolated and somehow introduced into a cell, that it would sometimes behave as a transforming principle with respect to *Gal* loci. Even if naked DNA does not penetrate *E. coli* by itself, it might be hoped that it would adhere to the outside of a nontransducing phage, and enter the host at the time the

[8] The preceding account is based largely upon the work of J. Lederberg, E. M. Lederberg, and M. L. Morse, and of E. L. Wollman and F. Jacob.

[9] By W. Arber, G. Kellenberger, and J. Weigle (1957), and by A. Campbell.

infecting phage contents do, in accord with the expectation mentioned on page 374. Indeed, this is known to occur;[10] that is, using nontransducing lambda as a carrier or "helper," DNA isolated from defective transducing phage is capable of *Gal* transformation.

You should have noticed, in the discussion of lambda, that such a temperate phage has two alternative pathways of action open to it upon infecting a sensitive bacterium. Either it enters the cytoplasm where it replicates faster than the chromosome, or it integrates with the chromosome where, as prophage, it resides associated with the *Lp* locus and is synchronously replicated as a regular chromosomal marker. *Accordingly, lambda, and probably most, if not all, other temperate phages are episomes.*

What is the difference between temperate phages capable of generalized and restricted

[10] From the work of A. D. Kaiser and D. S. Hogness (1960).

transduction? Extrapolating our reasoning regarding the episome F, it can be suggested that the nucleotide sequence held in common between prophage and chromosome is shorter for generalized transducing phages than it is for restrictive transducing phages, the former having a greater number of, and hence less specific, places of attachment as prophage than do the latter. Several experiments support the view that, at least sometimes, prophage may make the host cell immune to further infection by homologous phage, not by preventing the penetration of the DNA, but by preventing its replication. This action parallels the suppression of free-F replication by integrated F.

Transduction by temperate phages has been found to occur also in *Pseudomonas*, *Vibrio*, *Staphylococcus*, and *Proteus*. It would not be surprising to find that transduction can occur in a wide variety of cells, including human cells.

SUMMARY AND CONCLUSIONS

Genetic recombination of loci characteristically identified with the bacterial chromosome can be mediated by temperate bacteriophages in the processes of genetic transduction and genetic transformation.

A transducing phage is defective in its own genome. The deficient portion is probably replaced by a small segment of DNA acquired at the time the prophage deintegrated from its last host. The transduced segment may be derived from a wide variety of regions of the bacterial chromosome, as in generalized transduction, or from a narrowly limited region, as in restricted transduction. The DNA segment transduced may, by integration, replace a chromosomal marker of the host (as in complete transduction), or it may produce a merozygote, in which case the exogenote is still capable of acting cistronically, whether it can replicate (as can *Gal* exogenotes in *E. coli*) or cannot (as in abortive transduction in *Salmonella*).

Most, if not all, temperate phages are episomes, which when attached to the chromosome have some characteristics resembling those of attached F.

REFERENCES

Arber, W., Kellenberger, G., and Weigle, J., "The Defectiveness of Lambda-Transducing Phage" (in French), Schweiz. Zeitschr. Allgemeine Path. und Bact., 20:659–665, 1957; translated and reprinted in *Papers on Bacterial Genetics*, Adelberg, E. A. (Ed.), Boston, Little, Brown, 1960, pp. 224–229.

Jacob, F., and Wollman, E. L., "Spontaneous Induction of the Development of Bacteriophage λ in Genetic Recombination of Escherichia Coli K12" (in French), C. R. Acad. Sci., Paris, 239:317–319, 1954; translated and reprinted in *Papers on Bacterial Viruses*, Stent, G. S. (Ed.), Boston, Little, Brown, 1960, pp. 336–338.

Jacob, F., and Wollman, E. L., "Genetic Aspects of Lysogeny," pp. 468–500 in *A Symposium on the Chemical Basis of Heredity*, McElroy, W. D., and Glass, B. (Eds.), Baltimore, The Johns Hopkins Press, 1957.

Kaiser, A. D., and Hogness, D. S., "The Transformation of Escherichia Coli with Deoxyribonucleic Acid Isolated from Bacteriophage λdg," J. Mol. Biol., 2:392–415, 1960.

Morse, M. L., Lederberg, E. M., and Lederberg, J., "Transduction in Escherichia Coli K-12," Genetics, 41:142–156, 1956; reprinted in *Papers on Bacterial Genetics*, Adelberg, E. A. (Ed.), Boston, Little, Brown, 1960, pp. 209–223.

Ozeki, H., "Abortive Transduction in Purine-Requiring Mutants of Salmonella Typhimurium," Carnegie Inst. Wash. Publ. 612, *Genetic Studies with Bacteria*, 97–106, 1956; reprinted in *Papers on Bacterial Genetics*, Adelberg, E. A. (Ed.), Boston, Little, Brown, 1960, pp. 230–238.

Wollman, E. L., and Jacob, F., "Lysogeny and Genetic Recombination in Escherichia Coli K12" (in French), C. R. Acad. Sci., Paris, 239:455–456, 1954; translated and reprinted in *Papers on Bacterial Viruses*, Stent, G. S. (Ed.), Boston, Little, Brown, 1960, pp. 334–335.

Zinder, N. D., "'Transduction' in Bacteria," Scient. Amer., 199:38–43, 1958.

Zinder, N. D., and Lederberg, J., "Genetic Exchange in Salmonella," J. Bact., 64:679–699, 1952.

Norton D. Zinder,
about 1954.

QUESTIONS FOR DISCUSSION

41.1. How would you define the term *provirus*? How do the terms *merozygote* and *heterogenote* differ? How would you define a *homogenote*?

41.2. What characteristics are conferred upon a host cell infected by a nontransducing temperate phage which (1) becomes a prophage? (2) does not become a prophage?

41.3. How would you proceed to prove that there is only one exogenote in a microcolony of *Salmonella* produced following abortive transduction?

41.4. Discuss the statement: "Temperate phage has chromosomal memory, and the chromosome has temperate phage memory."

41.5. F particles are known which carry the prophage of λ as "memory." How could you prove the existence of such a particle?

41.6. Describe the procedure and genotypes you might use in demonstrating that *E. coli* can undergo genetic transformation with respect to *Gal*.

41.7. Is there any reason for believing that the close linkage of genes with related effects might be more advantageous in microorganisms than in higher organisms? Explain.

41.8. List the different ways that the *Gal* locus in *E. coli* may undergo recombination.

41.9. Would you say that temperate phages are good or bad for bacteria? Explain.

41.10. How would you define *sex-duction* or *F-duction*? Give an example of this process in *E. coli*.

41.11. Is a cell which has presumably stopped undergoing mutation, genetic recombination, and self-replication of its DNA still considered to contain genetic material? Explain.

Chapter *42

VIRUSES: RECOMBINATION
IN BACTERIOPHAGE (I)

IT HAS been already stated that the genetic material of bacterial chromosomes is DNA. It has been inferred (p. 366) that the episome F is also composed of DNA, and proof of this has been obtained. The possibility may not be excluded at the present time, however, that some episome other than F may have RNA for its unique genetic material, for this substance, too, could provide nucleotide sequences suitable for pairing with chromosomal segments of DNA. It is even possible to imagine that RNA might become integrated into a DNA chromosome.[1] (RNA episomal particles that deintegrate from the chromosome and retain a DNA segment as chromosomal memory could subsequently readily reintegrate.) Since we concluded near the close of the last Chapter that most, if not all, temperate phages are episomes, it would seem desirable at this point to discuss the morphology, chemical composition, and some details of the behavior of bacteriophages.

Different phages have different morphologies. Consider the structure of phages of the T-even group (T2, T4, T6), since these have been studied in some detail.[2] Such phages are tadpole-shaped, $0.1-0.2\mu$ long, or about a tenth the bacterial diameter (see Figure 42–1). The *head* has the form of a bipyramidal hexagonal prism, while the *tail* is cylindri-

cal and is the structure used for attaching the phage to the host cell. The membrane surrounding the head is composed of a large number of repeated subunits each having a molecular weight of about 80,000. The tail consists of an outer *sheath* which is composed of spirally arranged subunits which form a hollow cylinder. The sheath can contract in length as a consequence of which its diameter is increased but its volume is approximately unchanged. The sheath is composed of about 200 subunits, each of approximately 50,000 molecular weight. Beneath the sheath is the *core* of the tail. The core is a hollow cylinder with a central hole about 25 A in diameter. At the distal end of the core is a *hexagonal plate* to which six *tail fibers* are attached. Each tail fiber has a kink in the middle and seems to contain subunits with a molecular weight not less than 100,000. The head membrane, sheath and tail fibers are composed of proteins, each of whose digestion with trypsin gives a unique fingerprint. Therefore, each of these proteins is different. The core also is composed of protein. A serologically distinct protein, comprising 4–6% of the total protein, is found in the interior of the phage particle; polyamines, putrescine, spermadine, lysozyme, and a minor polypeptide are also reported in the phage interior.

In addition to the components already mentioned, the phage interior contains DNA whose volume is approximately equivalent to that of the total protein. This DNA is composed of a double helix about 200,000 nucleotides long. Since such a polynucleotide would be about 68μ long, it is clear that the DNA inside the phage must be highly coiled upon itself. No RNA is reported to be contained in these phages. However, not all phages contain DNA. At least one phage is known to contain RNA and no DNA. Moreover, the physical and chemical complexity of the T-even phages is not typical of all viruses. Certain plant viruses, like tobacco

---

[1] See reference to J. S. Krakow, H. O. Kammen, and E. S. Canellakis at end of Chapter.

[2] See reference to S. Brenner *et al.* (1959) at end of Chapter.

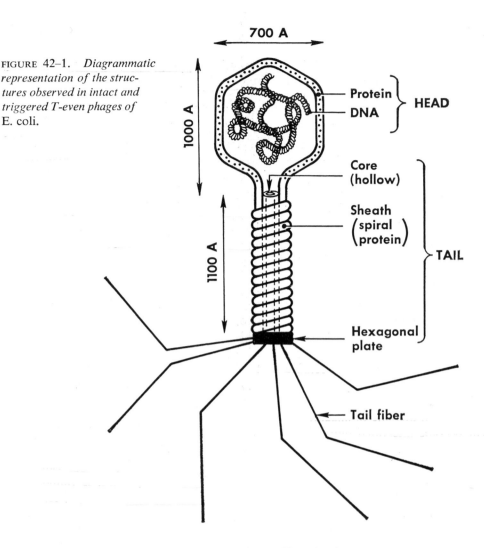

FIGURE 42–1. *Diagrammatic representation of the structures observed in intact and triggered T-even phages of E. coli.*

700 A

1000 A

1100 A

Protein
DNA } HEAD

Core
(hollow)

Sheath
(spiral
protein) } TAIL

Hexagonal
plate

Tail fiber

mosaic virus and turnip yellow mosaic virus, are relatively simple structures.

We are now in a position to examine the evidence concerning the chemical identity of the genetic material in typical DNA-containing phages. Since DNA contains no S and T2 phage protein contains no P, the DNA in one sample of phage can be labeled by feeding the *E. coli* host cells radioactive P^{32}, while the protein in another sample of phage can be labeled by feeding the host cells radioactive S^{35}. The two samples of radioactive phage are then permitted to infect nonlabeled cells.[3]

[3] This account follows the work of A. D. Hershey and M. Chase (1952).

It is found that all of the P^{32} (hence all of the DNA) enters the bacterium while all but about 3% of the S^{35} (hence almost all the protein) remains outside. As mentioned in the last Chapter (p. 374), protein portions of a phage can be shaken off the host cell by Blendor treatment without affecting the normal outcome of infection (transduction, lysis, lysogenation). This result is consistent with the view that it is DNA which is the carrier of phage genetic information.

It has already been mentioned (p. 379) that naked DNA does not penetrate normal *E. coli*. It is possible to remove the cell wall of *E. coli* by suitable culture conditions to produce what is called a *protoplast*. When protoplasts are exposed to almost naked DNA from phage T2, complete and typical T2 progeny phage are later released by lysis.[4] This result strongly suggests that it is the phage DNA which contains all the genetic information for the production of progeny phage. By various methods (treatment with phenol or $CaCl_2$), it is possible to remove all the protein coat from phage, leaving naked phage DNA. When protoplasts of *E. coli* are treated with naked, single-stranded DNA of phage $\phi X174$, typical $\phi X174$ progeny are produced, complete with the protein envelope characteristic of this phage.[5] (Note that there are only about 5,000 deoxyribotides per $\phi X174$ particle.) Accordingly, the *genetic material in DNA-containing phage is solely DNA.*

Following the tail-first attachment of a phage to a host cell, the course of events leading to lysis can be summarized as follows (Figure 42–2). All the DNA and a small amount of protein are injected into the host, possibly assisted by the contraction of the spiral sheath protein. Then follows an *eclipse period* during which no infective phage can be demonstrated in the recently infected bacterium (Figure 42–2, B–D), even if this is artificially lysed. In this period, the infected cell is said to carry *vegetative phage.* During the eclipse period the phage DNA is replicated to produce a pool of DNA units. From time to time, this pool of DNA is sampled and a fraction of it undergoes con-

densation into phage genomes which are surrounded by a new skin (head and tail), formed from a cycle of protein synthesis and organization (Figure 42–2D). The production of the first infective phage signals the end of the eclipse phase (Figure 42–2E). (If bacteria are prematurely lysed toward the end of the eclipse phase, one can find empty phage heads in the lysates.) About 20–40 minutes after infection, the bacteria produce *endolysins* which lyse the cell wall and liberate infective phage into the medium.

This completes the *lytic cycle* of a bacteriophage. This is the only cycle possible for virulent phages such as those of the T series attacking *E. coli*. This is also one of the two cycles possible for temperate phage, which has the other alternative upon entering a bacterium of establishing a relationship with the bacterial chromosome as a prophage and making the bacterium lysogenic. Of course, occasionally, the prophage dissociates from the chromosome, becoming vegetative phage whose replication produces infective phage released at lysis.

Methods for detecting the presence and amount of virulent phage are based upon the capacity of the phage to lyse sensitive bacteria grown either in liquid or solid medium. In the former medium, the assay is made by determining the time required for complete lysis of a liquid culture of sensitive bacteria; this is denoted by the clearing of the originally turbid culture. In the latter medium, the surface of an agar-containing plate is heavily seeded with sensitive bacteria whose clones grow together to form a continuous and somewhat opaque lawn. If a few virulent

[4] As shown by J. Spizizen and by D. Fraser, H. Mahler, A. Shug, and C. Thomas, Jr.
[5] By G. G. Guthrie and R. L. Sinsheimer.

FIGURE 42–2. (*opposite*). *Electron micrographs of growth of T2 virus inside the* E. coli *host cell. A. Bacillus before infection. B. Four minutes after infection. C. Ten minutes after infection. The thin section photographed includes the protein coat of T2 which can be seen attached to the bacterial surface. D. Twelve minutes after infection. New virus particles are starting to condense. E. Thirty minutes after infection. More than 50 T2 particles are completely formed and the host is about ready to lyse. (Courtesy of E. Kellenberger. Reprinted from the Scientific* American, 204:100, 1961.)

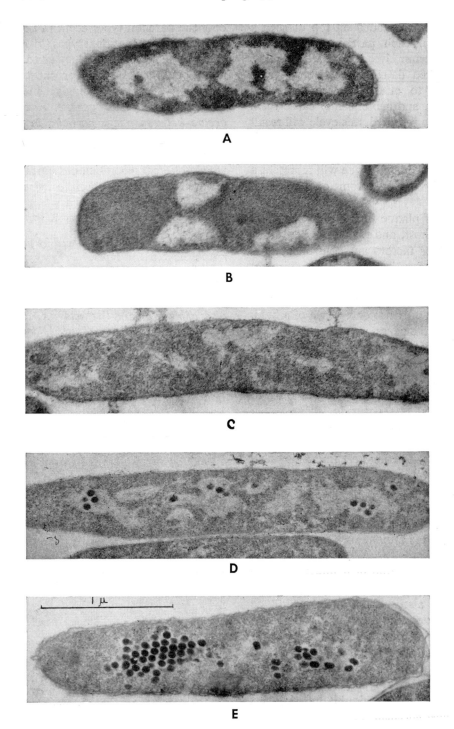

phage particles are added on top of such a *bacterial lawn*, each particle will enter a different bacterium, lyse it, and release up to several hundred daughter particles. These will proceed to attack bacteria near the original burst, and subsequently cause them to lyse. When repeated, this cycle will result in a progressively increasing zone of lysis which appears as a *clearing* or *plaque* in the bacterial lawn. Each plaque will represent a phage colony derived from one ancestral particle.

The type of plaque formed depends upon the medium, host, and phage. When, however, all other factors are controlled, it is found that genetically different virulent phages may produce characteristically different plaques. Differences in plaques may involve size, the presence or absence of a halo, the nature of the edges, and color differences on colored agar. One can, therefore, study the inheritance of phage mutants affecting plaque type. Genetically different phages also differ in the hosts which they are able to infect, and mutants occur in phage which change the range of hosts which may be attacked. Accordingly, the inheritance of phage mutants affecting host range may also be studied. What kinds of results are obtained when both types of mutants are involved simultaneously?

It is possible to obtain a strain of virulent T phage which is mutant both for *host range*, *h*, and *plaque type*, *r*. When sensitive bacteria are singly infected, the mutation rates to the wild-type alleles (h^+ or r^+) can be determined. It is also possible, using wild-type phages, to determine the mutation rates to the two kinds of mutant alleles. The sensitive bacterial strain also may be exposed to a high concentration of a mixture of the doubly mutant (*h r*) and wild-type ($h^+ r^+$) phages, as a result of which some doubly infected cells occur that carry both phage types. When the daughter phages from such exposures are harvested and tested, it is found that not

only the parental types occur (*h r* and $h^+ r^+$) but that recombinational types ($h^+ r$ and $h r^+$) occur in such high frequency as to exclude a mutational explanation for most of them (Figure 42–3). Accordingly, such experiments [6] prove that *genetic recombination occurs between phage particles in a multiply infected cell.* Using a variety of mutants, and on the basis of the relative frequencies with which different recombinants appear in phage released from multiply infected cells (this

[6] Following the work of M. Delbrück and W. T. Bailey, and of A. D. Hershey and R. Rotman.

FIGURE 42–3. *Plaques produced by parental and recombinant phage types. Progeny phage of a cross between* h r$^+$ *and* h$^+$ r *were tested on a mixture of suitable indicator bacteria. The small clear and the large turbid plaques are made by the parental types of phage progeny (*h r$^+$ *and* h$^+$ r, *respectively). The large clear and the small turbid plaques are produced by the recombinant types of progeny (*h r *and* h$^+$ r$^+$, *respectively). (Courtesy of A. D. Hershey.)*

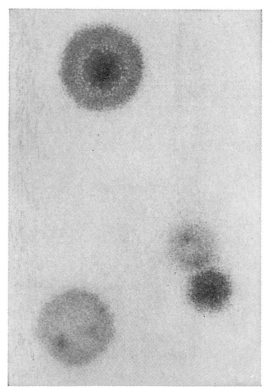

procedure being the equivalent of studying the results of "crossing" genetically different virulent phages), it is possible to construct a genetic map of phage in which the mutant loci are arranged in linear order.

Plaque mutant *r* is rapidly lysing and produces a larger plaque with sharper margins than is produced by the wild-type allele r^+. Mixed infections with *r* and r^+ phages usually yield progeny phages that produce plaques of one or the other type. However, two per cent of the plaques observed are mottled, that is, are plaques which appear partly r and partly r^+. When the phages in *mottled plaques* are tested, both (and only) r and r^+ types are found. Accordingly, such mottled plaques cannot be explained as being derived from single haploid recombinant progeny. These mottled plaques can be shown not to be due to some action by clumps of phage particles. Finally, such plaques cannot be explained as being due to mutations in unstable *r* mutants, for such unstable *r* phages are known to produce sectored, rather than mottled, plaques, whose phage contents when tested either yield sectored plaques again or r plaques, but none of r^+ type. From these results and others, it is proved [7] that the two per cent of phage that produce mottled plaques are heterozygotes for a short region including the *r* locus. It is also found that such heterozygotes are recombinant for genetic markers on opposite sides of the short heterozygotic region.[8] This suggests that, in phage, the processes leading to heterozygosis are the same as those leading to recombination.

One of the ways that heterozygosis and genetic recombination in phage can be visualized to occur is as follows. In a mixed infection, the DNA's of different vegetative phage particles repeatedly pair and unpair until the host lyses. It is during these "matings" that replication of new vegetative phage occurs. Suppose replication proceeds by a copy-

choice mechanism, and the two mating strands are genetically different at two closely linked points. If new phage DNA was formed by using the DNA of only one vegetative phage as template, the progeny phage receiving this would, of course, be nonrecombinant. If, however, as diagrammed in Figure 42–4, one vegetative phage is used as a template to make a partial replica that extends through one marked locus (a^+) and the other mate is used as a template to make a partial replica that extends through the other marked locus (b^+), synthesis may continue so that both partial replicas contain the short segment between the markers. A progeny phage which receives such overlapping partial replicas would be recombinant for the markers we are following and diploid for the segment between them. It is possible that the ends of the partial replicas may join to produce a single strand with a tandem duplication. Had the parent phages differed in the genic alternatives (x_1 vs. x_2) present in the segment which became diploid, the recombinant phage would also be partially heterozygous. Of course, should partial replicas overlap in some other region, the progeny phage containing the overlap would not be recombinant for the markers we have been following, and recombination would be identified only if this new region had been suitably marked genetically. It is known that a single phage particle can be heterozygous for several loci, provided these are located far enough apart. In fact, it is unlikely, contrary to the possibility already mentioned, that any phage is completely haploid. Considered in this way, phage recombination is a consequence of the occurrence of copy-choice in the formation of partial DNA replicas. This explanation receives support [9] from the fact that the observed frequency of heterozygotes is great enough to explain the observed frequency of recombination.

The preceding explanation of the mecha-

[7] A. D. Hershey and M. Chase (1951).
[8] As indicated by C. Levinthal.
[9] From work of C. Levinthal.

FIGURE 42–4.   *The hypothesized synthesis of over-lapping partial replicas.   The phage cross is* $a^+(x_1)b^- \times a^-(x_2)b^+$.

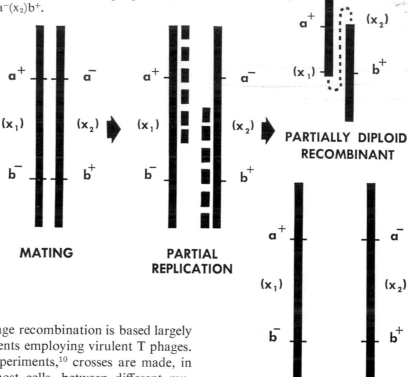

MATING

PARTIAL
REPLICATION

PARTIALLY DIPLOID
RECOMBINANT

PARENTAL

nism of phage recombination is based largely on experiments employing virulent T phages. In other experiments,[10] crosses are made, in unlabeled host cells, between different mutants of the temperate phage, lambda, of which one is unlabeled and the other is labeled with the isotopes C^{13} and N^{15}. Density-gradient ultracentrifugation is then used to determine the distribution of labeled parental DNA among both parental and recombinant genotypes.   It is found, from this and other experiments, that discrete amounts of the original parental DNA appear in the recombinant phages.   The simplest model accounting for the results is that recombinants are formed following breaks in the parental DNA strands.   Such results do not support, but do not exclude, the usual form of the hypothesis of phage recombination by a copy-choice mechanism, according to which the recombinant phage DNA should be made of entirely new, unlabeled, material.

[10] M. Meselson and J. J. Weigle (1961), and G. Kellenberger, M. L. Zichichi, and J. J. Weigle (1961).

A. D. HERSHEY, *about 1960.*

SUMMARY AND CONCLUSIONS

T-even phages are virulent in *E. coli*. Their morphology and lytic cycle are discussed, their genetic material identified chemically as DNA. Following multiple infection with phages carrying different genetic markers, genetic recombinants are found among the progeny.

From the results of such phage crosses a recombination map can be constructed in which the genes are arranged linearly. Recombinant phages are often also diploid for a short region between the recombinant markers. Both phage recombination and partial diploidy may sometimes be the consequence of a copy-choice mechanism of DNA replication during which there has been a switching of the templates utilized in the making of partial replicas. Sometimes, if not always, phage recombination involves parental strands which have broken.

REFERENCES

Brenner, S., Streisinger, G., Horne, R. W., Champe, S. P., Barnett, L., Benzer, S., and Rees, M. W., "Structural Components of Bacteriophage," J. Mol. Biol., 1:281–282, 1959.

Hershey, A. D., and Chase, M., "Genetic Recombination and Heterozygosis in Bacteriophage," Cold Spr. Harb. Sympos. Quant. Biol., 16:471–479, 1951; reprinted in *Papers on Bacterial Viruses*, Stent, G. S. (Ed.), Boston, Little, Brown, 1960, pp. 179–192.

Hershey, A. D., and Chase, M., "Independent Functions of Viral Protein and Nucleic Acid in Growth of Bacteriophage," J. Gen. Physiol., 36:39–54, 1952; reprinted in *Papers on Bacterial Viruses*, Stent, G. S. (Ed.), Boston, Little, Brown, 1960, pp. 87–104.

Kellenberger, G., Zichichi, M. L., and Weigle, J. J., "Exchange of DNA in the Recombination of Bacteriophage λ," Proc. Nat. Acad. Sci., U.S, 47:869–878, 1961.

Krakow, J. S., Kammen, H. O., and Canellakis, E. S., "The Incorporation of Ribonucleotides into Terminal Positions of Deoxyribonucleic Acid," Biochim. et Biophys. Acta, 53:52–64, 1961.

Meselson, M., and Weigle, J. J., "Chromosome Breakage Accompanying Genetic Recombination in Bacteriophage," Proc. Nat. Acad. Sci., U.S., 47:857–868, 1961.

QUESTIONS FOR DISCUSSION

42.1. Is the hole in the tail of T-even phages large enough for the passage of one or of two double helices of DNA? Explain. In what respect does your answer bear on the manner of entry of phage DNA into a bacterial host?

42.2. What are the advantages of studying phages using bacteria growing on solid, rather than in liquid, culture medium?

42.3. Do you think it would be feasible to study the genetic basis for different morphological or for different protein components of a phage? Explain.

42.4. If a phage is virulent in one strain of bacteria and not in another, is it temperate for the latter? Explain.

42.5. What is meant by a phage cross? Describe how you would know that you made one.

42.6. Are the genes which show recombination always diploid in a recombinant phage?

42.7. Does the fact that complete progeny phages are liberated after naked DNA from ϕX174 infects a protoplast mean that all the information for making ϕX174 DNA and ϕX174 protein is contained in the phage's DNA? Explain.

42.8. Are the hypotheses of phage recombination by breakage and by copy-choice mutually exclusive? Explain.

Chapter 43

VIRUSES: RECOMBINATION
IN BACTERIOPHAGE (II)

ALTHOUGH most of the work discussed in the last Chapter utilized virulent phages, the concluding portion mentioned that genetic recombination also occurs between temperate phages. It was mentioned specifically that multiple infection of sensitive cells by different mutants of lambda is followed by the occurrence of genetically recombinant phages among the progeny. From the frequencies of such recombinants it is possible to arrange the mutants in a single linear linkage map, just as was stated can be done for different mutants in the virulent T phages.

The difference between a virulent and a temperate phage lies in the capacity which the latter has to lysogenize its host. Is lysogeny itself dependent upon the phage genotype? When temperate phages infect sensitive bacteria, the plaques produced have a turbid region in their center due to the growth there of bacteria which were lysogenized, not lysed. In such a temperate strain, mutants can occur whose capacity for lysogenization is decreased or lost (in the latter case the phage becomes a virulent one), and are detectable because they form less turbid or clear plaques, respectively. This proves that lysogenization is based upon a part of the phage genotype which is expressed in the phenotype of its host. Moreover, "matings," between phages carrying different lysogenization mutants and other markers, show that these lysogeny loci are a regular part of the phage genetic map.

390

While certain mutations affecting lysogeny seem to affect the stability of prophage in the course of bacterial multiplication, the most important ones seem to affect the very process by which phage is converted to prophage. Mutants of the latter type are called c (clearing) mutants and these occur in a cluster of loci located within the genetic map of the phage. In lambda, there are three groups of c mutants arranged linearly in segments called c_3, c_1, and c_2 (Figure 43–1). Mutants in the c_1 segment no longer have any measurable capacity to lysogenize, whereas those on either side (being in c_3 or c_2) have their ability for lysogenization reduced to about .1 to .01 of that of wild-type lambda.

It has been possible to isolate more than a dozen temperate phages in E. coli, of which some show ultraviolet and zygotic induction and others do not. All seven of the viruses which give rise to inducible prophages were found to be associated with the chromosome at different loci (Lp or ly), all of which are located in a linear order close to and on the same side of Gal (Figure 43–2). These phages are all different, in the respect that a host lysogenic for one of them is immune to subsequent infection by the same phage, but is not immune to subsequent infection by any of the others.

When multiple infections are made, to cross lambda with any one of the other six phages, some genetic recombinations are found in the progeny phage in each case. However, the markers capable of recombination differ, and this is dependent upon the type of phage with which lambda is crossed. This demonstrates that these six phages differ in the number of loci they contain which are identical or homologous to loci in lambda. The results of crossing lambda and phage $\phi 434$ are particularly instructive. $\phi 434$ proves to have a genotype that is completely homologous to that of lambda, with the exception of one region. That is, it is possible to make a "hybrid" phage that is

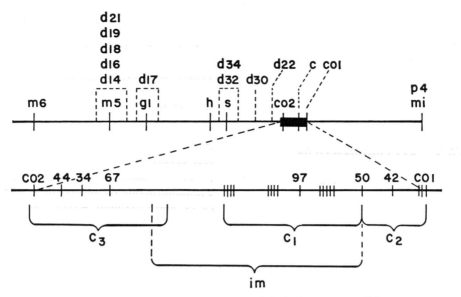

FIGURE 43–1. *Diagrammatic representation of the* <u>*linkage group of the temperate*</u> <u>*bacteriophage*</u> λ. *The upper diagram shows the linear arrangement of various markers for host range or plaque size or type. The* d *symbols refer to specific defective mutants. The* c *region is marked by a thicker line and is shown enlarged in the lower diagram. It is composed of three sub-regions,* c_3, c_1, c_2. Im *refers to the segment controlling immunity. (After F. Jacob and J. Monod.)*

completely lambda except for the c_1 region of the lambda genetic map. Such a hybrid 434 still behaves as 434 in the following respects. It still occupies only the 434 position in the *E. coli* map, and makes the cell immune only to subsequent infection by 434 or hybrid 434. We may conclude from this that the c_1 region of lambda is the only portion of the lambda genotype concerned with selecting its particular prophage site on the chromosome, and the only essential portion determining immunity to infection by homologous phage. Let us restate these results in terms of lambda prophage. Since the characteristics of prophage include its association with a particular chromosomal site and with the immunity of its host, it is concluded that both these traits of prophage are intimately associated only

with the c_1 portion of the phage genome. We shall also call c_1 the "prophage region" of other phage genomes.

Whereas different c_1 mutants of lambda can undergo recombination, there is no recombination between the c_1's of lambda and 434, indicating a genetic dissimilarity between them. It becomes clear that the presence of a given c_1 region inhibits the vegetative multiplication of superinfecting particles possessing the same c_1 regions. This immunity is found to be due to the occurrence of a repressor substance, in the cytoplasm, whose formation and specificity appear to be determined by the c_1 region.[1]

[1] The preceding discussion is based primarily upon work of F. Jacob and E. L. Wollman (1957), of A. D. Kaiser and F. Jacob (1957), and of F. Jacob and A. Campbell.

FIGURE 43–2. *Part of the* E. coli *linkage map showing the location of certain inducible prophages.*

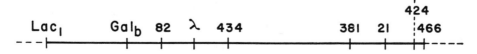

Prophage has another characteristic, namely, the capacity to produce infective phage. It should be noted that while the chromosomal locus and immunity properties of prophage are explicable on the basis of a small portion of the phage's total DNA content, the c_1 region, this does not necessarily mean that this region alone includes all the genetic information or specifications needed for prophage to become vegetative phage, and therefore infective phage.

The preceding discussion may suggest to you that not all of the genetic material present in a phage is essential for the existence of phage as an organism. This possibility should not be surprising, since we are already acquainted, in other organisms, with homozygous deficiencies (of euchromatic or heterochromatic regions) which still permit viability of the organism (even though such a change may be more or less adaptive). In these cases, then, there is genetic material present which is nonessential for the formation of the organism. Although we have seen that in order to have a phage organism at least the prophage loci in the c_1 region are essential, we do not have any way, at present, of determining how many additional loci are essential.

Let us assume, contrary to the expectation just mentioned, that all genes present in phage are essential for phage existence. If so, one would expect to find that progeny phage contain the same genetic material as the parent phage. Or, to put this expectation another way, the very DNA molecules present in the parental phage particle should be present in one or more progeny phage. This can be tested in the following way. The DNA of phage is labeled with P^{32}, by harvesting the phage that lyse bacteria growing in medium whose sole P source is P^{32}. The labeled phages are then permitted to infect unlabeled bacteria, and the total amount of label included in the harvested progeny is compared with the total amount present in the parent phage.

It is found [2] that only about 40% of the parentally labeled DNA is included in the progeny, that is, 60% of the specific DNA nucleotides (P atoms) present in the parents are not found in the offspring. Thus, 60% of the DNA of phage is nonconserved. There are several explanations possible for this. One possibility is that all or almost all of the genetic material of phage is essential but that replication and the formation of progeny phage is inefficient, so that not all the parental DNA is retained, 60% of it being replaced by unlabeled daughter DNA genetic material of exactly the same type. The presence of a mixture of labeled and unlabeled DNA in the same particle indicates the occurrence of genetic recombination (see p. 388). Even though the parental phage DNA is sometimes broken to produce genetic recombinant progeny, there is very clear evidence [3] that the DNA of phage T2 normally consists of a single unbroken molecule whose molecular weight is $130-160 \times 10^6$.

In discussing the advantages of bacteria as material for genetic studies (p. 330), it was noted that very large bacterial populations are readily manipulated experimentally. This makes it feasible to discover and study rare events of mutation and genetic recombination. Phage also has this particular advantage. Consider how this advantage may be put to use in the investigation of a particular kind of phage mutant,[4] whose study may reveal the characteristics of the fine structure of the genetic material.

We have already mentioned (on p. 387) that wild-type (r^+) T-even phages produce small, rough-edged plaques when plated on E. coli, whereas rapid lysis (r) mutants pro-

[2] By J. D. Watson and O. Maaløe, by C. Levinthal, and by others.
[3] From I. Rubenstein, C. A. Thomas, Jr., and A. D. Hershey (1961), and P. F. Davidson, D. Freifelder, R. Hede, and C. Levinthal (1961).
[4] The discussion following is based largely upon the work of S. Benzer (1955, 1957).

GENOTYPE	PLAQUES FORMED ON HOST STRAIN	
	B	K
rI or rIII Mutants	r	r
rII Mutants	r	None
r⁺	+	+

FIGURE 43–3. *Behavior of* r *mutants of T-even phages in the B and K strains of* E. coli.

duce large, sharp-edged plaques. When the *r* mutants are mapped they are found to occupy three distinct regions of the phage genetic map, rI, rII, and rIII. The *r* mutants in all three regions can be detected and harvested using *E. coli* strain B. However, the mutants in the rII region are unique in having an additional attribute, namely, that they cannot form plaques when their host is strain K of *E. coli* (which is lysogenic for lambda) although the rI and rIII mutants and *r*⁺ phages can do so (Figure 43–3). Thus, mutants in the rII region show a restriction in host range as compared with *r*⁺ or *r* mutants in other regions. We shall restrict our attention henceforth to the mutants of the rII group in phage T4.

The host range restriction of rII mutants is useful not only for their identification, but for the study of rates of mutation and of genetic recombination. After identifying a mutant as being in the rII region, its mutation rate to *r*⁺ can be determined readily by platings on strain K, since only *r*⁺ mutants will form plaques there. From a large number of rII mutants, those which were stable and had a low mutation frequency (sometimes as low as 1 per 10^8 phages) were selected for further study. Using high multiplicities of phage infection, the results with these showed that mutants in the rII region fall into one of two groups. If a bacterium is infected by one mutant from each of the two groups, both viruses can reproduce and lyse the cell. (In this case almost all the multiply infected K bacteria on a plate would lyse, clearing the entire plate in about half an hour.) This behavior can be explained by considering that the rII region is composed of two subregions, A and B. Each subregion in normal phage independently forms a phenotypic product, the products of both subregions being required to cause the r⁺ phenotype. So, a mutant defective only in the A subregion still makes proper B product, and vice versa. In a bacterium multiply infected with one phage mutant in A and another mutant in B,

FIGURE 43–4. *The occurrence or non-occurrence of complementation between different rII mutants.*

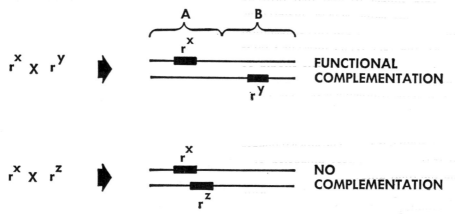

the two mutants can act phenotypically in a complementary manner, or show *complementation*, to produce the r+ phenotype (Figure 43–4).

On the other hand, if multiple infection occurs with two different mutants both located in subregion A (or B), they will not be capable of phenotypic cooperation to produce the r+ phenotype, since both phages produce defective or no A (or B) product. While the entire plate does not clear in about a half hour in this case, one may observe the occasional incidence of plaques in different regions of the plate. Sometimes the frequency of these plaques is no greater than one would expect to find due to the rate of spontaneous mutation of the two mutants. This would indicate the nonoccurrence of r+ genetic recombinants, which failed to appear either because the two mutants are located too close to each other on the genetic map and/or because both have a common nucleotide defect. Other times the frequency of plaques is so clearly larger than that expected from mutation that the excess can be attributed to recombination between the two A (or B) mutants which results in progeny phages whose rII region is normal (and produce the r+ phenotype) or is doubly mutant (and are undetected).

Two mutants in subregion A, *r1* and *r2*, may fail to show recombination with each other. However, one of these, say *r1*, shows recombination with mutant *r3*, while mutant *r2* does not. Such results can sometimes be shown to be due to the fact that mutant *r2* is deficient not only in its own locus but for all or part of *r1* and *r3* also. Accordingly, the mutant order must be *123* (or *321*) in such cases. Other mutants behave as point mutants, giving no evidence of deficiency. Of more than 1500 spontaneously occurring rII mutants typed, about 300 were different, that is, each was separable from all the others by recombination (Figure 43–5). Using overlapping deficiencies and mutants showing no

evidence of being deficiencies, it is possible to arrange all the *r* loci in the A and B subregions in a single linear sequence, the recombination rates between two mutants being constant in different tests. Thus, *even in its fine structure, the genetic recombination map of bacteriophage is linear.*

The great efficiency in detecting r+ mutants by the plating of rII mutants on strain K has already been implied by the statement that mutation rates as low as 1 in 10^8 can be detected. This method also has approximately the same efficiency for detecting recombinations. The smallest reproducible frequency of recombination, 0.02%, was found between the mutants *r240* and *r359*. Of numerous other mutants tested, all gave either no recombination or a higher percentage of recombination. Note that the methods used can detect recombination frequencies that are a hundred or even more times less frequent than 0.02%. Even so, none were found, as if 0.02% is close to the lower limit of recombination. To what use may we put this observation? Since the genetic material of phage T4 is DNA, a lower limit for recombination frequency may give us an idea to what degree DNA is finitely divisible for purposes of recombination. Can we translate genetic recombination distance into DNA nucleotide distance? Or, in other words, can we set any limits in terms of nucleotides to the size of the recon in phage T4?

In order to attempt to estimate the nucleotide scope of a recon we shall have to make the following primary assumptions: (1) the probability for genetic recombination is constant per molecular distance throughout the phage genetic map, and (2) phage DNA is present as a single copy in the form of a single double-stranded Watson-Crick helix. With reference to (1) it is further supposed that the genetic markers studied are representative of all loci present and that the total length of the genetic map is accurately estimated by the summation of a number of small distances. On these bases, then, the total genetic map of phage T4 can be calculated to be approximately 800 recombination units long, i.e., shows 800% recombination with respect to its total genetic content. (Recall that a recombination map based upon crossing over can be longer than 100 recombination [in this case, crossover] units.) With reference to the primary assumption (2) it may be recalled that there are about 400,000 nucleotides per phage, represented by a double helix of 200,000 linearly arranged nucleotides.

The fraction 800% recombinations/200,000 nucleotides equals 0.004%, and expresses the percentage of recombinations which occurs per linear nucleotide. On the reasonable assumption that recombination cannot take place within a nucleotide, there would be 199,999 points between nucleotides where exchange may occur if the phage chromosome is a rod, and 200,000 such points if the phage chromosome is a ring. Expressed in this particular way, we can say that if two r mutants each differ from their wild-type form by only a single nucleotide, and if the two nucleotides changed are adjacent in r^+, then recombinants (r^+ and double mutant) would be expected to occur among 0.004% of the progeny obtained by crossing the mutants.

Suppose that the lowest recombination frequency observed, 0.02%, is actually the minimal rate. This means that, on the average, only every fifth (.02/.004) internucleotide point is capable of undergoing recombination, so that the recon is estimated to be as small as five nucleotides in length. Because tests fail to give evidence that phage nucleotide sequence is interrupted by non-nucleotide material, it would seem reasonable that recombination could occur at any internucleotide position. Accordingly, in view of the fact that the observed value of 0.02% is a maximal value for the least amount of recombination, and in view of the uncertainties

which exist with regard to the length of the genetic map and the number of nucleotides in the phage genome, we can entertain *the working hypothesis that one recon equals one nucleotide*. [5] This is consistent with our expectation regarding the polarity of a recon (see p. 303). On this hypothesis, it should be clear that the term *allele* is properly restricted to the alternatives that occur for a particular recon. In this way we are describing *reconic alleles*, within which there can be no recombination or crossing over (see Chapter 22 and p. 290 for previous usage of the term *allele* in this sense).

Finally, let us consider the functional characteristics of the rII region. So long as we are considering the production of the r and r$^+$ phenotypes, the rII region has a single function. In this respect the whole region behaves as a single cistron. But the rII region is composed of two subregions, A and B, a mutant in one subregion being able to functionally complement a mutant in the other. Such complementation suggests that A and B are independent at this level of functioning, and therefore each may be considered to be a separate cistron having a different function. The whole rII region contains about 1000 linearly arranged nucleotides, each subregion containing hundreds of nucleotides. We do not know, but A and B may order the amino acid sequence in different polypeptide chains, both of which must be correctly specified in order to produce the r$^+$ phenotype. While the specification of a polypeptide chain is accepted as one kind of primary effect possible for a cistron, it should be noted again (refer to Chapter 32) that the primary effect of a cistron may not always be to specify a polypeptide. Substances other than polypeptides may be specified by the primary action of a cistron; these substances might conceivably be simpler than a polypeptide, for example single amino acids. In this

[5] Support for this view is found in work by D. R. Helinski and C. Yanofsky (1962).

FIGURE 43–5. *Genetic map of the rII region of phage T4. The breaks in the map indicate segments as defined by the ends of deletions. The order of the segments has been determined as shown. The order of mutants within any one segment has not been determined, but all give recombination with each other. The hollow circles and other filled-in symbols represent different types of phenotypic effects.* (Courtesy of S. Benzer and S. P. Champe, Proc. Nat. Acad. Sci., U.S., 47:1030–1031, 1961).

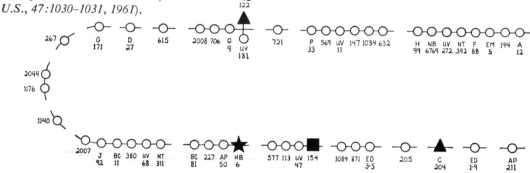

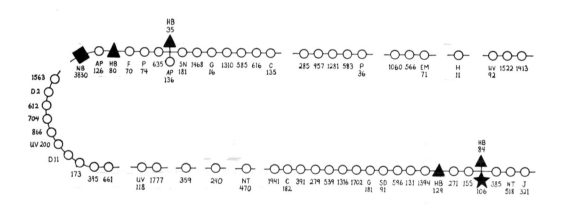

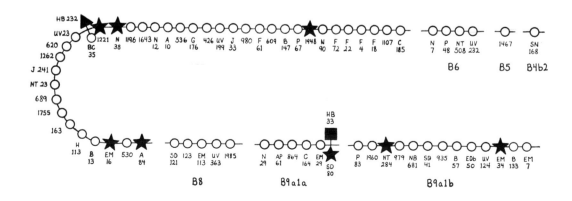

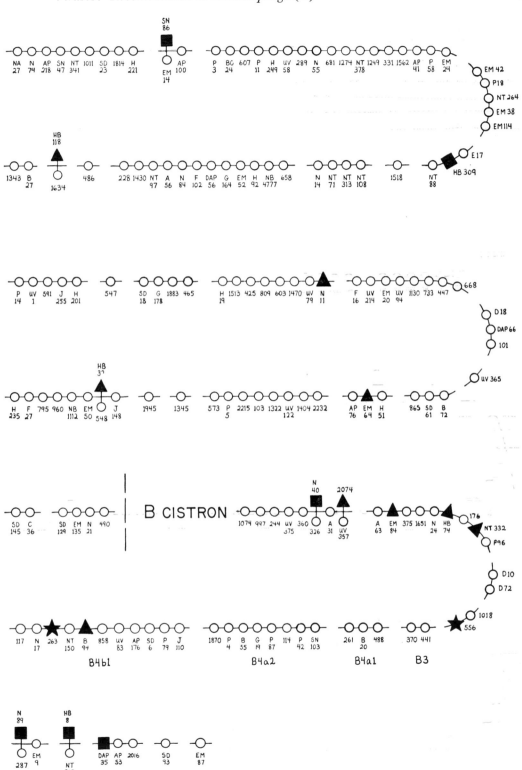

case we would also be correct to call a cistron the much shorter linear sequence of nucleotides required to specify a single amino acid. (Recall that it has been suggested on p. 370 that heterochromatin is composed of short cistrons that specify, not polypeptides, but a much simpler kind of chemical product.) It will be necessary, therefore, to realize that although a cistron is recognized as a linear sequence of nucleotides which produces a single primary phenotypic effect, the particular primary function under consideration will determine the complexity of the product and therefore the length of the cistron involved.

SEYMOUR BENZER, *in 1961.*

SUMMARY AND CONCLUSIONS

Genetic recombination can occur between temperate phages of different, but related, types, but not between their prophage regions. The prophage stage of a phage is (1) associated with a unique chromosomal site, (2) the cause of immunity, (3) essential for the subsequent production of infective phage. The first two properties of prophage are identified with the c_1 region of the phage genetic map. However, this region does not necessarily contain all the genetic material necessary for the production of complete infective phage. Not all of the parental phage DNA is conserved in subsequent phage progeny.

The genetic fine structure of the rII region of ϕT4 is revealed by studies of mutation, complementation, and genetic recombination. The data from this study and others suggest the hypothesis that one recon equals one nucleotide.

REFERENCES

Benzer, S., "Fine Structure of a Genetic Region in Bacteriophage," Proc. Nat. Acad. Sci., U.S., 41:344–354, 1955; reprinted in *Papers on Bacterial Viruses*, Stent, G. S. (Ed.), Boston, Little, Brown, 1960, pp. 209–219.

Benzer, S., "The Elementary Units of Heredity," pp. 70–93 in *A Symposium on the Chemical Basis of Heredity*, McElroy, W. D., and Glass, B. (Eds.), Baltimore, Johns Hopkins Press, 1957.

Benzer, S., "On the Topography of the Genetic Fine Structure," Proc. Nat. Acad. Sci., U.S., 47:403–415, 1961.

Benzer, S., "The Fine Structure of the Gene," Scient. Amer., 206 (No. 1):70–84, 1962.

Davidson, P. F., Freifelder, D., Hede, R., and Levinthal, C., "The Structural Unity of the DNA of T2 Bacteriophage," Proc. Nat. Acad. Sci., U.S., 47:1123–1129, 1961.

Helinski, D. R., and Yanofsky, C., "Correspondence between Genetic Data and the Position of Amino Acid Alteration in a Protein," Proc. Nat. Acad. Sci., U.S., 48:173–183, 1962.

Jacob, F., and Monod, J., "Genetic Regulatory Mechanisms in the Synthesis of Proteins," J. Mol. Biol., 3:318–356, 1961.

Jacob, F., and Wollman, E. L., "Genetic Aspects of Lysogeny," pp. 468–500 in *A Symposium on the Chemical Basis of Heredity*, McElroy, W. D., and Glass, B. (Eds.), Baltimore, Johns Hopkins Press, 1957.

Jacob, F., and Wollman, E. L., "Viruses and Genes," Scient. Amer., 204 (No. 6):92–107, 1961.

Kaiser, A. D., and Jacob, F., "Recombination Between Related Temperate Bacteriophages and the Genetic Control of Immunity and Prophage Localization," Virology, 4:509–521, 1957; reprinted in *Papers on Bacterial Viruses*, Stent, G. S. (Ed.), Boston, Little, Brown, 1960, pp. 353–365

Rubenstein, I., Thomas, C. A., Jr., and Hershey, A. D., "The Molecular Weights of 2T Bacteriophage DNA and its First and Second Breakage Products," Proc. Nat. Acad. Sci., U.S., 47:1113–1122, 1961.

Watson, J. D., and Maaløe, O., "Nucleic Acid Transfer from Parental to Progeny Bacteriophage," Biochim. et Biophys. Acta, 10:432–442, 1953; reprinted in *Papers on Bacterial Viruses*, Stent, G. S. (Ed.), Boston, Little, Brown, 1960, pp. 105–115.

See last portion of Supplement V.

QUESTIONS FOR DISCUSSION

43.1. In what respects is $\phi\lambda$ similar to and different from an F particle?

43.2. A temperate phage is known which is capable of transducing any known chromosomal marker in *E. coli*. Would you expect to be able to locate the chromosomal site for its prophage? Explain.

43.3. Does the finding that a single phage particle may transduce a bacterial fragment carrying not only a bacterial marker but two linked prophages have any bearing upon the essentiality of the entire phage genome for infection and/or the production of phage progeny? Explain.

43.4. How can you distinguish a mutant in the rII region from one in the rI or rIII region?

43.5. Describe how the trans test is used to show functional complementation between two mutants in phage.

43.6. What would you expect to be the near-maximum number of nucleotides transduceable by a phage which is still capable of phage activity? On what is your opinion based?

43.7. How would the estimated nucleotide length of a recon be affected if 80% of phage DNA was actually conserved? If the average protein-specifying cistron was 2000 nucleotides long, how many different proteins could be specified by T4? by ϕX174?

43.8. What do you consider to be the most remarkable feature of ϕX174?

43.9. Mutants which show functional complementation in the *pan-2* region of *Neurospora* can be arranged in the same linear order by complementation and by genetic recombination. Is it necessarily true that both maps also will be identical for other regions? Explain.

43.10. What is a cistron? How is your answer related to its length in nucleotides?

43.11. What have you learned in the present Chapter regarding the chemical nature of different genetic units?

VIRUSES: BACTERIAL, ANIMAL, AND PLANT

IN DISCUSSING the genetics of the rII region of the T4 phage genetic map, it was mentioned (p. 394) that the more than 1500 spontaneously occurring mutants tested could be explained as involving changes in one or more of about 300 different sites in the rII region. This means that some sites of mutation must have been involved more than once. In fact, the number of times different sites were involved in mutation is quite variable. In terms of DNA this must mean that certain nucleotides, singly or in groups, are much more likely to undergo spontaneous mutation than others, there being, so to speak, *mutational "hot spots"* within the rII region.

Since recombination studies permit the analysis of the rII region at the level of the nucleotide, the DNA of T4 may serve as material for studies on the nature of mutation which may lead to a clearer definition of mutation in chemical terms. It should be noted at this point that even-number T phages (T2, T4, T6) have 5-hydroxymethyl cytosine (Figure 33–2, and p. 296) instead of cytosine in their DNA. In all other respects, the DNA is typical. It was already noted, on page 325, that 5-bromo uracil (Figure 35–5) can substitute for thymine, and only thymine, in the synthesis of DNA *in vitro*. What would be the mutational consequence of incorporating 5-bromo uracil into T4 DNA? [1]

[1] The discussion following is based largely upon the work of S. Benzer and E. Freese (1958) and subsequent work by E. Freese and coworkers.

Addition of 5-bromo uracil to the normal culture medium in which T4-infected cells are growing would not necessarily result in the incorporation of this base analog in T4 DNA, since thymine could be synthesized by the bacterium and it, rather than the analog, might be utilized preferentially or exclusively in the synthesis of phage DNA. In order to assure that no thymine is synthesized or available as raw material for DNA synthesis, sulfanilamide is added to the culture medium. This drug, which by itself does not appreciably increase the mutation rate, inhibits nearly all syntheses leading to the addition of methyl or hydroxymethyl groups to compounds. Accordingly, the medium is supplemented with a variety of essential chemical substances already containing methyl and hydroxymethyl groups but not with the deoxyribotides of thymine or of 5-hydroxymethyl cytosine. (The latter deoxyribotide is omitted to prevent its possible conversion to an analog of thymine which might be incorporated in preference to the 5-bromo uracil.) In this way, the bacterium can properly function as a phage host, but cannot, for example, produce thymine (5-methyl uracil) by methylating the uracil which is present in abundance in the cytoplasm and its RNA. Under these conditions, then, 5-bromo uracil will be used as a substitute for thymine in DNA synthesis. It should be noted, however, that the base analog may also be falsely incorporated in place of 5-hydroxymethyl cytosine, or act in other ways, in producing a mutagenic effect.

Under these experimental conditions, it is found that 5-bromo uracil is highly mutagenic in the rII region. A comparison of 5-bromo uracil-induced and spontaneously occurring rII mutants reveals that the induced mutants also occur in clusters on the genetic map, but that the hot spots are in different positions. Moreover, contrary to the spontaneous mutants, very few of those induced are of gross (internucleotide) type, and almost all are subsequently capable of reverse mutation to, or near, the r⁺ phenotype.

Although the mutational spectra (see p. 200) for 5-bromo uracil, for other chemical mutagens, and for spontaneous mutants are all different at the nucleotide level, we cannot specify, with any certainty, the exact chemical basis for the induced mutations. This is so because there are a number of possible metabolic paths through which the mutagen may be producing its effect. It is clear that the chemical basis for mutagenic action is best studied when the pathway between mutagen and gene is the shortest possible.[2] In this connection, just as it is preferable to expose sperm rather than any other cell of that organism to a chemical mutagen, clearly it is more desirable to treat phage or transforming DNA directly, rather than indirectly, via its host.

What is the *molecular basis of mutation*? Since the genetic material is a linear array of nucleotides, consider how mutation might involve single whole nucleotides. Loss or gain of a single whole nucleotide might be expected to result from breaking the nucleotide string backbone at two or more places, followed by deletion of a whole nucleotide or its insertion in a new position. This might occur especially frequently after exposure to a physical mutagen which ionizes, and would involve, at least occasionally, only the already formed "old" gene material. However, single whole nucleotide change may also be produced by chemical mutagens without involving breakage. It has been suggested[3] that chemical mutagens like the acridines insert themselves between the nucleotides of a chain which is subsequently to replicate. A molecule of a chemical mutagen, intercalated this way between bases that are linear neighbors, could spread the chain 3.4A, and result in the addition of an entire nucleotide at this position to the complementary chain

made next. The possibility also exists that an unbound nucleotide or other normal substance might intercalate with similar results. This mechanism would involve changes in the new genes formed.

Before discussing the mechanisms possible for intra-nucleotide changes, consider what is known about the chemical behavior and mutagenicity of certain chemicals. Free T4 phage is known to be permeable to certain small molecules, such as nitrous acid (HNO_2) and hydroxylamine (NH_2OH), both of which are mutagenic. Nitrous acid removes NH_2 from, or deaminates, purines and pyrimidines. Thus, when cytosine is deaminated it is converted to uracil and adenine is converted to hypoxanthine (the structural formulae for these compounds are shown in Figure 35–5), while deaminated guanine becomes xanthine. Hydroxylamine acts in the reverse manner from nitrous acid, by adding an amino group, for example, to the 2—C atom of cytosine, forming a molecule that may function like thymine. Such chemicals and others probably act as mutagens by producing intranucleotide changes.

Such mutagens may ultimately cause one purine to be substituted by another purine (A ↔ G) or one pyrimidine for another (T ↔ C). Replacement by another base of the same kind (purine or pyrimidine) can be called *transition*, while replacement of a purine by a pyrimidine or the reverse (for example, A ↔ C or T ↔ G) can be called *transversion*.[4] Both transitions and transversions would act at the subnucleotide level.

What sequence of events may be involved in transition and transversion? A particular base pair T : A exposed to a mutagen may become T : A' (see Figure 44–1). Suppose, at the time of chain separation A' specifies C (instead of T), and at the next division C acts normally to specify G. The net result is that the original A strand eventually produces a granddaughter strand carrying G, so that

[2] As noted by I. H. Herskowitz (1955).
[3] By L. S. Lerman (1961).
[4] Following the terminology of E. Freese.

FIGURE 44–1.   *One postulated sequence of events leading to transition or transversion.*

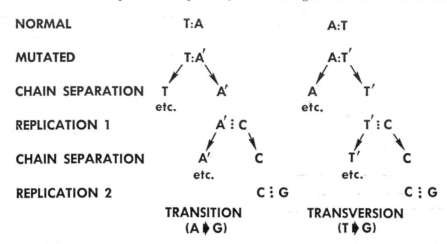

this is a transition. Or, given the original pair G ⋮ C, a mutagen may produce C′ which specifies A (instead of G), which in turn specifies T. So the net change from C to T also is a transition. If A ⋮ T becomes A ⋮ T′, after which T′ specifies C, and C specifies G, the net result is that T has been replaced by G, which is a transversion. Such transitions and transversions would be expected to be frequent following treatment with certain chemical mutagens. Penetrating radiations, especially ionizing ones, would be expected to be less selective than chemical mutagens in the nucleotides attacked this way. Note, in the examples mentioned, that the transitions and transversions were initiated by a change in the old gene. A second mechanism can be hypothesized in which the initial change leading to transition or transversion occurs in a base which is subsequently used in constructing a complementary DNA chain.

A third possible mechanism for intranucleotide change has been suggested [5] in which the members of a base pair undergo *rotational substitution* by breaking their bonds to sugar, rotating 180°, and rejoining. Thus, following rotational substitution, which may

be a frequent consequence of ion action, C ⋮ G would become G ⋮ C, the resultant double transversion being mutant.

A fourth possible mechanism for intranucleotide change involves the fact that the bases in DNA may change their configurations without changing their chemical content, that is, they can exist in several tautomeric forms. In the double helix configuration of DNA, the most likely tautomers of each base were assumed to obtain. Tautomers of the bases can differ in the exact positions where the hydrogen atoms are attached, so that the pairing characteristics are changed. Thus, for example, while the usual tautomer of adenine pairs with thymine, one of its less common tautomers could pair with cytosine (Figure 44–2). In this way an incorrect complement may be specified, leading to a transition or transversion.[6] Such *tautomeric shifts*, causing changes in the new gene code, may play an important role in spontaneous mutation.

You will agree that there would be no difficulty in identifying as mutant the completed transition or transversion or whole

[5] By H. J. Muller, E. Carlson, and A. Schalet (1961).

[6] See reference on p. 318 (J. D. Watson and F. H. C. Crick, 1953c).

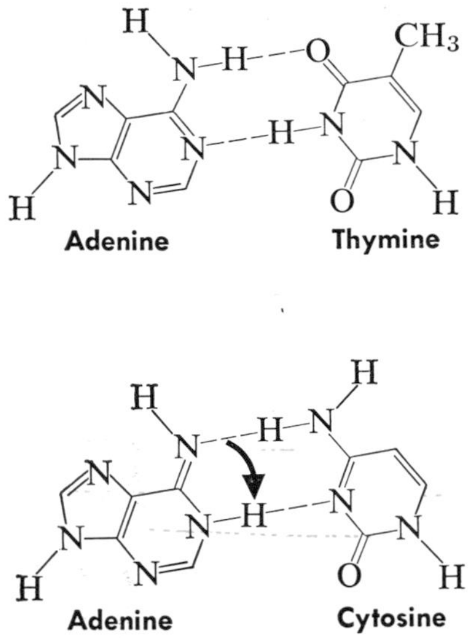

FIGURE 44–2. *Tautomeric shift of adenine which could change its complementary base from thymine to cytosine. Upper diagram shows adenine before, and lower diagram after, undergoing a tautomeric shift of one of its hydrogen atoms. (After* **J. D. Watson** *and* **F. H. C. Crick.***)*

nucleotide change. But at what point in a series of changes should one consider that a mutation has been first produced? The mutation can be said to be accomplished when, as in one of the mechanisms discussed, A is permanently changed to A'. You might object to this answer on the basis that A' may never be reproduced in a future replication. But, the product of a novel change need not be replicated or transmitted in order to be considered mutant. Such a novel product need only be more or less permanent in order to qualify in this respect. A' may be demonstrated to be more or less permanently different from A in five ways (as identified by five different operational procedures). First, A' may have a different chemical composition; second, it may have a different rate of change to a new chemical form; third, it may not specify T at all, or to the same extent as A did; fourth, it may change the phenotypic effect of the cistron in which it is located;

fifth, it may affect the recombination rate of itself or another recon. Operationally, then, it would seem desirable to *classify as a mutation any one or a combination of novel identifiable changes in the chemical, mutational, replicative, phenotypical, or recombinational properties of one or more nucleotides.* This new operational definition of mutation includes all aspects of the older one (a novel qualitative or quantitative change in the genetic material). Of course, at the present time, certain of the changes listed, which would identify a mutant, cannot be detected in specific individual nucleotides for technical reasons. Even so, it would seem fruitful to indicate even now all the possible operational ways we may be able to identify a mutant. It is also clear, from the preceding, that the smallest part of the genetic material whose change is mutant is presumably smaller than a nucleotide (and therefore smaller than a recon). Subnucleotide changes could involve the methyl, hydroxymethyl, or other groups or atoms in the base portion, as well as changes in the sugar or the phosphate portions of a nucleotide. Subnucleotide components should not be considered to be the smallest *units* of the genetic material capable of mutation, since the nucleotide is the smallest meaningful chemical unit of the genetic material. It is probably more fruitful to speak of *subnucleotide parts as furnishing a number of mutational sites within the nucleotide.*

Until now, our discussion of viruses has been restricted almost completely to DNA-containing phages. (Genetic recombination also occurs in the more complex *vaccinia virus*, that causes smallpox, whose DNA is probably single-stranded in the infective stage.) There is another group of viruses which contains no DNA but is entirely, or mainly, ribonucleoprotein in content. These viruses include many of the smaller animal viruses (causing poliomyelitis, influenza, and encephalitis, for example), at least one bacteriophage,[7] and many viruses attacking plants (notably including tobacco mosaic virus and turnip yellow mosaic virus).

Before considering the genetics of RNA viruses, it will be desirable to describe briefly some features regarding their assay and life cycle. Although these comments will pertain specifically to the *influenza virus*, many of them apply also to other animal and, to some extent, some plant viruses. Because influenza virus does not usually lyse the cell it infects, it cannot be assayed, like phage, by its production of plaques. In the case of this virus, and others that produce no clear host-lethal effect, the technique of *limit dilution*, to be described, must be used for their detection. This detection is facilitated, in the case of influenza, by the use of a viral strain which is capable of growing in the cells that line the fluid-containing cavities of the chick embryo. The virus produces a pathogenic effect in these cells. Accordingly, a sample to be assayed for influenza virus is sufficiently diluted, and aliquots inoculated into a series of eggs. Two or so days later, the eggs are examined for pathogenic effect, to determine the fraction which contain virus. If near-limit dilutions are used, so that the probability is low that an aliquot contains a single virus particle, one can estimate the virus content of the entire sample. Under these conditions, the progeny virus particles in a given egg comprise a clone.

The mammalian cell, which usually serves as host for the influenza virus, typically possesses a flexible shape and has an ambiguous cell membrane surrounded by a *mucoid coat*. This coat acts as a *virus receptor* since it serves as a substrate for an enzyme located on the virus surface. The virus has an outer protein coat, containing the mucin-reacting enzyme, and an inner core of RNA. (The virus cannot attach to the cell if the mucoid coat is removed by special treatment.) After attachment, the particle enters the cell, per-

[7] See reference on p. 305.

haps by being engulfed via the cell's normal pseudopodial activity. Once inside the cell, the particle enters an eclipse phase and multiplies vegetatively, during which period the cell's RNA content increases. Some hours after infection intact viral particles are liberated gradually, not in large spaced clusters.

FIGURE 44–3. *Electron micrographs of tobacco mosaic virus (TMV) showing its general configuration (top) and its hollow core (middle). The bottom photo shows a particle whose protein has been partially removed by treatment with detergent, leaving a thinner strand of RNA. (Courtesy of R. G. Hart.)*

The evidence suggests that the viral coat, which contains some material made before infection (by the host alone) and some made after (by host and virus together), is added around the RNA as this emerges from the host cell.

Two genetically different, haploid strains of influenza virus are available, SWE (having markers *a c*) and MEL (having markers *A C*). It is possible to multiply infect a chick's egg membranes with mixtures of the two strains. Such mixed infections give progeny particles which, when tested, yield pure clones, not only of the parental genotypes, but also of stable recombinant types (*A c* or *a C*). Since other explanations can be excluded, the results prove that *genetic recombination occurs also between RNA-containing viruses.*[8]

No evidence has been obtained for the occurrence of genetic recombination among viruses attacking plants. In the case of the *tobacco mosaic virus (TMV)*, infection is brought about experimentally by rubbing a sample of virus on the leaf surface. Even when a high concentration of virus is used, only a small fraction of the virus particles find and penetrate susceptible cells and give rise to a demonstrable lesion. For this reason, it is doubtful that one can multiply infect a tobacco cell, so that experiments that test for genetic recombination probably fail to find it because of the lack of mixed infections.

The TMV particle is a cylinder 3000 A long and about 160 A in diameter (Figure 44–3A). It has a molecular weight of about 40×10^6, of which 38×10^6 is protein and 2×10^6 is RNA.[9] The outer dimensions of TMV are

due to the helical aggregation of about 2200 identical protein subunits; each subunit has a molecular weight of about 18,000 and contains 158 amino acids in a single polypeptide chain (Figure 44–4). In cross section, the TMV particle is seen to have a hollow core about 40 A in diameter (Figure 44–3B), so the protein subunit adds about 60 A to the radius. The RNA in a particle (Figure 44–3C) is typically a single, unbranched strand, consisting of some 6400 nucleotides behaving as a single molecule, which is threaded through the protein subunits at a radius of 40 A. Accordingly, the RNA is normally covered externally by about 40 A of protein subunit. Since the protein subunits are arranged in a gently pitched helix (49 subunits per three turns), the RNA forms a helix of the same pitch.

When TMV is treated with phenol, the protein of the virus is destroyed, leaving the single RNA molecule intact. When tobacco is exposed to such RNA molecules, from which protein is removed, some infection occurs (the frequency is about 500 times less than that obtained using an equal number of whole virus particles), and typical TMV progeny (complete with TMV protein coats) are produced. Repeated phenol treatments do not decrease the infectivity of the RNA and no amount of protein can be detected chemically in these preparations. On the other hand, RNAase destroys the infectivity of the RNA fraction completely. It must be concluded, therefore, that *naked RNA is infective and carries all the genetic information to replicate itself.*[10] These experiments prove that TMV protein plays no part in the replication either of the RNA genetic material or of itself. This is further illustrated by what may be called *reconstitution experiments.* It is possible, under certain conditions, first to separate the protein and RNA of TMV, and then to have them recombine to produce the high

[8] Based upon the work of F. M. Burnet and others.
[9] The RNA content of different small viruses composed only of ribonucleoprotein is apparently constant, also contributing about 2×10^6 to the molecular weight of the virus particle. The protein contribution varies from 2×10^6 to 100×10^6, depending upon the number of protein subunits present.

[10] RNA isolated from a number of small animal viruses is also infective.

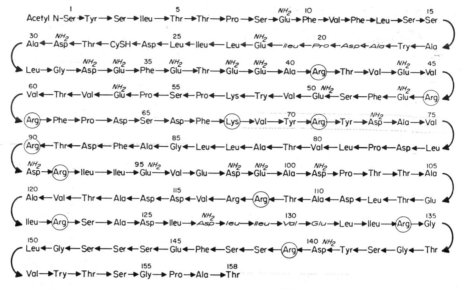

FIGURE 44–4. *Amino acid sequence in the protein building block of the tobacco mosaic virus (TMV). There are 158 amino acids in the sub-unit, the encircled residues indicate the points of splitting by trypsin.* (*Courtesy of A. Tsugita, D. T. Gish, J. Young, H. Fraenkel-Conrat, C. A. Knight, and W. M. Stanley, Proc. Nat. Acad. Sci., U.S., 46:1465, 1960.*)

infectivity of the original virus. Using two genetically different strains of this virus, the standard (TMV) and Holmes rib grass (HR), it is possible to construct a highly infective virus containing the RNA of TMV and the protein coat of HR. The progeny obtained are typically TMV with respect to RNA and protein coat. The reciprocal construct, a virus with HR RNA and TMV protein produces typical HR progeny in both their RNA and protein. Thus, *it is only the RNA of a TMV particle which specifies the RNA and protein of the progeny virus.*[11]

Mutations can be induced in TMV RNA by many of the agents which are mutagenic for DNA. For example, deamination of single bases by nitrous acid is mutagenic.

Such results and others prove that the biological activity of the RNA depends upon its primary (nucleotide content) and not its secondary (coiling pattern) structure.

The results mentioned prove that RNA is the genetic material in RNA-containing viruses. While the genetic information is carried by a single strand of ribotides within the RNA virus, we do not have any clear evidence with regard to the mode of replication or of function of the RNA once it is inside its host. It may be noted, in the case of ϕX174, whose DNA resembles RNA in being single-stranded, that there is some evidence suggesting that its replication involves the formation of a complementary DNA chain, which, however, does not become incorporated into mature phage. Even if the formation of a complementary chain proves to be true for this phage, it still remains to be seen whether this also occurs during the replication of RNA genetic material.

[11] The genetic experiments described for TMV are based largely upon work of H. Fraenkel-Conrat and R. C. Williams (1955), A. Gierer (1960), G. Schramm, and others.

SUMMARY AND CONCLUSIONS

There are mutational "hot spots" at the nucleotide level; these are different for mutants occurring spontaneously and for those induced by various chemical mutagens.

Mutation is defined operationally as any detectable novel change affecting the chemical constitution, mutability, replication, phenotypic effect, or recombination of one or more nucleotides.

Whole nucleotide mutations include additions and losses of single whole nucleotides; subnucleotide mutations may involve transitions and transversions. It is hypothesized that the components of a nucleotide serve as sites for mutation.

RNA is the sole carrier of genetic properties in certain viruses. Some RNA viruses can undergo genetic recombination.

REFERENCES

Benzer, S., and Freese, E., "Induction of Specific Mutations with 5-Bromouracil," Proc. Nat. Acad. Sci., U.S., 44:112–119, 1958; reprinted in *Papers on Bacterial Viruses*, Stent, G. (Ed.), Boston, Little, Brown, 1960, pp. 220–227.

Burnet, F. M., and Stanley, W. M. (Eds.), *The Viruses*; Vol. 1, *General Virology*, 609 pp.; Vol. 2, *Plant and Animal Viruses*, 408 pp.; Vol. 3, *Animal Viruses*, 428 pp. New York, Academic Press, 1959.

Fraenkel-Conrat, H., and Ramachandran, L. K., "Structural Aspects of Tobacco Mosaic Virus," Advances in Protein Chemistry, 14:175–229, 1959.

Fraenkel-Conrat, H., and Williams, R. C., "Reconstitution of Tobacco Mosaic Virus from Its Inactive Protein and Nucleic Acid Components," Proc. Nat. Acad. Sci., U.S., 41:690–698, 1955; reprinted in *Classic Papers in Genetics*, Peters, J. A. (Ed.), Englewood Cliffs, N.J., Prentice-Hall, 1959, pp. 264–271.

Freese, E., "The Difference Between Spontaneous and Base-Analogue Induced Mutations of Phage T4," Proc. Nat. Acad. Sci., U.S., 45:622–633, 1959.

Freese, E., Bautz, E., and Freese, E. B., "The Chemical and Mutagenic Specificity of Hydroxylamine," Proc. Nat. Acad. Sci., U.S., 47:845–855, 1961.

Gierer, A., "Ribonucleic Acid as Genetic Material of Viruses," in *Microbial Genetics*, Hayes, W., and Clowes, R. C. (Eds.), Cambridge, Cambridge University Press, 1960, pp. 248–271.

Herskowitz, I. H., "The Production of Mutations in Drosophila Melanogaster with Substances Administered in Sperm Baths and Vaginal Douches," Genetics, 40:76–89, 1955.

Lerman, L. S., "Structural Considerations in the Interaction of DNA and Acridines," J. Mol. Biol., 3:18–30, 1961.

Muller, H. J., Carlson, E., and Schalet, A., "Mutation by the Alteration of the Already Existing Gene," Genetics, 46:213–226, 1961.

Tsugita, A., Gish, D. T., Young, J., Fraenkel-Conrat, H., Knight, C. A., and Stanley, W. M., "The Complete Amino Acid Sequence of the Protein of Tobacco Mosaic Virus," Proc. Nat. Acad. Sci., U.S., 46:1463–1469, 1960.

QUESTIONS FOR DISCUSSION

44.1. Would you expect the mutational hot spots in the rII region to be different after exposing T4 to hydroxylamine from what they are after T4 is exposed to nitrous acid? Why?

44.2. How permanent need a change in a nucleotide be in order to qualify as being mutant?

44.3. Would you consider the substitution of P^{32} for P in the phosphate of a nucleotide as a mutation? Why?

44.4. What do you now think of the statement on page 199 that the only way we have of detecting changes in individual recons is by the phenotypic changes these produce?

44.5. What is meant by limit dilution? Is this technique used in studying TMV? Why?

44.6. What conclusions can you draw from the observation that the number of nucleotides is approximately constant in small RNA protein viruses?

44.7. What conclusions can you reach from the fact that within about a day after infection with a single particle of TMV, the cell can produce about 50,000 viral nucleic acid molecules and about 100×10^6 protein subunits?

44.8. How could you prove, using infections by naked RNA of TMV, that this RNA contains information for manufacturing TMV protein?

44.9. Compare transformation with infection by naked virus nucleic acid.

44.10. Discuss the view presented by F. Jacob that cancerous growths may originate because virus infection causes the activation of DNA replication.

Chapter 45

EXTRANUCLEAR GENES
AND THEIR INTERRELATIONS
WITH NUCLEAR GENES

WHEN a DNA phage enters the stage of vegetative replication, the synthesis of host DNA and protein ceases and the cell proceeds to make virus DNA and protein. While we do not know the detailed mechanism whereby this metabolic shift is produced, it could involve the utilization of the host's cistronic products as well as the direct suppression of host gene replication and/or cistronic functioning. It would seem of interest, in this connection, to discuss whether or not there is evidence of a direct interrelationship between chromosomal and nonchromosomal genes. We have already presented some evidence bearing on this during our study of episomes of F and temperate virus types. It should be recalled that when such episomes are associated with their chromosomal locus, replication, of the same episome located nonchromosomally, is repressed.

Is there any evidence for the occurrence of genes which are always physically unassociated with nuclear chromosomes, that is, genes which are not chromosomal or episomal but always extrachromosomal? It is possible that some virulent phages are composed of genes of this type. It is even possible that some of the genes in temperate phages are always extrachromosomal, in view of the fact that only the genes of the prophage are intimately associated with a chromosomal locus. We may now ask two questions: By

409

what means can we search for and prove the occurrence of extrachromosomal genes? If they exist, can we find any direct interactions between them and particular chromosomal genes? We can seek the answers to these two questions in investigations of organisms whose cells possess a definite nuclear membrane (and hence a definite nucleus). Accordingly, we shall be concerned with the identification of extranuclear genes and their interrelations with nuclear genes.

How are we going to recognize an extranuclear component as being genic? We can do so by testing whether that component is operationally genic — that is, by testing its chemical, recombinational, mutational, phenotypical, and replicative properties. If such studies reveal properties which satisfy our operational definitions of a gene, the component is genic.

Let recombination be the first operational method used in the search for extranuclear genes. To detect recombination we shall require that the extranuclear gene produce a recognizable phenotypic effect. We shall also require that such a gene be capable either of mutation or recombination, or both. In other words, we need to have changes, involving either the kind or quantity of such a gene, or both, so that we are provided with phenotypic alternatives having an inborn basis.

How would we actually proceed to look for an extranuclear gene in *Drosophila*? We would initially observe the occurrence of (preferably, clearly) different phenotypic alternatives which occur generation after generation under the same environmental conditions. By a series of crosses we would proceed to test whether the occurrence of the alternatives was associated with the presence of a particular chromosome (X, Y, II, III, IV) or a group of chromosomes. If it is, it is likely that the phenotypic alternatives are due to some genic factor linked to (hence located on) a chromosome. (Then by additional appropriate crosses and/or cytological studies, we could determine more about the precise nature of the nuclear gene change. As you may have surmised from the previous work discussed, the vast majority of gene-based traits that have been carefully analyzed are determined by genes contained in chromosomes. Thus, we would usually fail to find the extranuclear gene we started out to detect.)

But consider the genetic alternatives for resistance and *susceptibility to CO_2 gas*. One strain of *Drosophila* flies can be exposed to pure CO_2 for as long as 15 minutes and recover without apparent effect, while flies of another strain so exposed are almost invariably killed. Using marked chromosomes, it is found that CO_2-sensitivity is not linked to any chromosome of the normal genome. In fact, it is possible, by appropriate crosses, to replace each of the chromosomes present in the sensitive strain by a corresponding chromosome of the resistant strain. Yet, after this is done, the flies produced are still sensitive to CO_2! It is still possible, however, that the sensitive strain has somehow obtained an additional nuclear chromosome which, of course, would not be linked to any of the usual ones. Since the CO_2-sensitivity trait does not segregate in the progeny of hybrids between sensitive and resistant lines, this must mean that such a supernumerary chromosome cannot occur singly (in the individual that is hybrid for sensitivity) or as a pair (in flies of the pure sensitive strain). Moreover, cytological examination reveals no additional nuclear chromosome. Even so, the latter finding is not a conclusive argument against a nuclear locus for CO_2-sensitivity, since "chromosomes" so small that they escape cytological detection are known to exist from recombinational evidence.

It is found, however, that while the sensitive female regularly transmits CO_2-sensitivity to some progeny, the sensitive male does so only under special circumstances. It is still possible to conceive that a nuclear gene for sensitivity might somehow be preferentially excluded from a nucleus destined for a sperm but not from one destined for an egg. It seems much more reasonable, however, to attribute the nontransmission of CO_2-sensitivity through the sperm as being the consequence of the relatively minute amount of cytoplasm included in a sperm, as compared with the amount present in an egg of *Drosophila*. It is, therefore, very probable that CO_2-sensitivity is due to the presence of a body, called *sigma*, which is mutable and proves to have many of the characteristics of a virus, including infectivity by experimental means.[1] Sigma is not visible within the cell, and so we do not know more about its location.

Consider next another case, in *Drosophila*, already mentioned on p. 107. In this case, females mated to normal males give rise almost entirely to females. This trait has a genetic basis and also is not transmitted by males. Moreover, it is infective and unlinked to the usual chromosomes. It turns out that this female-producing-female trait is intimately associated with the presence of a spirochaete which can be seen in the blood. We might mention also the occurrence in corn of a phenotypic change which is associated with the presence of readily detectable, supernumerary, heterochromatic (so-called B) chromosomes.

None of the three cases just described conclusively demonstrates the existence of intracellular but extranuclear genes. However, they serve to illustrate the types of outcome which may be obtained, when investigations to prove the existence of such genes start with a study of genetic recombination. In view of such results, you can readily appreciate the advantage of correlating potentially extranuclear genes directly with objects observable in the cytoplasm. This advantage is held in the case of particles called *kappa*,

---

[1] Sigma has been studied mostly by P. L'Héritier, G. Teissier, and coworkers.

? leuk

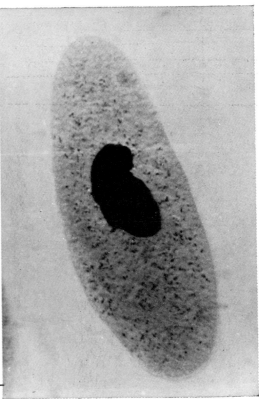

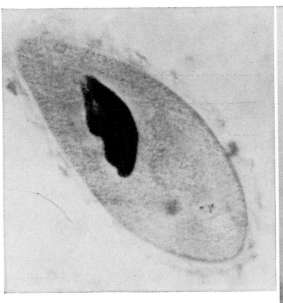

FIGURE 45–1. *Normal (above) and kappa-containing (right)* Paramecium. *(Courtesy of T. M. Sonneborn.)*

which are located in the cytoplasm of certain strains of the protozoan, *Paramecium*. Hundreds of kappa particles can be seen unstained in a single cell (Figure 45–1). They contain DNA and are self-reproducing. Individuals containing kappa are called killers, since animal-free fluid obtained from cultures of killer paramecia will kill sensitive (kappa-free) individuals.

Mutant kappas are known which produce different poisons. Kappa is liberated into the medium once it develops a highly refractile granule, which sometimes appears as a "bright spot" under the microscope. One "bright spot" kappa particle is enough to kill a sensitive individual. Kappa has a specific relationship to its host, in that a particular dominant host gene must be present in order for kappa to maintain itself, i.e., reproduce. Killer individuals that are homozygotes for

the recessive host allele partition the nondividing kappa among the two daughter cells, and this continues in successive divisions until a daughter receives none and is a kappa-sensitive cell.

Just what is kappa? In size and shape it resembles a bacterium and, like a bacterium, is known to be infective. But, kappa differs from bacteria in certain staining reactions and in internal morphology, particularly when kappa develops the bright spot, the refractile granule. Even though kappa looks like no known bacterium, the fact that it is infective and is not typically found in paramecia suggests that it is a foreign organism of some kind. Nevertheless, kappa furnishes our first example of genes which are extranuclear but intracellular in location.

The special significance of kappa is that it furnishes a model of how a parasitic or

FIGURE 45–2.   MARCUS M. RHOADES (*in 1959*) *examines striped corn plants in the foreground.   Unstriped corn plants are in the background.*

symbiotic microorganism can become so well-adapted to its host that it becomes a part of the host's genetic system and determines some of the traits of the host.   Like kappa, the rickettsial organism that causes Rocky Mountain spotted fever is visible and inherited through the cytoplasm.   These organisms, as well as the virus and spirochaete we have already discussed in this Chapter, also determine certain traits of their hosts.   Whereas each of the cases so far mentioned involves an organism which seems to be foreign to its host at present, we cannot be sure that the organism originated as a parasite or symbiont.   Could some of the now-foreign organisms located intracellularly originally have been part of the normal gene content of a cell?

This question is particularly pertinent when viruses are considered. From what has been learned in previous Chapters, we can no longer retain any preconceived notions either that viruses were always foreign infective agents, or that all presently known viruses are of this nature. Present-day virulent phages seem to be acting as foreign organisms when they lyse their bacterial hosts. But, the lytic capacity of phage depends upon its genotype and that of its host, so that under some genotypic conditions lysis is relatively rare. The decision as to normality or abnormality of present-day viruses is even more difficult when temperate phages are considered, for not only are they less lytic yet still capable of transduction, but the very genes characterizing their prophages seem to be associated with a part of a normal chromosome. As we learn more about viruses, particularly phage, our understanding of what is now genetically normal, and what is foreign, is undergoing radical revision.[2] With the future increase in our knowledge of the genetics of viruses and their "hosts," we will also be in a better position to postulate how they originated.

Let us continue our search for other extranuclear genes, restricting our attention now to cytoplasmic components which seem to be normal constituents of present-day cells, even though we shall make no decision as to their normality when they, or their precursors, first arose.

Many plant cells contain cytoplasmic bodies called *plastids*, which when green because of the presence of chlorophyll are called *chloroplasts*, and when white are called *leucoplasts*. In the absence of sunlight, chloroplasts lose their pigment and become leucoplasts, the process being reversed when the plastids are again exposed to sunlight.

Chromosomal genes are known in corn whose mutants affect the production of chlorophyll in plastids by interfering with the sequence of reactions leading to chlorophyll production. For example, such a nuclear gene may prevent plastids from producing any chlorophyll at all; thus there is a type of leucoplast which is incapable of becoming green for this reason. If a seedling possesses the appropriate nuclear genotype, it will be nongreen; it will grow until it exhausts the food supply in the seed, then die because in the absence of chlorophyll there is no photosynthesis and no sugar manufactured. Such nuclear genes act as lethals when they produce albino seedlings.

Corn plants are also known whose leaves are mosaic, having stripes of green and white (Figure 45–2), the white parts having only leucoplasts incapable of becoming green.[3] The white portions of the leaf survive because they receive nourishment from the green parts. What is the basis for this mosaicism? Is it due to nuclear genes causing different paths of differentiation in different portions of the leaf?

It is observed that the striping occurs not only within the leaves but also elsewhere, and seems to extend even into the reproductive organs, so that pollen and eggs can be obtained, derived both from green and from white parts. This may permit us to determine the answer to the question last posed. For, if the striping is due to a nuclear gene acting upon differentiation, such a gene should be transmissible through the male or female gamete, without relation to the whiteness or greenness of the tissue giving rise to the reproductive structures.

What is done is to obtain an ear of corn derived from an ovary which was likely to be mosaic, having originated partly from green and partly from white tissue. The kernels in such an ear are the F_1, and are grown in rows

---

[2] See A. Campbell (1961).

[3] The following account is based primarily upon work of M. M. Rhoades.

corresponding to their positions in the cob. What is observed is not all green seedlings, or all white, or all striped, or a randomly distributed mixture of types; instead, groups of green and of albino seedlings are found (Figure 45–3). This suggests that striping actually was present in the ovary also and that it persisted in the cob. Other tests of this strain show that the greenness or whiteness of a seedling has nothing to do with the color of the parental part giving rise to the pollen used in the fertilization which produced the seed. The only deciding factor proves to be the color of the tissue giving rise to the ovary. The fact that this effect is independent of the pollen grain suggests that the effect is not due to a nuclear gene acting differently in different tissues, and by appropriate crosses

it can be shown that none of the genes in the male chromosomes is involved. In other crosses this is also shown to be true for the nuclear genes contributed by the mother (a fact which you may have already suspected from the clustering of green and of albino seedlings already mentioned). We may conclude, therefore, that, in the present case, it is only the nature of the plastids contained in different ova which is important.

The fact that the pollen grain is not known to carry plastids, and, in the present case, has no influence on the type produced after fertilization, argues in favor of the view that plastids are derived only from pre-existing plastids, the color trait of the daughter plastids being determined only by the color potentiality of the parent plastid. This

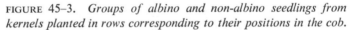

FIGURE 45–3. *Groups of albino and non-albino seedlings from kernels planted in rows corresponding to their positions in the cob.*

hypothesis may be subject to test in another way. What does one find in the cytoplasm of cells located at the border between white and green tissue? Here one finds cells which contain both fully green and completely white mature plastids, whereas cells within a green sector contain all green mature plastids, and cells in a white sector have only leucoplasts. (It should be noted that, when immature, all plastids are smaller and colorless.) Thus, even when the two kinds of mature plastids are present in the same cell, they have no influence upon each other, but develop according to their innate capacities. If a zygote (or other cell) contains both kinds of plastids it will, by the accident of producing daughter cells having only "white" or only "green" plastids, give rise to stripes of white and of green, respectively. We can conclude from the results presented, amply supported by others not mentioned, that plastids are self-replicating, do not arise except from plastids, and are capable of innate transmissible changes. Accordingly, *since plastids are self-replicating, mutable, and capable of replicating their mutant condition, they contain at least one extranuclear cytoplasmic gene.* We have already mentioned that it was proven, from other work, that the chlorophyll trait is also influenced by nuclear cistrons. Thus, a trait of a self-replicating cytoplasmic body is subject to modification both by the extranuclear gene(s) it contains, as well as by nuclear genes.

It has been found, after crossing two particular all-green corn plants, that some of the progeny are green-and-white striped. The striped plants prove to be homozygous for a recessive nuclear gene, *iojap* (*ij*), for which their parents were heterozygous. That the striped phenotype is not due to some interference by *ij ij* in the biosynthetic pathway leading to the production of chlorophyll pigment (or, in other words, that it is not due to some nuclear gene-caused error in metabolism) is demonstrated by the fact that the leucoplasts in albino cells remain colorless in subsequent generations of corn plants, even after the iojap recon is replaced by its normal allele. The only simple explanation for this effect is that, in the presence of *ij ij*, an extranuclear gene, which is located in the plastid and which is responsible for chlorophyll production, is caused to mutate to a form no longer capable of performing this function. This comprises proof that *mutation of an extranuclear gene can be induced by a nuclear gene.* A similar case, in which a nuclear gene controls chlorophyll production by mutating plastid genes, is known in the catnip, *Nepeta.*

We have already mentioned [4] that the cytoplasmic particle kappa can be transmitted from one generation of *Paramecium* to the next. The distribution of kappa to the next generation depends upon the way the new generation initiates. Since a new generation can be formed in several ways, we shall understand kappa-transmission better after a brief description of two such mechanisms.

One method of producing the next generation of *Paramecium* is asexual. A typical *Paramecium* contains a diploid *micronucleus* and a highly polyploid (about 1000N) *macronucleus* (or *meganucleus*). The individual can divide by *fission* to produce two daughter paramecia comprising the next generation. Both the micronucleus and macronucleus replicate and separate, so that when fission is completed, both daughter cells are chromosomally identical to each other and to the mother cell from which they were derived. Even though the cytoplasmic contents are not equally apportioned to the daughters, a killer mother will normally produce two killer daughters, since both of these receive some of the hundreds of kappa particles distributed throughout the cytoplasm of the parent cell. Should the daughters undergo

[4] The previous and following discussion of *Paramecium* is based largely upon the work of T. M. Sonneborn and coworkers.

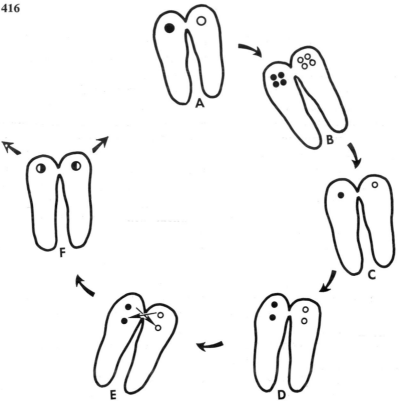

FIGURE 45–4. *Simplified representation of micronuclear events occurring during conjugation in* Paramecium. *Each conjugant has a single diploid micronucleus (A), which following meiosis produces four haploid nuclei (B). Three of these disintegrate (C), and the remaining nucleus divides once mitotically (D). The conjugants exchange one of the haploid mitotic products (E), after which fusion of haploid nuclei occurs (F) so that each of the conjugants, which later separate, contains a single diploid micronucleus.*

fission also, etc., a clone of chromosomally identical killer individuals will be produced. Successive fissions of a sensitive *Paramecium* produce, naturally, a clone of sensitive individuals.

A second process for forming new generations is sexual. The members of a clone are all found to be of the same mating type. But when clones of different mating type are mixed together, there is a *mating reaction*. This involves the sticking together of individuals of different mating types so that larger and larger clumps of paramecia are formed. This is followed by *conjugation* by

pairs, each member of a pair being of a different mating type. During conjugation (Figure 45–4), the micronucleus of each mate undergoes meiosis, at the conclusion of which, three of the four haploid nuclei produced disintegrate. The remaining nucleus divides mitotically once, producing two haploid nuclei. Then one of the two haploid nuclei in each mate migrates into the other mate and there joins the nonmotile haploid nucleus to form a single diploid nucleus in each conjugant. During conjugation the macronucleus disintegrates.

After conjugation the two paramecia separate, producing the exconjugants of what we shall consider to be the next generation. You will recognize that both exconjugants are chromosomally identical, since each conjugant contributes an identical haploid nucleus to each fertilization micronucleus. The chromosomal identity of exconjugants can be proven by the use of various marker genes. (Of course, if the conjugants were homozygous for different alleles, the exconjugants would be identical heterozygotes.) The diploid micronucleus in each exconjugant divides once mitotically, one product forming a new macronucleus, the other remaining as the micronucleus.

What would be the normal consequence of mating a killer with a sensitive individual? (Mating can occur before a killer can kill a sensitive individual; in fact, during conjugation, all conjugants are resistant to killing action.) Normally, the cytoplasmic interiors of conjugants are kept apart by a boundary which is probably penetrated only by the migrant haploid nuclei. As a result, little or no cytoplasm is exchanged, so that, kappawise, the exconjugants are the same as the conjugants, namely, one is a killer and one is a sensitive individual. However, using certain experimental conditions, a wide bridge can be seen to form between the conjugants through which the cytoplasmic contents of both mates can flow and mix (Figure 45–5). Moreover, the extent of cytoplasmic mixing can be controlled experimentally. If one of the conjugants is killer and the other sensitive, and if cytoplasmic mixing is extensive enough, both exconjugants are found to be killers because of the flow of kappa particles into the sensitive conjugant.

Consider now precisely how nuclear genes are distributed in conjugation. Suppose each conjugant is a micronuclear heterozygote, *Aa*. It would be a matter of chance in each mate which one of the four haploid nuclei produced by meiosis, *A, A, a, a*, fails to disintegrate, divides mitotically once, one of whose products migrates to help form the fertilization nucleus in the other mate. Accordingly, both exconjugants will be *AA* 25% of the time, both exconjugants will be *Aa* 50% of the time, and both *aa* 25% of the time. This result would be obtained whether or not the conjugants mix cytoplasms. Note again that, regardless of the genotype of the conjugants, the members of a pair of exconjugants are identical with respect to micronuclear genes and will give rise to clones phenotypically identical with respect to the micronuclear gene-determined trait under consideration. When dealing with a trait determined by a cytoplasmic particle like kappa, on the other hand, we have seen that the results may be different. In this particular example, a cross of sensitive with killer produces exconjugants whose type depends upon the occurrence or nonoccurrence of cytoplasmic mixing.

Suppose, to generalize, two paramecia, phenotypically different with respect to a given trait, are mated together. It may be found, when there has been no cytoplasmic exchange, that the two exconjugant clones remain different, each resembling its cytoplasmic parent in this trait. Suppose, moreover, that only when there is cytoplasmic mixing are the two exconjugant clones found to be the same phenotypically. Such results would prove that the trait under test is determined at least in part by an extranuclear

FIGURE 45–5. *Silhouettes of conjugating* Paramecium. *A. Normal, no cytoplasmic mixing. B. Wide bridge, permitting cytoplasmic mixing.*

gene. It becomes clear, therefore, that the occurrence and control of cytoplasmic mixing during conjugation provides a powerful tool for detecting and proving the occurrence of extranuclear genes in *Paramecium*.

With this background regarding the differential transmissive behavior of nuclear and extranuclear genes in *Paramecium*, consider the results obtained from the study of the genetic basis for two *different mating types*, calling one *alpha* and the other *beta*. It can be proven that there is a gene basis for these mating types in the macronucleus. However, exconjugants from a mating of alpha by beta form clones of different mating type only if there is no cytoplasmic mixing, and clones of the same mating type only if the mates mix cytoplasms. There is clearly, then, also an extranuclear gene basis for the mating-type trait. The extranuclear genes involved in this case are invisible and seem to be a normal component of the cell. So, just as is the case for chlorophyll production in corn, the mating type phenotype in *Paramecium* is affected both by nuclear and extranuclear genes.

Additional experiments clarify the role of both types of gene. Recall that the macronucleus degenerates during conjugation, and that one daughter nucleus produced by a mitosis of the fertilization nucleus forms the new macronucleus, which thereafter divides at every fission and goes to all daughter cells of a clone. At first this new macronucleus can be referred to as a *young macronucleus*, and later as an *adult macronucleus*.

Experiments demonstrate that if a young macronucleus is located in cytoplasm containing the alpha extranuclear gene, then as an adult macronucleus it comes to determine the alpha mating type; a genetically identical young macronucleus placed in cytoplasm containing the beta extranuclear gene becomes an adult macronucleus determining beta type. Clearly the young macronucleus carries the potentiality of producing either alpha or beta

mating type in the form of one or more macronuclear genes. Which alternative comes to phenotypic expression is dependent, however, upon the type of extranuclear gene carried. Once the macronucleus is mature, that is, is determined as an alpha or beta type, thereafter it and its daughters will persist in this condition. So this fixation of the macronucleus is irreversible.

On the other hand, it is found by suitable experimentation that a mature, fixed macronucleus produces, or determines the functioning of, extranuclear genes of the same mating type. For example, an adult alpha macronucleus causes the alpha cytoplasmic effect to be produced, which, in turn, is ready to determine the mating type of the young macronucleus produced in the next sexual generation. This mutual, circular, dependency between extranuclear and nuclear genes is an example of what may be referred to as a *feed-back system*. The extranuclear gene feeds instructions to the nuclear gene, which in turn feeds back instructions to the extranuclear gene, which feeds back instructions to the nuclear gene, etc.

Other traits in *Paramecium* are also known to be controlled by nuclear and extranuclear genes operating in feed-back systems. It should be noted, however, that when such systems operate, they may not always result in an irreversible fixation in the type of phenotypic alternative which either of the two kinds of genes may express. Moreover, it is not known whether the one kind of gene acts directly on the other kind of gene or on its products. Finally, it should be pointed out that in none of the cases mentioned, ignoring kappa, has it been proved that the extranuclear and the nuclear genes affecting the same trait differ except in location and in the consequences expected from this difference. Accordingly, we should not exclude the possibility that extranuclear genes may sometimes prove to be episomes or derivatives of episomes.

SUMMARY AND CONCLUSIONS

The cytoplasm can contain extranuclear genes which are not known to be episomes. In some cases the extranuclear genes seem to be foreign organisms (sigma probably, kappa), in other cases they appear to be normal constituents of the cell (chloroplasts, mating type).

Nuclear and extranuclear genes show the following interrelations: the former can mutate the latter; both may interact in the production of a particular phenotype, sometimes operating as a feed-back system.

REFERENCES

Beale, G. H., *The Genetics of Paramecium Aurelia*, Cambridge, Cambridge University Press, 178 pp., 1954.

Campbell, A., "Conditions for the Existence of Bacteriophage," Evolution, 15:153–165, 1961.

Rhoades, M. M., "Plastid Mutations," Cold Spr. Harb. Sympos. Quant. Biol., 11:202–207, 1946.

Rhoades, M. M., "Interaction of Genic and Non-Genic Hereditary Units and the Physiology of Non-Genic Inheritance," in *Encyclopedia of Plant Physiology*, Ruhland, W. (Ed.), Vol. 1, pp. 19–57, Berlin, Springer Verlag, 1955.

Sonneborn, T. M., "The Role of the Genes in Cytoplasmic Inheritance," Chap. 14, pp. 291–314, in *Genetics in the 20th Century*, Dunn, L. C. (Ed.), 1951.

Sonneborn, T. M., "Kappa and Related Particles in Paramecium," Adv. Virus Res., 6:229–356, 1959.

Sonneborn, T. M., "The Gene and Cell Differentiation," Proc. Nat. Acad. Sci., U.S., 46:149–165, 1960.

Tracy M. Sonneborn, *about 1960.*

QUESTIONS FOR DISCUSSION

45.1. What is revealed regarding nucleocytoplasmic interrelationships from the study of F? Of temperate phages?

45.2. What evidence can you present that CO_2-sensitivity is due to a virus rather than a normal chromosomal gene?

45.3. In proving the existence of extranuclear genes which operations (recombinational, mutational, functional, chemical) were we utilizing? Did we include their capacity for self-replication? Why?

45.4. Discuss the genetic control of chlorophyll production in corn.

45.5. Do you think the study of nucleocytoplasmic interrelations in *Paramecium* has any bearing upon differentiation processes in multicellular organisms?

45.6. What unique advantages does *Paramecium* have as an experimental organism for genetic investigations?

45.7. Certain paramecia are thin, due to a completely recessive nuclear gene, *th*. What is the phenotypic expectation for the clones derived from exconjugants of a single mating of $+ + \times + th$?
    Is your expectation affected by the occurrence of cytoplasmic mixing? Why?

45.8. According to the definition of a chromosome given on page 19, would you consider kappa to be, or contain, a chromosome? Explain.

45.9. Keeping in mind the difficulties of proving the existence of extranuclear genes, which do you think represents the primary genetic material in cellular organisms, nuclear or extranuclear genetic material? Explain your decision.

45.10. Does adaptive enzyme formation provide an example of a feed-back system? Explain.

Chapter 46

GENE ACTION AND OPERONS

THE extensive study of any organism reveals a large number of alternative traits which have a genetic basis. Some of these traits describe the presence or absence of genetic material (for example, the trait "cytoplasmic DNA" in *Paramecium* may be due to the presence of kappa). Other traits involve the relocation of genetic material (for example, changes in episomal state, or the inversion of a chromosomal segment). But such alternatives as the presence, absence, and movement of genetic material do not describe how the cell or organism is affected, or in what ways genetic material performs a function.

We are especially interested in studying those alternative traits which result from some action by, or involving, genetic material. One action, typical of what we have defined as genetic material, is self-replication. You will admit that self-replication must have *some* phenotypic consequences due to the removal of gene precursor material from the pool of metabolic substances and to the presence of new genetic material. Can *all* genic action be ascribed to the metabolic changes which take place because of genic self-replication? We know of several kinds of situations in which there is no evidence of gene replication, yet there is evidence of genic action. One example is found in the case of abortive transduction; another is provided by highly functional cells which never divide again, for example, neurons. We can conclude, therefore, that *conserved*

genetic material also functions by some mechanism other than self-replication. A study of inborn errors of metabolism, and of the pedigree of causes for pleiotropic effects of mutants, led us to hypothesize (Chapter 32) that a gene has a single primary function. You realize now that this hypothesis refers to some action by genetic material other than self-replication. Depending upon the particular trait we consider to be primary, the scope of genetic material essential for this function, that is, the length of a cistron, will vary (Chapter 42). The general hypothesis of one cistron-one function (besides self-replication) was tested in the specific form of one cistron-one polypeptide chain (Chapter 32). The results demonstrated that the specific form of the general hypothesis is acceptable.

It was mentioned, on p. 376, that *Salmonella* has at least eight closely linked loci (Figure 46–1), all having an effect upon the sequence of chemical reactions leading to the biosynthesis of histidine. Already four of the eight loci have been correlated with specific enzymes,[1] thereby providing additional evidence for the hypothesis one polypeptide-one cistron. Although it was also pointed out at that time that close linkage of genes controlling different parts of a biosynthetic sequence is not a universal phenomenon, let us consider some finer genetic details of the lactose, *Lac*, locus in *E. coli* which is, in this respect, similar to the histidine locus in *Salmonella*.

You may remember, from p. 369, that the *Lac* segment contains three cistrons. The y^+ cistron specifies the structure of the enzyme galactoside permease, while z^+ is the gene that specifies the structure of the enzyme β-galactosidase. (Certain alleles of z result in the synthesis of a modified, enzymatically inactive, protein, called Cz, which can be identified by its specific antigenic charac-

[1] See P. E. Hartman, J. C. Loper, and D. Šerman (1960).

421

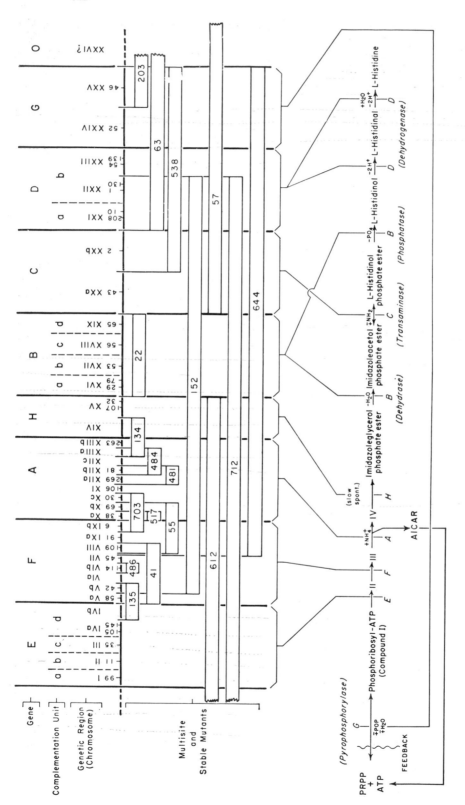

FIGURE 46–1.   *The histidine region in Salmonella.*   *(Courtesy of P. E. Hartman.)*

teristics.) The third cistron, i^+, specifies the synthesis of a *repressor substance* which prevents y^+ and z^+ from producing the permease and galactosidase, respectively. When the substrate upon which these enzymes act is present, however, the repressor substance made by i^+ is inactivated, so that the formation of these enzymes becomes possible. Accordingly, *E. coli* of genotype $y^+z^+i^+$ cannot produce galactosidase or permease *constitutively* (in the absence of substrate for these enzymes) but can do so *inductively* (in the presence of enzyme substrate). This genotype provides us with an example of the genetic basis for the phenomenon of induced enzyme formation. Note, in this connection, that it is often found that the formation of an enzyme is repressed by a high intracellular concentration of its product, so that a feed-back system is involved (cf. p. 418 and also Figure 46–1).

The order of these genes relative to themselves and others is: *TL . . . Pro . . . (Lac) y z i . . . Ad . . . Gal.* Note that all three *Lac* cistrons specify unique substances. Because i^+ produces a repressor substance, which in the absence of substrate is capable of pleiotropic effects — that is, of phenotypic suppression of both y^+ and z^+, i^+ can be called a *regulator gene.* What is the precise mechanism by which i^+ suppresses the action of two other genes which are themselves nonallelic, even if they are part of the same biochemical sequence?

With this question in mind, let us examine the consequences of certain mutations in the *Lac* region. Mutants capable of synthesizing permease and galactosidase constitutively might be due to the genotype $y^+ z^+ i$, in which the specific repressor is not produced, and the genes y^+ and z^+ are able to act under all circumstances. It is possible to construct *E. coli* which are hybrid for the *Lac* region, by introducing into F⁻ cells F particles containing the *Lac* region as chromosomal memory (see p. 369). Thus, one

can obtain an *E. coli* whose chromosome has $y^+ z i$ (which by itself would make permease and Cz protein constitutively) and whose F-*Lac* particle is $y^+ z^+ i^+$ (which by itself would make permease and galactosidase only in the presence of substrate). In the hybrid no products are formed in *noninduced bacteria* (in the absence of inducing substrate), while all three (galactosidase, Cz protein, and permease) are formed in *induced bacteria* (exposed to enzyme substrate). We must conclude from this that a single i^+ gene can manufacture repressor substance which prevents the products of both normal and mutant y and z genes from being formed constitutively but not inductively, whether or not these genes are located on the same chromosome segment. In other words, the repressor substance is diffusible and can act at a distance. There is some evidence that the repressor substance is RNA.

Another mutant is found which also permits y^+ and z^+ products to form constitutively, and is, therefore, presumably a mutation of i^+, say to allele i^x. When an F-*Lac* particle of the presumed genotype $y^+ z^+ i^x$ is placed in a cell whose chromosome is $y^+ z i$ (which by itself is known to produce permease and Cz protein constitutively), no Cz protein is formed constitutively in noninduced bacteria. Contrary to the assumption made, i^x must be i^+ since it is producing repressor capable of repressing Cz protein formation constitutively. If so, in what respect is the F-*Lac* particle mutant? Let us make the supposition that the F-*Lac* particle is mutant at a locus, o^+, the new allele being o^c, which permits only the y and z loci in the same chromosome or particle to act constitutively regardless of which allele of i may be present in the cell. If this is so, then the F-*Lac* particle is genotypically $y^+ z^+ o^c i^+$ while the genotype of the chromosome can be written $y^+ z o^+ i$, ignoring gene order for the present. On the new hypothesis, the hybrid ought to produce permease and galactosidase consti-

[Margin notes:]
i^+ on F able to repress $y^+ z$ on chromosome

Cz should be formed constitutively but F particle has O^c mutation behind it so repressor is still formed

tutively, and to produce Cz protein also inductively. This is found. The results obtained with this genotype are summarized in Figure 46–2. It is possible to construct other hybrids containing both the o^c and o^+ alleles. These are also listed in Figure 46–2 with the results obtained. For example,

$$y^+ \, z \, o^+ \, i^+ / F\text{-}Lac \, y^+ \, z^+ \, o^c \, i^+$$

produces y^+ and z^+ enzymes but no Cz substance constitutively, and produces all three in induced bacteria. Partial phenotypic analysis was made for two other genotypes. Thus,

$$y \, z^+ \, o^+ \, i^+ / F\text{-}Lac \, y^+ \, z \, o^c \, i^+$$

produces Cz protein but no galactosidase in noninduced bacteria, but produces both of these in induced bacteria. Finally,

$$y^+ \, z \, o^+ \, i^+ / F\text{-}Lac \, y \, z^+ \, o^c \, i^+$$

produces galactosidase constitutively, and it and permease inductively.

We conclude, therefore, that these results are consistent with the hypothesis that an operator gene, o^+, exists and that it is this gene which is sensitive to the repressor substance produced by the regulator gene, i^+. When the repressor substance is produced and is not inactivated by the presence of substrate, it reacts with o^+, and this prevents both z and y alleles from operating. When the mutant allele i is present, no repressor substance is produced, o^+ is not affected, and z and y alleles are capable of acting constitutively. However, a mutant allele of o^+, namely o^c, is insensitive to the repressor substance, so that z and y alleles can act constitutively regardless of the genotype with respect to i. Note that the behavior of the y and z alleles is dependent upon the particular allele of o which is in the same chromosome or F particle — that is, which is linked in the cis position. Thus, the constitutive mutant of operator, o^c, has a pleiotropic effect only on other genes in the cis position.

Other results demonstrate that the locus of o^c is between z and i. Still other mutants have been obtained which prevent the synthesis of permease and galactosidase under all conditions. These mutants undergo re-

GENOTYPE		NON-INDUCED BACTERIA			INDUCED BACTERIA		
Chromosome	F-Lac	P	G	Cz P	P	G	Cz P
$y^+ \, z^+ \, o \, i^+$	$y^+ \, z^+ \, o^c \, i^+$	33	36	nd	100	270	100
$y^+ \, z^+ \, o \, i^+$	$y^+ \, z^+ \, o^c \, i^+$	50	110	nd	100	330	100
$y \, z^+ \, o^+ \, i^+$	$y^+ \, z \, o^c \, i^+$	—	<1	30	—	100	400
$y^+ \, z \, o^+ \, i^+$	$y \, z^+ \, o^c \, i^+$	nd	60	—	100	300	—

P = Permease

G = Galactosidase

Cz P = Cz Protein

FIGURE 46–2. *Crosses, and their results, involving the* Lac *region of* E. coli. *nd = not detectable, — = not tested.*

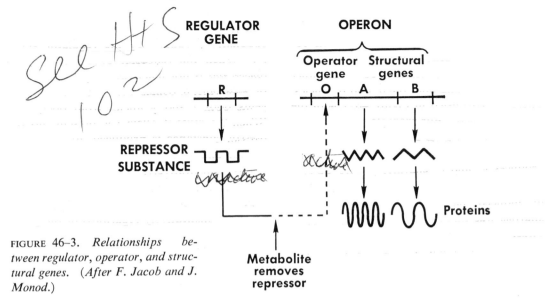

FIGURE 46–3. *Relationships between regulator, operator, and structural genes.* (*After F. Jacob and J. Monod.*)

verse mutation, show complementation neither with *z* nor with *y* mutants, are extremely closely linked to the *o^c* mutant, and are located between *z* and *i*. These mutants are clearly alleles of *o^+*, which we can call *o^o*.

It should be noted that the *operator gene* does not seem to produce any unique product which can be detected cytoplasmically. In this respect it may be considered a gene whose primary job is not the specification of a chemical product, such as the amino acid sequence in a polypeptide, but one *whose primary effect is to control the function of other genes.* Accordingly, operator genes may be called *genes for function* in contrast to those which specify chemical structures and are, therefore, *genes for structure* (Figure 46–3).

It is possible to explain the action of an operator gene on the basis that it shares nucleotides with an adjacent cistron which is controlled by the operator gene. When the operator gene is functional the adjacent gene cannot be read correctly, since some of its nucleotides are unavailable for this usage. On another occasion, the operator gene might not be functional, permitting the adjacent gene to act. Moreover, the operator gene could mutate in such a way that it is no longer ever functional, in which case the adjacent genes would always be functional, or in such a way that the operator gene is always functional, in which case the adjacent genes could never be functional.) (See pp. 370–372 for other applications of the hypothesis of nucleotide-sharing.)

We have seen that an operator gene coordinates the expression of adjacent genes. In the present case the genes controlled are related, in that they both affect the biochemical pathway involving lactose utilization. This suggests that there is, at least in some cases, a unit of gene function which is intermediate in size between the cistron and the chromosome, and which we may call an operon. *Operons, linear groups of genes whose structural activity is coordinated by a functional gene, or operator,* may be common in microorganisms. They may also occur in other organisms and may be more frequent than one might at first suspect.[2]

[2] The preceding discussion of operons and operator genes is based upon the work of F. Jacob, D. Perrin, C. Sanchez, and J. Monod (1960), and F. Jacob and J. Monod (1961).

SUMMARY AND CONCLUSIONS

DNA has a function other than self-replication. This additional function is clearly dependent upon its sequence of nucleotides. In terms of this additional capacity, DNA cistrons can be classified as being genes for structure and/or genes for function.

When acting as a gene for function, the cistron serves as an operator that controls the expression of structural genes which are its linear neighbors, the whole complex of genes comprising an operon. It is speculated that the operator gene may produce its different effects by sharing and not sharing nucleotides with structural genes in the operon.

REFERENCES

Gorini, L., "Antagonism Between Substrate and Repressor in Controlling the Formation of a Biosynthetic Enzyme," Proc. Nat. Acad. Sci., U.S., 46:682–690, 1960.

Hartman, P. E., Loper, J. C., and Šerman, D., "Fine Structure Mapping by Complete Transduction Between Histidine-Requiring Salmonella Mutations," J. Gen. Microbiol., 22:323–353, 1960.

Jacob, F., and Monod, J., "Genetic Regulatory Mechanisms in the Synthesis of Proteins," J. Mol. Biol., 3:318–356, 1961.

Jacob, F., Perrin, D., Sanchez, C., and Monod, J., "The Operon: A Group of Genes Whose Expression Is Coordinated by an Operator" (in French), C. R. Acad. Sci., Paris, 250:1727–1729, 1960; translated and reprinted in *Papers on Bacterial Genetics*, Adelberg, E. A. (Ed.), Boston, Little, Brown, 1960, pp. 395–397.

McClintock, B., "Some Parallels Between Gene Control Systems in Maize and in Bacteria," Amer. Nat., 95:265–277, 1961.

Yanofsky, C., and St. Lawrence, P., "Gene Action," Ann. Rev. Microbiol., 14:311–340, 1960.

QUESTIONS FOR DISCUSSION

46.1. How does the phenotypic effect of o^o differ from that of its alleles, o^+ and o^c?

46.2. How does an operator gene differ from a regulator gene?

46.3. Do you suppose the nucleotide sequence is longer in an operator gene than it is in the other genic members of an operon? Why?

46.4. Does prophage act as one or more regulator genes? Explain.

46.5. Some workers classify genes into three kinds: those for structure, for regulation, and for operation. Do you believe this distinction is basic? useful? Explain.

46.6. Hypothetically, what kinds of phenotypic effects might operons produce in man?

46.7. Discuss the hypothesis (of J. F. Danielli) that the nucleus controls the possibility of particular chemical substances appearing in cells, while the cytoplasm controls the way in which macromolecules are organized into functional units.

46.8. In what ways do genes function?

46.9. What is your present concept of the cistron?

Chapter 47

GENE ACTION
AND AMINO ACID CODING

IN THE last Chapter, we found that genes can act functionally, as operator genes, or structurally, to cause the production of particular substances. Restricting our attention to DNA, which seems to be the genetic material in most kinds of organisms, the question may be asked relative to structural gene action: What can DNA do, or have done to it, which would result in the formation of particular polypeptide chains? Since we are dealing with conserved DNA, that is, DNA which remains part of a polynucleotide, whatever it does must be done *in situ*. Since DNA is not protein, it is probably not an enzyme, and probably does not act as a catalyst in producing its cistronic effect. Accordingly, being inactive in this respect, DNA is thought to serve as a kind of template, so that things are done to it or with it. (In this respect DNA serves as a better inert template than does RNA, whose ribose sugar is more reactive than the deoxy-D-ribose in DNA, so that, as a substance, RNA is less stable than DNA.)

We know that following strand separation, each DNA strand apparently serves as a template for the formation of a complementary chain. If DNA is also used as a template for cistron functioning, we may ask what kind of template information it may contain. This information must be contained in the fact that in a linear sequence of DNA, there are usually only four different base pairs, A : T, T : A, C : G, G : C.

427

What information are these base pairs supposed to contain? Since their "primary" product is, at least in some cases, a specific polypeptide chain, consider what makes a polypeptide chain specific. Almost all polypeptide chains contain one or more of each of the twenty amino acids commonly found in organisms. These amino acids are shown in Figure 32–2, p. 285. Polypeptides usually differ only in the number and sequence of these amino acid building blocks. Clearly, then, our problem is to understand how 20 amino acids and their sequence can be specified by DNA. Both the polypeptide and DNA are linearly arranged, so this common trait helps us visualize the relation between the two. The sequence of nucleotides must be meaningful in specifying amino acid sequence. But how can a linear template of nucleotides, of which there are usually only four kinds, determine the linear sequence of amino acids, of which there are 20 kinds? We are presented with a *problem of DNA coding*.

Let us postpone further discussion of the nature of the genetic code, until we have completed a consideration of certain evidence regarding protein synthesis.

Given the template of conserved DNA, the question can be asked: Where in the cell does the information contained in DNA become translated into a polypeptide sequence? You might think that this specification takes place in the nucleus, using the DNA template directly. If so, it ought to be possible to demonstrate that the nucleus is the main or only site of protein synthesis. There is very good evidence, however, not only that some protein synthesis takes place in the nucleus isolated from its cytoplasm,[1] but that protein synthesis also occurs in the cytoplasm in the absence of the nucleus. The evidence even suggests that the cytoplasm is the major site of protein synthesis. Let us

[1] From work of A. E. Mirsky, V. G. Allfrey, and others.

$$2 \ (30s) + 2 \ (50s) \rightleftharpoons 2 \ (70s) \rightleftharpoons 1 \ (100s)$$

| MOLECULAR WEIGHTS $\times 10^6$ | $\sim .8$ | 1.8 | 2.7 | 5.4 |

FIGURE 47–1.   *Relation among ribosomes having different sedimentation rates.*

consider the nature of certain particular cytoplasmic components, because of the possibility that these may be concerned with protein synthesis.

Electron micrographs of thin sections of cells reveal numerous *ribosomes* in the cytoplasm of all cells which have been examined for them — plant, animal, or microorganismal. They vary in size from 100–200 A in diameter and are particularly abundant in cells actively synthesizing protein. (Some are also found in the nucleus.) It is possible to rupture cells and characterize these ribosomes by size according to their sedimentation rate in the ultracentrifuge. Thus, in terms of *sedimentation units, s* (the smaller the number of units the smaller the particle, although the relationship is not linear), there are four discrete sizes in *E. coli*: 30s, 50s, 70s, and 100s. There are two basic sizes, 30s and 50s, the larger ones being composites of these units, as indicated in Figure 47–1. Both the 30s and 50s particles contain 63% RNA and 37% protein. Several enzymes appear to be attached to the ribosomes, including much, if not all, of the cell's RNAase and part of the cell's DNAase.[2] The smaller particles aggregate into the larger ones when Mg^{++} or other divalent cations are added. Most (about 80%) of the RNA in a cell is contained in ribosomes. (Small amounts of RNA are also reported in mitochondria and plastids.) Analysis shows that the RNA in ribosomes has the relatively high molecular weight of .56–1.1 $\times 10^6$ (having about 1000–2000 bases).

A series of experiments can be performed[3] in which radioactive amino acids are injected into the body, and tissues rapidly synthesizing proteins examined at intervals. The first experiment involves injection of a large dose of labeled amino acid, and shows that the ribosomes become labeled almost immediately. A second experiment uses a very small dose of labeled amino acid, which is expected to be used up rapidly in protein synthesis. In this case, the label in the ribosome increases quickly at first, and then decreases. Finally, a third experiment can be performed which demonstrates that the labeled amino acid which moves out of the ribosomes is actually incorporated into protein, for example, hemoglobin. Here, then, is clear evidence that ribosomes are associated with protein synthesis. Moreover, it would seem that the manufacture of hemoglobin takes place in the cytoplasm. But the amino acid sequence in hemoglobin is supposed to be determined as the primary function of DNA cistrons (Chapter 34)! How can the DNA template, which apparently remains in the nucleus, function to order the amino acid sequence of hemoglobin, which is apparently manufactured in the cytoplasm? Clearly, in this respect, the DNA cannot be functioning as a template directly, but would have to be doing so indirectly.

Suppose the DNA made another template which was neither DNA nor protein, which could leave the nucleus, enter the cytoplasm, and there serve as template for protein synthesis. A reasonable candidate for this func-

[2] See M. Tal and D. Elson (1961).

[3] Following the work of P. C. Zamecnik and co-workers, and of M. Rabinovits and M. E. Olson.

tion is RNA which is also a nucleic acid and also has a four symbol code, A, U, C, G, in which uracil (U) occurs in place of thymine (T). We would then require the four symbol code of DNA to be translated directly into the four symbol code of RNA. There are several questions we may ask, whose answers will serve to test the hypothesis that *DNA nucleotide sequence specifies RNA nucleotide sequence which, in turn, specifies amino acid sequence*.

1. Where is RNA synthesized? Several experiments support the view that much, if not all, RNA is synthesized in the nucleus, after which it can be detected, by radioactive tracer studies, to enter the cytoplasm. There is no evidence, on the other hand, of a flow of RNA from the cytoplasm to the nucleus. These results are consistent with the hypothesis under consideration.

2. What happens to nucleus-synthesized RNA? Since the typical chromosome contains RNA, *chromosomal RNA*, some of the newly synthesized RNA must be retained in the nucleus where it appears as part of daughter chromosomes. Most of the newly made RNA leaves the nucleus, and a considerable portion is believed to be used in the manufacture of new ribosomes. (In *Neurospora*, ribosomal RNA is known to be synthesized in the nucleus.) Already formed ribosomes do not accept large quantities of newly formed RNA, since it is found, by labeling experiments, that only a relatively small amount of a ribosome's RNA shows turnover. Accordingly, the greater part of the RNA in ribosomes, *ribosomal RNA*, is usually incorporated at the time of ribosome formation. Note that the mechanism by which such nuclear RNA becomes incorporated as part of new ribosomes is still unknown.

3. What is the relationship between the RNA synthesized in the nucleus and the DNA in the nucleus? Bacteria manufacture RNA, and continue to do so even after being in-

fected with phage. The base ratio in the DNA of a particular phage is known to differ from that of the DNA of its host cell. After phage infection it is found that the RNA manufactured is different from that manufactured prior to infection, having, in fact, the base ratio of phage (substituting U for T). Moreover, only the RNA synthesized after infection can base pair *in vitro* with phage DNA (made single-stranded by annealing) to form a double strand — one strand being RNA and one DNA.

It is known that, under normal circumstances, RNA is first synthesized in the chromosomes and is then transferred to the nucleolus. Yeast cells can be fed radioactive phosphorus so that the RNA synthesized shortly thereafter is labeled. When such labeled RNA is analyzed for its base ratio it is found to have the same one as has yeast DNA (making the substitution of U for T). Other work [4] demonstrates that, in normal cells, freshly made nuclear RNA forms a complex with chromosomal DNA and protein. (RNA in such a complex is resistant to RNAase.) Such results support the view that there is a direct base-for-base correspondence between DNA and nucleus-synthesized RNA. We can call this RNA, which has the base ratio equivalent of DNA, *informational* or *template RNA*.

4. How is informational RNA synthesized? In experiments dealing with the *in vitro* synthesis of DNA (Chapter 35), it was found that DNA can replicate in the absence of RNA. This is very likely to be true also in the nucleus, although there might be subtle secondary interactions with RNA. There is evidence, already mentioned in answer to the previous question, in favor of the view that RNA synthesis is intimately related to DNA. It is found [5] that the

[4] By J. Bonner, R. C. Huang, and N. Maheshwari (1961).
[5] From the work of J. Hurwitz, of A. Stevens, of S. B. Weiss, of their colleagues and of others.

nucleus contains an enzyme, *RNA poly-merase*, which is necessary for RNA synthesis. This RNA synthesis can be performed *in vitro*, and requires also the presence of DNA, as well as all four riboside triphosphates; the RNA synthesized proves to have the same base ratio as the DNA (except that T is U). This situation is reminiscent of the synthesis of DNA, where the DNA polymerase takes directions from single-stranded DNA. Here RNA polymerase takes directions from DNA in the making of RNA polymer. It has been found that single-stranded DNA can serve as template for the RNA polymerase, and that an RNA polymer probably cannot serve as primer.

5. How do the amino acids destined to form polypeptides arrive at the ribosomes? Whereas ribosomal RNA has a relatively high molecular weight ($\frac{1}{2}$ to 1 million), as already mentioned, there is another kind of RNA in the cytoplasm which has the relatively low molecular weight of about 18,000 (having about 30 bases). Other evidence indicates that there are 80–90 bases per molecule. Since this RNA is soluble when ribosomal RNA is not, it is called *soluble RNA or sRNA*. There is also no experimental proof that sRNA is derived from nuclear RNA. Using radioactively labeled amino acids it can be demonstrated that the amino acids arrive at the ribosomes singly, each attached to a molecule of soluble RNA. All the soluble RNA molecules are similar in their terminal nucleotides, one end terminating with the base G and the other end with the base sequence —C—C—A. Otherwise, they are dissimilar, being of about 20 different types, each capable of carrying a different one of the amino acids typically found in protein. The transported amino acid is attached through its carboxyl (—COOH) group to the 2′ or 3′ hydroxyl group of the terminal adenosine.

Since sRNA serves to transfer the amino acids to the ribosomes, it can also be called *transfer RNA*.

6. What do we know about the formation of the amino acid-transfer RNA complex? It has been found that each of the 20 amino acids must be activated before it can be accepted by its particular transfer RNA. Both the activation of an amino acid and its attachment to soluble RNA may involve the activity of a single enzyme. There is probably a different activating enzyme for each kind of amino acid. Activation involves the combination of the amino acid at its carboxyl end to the adenosine triphosphate (ATP) located terminally, with the removal of two phosphates as pyrophosphate. This reaction can be summarized: amino acid + ATP $\rightleftharpoons$ amino acid adenylate + pyrophosphate.

7. What determines which transfer RNA molecules are to be attracted to a ribosome? It has been mentioned already that, after a phage infects its host, RNA is made having the base ratio of the phage DNA. It has been found that polynucleotides of this phage-specific RNA become attached to a small percentage of already formed ribosomes. This suggests that many ribosomes do not automatically carry a template of RNA, containing information for specifying amino acid sequence, which it obtained from the DNA template. Such ribosomes are capable of receiving segments of template RNA which carry the code for making phage-specific polypeptides. Thus, there is a third type of cytoplasmic RNA, *messenger RNA*, which carries information for cistronic action from phage DNA to the ribosome. It is the messenger RNA which attracts the various molecules of transfer RNA, each of which is carrying individual amino acids. It has also been shown [6] that messenger RNA is used in sending cistronic template information from the regular DNA content of a cell to its

[6] By M. Hayashi and S. Spiegelman (1961).

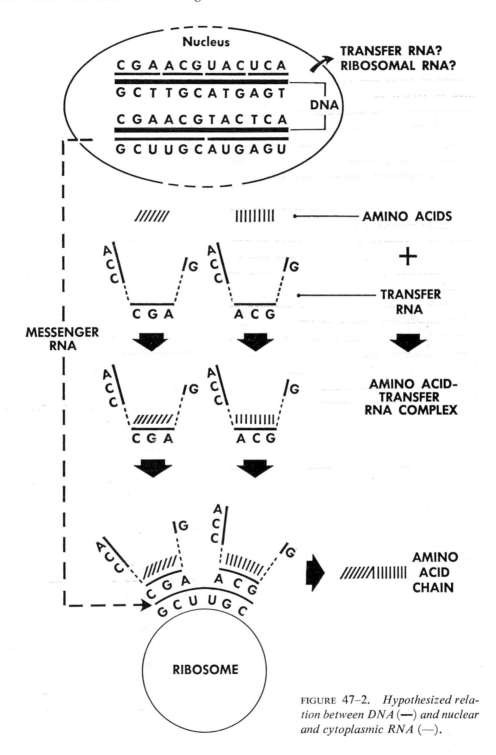

FIGURE 47–2. *Hypothesized relation between DNA (—) and nuclear and cytoplasmic RNA (—).*

ribosomes. (Guanosine triphosphate is required in order that the labeled amino acids, carried by transfer RNA, appear attached to the ribosome.)

It can be hypothesized (as illustrated in Figure 47–2) that each of the two DNA strands (which are complements) specifies an RNA complement (the two RNA strands would then also be complementary and comprise informational or template RNA). Large segments of one of the informational RNA templates leave the nucleus as messenger RNA and become located in already formed ribosomes, while the complementary RNA template is broken into segments which are used to make transfer RNA and possibly other RNA's (such as ribosomal RNA). In this event, transfer RNA and messenger RNA would be complementary, they could pair at the ribosome in the cytoplasm, and, in doing so, would place the transported amino acids in proper sequence. These amino acids could then be enzymatically joined to form a polypeptide, which could be freed from transfer RNA, which, in turn, could be liberated from pairing with its messenger complement.

The mechanism of protein synthesis can be studied using a suspension of ruptured cells. Such a cell-free system can be prepared from *E. coli.* The activity of the cell-free system can be preserved by the addition of mercaptoethanol. Also added to the mixture are the triphosphates of the ribonucleosides of A, G, C, and U, as well as all 20 of the amino acids in their L forms. The synthesis of protein can be readily detected if one of the added amino acids is radioactive. If the labeled amino acid is valine, for example, valine is found to become incorporated into protein. This incorporation can be stopped by the addition of DNAase, which destroys the DNA, thereby halting the production of messenger RNA. In the absence of new messenger RNA, protein synthesis stops.

That this effect of DNAase concerns the production of messenger RNA is demonstrated (1) by the absence of valine incorporation when sRNA or ribosomal RNA is added to the system, and (2) by the resumption of valine incorporation when the RNA from washed ribosomes is added to the system. The informational RNA added may come from various sources. Some experiments have studied the *in vitro* conditions for the synthesis of β-galactosidase [7] (see Chapter 46), using messenger RNA obtained from genetically different induced and noninduced *E. coli.* It is even possible to add TMV RNA to the bacterial cell-free system and detect the synthesis of TMV protein.[8]

Using a bacterial cell-free system it is also possible to study whether the addition of synthetic polyribonucleotides has any effect on protein synthesis. First, pure polyribotides containing only one base, A, or C, or U, are added. The first two fail to result in amino acid incorporation. However, the addition of polyuridylic acid causes L-phenylalanine to be incorporated into protein.[8] It is found, moreover, that the protein formed is poly-L-phenylalanine, and that no other amino acid is incorporated. It is also found that phenylalanine linked to sRNA is an intermediate in this process. This surely means that wherever an appropriate sequence of U's appears in normal messenger RNA, the protein being synthesized will incorporate L-phenylalanine. This is the first crack in *the RNA code*, that is, the first determination of a sequence of messenger RNA nucleotides which specifies the incorporation of a particular amino acid into protein. Note that the problem of DNA coding, mentioned on page 427, has become a problem of RNA coding.

The results mentioned also tell us that certain ribonucleotide sequences do not have

---

[7] In work of G. D. Novelli and coworkers.
[8] M. W. Nirenberg and coworkers.

amino acid meaning in the RNA code, since regardless of the length of the polyribotides of A or C added, no amino acid is incorporated into protein. But even if each single ribonucleotide specified a different amino acid, only four amino acids would be encoded. But 20 amino acids need be encoded! Can we circumvent this difficulty by assuming that a sequence of two nucleotides specifies an amino acid? (This would be like having an alphabet of only four letters and a language composed only of two-letter words.) In this case, since the first letter can be any one of four, as can the second, there are 4×4, or 16, different doublets (or words) possible, if the presumption is made that the RNA code can be read only in one direction. Unidirectional reading seems reasonable, since a single strand of RNA is polarized, just as is a single strand of DNA. Still, this will not be enough to specify 20 amino acids, unless other assumptions are made. (For example, it could be hypothesized that a given doublet encodes more than one kind of amino acid, in which case we would be dealing with a *degenerate code*.) If, however, a sequence of three nucleotides, that is, a triplet, encodes an amino acid, there would be $4 \times 4 \times 4$, or 64, different unidirectional sequences possible. This provides more than enough triplets to encode 20 amino acids. (The code would also be degenerate if different triplets encoded the same amino acid.)

There are, however, other characteristics of RNA which have a bearing on the nature of its code. Since the number of consecutive ribotides may be in the hundreds or thousands, there are no spaces (or non-nucleotide punctuation) to indicate where one triplet should stop and the next should begin. Accordingly, we are dealing with what may be called a *comma-free code*. Suppose we had six ribotides arranged linearly, in positions called 123456. If triplet 123 specifies amino acid A and 456 amino acid B, errors would

be possible if the overlapping triplets 234 or 345 served to encode different amino acids, and if the reading of different meaningful triplets were performed independently. In this event, the last two triplets would have to be eliminated as words in the code to avoid errors. Accordingly, the entire code has to be examined, and all overlapping triplets eliminated from being meaningful, that is, from specifying an amino acid. When, of the 64 possible triplets, all overlapping ones are eliminated, 20 nonoverlapping triplets (amino acid-specifying "words") remain. However, the question of overlapping triplets can be avoided to a great extent if the reading of the message can start only at a given place and triplets are read in succession. In this case, the punctuation is provided by the mechanism for reading the code. The least we can conclude from the present discussion is that it requires a sequence of more than one ribotide to encode an amino acid.

When the synthetic polyribotide of U is mixed with the synthetic polyribotide of A, so that several strands are likely to base pair or wrap about one another, incorporation of phenylalanine is partially or completely reduced. Thus, the synthetic polymer is most effective in synthesis when it is single-stranded, as is apparently also true for normal messenger RNA.

It is also possible to study the effect on amino acid incorporation into protein of the presence of different nucleotides in the same polyribonucleotide. Using polynucleotide phosphorylase, one can enzymatically synthesize *in vitro* polyribotides containing two or more different ribotides which are apparently in a random order. The analysis[8,9] is greatly expedited by the fact that polyphenylalanine is insoluble in the cell-free system. In practice, then, in forming any mixed polynucleotide, an excess of uridylic acid is used, in order to obtain the synthesized protein as a precipitate, which

[9] By S. Ochoa and coworkers.

can then be analyzed for the amount and kind of amino acids, besides phenylalanine, which are present. Thus, to synthesize polyuridylic-adenylic acid, polyuridylic-cytidylic acid, and polyuridylic-guanylic acid, five times as much uridine diphosphate is used as the diphosphates of adenosine, cytidine, or guanosine, respectively. To make mixed polynucleotides containing UAC, UCG, or UGA, ten times as much uridine diphosphate is used as the nucleoside diphosphates of A, C, or G.

For example, a mixed polyribotide composed of U and C is added to the cell-free system, which is then tested to determine whether any amino acid besides phenylalanine is incorporated into protein. With this particular mixture, proline and serine are among the amino acids incorporated. The code letters for these amino acids include, therefore, at least one U and one C. One can also determine, in the same way, the effects of other mixed polyribotides on amino acid incorporation. It is found that some amino acids, such as alanine and arginine, require three different nucleotides to be encoded, so that the *coding ratio* (the number of nucleotides required to code one amino acid) is at least three. (No amino acid is found which requires the presence of all four types of nucleotides. Were the coding ratio four, there would be 24 different sequences possible in quartets composed of AUGC, some of which might be expected to encode an amino acid.) In view of these results (and of others [10] suggesting a low coding ratio) it is hypothesized that triplets of nucleotides of messenger RNA have amino acid meaning, that is, that we are dealing with a *triplet RNA code*.

By varying the proportions of uridylic acid and cytidylic acid in a mixed polynucleotide, it is discovered that less proline than serine is incorporated when there is an excess of polyuridylic acid. However,

[10] Obtained by A. Garen (190).

when there is a relative excess of cytidylic acid in the polymer, the reverse occurs, namely, more proline than serine is incorporated. In terms of triplets, proline must be specified by UCC and serine as UUC (see Figure 47-3), although the sequence of nucleotides in the triplet and the order in which they are read are still undetermined. In other words, although the messenger RNA triplet code letters are UCC for proline, we cannot say whether the sequence is UCC, CUC, or CCU. (The first and last triplets are different, since the single-stranded messenger RNA molecule is polarized.)

Starting with ribotides of U and C in the relative frequencies 5 : 1, we can predict the relative frequencies of different triplets in the synthesized polymer. UUU should occur with a frequency of $\frac{5}{6} \times \frac{5}{6} \times \frac{5}{6}$, or $\frac{125}{216}$. While there are three arrangements possible for the code letters UUC, any particular sequence should occur with a frequency of $\frac{5}{6} \times \frac{5}{6} \times \frac{1}{6}$, or $\frac{25}{216}$; any one of the three possible arrangements of UCC should occur with a frequency of $\frac{5}{6} \times \frac{1}{6} \times \frac{1}{6}$, or $\frac{5}{216}$, while CCC should occur with a frequency of $\frac{1}{216}$. These particular sequences are, respectively, in the relative frequencies 125, 25, 5, and 1. Accordingly, if a triplet code is the correct one, then when this particular polyribotide is studied for protein synthesis, one would expect five times more phenylalanine incorporated than serine, and 25 times more phenylalanine incorporated than proline. Although the results actually obtained [11] using various synthetic polymers sometimes differ by a factor of two or so from those expected according to the present analysis, the over-all agreement is striking, and offers very strong support for a triplet RNA code.

(If an amino acid is incorporated at a rate lower than expected, this may be due to the fact that a given nucleotide, *U*, is in a sequence which can be read meaningfully in more than two ways. If the sequence is UU*U*CCC, sometimes the triplet read may be UU*U* (phenylalanine), or U*U*C (serine?), and still other times *U*CC (proline?). Thus, nucleotide-sharing may be partially responsible for actual incorporation rate deviating from that expected.)

You should be able to work out that a polymer synthesized from ribotides of U, A, and C in the relative amounts of 6, 1, and 1, respectively, has the triplet code letters, UUU, UUA, AAU, UAC, AAA, CCC, in a given sequence in the relative frequencies 216 : 36 : 6 : 6 : 1 : 1, respectively.

Using synthetic polyribotides, the triplet code letters have been determined for 19 amino acids [11] and predicted for one amino acid, and it is these which are given in Figure 47–3. All meaningful triplets in the experimentally detected code contain U. This does not seem to be dependent solely upon the fact that, for technical reasons, each mixed polynucleotide contained U. For no amino acid was incorporated following treatment with pure polyribotides of A or of C. It seems reasonably certain that *all meaningful triplets in the messenger RNA code for amino acids normally contain uracil*. (This does not preclude the occurrence of mistakes, as the result of which a given amino acid is encoded by another triplet which may or may not contain U.)

Of the 64 unidirectionally read triplets possible using A U G C, 37 have one or more U's and 27 have none. (The chance a triplet has no U is $\frac{3}{4} \times \frac{3}{4} \times \frac{3}{4}$, or $\frac{27}{64}$.) It is reasonable, therefore, to expect that triplets which do not contain U do not appear in messenger RNA, except possibly to interrupt the message in order to end a polypeptide chain. If the presence of U in each triplet is characteristic of messenger RNA, then this RNA must have been the complement of a DNA strand which characteristically has triplets containing A. Moreover, the complementary DNA chain would be characterized by the usual presence of T in its trip-

[11] By S. Ochoa and coworkers.

AMINO ACID	TRIPLET CODE LETTERS (Sequence unknown)
Alanine	UCG
Arginine	UCG
Asparagine	UAA (UAC?)
Aspartic acid	UAG
Cysteine	UUG
Glutamic acid	UAG
Glutamine	UGC (predicted)
Glycine	UGG
Histidine	UAC
Isoleucine	UUA
Leucine	UUC (UUA?, UUG?)
Lysine	UAA
Methionine	UAG
Phenylalanine	UUU
Proline	UCC
Serine	UUC
Threonine	UAC (UCC?)
Tryptophan	UGG
Tyrosine	UUA
Valine	UUG

FIGURE 47–3. *Messenger RNA code for amino acids.* (*After Speyer, J. F.,* et al., *Proc. Nat. Acad. Sci., U.S., 48:441–448, 1962.*)

lets and the template RNA made from it should contain A in almost every triplet. This RNA would not be used as messenger. We have already presumed (see Figure 47–2 and its discussion in the text) that part of this RNA is used to make sRNA. This is supported by the fact that although only one triplet of sRNA is known, it is ACC. We are led to suppose that sRNA has a different triplet which pairs with a triplet of messenger RNA, and that it contains at least one A. It is also supposed that this is the same triplet which directs a particular activating enzyme to join a particular kind of amino acid to a specific sRNA.

Therefore, we expect that (1) if a portion

of one DNA strand is rich in successive triplets containing at least one A, this portion is used to make U-containing messenger RNA, and that (2) there is a corresponding segment in the complementary DNA strand, each of whose triplets contains T, which is used not to make messenger RNA but A-containing sRNA. It is not necessary to assume that all portions of a given DNA strand are used to make the same type of informational RNA (messenger RNA or sRNA). For it is possible, via mutation, to invert a segment of double-stranded DNA; sometimes the length of the inverted segment would correspond exactly with a protein-specifying cistron or operon. If this occurs, some parts of a given DNA strand may be used to make messenger RNA, and other parts to make sRNA.

SUMMARY AND CONCLUSIONS

The translation of DNA nucleotide sequence into amino acid sequence involves the following events: Each of the single strands of double-helix DNA serves as template for RNA polymerase, which synthesizes two complementary single strands of informational RNA. Segments of informational RNA which are composed primarily of U-containing nucleotide triplets attach to ribosomes in the cytoplasm and function as messenger RNA. Segments of informational RNA which are complementary to messenger RNA, and hence have at least one A per triplet, are used to make transfer (soluble or s) RNA. Each kind of amino acid is individually activated and attached to a different kind of sRNA in the cytoplasm. The sRNA molecules, each carrying an amino acid, apparently base pair with complementary regions of messenger RNA, so that the transported amino acids are arranged in a specific linear sequence on the ribosome. The amino acids are then linked enzymatically to form a polypeptide which is freed from sRNA, after which the sRNA molecules are liberated from pairing with messenger RNA, and each is free to receive another amino acid for transfer.

It is assumed that sRNA possesses a nucleotide triplet, containing at least one A, and that this triplet serves both to specifically attract a particular amino acid and to pair with its complementary triplet in messenger RNA. The code letters in this sRNA triplet and in messenger RNA would be complementary. The code letters in messenger RNA have been determined for almost all amino acids (each triplet contains at least one U), although the sequence of the letters within the triplet and the order in which they are read are still largely undetermined.

The comma-free, triplet RNA code for specifying amino acids is essentially solved, although some of the details are unknown at this time.

REFERENCES

Allfrey, V. G., and Mirsky, A. E., "How Cells Make Molecules," Scient. Amer., 205:74–82, 1961.

Bautz, E. K. F., and Hall, B. D., "The Isolation of T4-Specific RNA on a DNA-Cellulose Column," Proc. Nat. Acad. Sci., U.S., 48:400–408, 1962.

Brenner, S., Jacob, F., and Meselson, M., "An Unstable Intermediate Carrying Information from Genes to Ribosomes for Protein Synthesis," Nature, London, 190:576–581, 1961.

Crick, F. H. C., "Nucleic Acids," Scient. Amer., 197:188–200, 1957.

Crick, F. H. C., "On Protein Synthesis," Symp. Soc. Exp. Biol., 12:138–163, 1958.

Furth, J. J., Hurwitz, J., and Goldman, M., "The Directing Role of DNA in RNA Synthesis," Biochem. Biophys. Res. Commun., 4:362–367, 1961.

Garen, A., "Genetic Control of the Specificity of the Bacterial Enzyme, Alkaline Phosphatase," in *Microbial Genetics*, Hayes, W., and Clowes, R. C. (Eds.), Cambridge, Cambridge University Press, 1960, pp. 239–247.

Speakers (l. to r.) M. W. NIRENBERG, F. LIPMANN, *and* S. OCHOA *at a symposium on the RNA code held January, 1962 at Indiana University.*

Gay, H., "Nuclear Control of the Cell," Scient. Amer., 202 (No. 1):126–136, 1960.

Geiduschek, E. P., Nakamoto, T., and Weiss, S. B., "The Enzymatic Synthesis of RNA, Complementary Interaction with DNA," Proc. Nat. Acad. Sci., U.S., 47:1405–1415, 1961.

Goldstein, A., "Chain Growing of Proteins: Some Consequences for the Coding Problem," J. Mol. Biol., 4:121–122, 1962.

Gross, F., Hiatt, H., Gilbert, W., Kurland, C. G., Risebrough, R. W., and Watson, J. D., "Unstable Ribonucleic Acid Revealed by Pulse Labelling," Nature, London, 190:581–585, 1961.

Hall, B. D., and Spiegelman, S., "Sequence Complementarity of T2–DNA and T2–Specific RNA," Proc. Nat. Acad. Sci., U.S., 47:137–146, 1961.

Hoagland, M. B., "Nucleic Acids and Proteins," Scient. Amer., 201 (No. 6):55–61, 1959.

Hurwitz, J., and Furth, J. J., "Messenger RNA," Scient. Amer., 206 (No. 2):41–49, 1962.

Kurland, C. G., "Molecular Characterization of Ribonucleic Acid from *Escherichia Coli* Ribosomes," J. Mol. Biol., 2:83–91, 1960.

Martin, R. G., Matthaei, J. H., Jones, O. W., and Nirenberg, M. W., "Ribonucleotide Composition of the Genetic Code," Biochem. Biophys. Res. Commun., 6:410–414, 1962.

Nirenberg, M. W., and Matthaei, J. H., "The Dependence of Cell-Free Protein Synthesis in *E. Coli* upon Naturally Occurring or Synthetic Polyribonucleotides," Proc. Nat. Acad. Sci., U.S., 47:1588–1602, 1961.

Novelli, G. D., Kameyama, F., and Eisenstadt, J. M., "The Effect of Ultraviolet Light and X Rays on an Enzyme-Forming System," J. Cell. Comp. Physiol., 58 (Suppl.):225–244, 1961.

Schulman, H. M., and Bonner, D. M., "A Naturally Occurring DNA–RNA Complex from *Neurospora crassa*," Proc. Nat. Acad. Sci., U.S., 48:53–63, 1962.

Speyer, J. F., Lengyel, P., Basilio, C., and Ochoa, S., "Synthetic Polynucleotides and the Amino Acid Code, II," Proc. Nat. Acad. Sci., U.S., 48:63–68, 1962.

Stevens, A., "Net Formation of Polyribonucleotides with Base Compositions Analogous to Deoxyribonucleic Acid," J. Biol. Chem., 236 (No. 7), PC 44, 1961.

Strauss, B. S., *An Outline of Chemical Genetics*, Philadelphia, Saunders, 1960.

Tal, M., and Elson, D., "The Reversible Release of Protein, Ribonucleic Acid and Deoxyribonuclease from Ribosomes," Biochim. et Biophys. Acta, 53:227–229, 1961.

Zamecnik, P. C., "The Microsome," Scient. Amer., 198 (No. 3):118–124, 1958.

Zamecnik, P. C., "Historical and Current Aspects of the Problem of Protein Synthesis," Harvey Lect., 54:256–281, 1960.

QUESTIONS FOR DISCUSSION

47.1. Would you expect the RNA code for amino acids to be the same in all free-living organisms? Explain.

47.2. Compare the replication of RNA virus with that of polypeptide chains.

47.3. If a polypeptide chain is specified by a sequence 2000 or so nucleotides, what would you conclude regarding the presence of non-nucleotide material as punctuation between cistrons?

47.4. To what use can you put the fact that the spacing between nucleotides in a DNA chain is nearly the same as it is between amino acids in a polypeptide chain?

47.5. Discuss the hypothesis that ribosomes are viruses.

47.6. Make a report on advances in our understanding of the genetic code since the present account was written (February 1962).

47.7. What evidence can you present that the attachment of messenger RNA to the ribosome does not involve extensive complementary base pairing?

47.8. Give evidences that messenger RNA is single-stranded.

Chapter **48**

THE BIOCHEMICAL EVOLUTION
OF GENETIC MATERIAL

IN THE course of studying the nature and effects of genes, you may have wondered about the origin of genetic material on earth. This would involve the first occurrence of a chemical substance capable of replicating itself and some of its modifications. At present we know of only two substances having these properties, DNA and RNA. Some understanding of the problems involved in explaining gene origin may be obtained from a consideration of our knowledge of present-day genes and of biological evolution.

Let us assume that the first gene was either DNA or RNA. Given the presence of the first gene, how did it manage to replicate? We already know something regarding the mechanism of biological replication of DNA. The simplest DNA system capable of replicating *in vitro* requires the presence of (1) energy to separate the double-stranded helix, (2) four kinds of deoxyriboside triphosphates, and (3) the enzyme DNA polymerase, not to mention water, at the correct pH, which contains the ions necessary to activate the enzyme. It does not seem very likely that the first gene was a DNA polymer which replicated in this manner. One reason for this opinion is based upon the essential role played by the enzyme. According to our present understanding, the amino acid sequence in such an enzyme is specified by a gene. It seems improbable that so complex an enzyme could be formed independently of gene action. However, one

439

might require that the first gene be capable of specifying DNA polymerase which would then be available for subsequent DNA synthesis. Even so, one would have to be convinced that the amino acids in the enzyme, the nucleoside triphosphate building blocks, and the energy for chain separation are components likely to be present in the environment of that time. The difficulty of chain separation would be avoided if the first gene were RNA, since this nucleic acid is usually single-stranded. Unfortunately, we do not know nearly as much about the biological replication of RNA genes as we do about DNA genes.

The complexity of present-day replication of DNA should not automatically exclude it or RNA as being the material basis of the first gene. Before making any decision on this matter, we would need to have more information relative to DNA synthesis, including answers to such questions as: (1) Can any other simpler substance substitute, no matter how inefficiently, for the polymerase? (2) What is the shortest nucleotide sequence capable of self-replication? (3) What, if any, simpler substances can replace the triphosphates?

Although DNA and RNA are recognized as being genetic material today, it is possible that the first genes were of neither type, but of a related chemical composition. We may even wonder if, at present, there are genes which are neither DNA nor RNA. Note that we have thus far bypassed the problem of the origin of the first gene, and have considered only the matter of its replication were it DNA or RNA. Although we initially inquired about the origin of genes, clearly the answer we suggest regarding the mechanism of its replication will depend upon the chemical identity we hypothesize for the first gene.

In considering the origin of the first gene we should keep in mind the possibility that its nongenic predecessor might have been capable of some degree of self-replication, but might not have been able to replicate any of its mutant forms. The search for information regarding nongenic systems having some but not all of the properties of genetic material is clearly highly desirable. Such information may be sought in studies of various polymers under test tube conditions. Subgenic chemicals may occur in present-day cells. Several constituents of the cytoplasm other than plastids are able to self-replicate. These include the centriole and the kinetosome (which have already been discussed on pages 369–370 in connection with episomes). If these structures prove to be mutable and are still able to self-replicate, they can be classed as cytoplasmic or extra-nuclear genes. Experimental study of these organelles will be expected to reveal the details of their chemistry, and whether they possess only the self-replicating capacity of genes, never having had, or having lost, the ability to reproduce themselves after mutation. In any event, our knowledge of genes will be increased by such studies. We would also wish to know a great deal more about the synthesis of RNA genes, and whether ribosomes, which have the chemical composition of RNA genes,[1] are self-replicating and mutable, in order to speculate fruitfully upon the nature of the pregenic and the first genic material.

While we must conclude that we do not yet have sufficient information to decide which pathway led to the chemical evolution of the first gene, we do have some evidence on the subsequent history of genes. The only genetic material found exclusively in free-living organisms today is DNA, and this is found in all such organisms, whether they be unicellular or multicellular, plant, animal, or microorganismal. Whether or not other types of genes exist or have existed, DNA genes must have a selective advantage for survival, having persisted as the main

[1] See A. Van Kammen (1961).

genetic material for about a billion years, which is approximately the period that plants and animals have been separate in their evolution. Moreover, it is likely that the formation of chromosomes with telomeres and with centromeres, as well as the establishment of special methods of separating daughter and homologous chromosomes (by mitosis and meiosis), and of recombining them (fertilization), were innovations involving DNA which were established some time prior to the divergence of the plant and animal kingdoms.

Not only must there have been a chemical evolution in DNA and the accessory material which packages and recombines it, but there probably was also an evolution in gene activity. It is likely that the primitive earth accumulated large amounts of different, more or less complex, organic materials which remained undegraded before the advent of the first genetic material. As the first gene-containing organisms used up these resources in their metabolism, however, there would have been a selection in favor of mutants capable of synthesizing such organic materials from simpler organic, or from inorganic, components. This means that natural selection acted against those genes which functioned *auxotrophically* (that is, which were incapable of directing synthesis of nongenetic material or directed the formation of no meaningful synthetic product) in favor of those genes which functioned *prototrophically* (that is, which specified the synthesis of a component no longer available in the environment). Prototrophism would also be advanced by the physical association of genes involved in different portions of a given biochemical sequence. This would lead eventually to the selection of mutant genes whose function, other than self-replication, was to regulate the functioning of other genes. Thus, in addition to genes for structure, there would be expected to evolve genes for function — operator genes located in operons.

A study of the comparative biochemistry of present higher plants and animals, bacteria, and many viruses, shows that they all form or require the same 20 or so amino acids. Accordingly, nucleic acid and protein are, perhaps, the most durable geochemical features of the earth, having persisted more than a billion years. Because of the intimate relationship between amino acids and genetic material, it would seem highly desirable to learn about the evolution of all kinds of organic (carbon-containing) compounds, including amino acids and polypeptides, energy-rich compounds (like ATP), catalysts (like iron-containing compounds), and energy-capturing compounds (like chlorophyll).

Our present understanding is that at an early stage in the history of the earth there was a *reducing atmosphere*, which was rich in water, hydrogen, methane, and ammonia, but poor in free oxygen and CO_2. Using mixtures of gases predicated as being present in such a reducing atmosphere, and exposing such mixtures to heat, ultraviolet light, or electrical discharges (man-made lightning), it has been possible to produce large amounts and a large variety of amino acids. Other experiments have, by heat treatment, converted amino acids into polypeptides, and have produced purines like adenine from simpler components. Such experiments are expected to lead us to understand better the organic evolution which took place on earth prior to the formation of the first genes or organisms.

We are not restricted to this planet, however, in our search for information regarding either pregenic, preorganismal evolution, or postgenic, postorganismal evolution. The present universe is about ten billion years old, the earth being about half this age. Because the universe contains vast numbers of stars (suns) with planets, there must be numerous suns the size of our own that have planets which are about the same size as the earth and which are about the same distance from their suns. Some of these planets are surely younger and others older than our own. What is the possibility that a chemical and biological evolution similar to that which occurred on earth would take place on these or other planets? The answer to this question will depend, of course, upon the chemical composition of these other planets.

Most of the universe is composed of hydrogen and helium (most of the earth's hydrogen having escaped from its atmosphere in the distant past). Of the remaining atoms, however, the universe has abundant oxygen and nitrogen and, in fact, is relatively richer than the earth in carbon, the atom essential for the organic compounds which have played so important a role in chemical and biological evolution on earth. It is, therefore, likely that there are numerous places in the universe where the initiation of an organic chemistry of biological interest would be possible. Since the earth is a relatively poor place for such an evolution (which nevertheless occurred), there are almost surely numerous planets in the universe like our own, which contain earlier stages in chemical evolution, similar stages in biological evolution, as well as those which are older, and very probably have more advanced types of organisms.

We already have evidence for the occurrence of organic radicals like CH, CN, CC, and CO in comets, and for organic molecules of an asymmetric type on Mars. Astronomers have also reported variations in apparent color and texture of Mars with changes in season. These evidences are very strong that Mars contains appreciable quantities of organic matter, although one cannot yet decide whether these have a preorganismal or an organismal origin.

Further information about the chemistry of the sun and planets will doubtless be provided by telescopes of various kinds placed into orbit above our atmosphere. In this position, such telescopes would not be impeded, as they are now, by the absorption of energy by the contents of our own atmosphere. Interplanetary research is now in progress to send instruments to or near various planets in the near future. Such missions will be capable of telling us the detailed chemistry of any of our neighboring planets, and will, of course, also be designed to detect the presence of organisms and of DNA. We are already sending radio signals into space in an attempt to contact other organisms capable of replying.

It will become apparent to you that in any space mission it is important to avoid the accidental transplantation of terrestrial genotypes to other planets. For, if a single bacterium, like *E. coli*, were to be placed on a planet containing a suitable medium, the progeny would occupy a volume the size of the earth in about 48 hours. Such an unscheduled transplantation would be disastrous to any plan we would have for a later study either of the preorganismal evolution of organic compounds or of any indigenous organisms. This is why objects sent beyond our atmosphere are carefully sterilized.

Which heavenly objects, likely to be investigated in the near future, are interesting from the point of view of preorganismal and organismal evolution? We have already mentioned the desirability of exploring Mars. Consider Venus, whose surface is unknown, being hidden completely by an opaque, highly reflecting, cloud layer, containing abundant CO_2 and water. While estimates of Venus' temperature vary widely, and it is thought that its surface is dry and hot, we cannot assume that organic chemistry or even biological activity is impossible there. After studying its chemistry in sufficient detail, it is possible that we might wish to colonize Venus, perhaps first by placing a chlorophyll-containing microorganism in its outer atmosphere. In a very short period, such an organism, by using huge quantities of the atmospheric components for growth and reproduction, might change the entire climate on Venus. Missions to other planets in our solar system would be expected to reveal the kind of chemical evolution which occurs under other environmental conditions.

Our own satellite, the moon, has no atmosphere, and probably no water. Accordingly, the presence there today of earthlike life is out of the question. However, it is possible that the moon is just about as old as the earth and may have had an organic and even a biological evolution similar to our own before it lost its atmosphere. So, it will be interesting to obtain and analyze samples of its surface and, particularly, its subsurface material. It has been suggested that the moon might act as a gravitational trap for fossil spores which may have drifted between planets. Although improbable, the very possibility of an interplanetary gene flow is too important to ignore in our plans to explore and exploit space. Planetary research has many motivations, but the search for evidence of chemical evolution, DNA, organisms, and life would seem to be among the most significant.

SUMMARY AND CONCLUSIONS

DNA has been the primary genetic material on earth for about a billion years. During this time DNA together with accessory material has undergone a structural evolution leading to the establishment of chromosomes and of mechanisms for genetic recombination. There has probably been also a functional evolution of genes, which proceeded from those which serve as genes for structure (specifying the organization of nongenic compounds) to those which serve as genes for function (and act as operator genes in operons).

Further information regarding pre- and postgenic evolution can be expected to be obtained from experiments with polymers, DNA, RNA, and various cell organelles, as well as from experiments involving other planets. It is expected that biochemical and biological evolution will also be found elsewhere in the universe.

REFERENCES

Abelson, P. H., "Extra-Terrestrial Life," Proc. Nat. Acad. Sci., U.S., 47:575–581, 1961.

Blum, H. F., "On the Origin and Evolution of Living Machines," Amer. Sci., 49:474–501, 1961.

Calvin, M., "The Origin of Life on Earth and Elsewhere," Ann. Int. Med., 54:954–976, 1961.

Clark, F., and Synge, R. L. M., (Eds.), *The Origin of Life on the Earth*, New York, Pergamon Press, 1959.

Huang, S.-S., "Life Outside the Solar System," Scient. Amer., 202 (No. 4):55–63, 1960.

Lederberg, J., "Exobiology: Approaches to Life Beyond the Earth," Science, 132:393–400, 1960.

Lederberg, J., and Cowie, D. B., "Moondust," Science, 127:1473–1475, 1958.

Miller, S. L., and Urey, H. C., "Organic Compound Synthesis on the Primitive Earth," Science, 130:245–251, 1959.

Oparin, A. I., *The Origin of Life on the Earth*, 3rd Ed., New York, Academic Press, 1957.

Penrose, L. S., "Self-Reproducing Machines," Scient. Amer., 200 (No. 6):105–114, 1959.

Rose, H. H., *A Synthesis of Evolutionary Theory*, Englewood Cliffs, N.J., Prentice-Hall, 1962.

Sagan, C., "The Planet Venus," Science, 133:849–858, 1961.

Sagan, C., "On the Origin and Planetary Distribution of Life," Rad. Res., 15:174–192, 1961.

Sinton, W. M., "Further Evidence of Vegetation on Mars," Science, 130:1234–1237, 1959.

Tax, S. (Ed.), *The Evolution of Life*, Vol. 1 of *Evolution after Darwin*, Chicago, University of Chicago Press, 1960.

Van Kammen, A., "Infectious Ribonucleic Acid in the Ribosomes of Tobacco Leaves Infected with Tobacco Mosaic Virus," (PN 941), Biochim. Biophys. Acta, 53:230–232, 1961.

See Supplement VII.

QUESTIONS FOR DISCUSSION

48.1. Which do you think came first in evolution, the gene or what we now consider "gene product"? Explain.

48.2. Do you consider it a fact that the genetic material on earth has undergone a biochemical evolution? A structural evolution? A functional evolution? Why?

48.3. Do you believe there are "superhumans" on other planets? Why?

48.4. Do you suppose, in the future, that we will need to be just as careful to avoid the accidental transplantation of genotypes from other planets to our own, as we now are to avoid the reverse? Why?

48.5. In what respects would you expect the environment of Venus to be changed by explantation of a photosynthesizing microorganism to its atmosphere?

48.6. What kind of information would you seek to discover from landings on the moon? Mars? Venus?

48.7. What characteristics would you expect genes from other planets to have?

Chapter *49

GENES — NATURE
AND CONSEQUENCE

IN THE first Chapter, we postulated the occurrence of genetic material responsible for phenotypic similarities and differences between organisms. We later required that the genetic material be self-replicating and capable of self-replicating some of its chemical changes. Most of this book has been concerned primarily with the further definition or delimitation of the nature of the genetic material. Each different way of studying segments of the genetic material, or genes, revealed additional properties of the genetic material which were expressed in terms of the operation used to detect them. Thus, in the study of the chemical basis of the genetic material, it was demonstrated that all known genes are inseparable from nucleotides of either RNA or DNA, the latter being the typical genetic substance of chromosomes and of free-living organisms. RNA is usually single-stranded and DNA double-stranded.

The biological replication of DNA involves strand separation and the action of a polymerase that takes directions from the single DNA chain, in the utilization of deoxyriboside triphosphates to manufacture the complementary DNA chain. Though DNA is self-replicating, this does not mean that the process is accomplished in one step. In fact, it requires two replications before a given strand can result in a copy of itself, the first replication producing the complementary strand and the second replication

producing a copy of the first strand. It is probably justified to think of self-replication as occurring in this indirect way for several reasons. First, DNA replication is by single strands, each of which apparently acts independently of the other. Second, DNA occurs in organisms like ϕX174 in the single-stranded condition, all strands being the same complement. Here self-replication must be considered a two-step process. Third, it is possible that one of the two strands in a double helix may be defective (mutant), so that it is, at least in some places, incapable of replicating a complement. Such a chain would be incapable of both replication and self-replication in its defective portion, while its normal, complementary chain would be capable of both.

The preceding dealt with self-replication at the chemical level. When does self-replication occur at the informational level? The transforming ability of hybrid DNA double helices proves that a single DNA strand is capable, subsequent to replication, of providing all the information contained in a double-stranded helix possessing correct complementary pairs. It is likely that either single strand of a normal double helix can furnish this information after it has replicated once. However, all or part of the information used to make messenger RNA may be carried by only one DNA strand. Therefore, in order to carry the same functional (messenger, or sRNA, or other) information, DNA probably has to self-replicate. It would seem desirable, therefore, to recognize the difference between replication and self-replication, at both the chemical and informational levels.

Does pure DNA have any of the properties of the genetic material? It is still an assumption, however likely, that the DNA primer placed *in vitro* has come from the replication of DNA *in vivo*, rather than being the product of the activity of some other substance, like protein or RNA. Accordingly, we cannot use the origin of the DNA primer as part of a proof that it is genic. But, consider certain chemical characteristics possessed by the DNA primer. It is self-replicating under *in vitro* conditions, and, moreover, replicates precisely certain chemical modifications of itself. This is demonstrated directly by the extensive synthesis which occurs after uracil is substituted for the thymine in the substrate (cf. p. 325), and is demonstrated indirectly, using the normal substrate, by the synthesized product having the same $A + T/C + G$ ratio as the primer, regardless of what variation in this ratio the primer may show. We conclude, therefore, that DNA synthesis *in vitro* fulfills one of the requirements of our definition of genetic material. The detection of genetic material was originally dependent upon its presence in organisms and its production of a phenotypic effect. In the course of this book, however, we have apparently dispensed with these requirements. Pure virus DNA in a test tube is considered genetic material, even though it is no longer intraorganismal, recombining, mutating, replicating, or performing any phenotypic function. This is valid on the basis that this DNA either is known or expected to possess such properties when introduced into an organism, or is chemically indistinguishable from organismal DNA known or expected to have these properties. The DNA synthesized *in vitro* is chemically indistinguishable from organismal DNA, is capable of self-replicating itself and some of its modifications, and of undergoing strand separation and recombination. Since it possesses these characteristics it would seem reasonable to consider that it, too, is genetic material, even though, until now, attempts to detect a cistronic effect via transformation have been unsuccessful. According to this view, then, genetic material has already been synthesized in the test tube.

We have just reasoned that DNA may be identified as genetic material, using solely the operation of chemical investigation. Using living cells there are other operations which can be employed to study and identify genes, including recombination, mutation, and phenotypic function. These other methods of studying genes have led to our present understanding of the recon and cistron. Chemically, we have found that the recon may be a single nucleotide, while the cistron is composed of several or many recons. What is the smallest chemical unit of genetic material capable of (chemical and informational) replication? We do not know.

The phenotypical, mutational, and recombinational operations employed to study gene properties are different from the study of genes by chemical methods in two respects. First, they require that the gene produce a phenotypic effect. Second, they require a genetic alternative which produces a detectable change in phenotype. Let us make some additional observations regarding each of these three operations in turn.

It should be made clear that just because all three of these operations depend upon phenotypic effects for their detection does not necessarily mean that these operations automatically characterize cistrons. For cistrons are genetic units as defined from the study of what are apparently the single primary phenotypic effects of genes. If we study the mutation from dull red to white eye in *Drosophila*, for example, or the recombination of such mutants, we are not necessarily concerned with whether we are dealing with the primary effects of genetic units; merely studying the effects of genes undergoing mutation and recombination does not automatically reveal information on how cistrons are related to the traits produced. The cistron has meaning only when it is hypothesized that the genetic material has a single effect other than replication, and only after the decision is made as to which effect is to be considered primary can the scope of the cistron be identified by experimental means.

Let us examine the basic premise involved, which states that one genetic unit, or cistron, has one primary function besides replication. This was presented as a working hypothesis in the hope that its acceptance would lead to experiments which would result in a better understanding of the functional unit of genetic material. This hypothesis, however fruitful may have been the consequence of its acceptance, has never been proved (refer to p. 278). What basis have we for such a conclusion? Suppose we start with a morphological or biochemical pleiotropism whose pedigree can be traced back to fewer and fewer causes. If, after tracing the pedigree back as far as our techniques permit, we find there are still two or more apparently unrelated effects, the proponent in favor of the one cistron-one function hypothesis can always claim that had we searched longer with better techniques, we would find this pleiotropism has a single basis. Or, if we are able to trace a group of pleiotropic effects back to a single origin, opponents of this hypothesis can still state that had we looked harder and better we would find still other, not yet known, effects which would be unrelated to the single factor which explains all the presently known pleiotropic effects. We must conclude, therefore, that we cannot decide what a primary effect of a gene is merely from the number of effects detected.

However, we have used the idea, that if we find a one-to-one correlation between any effect and a gene change, the phenotypic effect is directly, hence primarily, the result of gene action. In this way, for instance, we tested the idea that polypeptide sequence is determined in a primary way by nucleotide sequence. We found, in the case of hemoglobin, that mutation was directly associated with a change in its amino acid composition. Acceptance of the hypothesis one polypeptide-one cistron, however, does not mean that the reverse is true, namely, one

cistron-one polypeptide, that is, that all cistrons have as their primary function the specification of polypeptides. The reservation was made that cistrons also might act in a primary way to specify other substances. In this connection, it should be mentioned that operator genes are recognized by having a primary effect upon the functioning of other genes, and that thus far such genes have not been demonstrated to specify any chemical product whatsoever.

When we speak of a phenotypic result as being affected by a gene in a primary way, do we mean anything other than that there is a one-to-one relationship between gene and phenotype? Do we mean that the first action of a gene is, at least in some cases, the specification of amino acid sequence? No! For we have evidence from hemoglobin and other proteins that their synthesis takes place in the cytoplasm, physically isolated from conserved DNA. In these cases the amino acid sequence is specified by messenger RNA nucleotide sequence. In such cases, then, it is clearly more correct to consider RNA specification as being caused in a primary way by genic action than it is to claim the same for amino acid sequence.

Let us discuss the matter of gene action by starting not from a phenotypic result and working back toward the gene, but from the other direction, starting with the gene. The genetic activity we know most about directly is replication. In DNA replication the single DNA strand is remarkably passive, in that it is neither energy-supplying, nor appreciably modified in its own structure, nor irreversibly changed in any directional manner, nor acting enzymatically. What then are the properties of DNA which are responsible for its capacity to serve as template? These properties must include the physical configuration of linearly arranged nucleotides as well as the specific pattern of their electrical charges, both of which seem to act more in a physical than in a chemical capacity. The utilization of the DNA template for DNA replication is, therefore, a relatively passive process with regard to the DNA strand, and an active, chemical one relative to the highly specific action of DNA polymerase. If the DNA fiber which serves as a template for DNA polymerase action is mostly a passive chemical, it should be not at all surprising that DNA serves as a template which is utilized by other enzymes, provided that the raw materials collected on the template are sufficiently similar to deoxyribotides in physical and electrical properties. This has, in fact, been found true for polyribotides synthesized by RNA polymerase which uses DNA as template. Whether nucleotides other than those in DNA and RNA, or still other substances, make use of the DNA template in a similar or different manner has yet to be determined. Be that as it may, it is suggested that the simplest and broadest working hypothesis is that all the functional characteristics of genes depend upon the linear sequence of nucleotides and the ways this can be used as template by various substances and enzymes. _In accordance with this view, serving as template is the primary and only function of DNA._ The DNA template would have at least two uses to which it is put, one involving the making of DNA and another the making of RNA polymers.

We come then to a new definition of *the gene, as being any template whose use eventually results in self-replication of the template, and which either retains this property after mutation or is derived from a template which can do so.* We can still consider as genetic any substance producing the same phenotypic effects as a known gene. In these terms, the RNA in plant viruses is genetic material, just as is conserved chromosomal DNA. We do not know how viral RNA functions in replication and self-replication, although there are several possibilities. The host cell may contain a special

RNA polymerase which uses the virus RNA as template, the second replication being virus RNA. Or, the virus RNA may be used as template by a special host DNA polymerase, and the DNA chain produced might then be used in a replication by regular RNA polymerase which would produce virus RNA. In either case, chemical and informational self-replication would be a two-step process, as is probably the case for DNA genes.

Is chromosomal RNA genic? Only future experimentation will provide the answer. We need to know whether nuclear polymers of RNA (synthesized using DNA as template) can be used as template in a manner suggested for virus RNA. If it is, it can probably self-replicate some of its mutants.

Because the DNA template contains particular nucleotides, each individual one has meaning at least for the specification of other complementary nucleotides (of DNA and RNA type), and groups of these in some cases eventually have purpose in the alignment of amino acids in polypeptides. It should be recalled that some protein synthesis apparently takes place in the nucleus. Does this synthesis involve the use of the RNA, or the DNA, or both, as template material? In this connection it may be remarked that the hypothesis of nucleotide-sharing translates into a phenomenon in which a segment of DNA or RNA template is utilized for two different purposes. Such purposes may be to make more DNA (to be conserved or not), more RNA (to be conserved or not), or to order amino acids or other substances. We need not specify whether this template-sharing should occur in the nucleus or the cytoplasm.

We have already been successful in the study of the replication and mutation of DNA *in vitro*, dissociated from protein. Recent studies [1] suggest that it may be possible also to study the enzyme-specifying cistron *in vitro*. The one-to-one relation-

[1] By D. Novelli and coworkers.

ship between cistrons and polypeptides is also expected to be extremely useful for determining the details of the DNA and RNA codes, and the nature of mutation. We have discussed several genetic systems which seem of special interest in these respects. One involves the genetic determination of hemoglobin. In this case, however, while the amino acid sequence of some of the protein is known, it is a difficult undertaking to determine the corresponding nucleotide sequence because of the large amount of nucleotide material in the genome. Several other systems should be mentioned. All involve viruses, which have a relatively small number of nucleotides per genome.

The amino acid sequence in the protein building block of tobacco mosaic virus is now known (see Figure 44–4). We need now to determine the sequence of ribotides in TMV. This is a formidable undertaking technically, whose success is hoped for, but is not assured. Progress along these lines is evidenced [2] by the finding that the terminal 5′ linked nucleotide in isolated TMV–RNA is adenosine, unphosphorylated at the 2′ and 3′ positions. Another line of attack attempts to correlate the details of the protein coat of phage with phage nucleotide sequence.

Still another line of investigation [3] involves the rII cistron in phage, whose fine structure is analyzable down to the nucleotide level, but whose phenotypic effect is not understood in detail chemically. Nevertheless, it is possible to determine the nucleotide basis for certain point mutants in the rII region. Suppose, in r^+, that the DNA strand "making" messenger RNA has a G in a certain triplet, and that this is replaced by A in a particular r point mutant. This mutant

[2] From work of T. Sugiyama and H. Fraenkel-Conrat, in 1961.
[3] Pursued by S. Benzer with S. P. Champe and other coworkers, and by others. (See reference in legend to Figure 43–5.)

phage may not lyse the K12 strain of *E. coli* because its messenger RNA is abnormal and contains U instead of C, and wrongly made r^+ product results. It has been found that 5-fluoro uracil, FU, is not mutagenic, but can substitute for the U in RNA when added to the diet of K12. When FU substitutes for U in messenger RNA, the FU may sometimes be mistaken for C by an sRNA molecule. So, in the case of the mutant under discussion, the sRNA paired with abnormal messenger RNA may be wrong, but it may be the one which carries the amino acid brought to this position in normal, r^+, messenger RNA. As a result, the normal amino acid would be incorporated, r^+ product would be formed, and the host cell would lyse. So, those r mutants, which can lyse only when FU is added, most probably have G on the r^+ DNA strand which "makes" messenger RNA, and C on the complementary DNA strand. Those mutants which do not lyse in the presence of FU may have T, A, or C at this locus in the DNA strand "making" messenger RNA. Using various chemical mutagens as well as FU, it is often possible to determine when T, or A, or C is present on the r^+ messenger-producing DNA strand.

It is sometimes found that a single phage mutant may simultaneously suppress the effects of point mutants at a number of other nucleotide sites. Suppose, in some of these cases, that all the latter point mutants have the same triplet modified by the same base substitution, and the result is that the same abnormal amino acid is incorporated into the different cistronic products. One way to suppress the effects of all of these mutants would be for a mutation to occur in the DNA which specifies the enzyme which determines which amino acid is transported by the specific sRNA which pairs with the abnormal triplet in the messenger RNA. In this case, an abnormal amino acid may be transported to the abnormal messenger RNA, and this amino acid may be the one which is normally incorporated at that position in the cistronic product. So, mutants which make wrong messenger RNA may still form the correct protein product, if the additional, compensating error is made of having sRNA carry a specific wrong amino acid. Through these and other studies in phage we can expect to learn a great deal about the sequence of nucleotides in DNA strands, the nature of the genetic code and of mutation. Further advances are expected from our increasing biochemical capabilities to determine nucleotide sequence in biologically made RNA and to synthesize specific sequences of ribonucleotides.

In order to study mutation, it has always been necessary in the past to observe a change in the phenotype, that is, some morphological, physiological, or biochemical change in a trait. Since additions, subtractions, or shifts of chromosomal material can be observed directly under the microscope, without any attempt being made to determine whether an extrachromosomal trait is involved, you might at first think such changes are not changes in phenotype but only changes in genotype. But the chromosome is surely just as much a part of the phenotype as is some nongenic portion of the organism. For example, the kappa particles (themselves genic) are properly described as being part of the *Paramecium's* phenotype (and also as part of its genotype). One can speak of the change in nuclear morphology (hence phenotype) which occurs when cells become polyploid or polytene (such changes having a genic basis). One can discuss changes in chromosomal phenotype during different stages of mitosis (even though there may be no gene change involved). It is clear, then, that the genotype refers to all the genes present, while the phenotype refers to all the genic and nongenic traits of the system. Of course, when one is working at the macroscopic level the phenotype cannot

include chromosomal or other genic traits, and deals only with the consequences of the interactions between genes and their environment.

The phrase, *a novel phenotype based upon genic change,* partially defines what we have previously called a mutant (see p. 403). The word "novel" requires some additional consideration. It would have been entirely correct to consider the first case of segregation as being a mutation, since it certainly was a novel change in the genetic material, one that had never before been recognized. When, however, other gene pairs were studied, it was found that segregation was not a novelty after all, but the rule for paired nuclear genes. We, therefore, include segregation as a means of genetic recombination, not of mutation. Similarly, genetic transformation was first considered to be a rare genetic change, and so was referred to as mutation. But once a variety of species exhibited this phenomenon, and once transformation was recognized as being a frequent event within certain species, it became clear that, usually, the process is better considered as a mechanism for genetic recombination. Recall also the discussion of *Modulator* and *Dissociation.* Although the position effects these genes apparently cause were not considered mutations, the movements of *Modulator* and *Dissociation* were. More and more cases of the latter type of change are being discovered. Are we still justified in considering these as being mutational? We will probably soon consider cases like these to be examples of another mechanism for genetic recombination, at least in certain organisms. Finally, you may recall that the integration and deintegration of F were classified as genetic recombinations, and not as mutations. You may have been surprised at this at the time, but this interpretation was given in the light of knowledge (which had not yet been presented) that other types of episomes were known. In this case, the evolution in terminology, from mutation to recombination, was purposely short-circuited.

Since what first appears to be a novel genetic change may prove, upon further investigation, not to be novel, we are always subject to reclassifying mutation as genetic recombination. Under these circumstances, today's mutations are possibly tomorrow's new mechanisms for genetic recombination.

The type of mutational change which seems to be most immune to reclassification as recombination is subnucleotide change. Clearly a substitution of 5-bromo uracil for thymine is a mutation. But even at this level, such immunity to reclassification is not absolute! Rotational substitution (A : T becomes T : A), now considered a possible type of mutation, may be found to be a normal mechanism of genetic recombination in some organisms.

It seems desirable to restrict the term *mutation* to describe *nucleotide changes which are unnatural* rather than novel. You may recall that we have already refrained from calling mutations certain genetic changes which occur naturally in the life cycle (polyploidy in liver cells, chromosome elimination in *Sciara*), although these same changes can be considered mutations at least when induced by extra-organismal factors.

What have we learned about recombination, the operation we used first to investigate the genetic material? We have found a variety of mechanisms which result in new genetic combinations, that is, changes in position or amount of naturally occurring nucleotide material. For chromosomal genes, these mechanisms include segregation, independent segregation, nondisjunction, crossing over, fertilization, polyploidy, polyteny, aneusomy, structural changes in chromosomes caused by breakage (such as deletion, duplication, inversion, translocation, transposition, and shift), transformation, transduction, and strand recombination *in vitro*. For extranuclear genes, we have found recombination to involve variation in number or kind of these genes; for episomes, we have the same recombinations as for extranuclear genes plus the pairing of episomes with, or their integration in, the chromosome.

In cases of transformation, strand recombination *in vitro*, and phage or plant virus infection, genetic recombination may require the addition or presence only of DNA or RNA. In most cases, however, it is not possible to make such a direct association, since, at the time of genetic recombination, the nucleic acid is apparently bound to protein in the form of nucleoprotein. Thus, for example, we cannot attribute chromosome breakage or crossing over to an action on or by DNA alone. It should also be realized that mutation (with the exception of certain virus-induced mutations) and template usage for gene action probably occur when the nucleic acid is in the form of nucleoprotein. For example, while the information may be carried solely by genetic RNA or DNA, this information is probably often used while the nucleic acid is bound to protein. Accordingly, our understanding of the usual recon and cistron will have to be expressed in terms of nucleoprotein activity, until such time as special materials and techniques are available.

Finally, you will realize that this book has been restricted largely to those consequences of genes which may reveal something of the nature of the genetic material. In comparison with what is known, very little has been said about the applications of genetic principles. We have had some brief discussions of how genetics plays a central role in our understanding of biological evolution, of differentiation, and of development. We have mentioned briefly some of the uses of genetics in plant and animal breeding, and in the understanding of inborn and infectious diseases. Some discussion of the past, present, and future uses and importance of genetics is given in Supplement V. Some of the questions posed at the ends of various Chapters also indicate various uses to which genetics has been or may be put.

We have come to the end of our thinking game, which I trust you have found stimulating. But I also hope the adventure is not completed for you, as it surely is not for me. Let us look to a future in which we continue rapidly to increase our knowledge about the nature and consequence of genes.

REFERENCES

Allen, J. M. (Ed.), *The Molecular Control of Cellular Activity*, New York, McGraw-Hill, 1961.

Cellular Regulatory Mechanisms, Cold Spr. Harb. Symp. Quant. Biol., 26, 1962.

Champe, S. P., and Benzer, S., "Reversal of Mutant Phenotypes by 5-Fluorouracil: An Approach to Nucleotide Sequences in Messenger-RNA," Proc. Nat. Acad. Sci., U.S., 48:532–546, 1962.

Fresco, J. R., and Straus, D. B., "Biosynthetic Polynucleotides: Models of Biological Templates," Amer. Sci., 50:158–179, 1962.

Mitchell, J. S. (Ed.), *The Cell Nucleus*, New York, Academic Press, 1960.

Muller, H. J., "Genetic Nucleic Acid: Key Material in the Origin of Life," Perspectives in Biol. and Med., 5 (No. 1, Autumn):1–23, 1961.

Niu, M. C., Cordova, C. C., and Niu, L. C., "Ribonucleic Acid-Induced Changes in Mammalian Cells," Proc. Nat. Acad. Sci., U.S., 47:1689–1700, 1961.

Sager, R., and Ryan, F. J., *Cell Heredity*, New York, Wiley, 1961.

Strauss, B. S., *An Outline of Chemical Genetics*, Philadelphia, Saunders, 1960.

QUESTIONS FOR DISCUSSION

49.1. Of what value are operational definitions of a gene?

49.2. What is your present definition of a gene?

49.3. In what respects has the concept of the gene been static and in what respects has it been dynamic, in the course of this book?

49.4. Define the recon and the cistron in chemical terms.

49.5. Ignoring its chemical composition, what are the other characteristics of a cistron? A recon?

49.6. How would you now define a mutant?

49.7. Is the recon a single nucleotide or a single nucleotide pair? Explain.

49.8. Discuss two areas of future investigation which you believe might provide basic information relative to the nature of the gene.

49.9. If a "replicon" is defined as the smallest unit of the genetic material capable of replication, discuss what is already known about it. What questions can you ask about it; whose answers are yet unknown?

49.10. The work of R. W. Briggs and T. J. King on nuclear transplantation proves that development involves irreversible changes in the nucleus. Should such changes be described as mutations? Explain.

49.11. Compare the terminal nucleosides of TMV and transfer RNA. What can you imply from this comparison?

49.12. What do you consider to be the essential characteristics of genetic material?

AUTHOR INDEX

Italicized page numbers refer to photographs.

Abelson, P. H., 443
Adams, J. N., 378
Adelberg, E. A., 292, 318, 338, 348, 354, 359, 360, 361, 362, 363, 364, 367, 372, 380, 426, s-49, s-76
Adler, J., s-64
Alexander, P., 184, 202
Allen, J. M., 451
Allfrey, V. G., 427, 436
Allison, A. C., 236
Amano, T., s-38
Ames, B. N., s-49
Anderson, T. F., 357, s-74
Arber, W., 379, 380, s-74
Auerbach, C., 250
Avery, O. T., 340, 348, s-63
Bacq, Z. M., 184
Baglioni, C., 288
Bailey, W. T., 386
Bangham, A. D., 109
Barclay, R. K., s-63
Barnett, L., 389
Baron, L. S., s-74
Basilio, C., 438
Bateson, W., *55*
Baumiller, R. C., 242, 370.
Bautz, E. K. F., 407, 436
Beadle, G. W., *126*, 272, 281, 292, s-*3*, s-38, s-39, s-49, s-63
Beale, G. H., 419, s-38
Bearn, A. G., 161, 280
Becker, E., s-38
Belling, J., 139, 144, 162
Bennett, D., 266
Bensch, K. G., 317
Benzer, S., 389, 392, 396, *397*, 400, 407, 448, 451, s-49, s-75
Berg, P., s-77
Bergmann, F. H., s-77
Bessman, M. J., s-64
Beutler, E., 269
Binnington, J. P., 184
Blakeslee, A. F., 139, 144, 162
Blum, H. F., 443
Boedtker, H., s-75
Bollum, F. J., s-64

Bonner, D. M., 438, s-49
Bonner, J., 429
Brachet, J., 21, 31
Brehme, K. S., 148
Brenner, S., 382, 389, 436
Bridges, C. B., 87, *92*, 104, 109, 142, 148, 186, 195
Briggs, R., 271, 451, s-75
Brink, R. A., 216, 217, *222*, 223
Brown, B., s-49
Bryson, V., s-75
Burnet, F. M., 405, 407, s-75
Burnham, C. R., *126*
Burns, S. N., 362, 363, 367, 372
Burrous, J. W., s-76
Butenandt, A., s-38
Calef, E., s-49
Calvin, M., 443
Campbell, A., 379, 391, 413, 419, s-75
Canellakis, E. S., 382, 389
Carey, W. F., s-74
Carlson, E., 402, 407
Carlson, J. G., 179
Case, M. E., s-49
Cavalli, L. L., s-76
Cavalli-Sforza, L. L., s-75
Champe, S. P., 389, 396, 448, 451
Chargaff, E., 305, 372, s-63
Chase, M., 383, 387, 389, s-75
Chesley, P., 266
Chevais, S., s-49
Chu, E. H. Y., 184, 250
Clark, F., 443
Claus, W. D., 184
Cleland, R. E., 24, 25, 26, 162, 166, *167*, 172
Clowes, R. C., 363, 436
Cohen, S. S., s-64, s-75
Cohn, M., s-49
Cordova, C. C., 451
Correns, C., 14
Cowie, D. B., 443
Crawford, I. P., 292, s-77
Creighton, H. S., 125, 126
Crick, F. H. C., 308, 309, 312, 318, 402, 403, 436, s-63, s-75, s-77
Crow, J. F., *235*, 236, 241, 242, 250
Darlington, C. D., 370
Davidson, J. N., 305
Davidson, P. F., 392, 398
Davis, B. D., s-49
Dawson, M. H., 340
DeGeorge, F. V., 79
Delbrück, M., 386, s-75
Dellweg, Z., s-64
Demerec, M., 158, 376, s-38, s-75
DeRobertis, E. D. P., 31
DeVries, H., 14, 162, *172*

Dewey, V. C., s-64
Dieckmann, M., s-77
Dobzhansky, Th., 7, 14, 60, 68, 73, *227*, 236, 239, 240, 250, 253, 254, 261
Dodge, B. O., s-49
Dodson, E. O., 14, 261
Doty, P., 345, 348, s-75
Doudney, C. O., s-75
Dunn, D. B., s-64
Dunn, L. C., 7, 14, 60, 261, 263, 266, 268, 419
du Vigneaud, V., s-49
Eagle, H., s-49
Edwards, P. R., s-76
Ehrensvärd, G., s-49
Eigner, J., 345, 348
Eisenstadt, J. M., 438
Elson, D., 428, 438
Emerson, R. A., *126*
Emerson, S., 162
Ephrussi, B., 272, *280*, s-38, s-49
Ephrussi-Taylor, H., *280*, 341, 348
Epling, C., 254
Fairbanks, V. F., 269
Falconer, D. S., 60
Ferguson-Smith, M. A., 147
Feughelman, M., s-63
Fincham, J. R. S., s-49
Flaks, J. G., s-64
Flemming, W., 21
Fling, M., s-38, s-39, s-49
Fogel, S., 21, 31, 98, 115, 126, 202, 227
Fox, S. W., s-38
Fraenkel-Conrat, H., 406, 407, 448
Francis, T., 266
Fraser, D. K., 384, s-76
Freese, E., 400, 401, 407, s-75
Freese, E. B., 407
Freifelder, D., 392, 398
Freiman, A. E., s-49
Freire-Maia, N., 250
Fresco, J. R., 451, s-75
Fries, N., s-49
Furth, J. J., 436, 437
Gabriel, M. L., 21, 31, 98, 115, 126, 202, 227
Garen, A., 434, 437
Garnjobst, L., s-49
Garrod, A. E., 275, s-38
Gay, H., 437
Geiduschek, E. P., 437
German III, J. L., 161
Gierer, A., 406, 407
Gilbert, W., 437
Giles, N. H., 184, 250, s-38, s-49
Gish, D. T., 406, 407
Glass, B., 381, 398, 399, s-76
Glover, S. W., s-38, s-75

453

Glucksohn-Waelsch, S., 269
Goldman, M., 436
Goldschmidt, R. B., 73, 109, *269*
Goldstein, A., 437
Golomb, S. W., s-75
Gorini, L., 426, s-49
Gots, J. S., s-38, s-75
Gowen, J. W., 236
Griffith, F., 340, s-75
Gross, F., 437
Gross, S. R., s-49
Guthrie, G. G., 384
Haagen-Smit, A. J., s-49
Haas, F. L., s-75
Hadorn, E., 67, 69, 73, 269
Haldane, J. B. S., s-38
Hall, B. D., 436, 437
Hallmann, G., s-38
Hamburger, V., 263
Hamilton, L. D., s-63
Hannah-Alava, A., 98
Hardy, G. H., 227
Harford, C. G., s-64
Harris, H., 280, 292
Hart, R. G., 404
Hartman, P. E., 376, 377, 421,
    422, 426, s-38, s-49, s-75
Hartman, Z., s-38, s-75
Haselkorn, R., s-75
Hayashi, M., 430
Hayes, W., 356, 358, 363, 364,
    436, s-77
Hecht, L. I., s-75
Hede, R., 392, 398
Heinrich, M. R., s-64
Helinski, D. R., 395, 399
Herriot, R. M., 348
Hershey, A. D., 383, 386, 387,
    388, 389, 392, 399, s-63, s-75
Herskowitz, I., *76*
Herskowitz, I. H., 55, 209, 242,
    250, 370, 372, 401, 407
Herskowitz, J., *76*
Hiatt, H., 437
Hiraizumi, Y., 223
Hirota, Y., s-75
Hoagland, M. B., 437
Hogness, D. S., 380, 381
Hollaender, A., 161, 212
Holtz, A. M., 73
Hooper, C. W., s-63
Horne, R. W., 389
Horowitz, N. H., s-38, s-49
Hotchkiss, R. D., 348, s-75
Houlahan, M. B., s-49
Hsia, D. Y.-Y., 280, 292
Hsu, T. C., 146
Huang, R. C., 429
Huang, S.-S., 443
Hurwitz, J., 429, 436, 437
Hutner, S. H., s-77

Iijima, T., s-75
Iino, T., s-76
Ingram, V. M., 286, 288, 292,
    s-49
Iritani, H., s-38
Itano, H. A., 286, 292
Jacob, F., 357, 359, 362, 363,
    364, 367, 369, 372, 379, 380,
    381, 391, 399, 425, 426, 436,
    s-75, s-77
Jesaitis, M. A., s-64
Johannsen, W. L., 1, *6*
Johnston, A. W., 147
Jones, O. W., 437
Josse, J., s-64
Kaiser, A. D., 380, 381, 391, 399
Kallman, F. J., 79
Kameyama, F., 438
Kammen, H. O., 382, 389
Karpechenko, G. D., 260
Kaufmann, B. P., 142, 159, 160
Kellenberger, E., 330, 379, 380,
    384, 388, 389
Kempthorne, O., 60
Khouvine, Y., s-49
Kidder, G. W., s-64
King, D. W., 317
King, T. J., 271, 451, s-75
Kjeldgaard, N., s-76
Klein, E., s-49
Klein, G., s-49
Kluyver, A. J., s-75
Knight, B. C. J. G., s-75
Knight, C. A., 406, 407
Knox, W. E., s-39
Kögl, F., s-49
Kornberg, A., 321, 328, s-4, s-63,
    s-64, s-75
Kornberg, S. R., s-64
Koshland, D. E., Jr., s-64
Kossikov, K. V., 196
Krakow, J. S., 382, 389
Krieger, H., 250
Kurek, L. I., s-49
Kurland, C. G., 437
Landauer, W., 263, 269
Landsteiner, K., 35
Lane, D., 345, 348
Langridge, R., s-63
Laughlin, J. S., 209
Law, L. W., s-49
Lederberg, E. M., 334, 335, 338,
    339, 379, 381, s-75, s-76
Lederberg, J., 334, 335, 338, *339*,
    349, 353, 354, 374, 377, 379,
    381, 443, s-4, s-49, s-75, s-76
Lehman, I. R., s-64
Lehrmann, H., 286
Lengyel, P., 438
Lennox, E., 376
Leopold, U., s-39

Lerman, L. S., 341, 345, 348,
    401, 407
Levene, H., 7, 60
Levine, P., 35
Levinthal, C., 387, 392, 398
Levy, M., s-49
Lewis, E. B., 191, 193, 194, 196
L'Héritier, P., 410
Li, C. C., 227
Lichtenstein, J., s-64
Lima de Faria, A., 370
Lindegren, C. C., s-49, s-77
Lindegren, G., s-77
Lipmann, F., *437*
Litt, M., s-75
Lively, E. R., s-76
Loeb, T., 304, 305, 357
Loper, J. C., 421, 426
Luria, S. E., 378, s-76
Lwoff, A., s-39
Maaløe, O., 392, 399
Maas, W. K., s-49
McCarty, M., 340, 348, s-63
McClintock, B., 125, *126*, 214,
    215, 222, 426
McCoy, A., s-76
MacDowell, E. C., 266
McElroy, W. D., 381, 398, 399,
    s-76
MacLeod, C. M., 340, 348, s-63
Maheshwari, N., 429
Mahler, H., 384
Marmur, J., 345, 348
Martin, R. G., 437
Matthaei, J. H., 437, 438
Mazia, D., 21
Melechen, N. E., 332, 335
Mendel, G., 8, 14, 39, 47, s-*1*
Merrill, D. J., 261
Meselson, M., 312, 314, 318, 388,
    389, 436, s-76
Metz, C. W., 173
Metzenberg, R. L., s-49
Miller, S. L., 443
Mirsky, A. E., 31, 427, 436
Mitchell, H. K., 280, s-39, s-49
Mitchell, J. S., 451
Mohr, O. L., 37
Monod, J., 391, 399, 425, 426,
    s-49, s-76
Montagu, A., 79
Moore, J. A., 7
Morgan, D. T., Jr., 158
Morgan, T. H., 83, 92, 115, s-*2*
Morse, M. L., 379, 381, s-76
Morton, N. E., 241, 242, 250
Muller, H. J., vi, 55, 161, 182,
    186, 196, 202, 203, 204, 209,
    210, *212*, 241, 242, 250, 402,
    407, 451, s-*2*, s-39, s-76
Nagel, E., s-76

Nägeli, C., 14
Nakamoto, T., 437
Nanney, D. L., s-76
Neel, J. V., 37, 286
Nelson, N. J., s-49
Newman, H. H., 79
Nirenberg, M. W., 432, *437*, 438
Niu, L. C., 451
Niu, M. C., 451
Novelli, G. D., 432, 438, 447
Novick, A., 336, 338, s-76
Nowinski, W. W., 31
Nyc, J. F., s-49
Ochoa, S., 433, 435, *437*, 438
O'Conner, C. M., s-77
Oehlkers, F., 162
Ofengand, E. J., s-77
Olson, M. E., 428
Oparin, A. I., 443
Ørskov, F., s-77
Ørskov, I., s-77
Osborn, F., 79
Oyama, V. I., s-49
Ozeki, H., 377, 381, s-38, s-75
Pardee, A. B., s-49
Parks, R. E., Jr., s-64
Partridge, C. W. H., s-49
Passano, K., 184, 250
Pateman, J. A., s-49
Pauling, L., 286, s-76
Penrose, L. S., 443
Perrin, D., 425, 426
Perutz, M. F., 286
Peters, J. A., 6, 14, 31, 126, 136, 196, 202, 222, 227, 292, 318, 348, 407
Peterson, P. A., 222
Peterson, W. H., s-49
Pintner, I. J., s-77
Pirie, N. W., s-77
Pollister, A. W., 7, 370, 372
Pollister, P. F., 370, 372
Pond, V., 184
Potter, V. R., 305, s-64
Preiss, J., s-77
Prokofyeva-Belgovskaya, A. A., 196
Provasoli, L., s-77
Puck, T. T., 177, 184, s-49
Rabinovits, M., 428
Race, R. R., 67
Radding, C. M., s-64
Ramachandran, L. K., 407
Rasmuson, M., 228
Rees, M. W., 389
Renner, O., 162
Révész, L., s-49
Rhoades, M. M., 29, 31, *126*, 160, *412*, 413, 419
Richter, A. A., s-77
Risebrough, R. W., 437

Robinson, E. A., 292
Rose, H. H., 443
Rotman, R., 386
Rous, P., s-49
Rubenstein, I., 392, 399
Rudkin, G., 316
Rudnick, D., 263
Ruhland, W., 419
Ryan, F. J., 7, 451, s-77
Saez, F. A., 31
Sagan, C., 443
Sager, R., 451
St. Lawrence, P., 426
Sanchez, C., 425, 426
Sandler, I., 223
Sandler, L., 223
Sanger, F., s-77
Schachman, H. K., s-64
Schalet, A., 212, 402, 407
Schildkraut, G., 345, 348
Schlossberger, H., s-38
Schrader, F., 7, 21, 370
Schramm, G., 406
Schreil, W. H. G., 330
Schrödinger, E., s-77
Schull, W. J., 37
Schulman, H. M., 438
Schultz, J., 294
Seeds, W. E., s-63
Šerman, D., 421, 426
Shettles, L. B., 107, 108, 109
Shug, A., 384
Sia, R. H., 340
Siminovitch, L., s-76
Simms, E. S., s-64
Sinnott, E. W., 14, 60
Sinsheimer, R. L., 384, s-64
Sinton, W. M., 443
Slatis, H., 242
Smith, J. D., s-64
Smith, P. E., 266
Snell, G. D., 266
Sonneborn, T. M., 411, 415, *419*
Sparrow, A. H., 184
Spencer, J. H., 372
Speyer, J. F., 435, 438
Spiegelman, S., 430, 437, s-77
Spilman, W. M., s-74
Spizizen, J., 384
Stadler, L. J., vi, *203*
Stahl, F. W., 312, 314, 318, s-76
Stanley, W. M., 406, 407
Stebbins, G. L., 261
Stent, G. W., 318, 380, 381, 398, 399, 407, s-75, s-77
Stephenson, M. L., s-75
Stern, C., 37, 64, 78, 125, *126*, 210, 228, 242
Stevens, A., 429, 438
Stocker, B. A. D., 377, s-77
Stokes, A. R., s-63

Straus, D. B., 451
Strauss, B. S., 438, 451
Streisinger, G., 389, s-64
Sturtevant, A. H., 100, *109*, 136, 162, 186, 196, s-39
Sueoka, N., 318
Sugiyama, T., 448
Suskind, D. R., s-49
Sutton, W. S., 31
Swanson, C. P., 21, 31
Swartz, M. N., 328
Synge, R. L. M., 443
Szilard, L., *280*, 336, 338
Szybalski, W., s-75
Tal, M., 428, 438
Tatum, E. L., 281, 292, 349, 354, s-3, s-38, s-39, s-49, s-76, s-77
Tax, S., 443
Taylor, A. L., 359, 360, 361, 364
Teissier, G., 410
Tessman, I., s-77
Thomas, C. A., Jr., 384, 392, 399
Todd, A., s-77
Tolmach, L. J., 341, 345, 348
Torii, M., s-38
Trautner, T. A., 328
Tschermak, E., 14
Tsugita, A., 406, 407
Umbarger, H. E., s-49
Urey, H. C., 443
Van Beneden, E., 31
Van Kammen, A., 440, 443
van Niel, C. B., s-75
van Schaik, N. W., 223
Vogel, H. J., s-49
Volkin, E., s-64
von Euler, H., s-75
Wacker, A., s-64
Waddington, C. H., 269
Wagner, R. P., 280, s-39
Wallace, E. M., 52, 81, 102, 103, 143
Watson, J. D., 308, 309, 312, *318*, 392, 399, 402, 403, 437, s-63, s-77
Weidel, W., s-38
Weigle, J. J., 379, 380, 388, 389, s-64
Weinberg, W., 228
Weiss, S. B., 429, 437
Welch, L. R., s-75
Wexler, I. B., 67
Weygand, F., s-64
Wiener, A. S., 67
Wilkins, M. H. F., s-63
Williams, R. C., 406, 407
Wilson, E. B., *31*, 98
Wilson, H. R., s-63
Wollman, E. L., 357, 359, 362, 363, *364*, 369, 372, 379, 380, 381, 391, 399, s-75, s-77
Wolstenholme, G. E. W., s-77

Wood, H. G., s-49
Wright, S., *227*, 269, s-39
Wyatt, G. R., s-64
Yanofsky, C., 286, 292, 395, 399, 426, s-39, s-49, s-77

Yates, R. A., s-49
Yeh, M., 269
Young, J., 406, 407
Yura, T., s-38, s-49, s-75
Zamecnik, P. C., 428, 438, s-75

Zelle, M., 354
Zichichi, M. L., 388, 389
Zimmerman, S. B., s-64
Zinder, N. D., 304, 305, 357, 374, 377, *381*, s-76, s-77

SUBJECT INDEX

Italicized page numbers refer to illustrations.

abnormal abdomen in *Drosophila*, 72
abortion, 106, 243
absorbency, 302, 312, *314*, 315, 345
achondroplastic (chondrodystrophic) dwarfism, 230, 242
acridine, 356, 362, 363, 368, 401
activation, 176, 430
Activator (Ac), 215, 360
adaptive value (*see* fitness, biological)
adenine (A), 284, 291, 296, *297*, 304, 306, 337, 371, 401, 402, *403*, 441
adenosine, 430, 448
adenosine triphosphate (ATP), *320*, *321*, 441
adenylosuccinase, 284, 290–*291*
adolescence, 234
age, 72, 106, 130, 147, 201, 245, 249, 336, 341
agglutination, 70, 340
air, 178, 275
albinism, 32, *34*, 49, 63, 68, 277, *414*
alcapton (homogentisic acid), 275, *276*
allele, 10, 185, 191–195, 287–291, 395
    iso-, 65, 214, 239
    multiple, 35–36, 62–65, 191, 198
allopatric, 255
America, 252
amino acid, 69, 231, 262, 276, 281, *285*, 332, 395, *406*, *431*, *435*, 441
amorph, 210, 371
amphiploidy (allopolyploidy), 143, 255, *258*, 259
anaphase, *17*, *18*, *25*, 26, *28*, *29*, 370
anemia, 36, 69, 70, 234
    sickle cell, *70*, 242, 269, 287, 289, 290
aneusomy, 214
Angstrom unit (A), 286
anlage (imaginal disc), 265, *272*
annelids, 94, 95
anthranilic acid, 376
anthropology, 253
antibiotics, 244, 284
antibodies and antigens, 34, 62, 68, 340, 421
Antirrhinum (snapdragon), 65
antiserum, 35, 340, 375
apricot eye color (*wᵃ*, *apr*), 62, *122*, 191, 204, 211
arginine, *285*, 287
Arizona, 253, *254*
Arrowhead inversion, 253, *254*
Artemia (water shrimp), 140, 317
arthritis, 275

Ascaris, 140, 197, 198, 213
ascospore and ascus, 121, *123*, *283*, 291
Asia, 252
Aspergillus, 193
assay, 384–385, 404
aster, 257
asynaptic gene in corn, 198, 213
ataxia, 34
atmosphere, 441
atom, 177, 247, 303
attached-X's, 121, *122*, 191, *192*
autopolyploidy, 140
autosome, 81, 101
auxotrophy, 333, 349–354, *350*, 356, 440
azaguanine, 337
Bacillus, 341
backcross, 43, *44*, 82, 111
bacteria, 214, 222, 312, 329–*335*, *332*, 369
    conjugation in, 349–354
bacteriophage (phage, ϕ), 296, 304, 374–380, 382–405, 429–430, 448
    lambda or 434, 378–380, 388, 390, *391*
    P1 or P22, 375, 376
    pro-, 375, 378, 390, *391*, 392
    T series, *307*, 311, 336–338, 353, 382–388, 393–*397*, 448
    X174 or S13, 311, 325, 347, 384, 406, 444
balanced lethals, *163*, 164–165, 207
balancers (halteres), 193, *194*
Bar (B) or Bar-like eye, 186, *187*, *188*–190, 206, *207*
Basic technique, 204, *205*, 206
base, organic, 295
bean plant, 1
benzene, 294, *295*
biochemistry, 69, 173, 266, 269
biophysics, 269
biotin, 281, 349–354
birds, 12, 84 (*see also* chicken)
bithorax (bx), 193, *194*, 195
bivalent, 24, *25*
black body color (b), 116
Blendor, 358, 362, 374, 383
blood, 69, 275
blood eye color (wᵇˡ), 62
blood type or group, 34, 62, 234
    ABO, 35, *36*, 49, 75, 252, 253
    MN, *35*, 49, 68, 75
    Rh (Rhesus), 36, 75
bobbed bristles (bb), 114, 208, 210
bone, 95, 247, 275
Bonellia, 95
Brachyury (Brachy) (T), 266–268
brain, 69
branched track method, 40, *42*
bridge-breakage-fusion-bridge cycle, 151, 152
brown eye color (bw), 272–274
Brownian movement, 150
buff eye color (wᵇᶠ), 62
cabbage, 259, *260*
caffeine, 337
calcium chloride, 384

457

California, 253, *254*, *260*
cancer, 213, 306
carbamates, 200
carbon, 247–248, 293, 294, 338, 441
carbon dioxide, 147, 410, 441, 442
carmine eye color (*cm*), 206, *207*
carnation eye color (*car*), 189, 206, *207*
cartilage, 265, 275
catalase, 337
catnip (*Nepeta*), 415
cattle, 257
cell and its division, 5, 16, 201, 245, 383
centrifugal forces, 181
centriole and centrosome, 369, 440
centromere, 16, 27, 120, 130, 152, 169, 181, 182, 197, 282, *283*, 369, *370*
cesium, 247–248, 312
chain of chemical reactions, *273*
chemical messenger, 95, 266, *267*
chemorecovery, 200
chiasma, 24–*28*, *26*, *30*, 44, 116–126, *120*, 128–135, 282, *283*
chiasmata, 100, *131*, *133*, 134
chicken, 12, 53, *54*, 84, *263*, *264*, 265, 306, *307*, 404
Chlamydomonas, 96, 315
chloramphenicol, 336
chlorophyll, 65, 96, *412*–415, 441
chromatid, 16, 18, 360
chromatophore, 96
chromocenter, 181
chromosome, 16, 19, 174, 181, 293, 410, 440 (*see also* gene)
  acentric, 150, *151*
  aneucentric, 154, *155*
  bacterial, 329, *330*, *391*
  balance, 104, 158
  blocks in, 181
  breakage, 150–153, *151*, 157, 173, 176–*179*, 181, 197, 214, 343, *344*, 360, 450
  bridge, *151*
  buckles and loops, 160
  changes, 137, 150–160, 180, 186, 257, 343, *344*, 450
    natural and induced, 20, 173–183, 249
  coils or gyres, 141, 179, 180, 181
  complexes, *171*
  cross-bands in, 141, *142*
  cytology, 86, 249
  dicentric, 150, *151*, 177, 214
  disjunction, 157, 167
  DNA content, 300, 341, 360
  doublet in, 195
  doubling of, 141
  duplicate parts of, *156*
  ends, 150, 179, 180, 181, 197
  eucentric, 154, *155*
  eutelomeric, 156
  fragment, 150, 198
  as genetic material, 20, 90–91
  heteromorphic, 87, 140
  homologous, 19, 102, 103, 125, 157
  human, *108*, *146*, *147*, *177*, 249
  hydration, 181
  iso-, *151*
  loss, 97, 106, 159, *209*
  maternal and paternal, 27
  metaphase plates, *174*
  movement, *167*, 181
  and nondisjunction, *89*, 90
  number, 21, 98, 106, 146, 181, 182
  polycentric, 197, 214
  puffs in, *316*
  ring and rod, 152, *153*, 174, *175*, 359–*361*
  salivary gland, 20, 141, *142*, *158*, *159*, *160*, 173, 195, 198, 213, *294*, 302, *316*
  segregation, 90, *168*
  shape or size, 173–*175*, 179, 181, 182
  shift and transposition, 158, 159, 173, 220
  sister strand, 120
  splint effect in, 181
  structural linearity, 19, 197
  volume, 179
chymotrypsin, 287
cilia, 95, 370
cinnabar eye color (*cn*), 272–274
cinquefoil (*Potentilla*), 254–255
circle of chromosomes, *166*, *167*, *168*
cis and trans positions, *189*, 190, 193
cistron, 279, 281–291, 293, 304, 317, 347, 368, 370–371, 377, 395–*396*–*397*–398, 415, 421–426, 430–436, 445–448, 450
civilization and races, 256
climate and mutability, 214
clone, 96, 329–338, *332*, *334*, 349–354, 416
cloud, 442
clubfoot, 77
cn+ substance, *273*
coding of amino acids, 427–436
coincidence, coefficient of, 132
colchicine, 141, 259
cold and autopolyploidy, 141
colicine, 369
collochore, 182, 213
color-blindness, 87, 114
comb types, 53, *54*
comet, 441
competence, 215, 267–268, 341
complementation, *393*–395
concordance vs. discordance, 76, 77
congenital abnormalities, 146, *233*
conjugation, 349–354, 356, *357*, *416*
constitutive enzyme, 423
continuous traits, 56–60, 104, 108, 262
Cooley's anemia (thalassemia major), 36, 289, 290
copy-choice, *344*, 387, *388*
coral eye color (*w^co^*), 62
core, 382, *383*
corn, Indian (maize, *Zea mays*), 19, 29, 126, *158*, *160*, 193, 214–222, *235*–*237*, 302, 360, 369, 370, *412*–415
cotton, 193, 259
coupling, 114
crab, 371

Creeper (*Cp*), *263*, *264*, 265
crops, 236
crossing over, 112, 116–126, *120*, 130, 131, 167, 182, 186, 259, 343, *344*, 450
  and cis-trans positions, 189, 190
  within cistron, 290–291
  frequency, 114, 116, 128
crossovers, 112, 124, 128, 130, *133*, 189
  genetical and cytological, 125
crossveinless wings (*cv*), 117, 119, 128
cubitus interruptus wing (*ci*), *64*, 81
curled wing fly, *52*
cut wings (*ct*), 117, 119, 128, *129*, 206, *207*
cyclosis, 181
cystine, 69, *285*, 349–354
cytochemistry, 300
cytogenetics, 125, 141, 159, 162–171, 199, 357
  of sex, 90, 100
cytoplasm and cytosome, 16, 141, 427
cytoplasmic mixing, *417*
cytosine (C), *296*, 304, 306, 400–*403*
  derivatives of, *296*, 325, *326*, 400
Datura (Jimson weed), 139, 140, *144*, *145*
deamination, 401
death, *233*, 240, 241, 242–246
DDT, 244
deficiency, 152–*153*, 159, 173, 179, 185, 395
deletion, 175, 214, 401
Delphinium (larkspur), 259, *260*
density gradient ultracentrifugation, 312, *314*, 388
deoxyadenosine, 298, 299, *301*, 304
deoxycytidine, 298, *299*, *301*, 304
deoxyguanosine, 298, *299*, 304
2'-deoxy-D-ribose (deoxyribose), *298*, 304, 427
deoxyribonuclease (DNAase), 302, 320, 323, 327, 340, 342–346, 352, 361, 375, 428
deoxyribonucleic acid (DNA), 324, 340–348, 356, 368, 369, 375, 379, 382, *383*, 384, 387, *388*, 411, 427, 439–450 (*see also* gene, recon, cistron, mutant)
  bases in, 306, 309, *310*, 315, 325, 327, 345
  biological synthesis, s-50–s-64
  chain growth, *323*
  chemical composition, 294–303
  coiling, 309
  conserved vs. nonconserved, 316–317, 345, 392
  denatured or renatured, 315, 324, 345
  density, 345
  enzymatic degradation, *323*, *324*
  evolution of, 439–440
  H-bonding in, 309
  homologous vs. heterologous, 346, 349, 374
  hybrid, 313, 346–347, 429
  molecular weight, 324, 342, 345, 346, 360, 392
  nearest nucleotide neighbor in, 327
  nucleoside and nucleotide ends, 322, *323*
  polymerase, 325, 328, 430, 447
  primer, 322, 325, 445
  replication, 312–*313*–*314*–315, 320–328
  and RNA interrelationship, 427–436, *431*
  single-stranded, 311

strand recombination, 345–347, 450
structure, 294–*302*, *308*, 309, 311
synthesis, 316, 322, 327, 352
unnatural bases in, 325, *326*
in vitro, 320–328
in vivo, 306–317
Watson-Crick model, 306–312, *308*, *311*, *318*
deoxyribonucleoprotein, 294
deoxyribonucleotide (deoxyribotide), 299, *300*, *301*, *302*, 304, 320
deoxyriboside, 298, *299*, *300*, 304, 321, 322
deoxyuridine, 5-bromo, 371
detergent, *404*
detrimental equivalents, 241
development, 74, 141, 201, 245, 257, 266, 272, 316
diabetes, 243
diakinesis, *25*, *26*, *28*
differentiation, 95, 100, 105, 265, 268, 316
diffuse (growth) stage, 26
Diplococcus (*see Pneumococcus*)
diploid, 10, 353, 379
diplonema, *25*, *26*, *28*, 123
Diptera, 159, 213
Dissociation (*Ds*), 214, *215*, 216, 360, 371, 449
dogs, 255
dominance, 12, 13, 47, 49, 53, 67, 111, 138
  complete or nearly complete, 210
  and mutation, 185
  phenotypic effect of, 58, 59, 72
  in populations, 225, 252
double cross, 236, *237*
doubling dose, 247
drift, random genetic, 226, 242, 245, 253
Drosophila, 52, 53, 69, 70, 72, 116, 121, 122, 140, 173, 174, 193, 214, 222, *294*, 360, 369, 371, 409–410
  bibliographies, 55
  eye, 62, 68, 83, 114, 186, 271–*272*–*273*–274
  larva and pupa, 69, 141, 144, *272*
  melanogaster, *81*, 128, *142*, *143*, 151, 176, 182, 204–209
  persimilis, 257
  pseudoobscura, 234–235, *239*, *240*, 253, *254*
  and sex, 83, 96, 100, 101, 106
  wing, *64*, 116, 117, 193
drug, 141, 259, 332–336, 400
duplicated parts and penetrance, 72
duplication, *156*, 159, 173, 179, 185, 186, 195, 206, *207*, 370, 387, *388*
dusky wings (*dy*), 206, *207*
dwarfism, 230, 242, 265, 266, 267
dyad, 26, 88, *120*, 124
ear, 275
Earth, 224, 439, 441, 442
earthquakes, 256
earthworm, 94
ebony body color (*e*), 81
Echinus (sea urchin), 140, 306, *307*
echinus, rough eyes (*ec*), 206, *207*
eclipse phase, 284, 404
ecology, 173, 254, 256
egg, 5, 91, 95, 97, 124, 249, 370, 404

electricity, 108, 441
electron, *142*, 176, 177, *209*
electron microscope, *330*, 345, 357
electrophoresis, 340
embryo, 263, *264*, 265–268, 289
encephalitis, 304, 403
endolysin, 384
energy, 179, 320
England, 87
environment, 1, 56, 72, 79, 95, 252
    and mutants, 200, 241, 244
enzyme, 68, 70, 274, 277, 281–286, 293, 302, 320, 328,
    404, 421–425
episome, 356–372, 374–380, 382, 409, 418, 421, 449
epistasis, 53, 72, 74, 101, 252
epoxide, 200
equivalents, lethal or detrimental, 241
Escherichia coli, 286, *307*, 321, 329, *330*, 341, 346, 349–
    369, *361*, 375–*385*, *393*, 421–425, 428, 432, 442,
    448
ethology, 256
euchromatin, 181, 186, 194, 198, 316, 370–371
Europe, 252
evening primrose (*see Oenothera*)
evolution, 143, 147, 158, 195, 208, 213–214, 224–226,
    244, 245, 255
    biochemical, 439–442
    biological, 94, 226, 450
    in various species, 170, 173, 176
exogenote, 377
expressivity, 70–73, 241
eye, 186, 206, 272–274
    color in *Drosophila*, 53, 62, 68, 69, 83, 117, 186,
        189, 224, 271, *272*, *273*, 274
F_1, F_2, 9
F episome, 356–369, 380, 381, 382
fallout, 247–248
family method, 32, 275
feather, 84
feed-back system, 418, *422–425*
ferns, 222
fertility and fecundity, 9, 90, 208
fertilization, 1, 5, 8, 97, 232, 256, 302
    random, *42*, 74, 90
    cross-, in populations, 224–226
Feulgen-Rossenbeck technique, 19, 20, 108, 300, 316
fibroblast, *177*, 317
filtration, 284, 352, 375
"fingerprints," 287, *288*, 382
fingers, 71, 265
fish, 293, 296, 306, *307*
fission, 415
fitness, biological (adaptive value, reproductive poten-
    tial), 208, 211, 224–226, 229, 245, 253–254, 329
flagellum, 96, 330, 370
flavin mononucleotide, 320, *321*
flight, insect, 244
flowers, 8, 9, 39, 114, 139
forked bristles (*f*) 97, 118, 119, *122*, 128, 189, 206, *207*
fowl (*see* chicken)
France, 240

frogs, 140, 271
fruiting bodies, 121, *123*
fungi, 222, 254, 302
fungus gnat (*Sciara*), 316, 450
galactose locus (*Gal*), 358, 378, 390, *391*
β-galactosidase, 369, 421–*424*, 425
gametes, 5, 88, 94, 152, 166, 246, 302
gametogenesis, 106, 157, 166, 214, 248, 317
gametophyte, 95, *163*
garnet eye color (*g*), 206, *207*
gene (*see also* mutant, DNA, RNA), 10, 14, 63, 91,
    100, 101, 120, 137, 164, 185, 262
    action, 70, 152, 185, 186, 193, 215, 262, 271–292,
        395, 398, 409–440
    arrangement, 128–135, 185, *189*
    balance, 104, 144
    chemical nature of, 293–304, 341
    and chemical reactions, s-27–s-49
    and chromosomes, 44–46, 90, 198
    code, 402
    defined, 199, 278–279, 447
    dominant and recessive, 12, 138
    essential vs. nonessential, 392
    extrachromosomal or extranuclear, 363, 408–418,
        450
    for function vs. structure, *425*, 440
    functional, 278–279
    interaction, 49–54, 56–60, 104, 236
    linear order of, 182, 197, 354
    linked, 112, 113, 116, 128, 197
    material basis of, 19, 30, 44, 90
    modifier, 210
    mutability controlled, 213–222
    mutable, 200
    and mutation, 197–202, 216
    mutator, 214
    nature of, 278–279, 317, 444–451, s-11–s-14
    normal, 111, 210
    number, 116, 158, 159, 195
    operational, 137, 199
    origin of, 439–442
    pairs, 10, 40
    phenotypic effect, 65–70, 210–211, 224, 262
    polarity, 197
    pool, 213, 224–226, 229, 242–243, 253–255
    precursor and mutation, 201–202
    recombinational, 199
    regulator, 423–*425*
    segregation, 8–14
    self-replication of, 20, 137, 213, 320–328, 363, 368,
        377, 405, 415, 421, 439–440, 444–445, 447
    self-sterility, 63
    size, 195, 198, 279
    and speciation, 257
    stable, 199
    suppressor, 214–216
    as template, 446–447
    transformer, *101*, 105
    transmission, 73
    untainted, 10, 20
genetic death, 242–246

genetic drift, random, 226, 242, 245, 253
genetic equilibrium, 224–226, *246*
genetic factor, 1
genetic fine structure, 394–*397*, 448
genetic imbalance, 144
genetic information, 347, 383–384, 405, 427–436, 450
genetic material, 1–6, 9, 10, 14, 116, 137, 199, 278, 293, 363, 367, 377, 384, 403, 406, 421, 439–442, 444–451
genetic polymorphism in races, 252
genetic stability and variability, 137, 213, 239, 240
genetic units, 10
genetics, applied, 236, 450
  bacterial, 329–380
  biochemical, 69–70, 208, 271–292
  comparative, 173
  developmental, 262–268
  pheno-, 262
  physiological, 269
  a view of, s-65–s-77
genitalia, 105, 257
genome, 30, 103, 137–143, 345, 448
genotype, 1, 72, 74, 130, 147, 208, 258, 294, 449
geography, 253–256, *254*
germ line, 106, 118, 146, 152, 197, 205, 293
Globe seed capsule, *144, 145*
glutamic acid, *285*, 287
glutamine, 69
glycine, *285*, 287
goatsbeard, 259
gonad, 94, 105, 246
grasshopper, 96, *179*
gravity, 181
growth, 26, 265, 267, 284, 337–338, 349–354
  of virus, 384, *385*
guanine (G), *297*, 298, 304, 306, 401, 432
guinea pigs, 72
gynandromorph (gynander), 96, *97*
half-life, 248
halteres (balancers), 193, *194*
haploid (monoploid), 10, 105, 139, 141, 144, 353, 379
Hardy-Weinberg equilibrium principle, 225n
head, 34, 252, 382, *383*
heart, 69, 265
helium, 441
Helix (snail), 94, 95, 317
helix, 286, *308*
hemizygous, 84
hemoglobin, 70, 238, 271, 286–*288*–289–290, 428, 446, 448
hemophilia, 87, 114
Hemophilis, 341
heredity, 15
hermaphrodite, 94
heterochromatin, 181, 186, 194, 198, 204, 214, 316, 370–371, 410
heterogametic females, 92
heterogenote, 377, 379
heterosis (hybrid vigor), 233–237
heterozygote (hybrid), 11, 42, *43, 130*, 134, *135*, 163, 207, 232–236, 256, 354, 387

Hexaptera, 137, *138*
histidine, *285*, 376, 421, *422*
histochemistry, 300, 306, *307*
histone, 293–294
homogenote, 381
homozygote, 11, 232–233
hormones, 98, 105, 266, *267*, 268, 271
horse, 257, 286
host range, 386, *393*
"hot spots" in mutation, 400
human genetics, 19, 32–37, 71–72, 74–79, 98, 105–108, 146–147, 177, 224–226, 229–234, 240–249, 252–253, 274–278, 286–290, *307*, 315
hybrid vigor (heterosis), 233–237
hybrids, 234–237, *258–260*
hydrogen, 309, 441
hydroxylamine, 401
hyperploid vs. hypoploid, 152
hypomorph, 210
hypostasis, 53, 72, 101
hypoxanthine and its derivatives, *326*, 401
Iceland, 252
imaginal disc (anlage), 265, *272*
imidazole ring, 295, *297*
immunity, 375, 377, 379, 380, 390, *391*
inborn error of metabolism, 275, 450
inbreeding, 32, 232–237, *233*, 241
India, 252
Indians, American, 252
indol, 284, 376
induction, 267–268, 378, 390, 423–*425*
influenza, 304, 403–404
insects, 296 (*see* specific types)
insulin, 243
integration, 343–*344*, 349, 353, 357, 360, 363, 366, 382, 391, 449
interference, 131, 132, 134
International Commission on Radiological Protection, 248
interphase, *17, 18*, 25, 26, *29*, 302
intersex, 102, *103*, 105, 140
interspecific hybridization, 258–260
intestine, small, 245
introgression, 260
inversion, *153–158, 155*, 173, 179, 204, 206, *207*, 214, 235, 253, *254*
iodine-131, 251
iojap (*ij*), 415
ions, 176–178, 345–346, 401–402
Ireland, 252
iron, 441
isogenic strains, 69
isotope, 303, 312, 388
Italy, 37
Japan, 32, *233*
Jimson weed (*Datura*), 139, 140, *144, 145*
juvenile amaurotic idiocy, 230, 242
kappa, 410, *411*, 415–417, 449
keto form, 296
kidney, 69
kinetosome, 370, 440

Klinefelter's type male, 98, 146
knuckle, 275
kynurenine and its derivatives, *273*, 274
lactate, 336
lactose locus (*Lac*), 358, 363, 366–369, 421–425, *424*
larkspur (*Delphinium*), 259, *260*
law of parsimony (Occam's rule), 10, 62, 199
lawn, bacterial, 384, 386
leptonema, 24, *28*
lethal equivalents, 241
leucine, *285*, 349–354
life, expectancy or span, 201, 249
light, ultraviolet, 176, 178, 200, 201, 302, 312, *314*, 336, 337, 349, 357, 441
    visible, 176, 200, 301
lily meiosis, *24*, *25*, *26*
limit dilution, 404
linear gene order, 128, 354
linkage, 111–*117*, 169, *361*, 376
    sex-, 81–92
lipid, 340, 369
lithium, *308*
liver, 141, 213, 275, 277, 450
load of mutants, 239–249
locus (loci), 120, 121, 193, 222, 343, 366
locust, 306, *307*
lysine, *285*, 287
lysis, 352, 353, 363, 375, 378, 384
lysogeny, 375, 377, 378, 390
lysozyme, 382
macromolecule, 307, 315
magnesium, 320, 321, 322, 336, 428
maize (*Zea; see* corn)
malaria, 234
male, Lfr, Hfr, or Vhf, 357, *359*, 360, *361*
Malpighian tubules, 211
mammal, 296, 345, 404
manifold effects (*see* pleiotropism)
mannitol, 343
maps, 124, 135, 182, *183*, 189, *361*, 390, *391*, 395–*397*, s-12
markers, selective vs. unselected, 352–353
marriages, cousin, 32, *233*, 241
    nonrandom vs. random, 231–236, *233*, 256
Mars, 224, 441, 442
mathematics, 227
mating, assortive, 231–232
    interspecific, 342
    in microorganisms, 387, 416, 418
    reciprocal, 9, 82, *117*
maximal permissible concentration, 248
Maxy technique, 206, *207*
mean, statistical, 58
measles, 78
medicine, 241, 243, 244, 247, 404, 450
medium, basic minimal, 281, 332
meiosis, 23–30, *24*, *25*, 95, 121, *122*, 124, 213, *416*–417, 440
    in various organisms, *29*, 88, 96, 154, 167, 282, *283*
melanin, 50, 277
"memory," 367, 423

mentality, 78, 79, 231, 277
mercaptoethanol, 432
meromixis and merozygote, 359, 368, 379
metabolism, 266, 271, *275*–*278*, 303, 332, 440
    and mutability, 181, 214, 337–338
    of phenylalanine, 231
metafemale and metamale, *103*
metaphase, *17*, *18*, *25*, 26, *28*, *29*, 86, *87*
methane, 441
methionine, *285*, 332, 353, 375–376
methods for detecting point mutants, 204–208
methyl green, 301
metronome, 78
Mexico, 239
Micrococcus, 346
microcytemia, 36
micromanipulation, 271, 331, 357
micron, 178
microorganisms, 193, 244
microspectrophotometry, 301
migration, 226, 242, 245, 253
miniature wings (*m*), 114, 117, 119, 128, *129*
mitochondria, 428
mitosis, 16, *17*, *18*–21, 24, 147, 213, 302, 440, 449
Modulator (*Mp*), 218–222, 449
moisture and penetrance, 72
mold (*see* template)
mold, bread (*see Neurospora*)
mollusc, 370
monad, 26, 120
Mongolism, 146, *147*
monoecious, 94
monoploid (*see* haploid)
monosomic (haplosomic), *143*, 145, 147
Moon, 442
morphology, 68, 173, 256–257, 262
mosaics, 96, 105, 186, 268, 329, 354, 371, *412*–415
mosquito, 257
mosses, 95
moths, 87, 98, 140
mountains, 256
mouse, 65–68, 162, 193, 201, 248, 257, 263, *264*, 266, *267*, *268*
mucoid coat, 404
muscle, 95, 269
mustard gas, 200
mutability, 181, 200, 245, 248, 249, 336, 415
    genetic control of, 213–222
mutagens, 200, 214, 245–249, 281, 302, 332, 333, 336, 340, 349
    anti-, 337–338
    types of, 338, 400–402
mutant (*see also* gene, DNA, RNA), 3, 5, 111, 137, 206, 241, 245, 248–249
    clearing, 390, *391*, 392
    detection of, 138, 199, 204–206, *205*, 281–282
    detrimental, 206, 208, 210, 229–231, 241
    dosage, 208
    intra-nucleotide, 400–402
    lethal, 62, 65–66, 69, 152, 156, *163*, 208, 229, 234, 239, *240*, 241

balanced, *163*, 164–165, 207
recessive, 65, 68, 152, 163, 204, *205*, 206, *207*, *209*, 211, 229, *230*, 231, *263*, *264*, 265–268
phenotypic effect of, *66*, 185, 206, 208, 210, 211, 239, *240*, 244, 246
point, 204–208, 448
pre- vs. postadaptive, 333–336
rare, in population, 229–231, 242–243
semilethal, 239, *240*
twin, *218*
"visible," 204, 206, *207*, 208
mutation (*see also* mutant), 5, 13, 71, 75, 87, 94, 137, 138, 150, 158, 188, 304, 340–341, 349, 400–*402–403*, 406, 415, 440, 447, 449–450, s-15–s-26
in bacteria, 329–338
in bacteriophage, 392–394
and gene precursor, 201–202
germinal, 246–249
nature of, 144, 199–200, 201
point and gene, 197–202, 204–208, 216
and populations, 225
prevention or recovery from, 200, 213
rate, 200, *209*, 214, 229–230, 247, 336, 386
and selection, 229–231
somatic, 245–246
and speciation, 256
at specific locus, 204, 340
spontaneous, 200, 333, 350–354, 394
and time, 201, 248
units of, 213
mutational loads, 239–249
mutational site, 199, 400–403, 450
mutational spectrum, 200–201, 400–401
National Research Council, 248
nature vs. nurture, 74
Neisseria, 341
neomorph, 210
nerve cell or tissue, 245, 266, 269, 421
Neurospora, 121, *123*, 124, 132, 154, 281–286, *231*, 332, 429
neutrons, 176, 178–180
New Mexico, 253, 254
Nicotiana (tobacco), 63
nicotinamide mononucleotide, 320, *321*
nitrogen and its compounds, 179, 281, 294, 296, 312–315, *314*, 336, 346, 388, 441
nitrous acid, 401, 406
nondisjunction, *89*–91, 106, 143, 146, 147, 188, 207, 214, 247
nose, 275
notochord, 266–267
novel phenotype, 137, 138, 403, 449
no-wing fly, *52*
nuclear war, 249
nucleoprotein, 303, 450
nucleoside, 303, *304*
nucleotide, 303, *304*, 307, 368, 371, 380, 394–395, 400–403, 426–436, 450
di-, 320, *321*, 327
-sharing, 370–372, 376, 425, 435, 447

nucleus and its parts, 16, 20, 121, 152, 181, 271, 300, 307, 329, 359, 370, 409, 429
macro- (mega-) vs. micro-, 415, *416*, 418
nurse cell, 317
nutrition, 130, 265, 266, 332, 337–338, 349–354
ocelliless (*oc*), 206, *207*
Oenothera (evening primrose), 139, *162*–171, 176, 194–195
ommatidia (eye facets), 186, 188
one polypeptide-one cistron view, 286
onion, *17*, *18*
operations (techniques), vi, 7, 13, 137, 278, 293, 403, 444
operon and operator gene, 421–425, 440, 446
Ophryotrocha, 95
organelle, 274, 369, 370, 371, 440
outstretched wing, small eye (*odsy*), 206, *207*
ovary and ovules, 63, 105, 163, 414
oxygen, 178, 179, 200, 201, 214, 287, 337, 441
P_1, P_2, 9
pachynema, 24, *25*, *28*, *158*, *160*
panmixis, 238
paracentric vs. pericentric, 152
paralysis, 69
Paramecium, 410, *411*, 415–418, 449
parasite, 95, 107, 411
parsimony, law of, 10, 62, 199
parthenogenesis, 140, 141
pea, garden, 8, *12*, 39, 81, 111, 162, *163*
sweet, 114
pedigree, 32, *34*, *71*, *87*, *231*, 233, 275
of causes, 70, 244, 271, 278, 287, 421
penetrance, 70–73, 241
penicillin, 341, 343
pentose sugar, *298*, *304*
peptides, 69, 287, *288*
pericarp variegation, 216–222
persistence, 242
personality, 78
phagocytosis, 317, 342
phenogenetics, 262
phenol, 384, 405
phenotype, 2, 57, 70, 111, 116, 138, 185, 210–211, *233*, 278, 394, 449
phenotypic expression, 49–54, 63, 137
phenylalanine, 231, *276*, 277, *285*, 349–354, 433–436
phenylketonuria, *231*, 233, 277
phenylpyruvic acid, *277*
phenyl thiocarbamide (PTC), 228
phokomelia, 265
phosphate, 299, 304, 320, 345, 403, 430
phosphorus, 281, 341, 383, 392, 429
photorecovery, 200
photosynthesis, 65, 413
physics, 189
physiology, 173, 198, 254, 256, 257, 266
Pikes Peak inversion, 253, *254*
pigment, 214–222, 271–274, 277
pistil, 63
pituitary, 266, *267*, 271
placenta, 266

planet, 441–442
plants, flowering, 222, 259
plaque, *386*, 387
plastid, 413–415, 428, 440
plate, hexagonal, 382, *383*
pleiotropism (manifold effects), 68–70, 163, 208, 210,
    234, 244, 265, 271, 275, 277, 279, 287, 421, 446
ploidy, *139*, 181, 245, 246
  eu- vs. aneu-, 143
Pneumococcus (*Diplococcus*), 340–342, 345, 346
point mutation, 197–202
polar bodies, 88
polarity, 197, 300, 303
poliomyelitis, 77, 304, 403
pollen, 63, 114, 121, 152
polyamine, 382
polydactyly, *71*, 74
polydeoxyribonucleotide, 300, *302*, 303, *308*, *311*
polygenes, 56, 108
polymer, 300, 303, 371, 433–440
polymorphism, balanced, 242
polynucleotide phosphorylase, 433–436
polypeptide, 286–290, *289*, 293, 309, 382, 395
polyploidy, 139–141, 147, 213, 302, 306, 449, 450
polyribonucleotide (polyribotide), 303, 433–436
polysaccharide, 340, 342
polysomy, *143*, *145*, 249
polyspermy, 97, 317
polyteny, 141, 213, 303, 316, 317, 449
population, 32, 210, 254, 275, 330
  genetics, 224–226, 229–236, 239–249
  natural, 170, 173, 176, 253, *254*
position effect, 185–195, 215, 235, 371, 449
  and mutation, 185, 222, 245
postbithorax (*pbx*), 193, *194*
potassium, 345
Potentilla (cinquefoil), 254–255
precursors, *273*, *278*, 282
probability, 11, 130, 132
proboscis, 95
proline, 69, *285*, 353, 369
prophase, 16, *17*, *18*, 24, *25*, 26, *28*, *29*
protamine, 293–294
protein, 262, 277, 284, 293, 340, 382, 406, 421–425, *424*
  synthesis, 427–436, 447
Proteus, 380
proton, 176
protoplasm, 150, 181, 274, 281, 293
protoplast, 384
prototrophy, 332, 349–354, *351*, 356, 440
prune eye color (*pn*), 206, *207*
Pseudomonas, 366, 380
pseudopod, 404
pure line, 2, *3*, 8, 84, 138, 162, 171, 252
purine and its derivatives, 281, 295–298, *297*, 304, 337,
    401, *402*, 441
putrescine, 382
pyrimidine, 281, 282, 294, *295*, *296*, 304, 337, 401, *402*
quadrivalent, 259
quadruplets, identical, 74
quantitative traits, 56–60, 104, 108, 262

quantum, 201
r region in T4, 393–*397*, 448
r (roentgen) vs. rad unit, 178
rabbit, 4, 35, 62, 63, 68, 141
race, 170, 226, 252–258
radiation and mutation, 141, 147, 176–180, 200, 201,
    245–249, 336–337, s-15–s-26
radicals, 441
radio, 442
radioactivity, 147, 247–248, 303, 321–323, 383, 392,
    428–432
radish, 259, *260*
raspberry eye color (*ras*), 206, *207*
ratios, phenotypic and genotypic, 49, *51*
ravelase, 347
reaction, norm or range of, 4
receptor, 357, 404
recessive, 12, 43 (*see also* dominance)
recombination, genetic, 13, 79, 94, 112, 134, 137,
    245, 290–291, 329, 409–410, 449–450
  in bacteria, 340–347, 349–354, 356–380
  in viruses, 382–405
recon, 279, 290–291, 303, 304, 345–346, 395, 445, 450
reconstitution, 13, 405
red blood cells (corpuscles), 34, *70*, 287
regression, 58
replica, partial, 387, *388*
  -plating, 349–354, *350*, *351*
replication, 9, 181, *344*, 444 (*see also* gene)
replicon, 451
repressor, 369, 391, 423–*425*
reproduction, asexual or sexual, 5, 74, 94, 329, *330*
reproductive barriers, 256, 257
reproductive disadvantage of mutants, 154–157
reproductive generation, 247
reproductive isolation, 255–260
reproductive potential (*see* fitness, biological)
repulsion, 114
research, 442, 451
respiration, 247
retinoblastoma, 229, 242
Rhyncosciara, *316*
ribonuclease (RNAase), 303, 340, 375, 405, 428
ribonucleic acid (RNA), 303–304, 309, 382, 403–406,
    427–436, *431*, 439, 441, 447, 448
  coding, 431–436
  polymerase, 430, 447
  various types of, 429–436
ribonucleoprotein, 303, 304, 403, 405
ribonucleoside (riboside), 303, *304*, 430–432
ribonucleotide (ribotide), 303, *304*, 320, 406
D-ribose (ribose), *298*, 303, *304*, 427
ribosome, *428*–436
rickettsia, 412
rotational substitution, 402, 450
roundworm, 140, 197
ruby eye color (*rb*), 206, *207*
rye, blue wild, 257
Saint Louis, Mo., 247
salamander, 140, 141
Salmonella, 341, 346, 366, 375–379, *377*, 421–*422*

schizophrenia, 79
Sciara (fungus gnat), 316, 450
scute bristles (*sc*), 204, 206, *207*
sea urchin (*Echinus*), 140, 306, *307*
sedimentation, 324, 375, 428
seed, 39, 111, 139, *144*, *145*, 216, 260
seedling, *414*
segregant, 353
segregation, 10, 168, 282–*283*, 360, 449, s-5–s-10
   gene, 8–14
   independent, 39–47, 74, 82, 111, s-5–s-10
   in man, 32–37
selection, 2, 59, 106, 195, 210, 226, 231, 245, 248–249,
   256, 440
   coefficient, 229–234
   and mutants, 208, 213, 229–231, 242–243
serine, 284, *285*
serology, 173, 340
sex, 5, 94, 95, 103, 104, 114, 201, 213, 256
   in bacteria, 349–354, 356–368
   chromosomes, 81, 90, 104, 179, *207*
     in man, abnormal, 98, 106, 146
   determination, 90, 94–98, 100–109
   -duction, 381
   genetic basis for, 81, 100, 101
   -linked, 83, 112
   ratio, 81, 100, *101*, 105–108
   super-, 103
sheath, 382, *383*
Siamese cat, *4*
siblings, 74, 232, 289
sigma, 410
singed bristles (*sn*), 206, *207*
sister strands, 120, 131, 150, *151*
site, 199, 342
size, 1, 95, 252
skin, 69, 252
smallpox, 403
snail (*Helix*), 94, 95, 317
snake venom diesterase, *324*
snapdragon (*Antirrhinum*), 65
Solenobia, 140, 141
somatic line, 23, 118, 141, 152, 197, 293
sonication, 315, 322, 343
Spain, 252
species, 5, 173, 200, 226, 255–260, 342
   DNA in different, 306, *307*
spectroscopy, 340
sperm, 5, 69, 95, 96, 106, *107*, 108, 121, 124, 178, 180,
   201, 205, 293, 336, 370, 401
spermadine, 382
spermatheca, 69
spermatids, 106, 201, 336
spindle, 17, 141, 369
spirochaete, 107, 410
spleen, 69
splenic phosphodiesterase, *323*, 327
split bristles (*spl*), 128, 189
spore, 121, 123, 124, 281–*283*, 442
spotted fever, Rocky Mountain, 412
Standard gene arrangement, 253, *254*

Staphylococcus, 380
star (sun), 441
starchy, 221
starvation, 141, 265
statistical methods, 58, 60, 249
sterility, 102, 239, *240*, 256
stigma, 63
stillbirths, *233*
stratosphere, 248
streaking method, *332*
Streptococcus, 346
streptomycin, 333–336, *334*, *335*, 342, 343, 346, 347,
   356, 357
strontium-90, 247–248
style, plant, 63
succinic acid, 284
sugar, 281, *298*, 304, 403
sulfanilamide, 400
sulfur, 281, 336, 383
superfemale vs. supermale, 102, *103*
superposition, 50
suppression, 371, 448
surface-volume relationships, 141
survival of human species, 249
Sweden, 32, 108
symbiont, 412
symbols, 32, *33*, 62, 111, 206
sympatric, 255
synapsis, 24, 100, 157, 181, *187*, 198, 213, 258, *259*,
   342, 343
   eu- vs. aneu-, *187*
   somatic, 141, *142*, 194
tail and tail fibers, 382, *383*
tarweeds, 257
tasters, 228
tautomeric shift, 402, *403*
taxonomy, 226
telescope, 441
telomere, 150, 181, 197, 440
telophase, *17*, *18*, *25*, *26*, *29*
temperate (nonlysogenic), 375
temperature, 63, 68, 130, 176, 200, 442
template, 312, *313*, 320, 344, 427–435, 446–447
tempo preference, 78
tendon, 275
tendrils, 111
territory, 253–255
test cross, 43, *44*, 84
tetrad, 24, *25*, 88, *120*, 160
tetraploid, 104, 139, 140, *145*
Texas, 253, *254*
Thailand, 238
thalassemia, 36, 289, 290
theophylline, 337
thiamin, 281, 349–354
thiazole, 281, 282
threonine, *285*, 332, 349–354, 375–376
thymidine, *298*, *299*, 304
thymine (T), *296*, 304–306, 338, 371, 400–*403*, 445
thymus, calf, 324, 346
Tibet, 257

tissue, 176, 178, 265, 267–268
  culture, 141, 265, 267, 317
tobacco (*Nicotiana*), 63
tobacco mosaic virus (TMV), 304, 382, *404–406*, 448
toes, 71, 265
traits, continuous (quantitative), 56–60, 104, 108, 262
transduction, genetic, 374–380, *377*, 421
transformation, genetic, 340–347, 352, 379–380, 444–445, 449–450
transformer (tra), *101*, 105
transition vs. transversion, 401, *402*
translocation, 156–*157*, *160*, *169*, 173, *175–177*, 180, *209*
transmission genetics, 8, 56, 66, 71, 73, 84, 112, 162, 340–341
transplantation, 265, 272–274, 442
transposition, 158, 173, 218, 220
triplet code, 434–*435*, 448
triplets, identical, 74
triploidy, *102*, 139, 140, 144, 147
trivalent homologs, 102, 103, 259
trypsin, 287, *288*, 328, 382, *406*
tryptophan, 284, *285*, 336, 376
  synthetase, 284, 286, 291
tuberculosis, 77, 78, 306, *307*
Turner's type female, 98, 146
turnip yellow mosaic virus, 383, 404
turnover, atomic, 303
twin mutant spots, *218*
twins, human, 32, 33, 74–79, *76*
typhoid, 375
tyrosine, *276*, 277, *285*
ultracentrifugation, 312, *314*, 340, 346
union, cross- (nonrestitutional, exchange), 150, 180, 181, 185, 371
unit, Angstrom (A), 286
  chemical, 403
  map, 124, 353–354
  mutational, 197, 213, 403
  sedimentation, 428
United Nations' report, 247
U.S.S.R., 108, 248

United States, 239, 247, 248, 253, *254*
univalent, 26, 120
uracil, *296*, 303, *304*, 325, *326*, 401, 433–436, 445
  5-bromo or 5-fluoro, 325, *326*, 400–401, 448, 450
urine, 274, 275, 277
v⁺ substance, *273*
vaccinia, *307*, 403
valine, *285*, 287
variance, 58
variation, 2, 7, 73, 78, *235*
variegation, 186, 214, *215*, *216*, *217*, *218*, 371
vegetative phage, 384
Venus, 442
vermilion eye color (v), 193, 195, 206, *207*, 272–274
vertebrae, 267
vestigial wings (vg), 116, 244
viability, 9, 66, 128, 129, 239, *240*
Vibrio, 380
virulence, 384, 390
virus, 304, 332, 341, 352, 353, 356, 357, 381, 403–404, 410, 412–413, 441, 447
water, 214, 256, 281, 307, 308, 441, 442
water shrimp (*Artemia*), 140, 317
Watson-Crick model of DNA, *308* (*see also* DNA)
waxy, 221
wheat, 143, 296
white eye (w), 62, 65, 69, 83, 114, 117, 119, 122, 128, 186, 206, *207*
wild-type, 65
X chromosome, 81, 90, 91, 97, 100, 146, 204, *205*, 206, *207*
Xanthomonas, 341
X ray, 176–180, *179*, 200, 206, 349 (*see also* radiation, mutation)
X ray diffraction pattern, 307, *308*, 340
Y chromosome, 81, 90, 91, 100, 106, 114, 146, 175, 182, 186, 206, 371
yak, 257
yeast, *307*, 429
yellow body color (y), 117, 119, 128, 188, 189, 206, *207*
Zea (*see* corn)
zygonema, 24
zygote, 5, 354

Irwin H. Herskowitz

GENETICS

SUPPLEMENTS

SUPPLEMENT I

Part of a Letter (1867)
from Gregor Mendel to C. Nägeli

*Translated from German by Leonie Kellen Piternick
and George Piternick. Reprinted from* The Birth of
Genetics, *Supplement to* Genetics, *Vol. 35, No. 5,
Part 2 (1950), by permission of Genetics, Inc.*

GREGOR MENDEL (1822–1884)

SUPPLEMENT II

Nobel Prize Lecture (1934)
of Thomas Hunt Morgan

Reprinted by permission of The Nobel Foundation for Les Prix Nobel. The complete lecture is published in The Scientific Monthly for July 1935. Only the first portion is reprinted here.

THOMAS HUNT MORGAN (1866–1945)

By permission of The American Genetic Association, The Journal of Heredity, frontispiece, Vol. 24, No. 416, 1933.

SUPPLEMENT III

Nobel Prize Lecture (1946)
of Hermann Joseph Muller

Reprinted by permission of The Nobel Foundation for Les Prix Nobel. Published in The Journal of Heredity, 38: 259–270, 1947.

HERMANN JOSEPH MULLER (1890–   )

SUPPLEMENT IV

Nobel Prize Lecture (1958)
of George Wells Beadle

*Reprinted by permission of The Nobel Foundation for
Les Prix Nobel. Published in* Science, *129:1715–1719,
1959.*

GEORGE WELLS BEADLE (1903–   )

SUPPLEMENT V

Nobel Prize Lecture (1958)
of Edward Lawrie Tatum

*Reprinted by permission of The Nobel Foundation for
Les Prix Nobel. Published in* Science, *129:1715–1719,
1959.*

EDWARD LAWRIE TATUM (1909–   )

SUPPLEMENT VI

Nobel Prize Lecture (1959)
of Arthur Kornberg

Reprinted by permission of The Nobel Foundation for
Les Prix Nobel. *Published in* Science, *131:1503–1508,
1960.*

ARTHUR KORNBERG (1918–   )

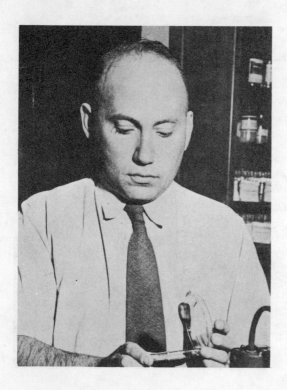

SUPPLEMENT VII

Nobel Prize Lecture (1959)
of Joshua Lederberg

Reprinted by permission of The Nobel Foundation for
Les Prix Nobel. *Published in* Stanford Med. Bull.,
17:120–132, 1959; and in Science, *131:269–276, 1960.*

JOSHUA LEDERBERG (1925–   )

PART OF A LETTER

(1867)

from

GREGOR MENDEL

to

C. NÄGELI

HIGHLY ESTEEMED SIR:

My most cordial thanks for the printed matter you have so kindly sent me! The papers "die Bastardbildung im Pflanzenreiche," "über die abgeleiteten Pflanzenbastarde," "die Theorie der Bastardbildung," "die Zwischenformen zwischen den Pflanzenarten," "die systematische Behandlung der Hieracien rücksichtlich der Mittelformen und des Umfangs der Species," especially capture my attention. This thorough revision of the theory of hybrids according to contemporary science was most welcome. Thank you again!

With respect to the essay which your honor had the kindness to accept, I think I should add the following information: the experiments which are discussed were conducted from 1856 to 1863. I knew that the results I obtained were not easily compatible with our contemporary scientific knowledge, and that under the circumstances publication of one such isolated experiment was doubly dangerous; dangerous for the experimenter and for the cause he represented. Thus I made every effort to verify, with other plants, the results obtained with Pisum. A number of hybridizations undertaken in 1863 and 1864 convinced me of the difficulty of finding plants suitable for an extended series of experiments, and that under unfavorable circumstances years might elapse without my obtaining the desired information. I attempted to inspire some control experiments, and for that reason discussed the Pisum experiments at the meeting of the local society of naturalists. I encountered, as was to be expected, divided opinion; however, as far as I know, no one undertook to repeat the experiments. When, last year, I was asked to publish my lecture in the proceedings of the society, I agreed to do so, after having re-examined my records for the various years of experimentation, and not having been able to find a source of error. The paper which was submitted to you is the unchanged reprint of the draft of the lecture mentioned; thus the brevity of the exposition, as is essential for a public lecture.

I am not surprised to hear your honor speak of my experiments with mistrustful caution; I would not do otherwise in a similar case. Two points in your esteemed letter appear to be too important to be left unanswered. The first deals with the question whether one may conclude that constancy of type has been obtained if the hybrid Aa produces a plant A, and this plant in turn produces only A.

Permit me to state that, as an empirical worker, I must define constancy of type as the retention of a character during the period of observation. My statements that some of the progeny of hybrids breed true to type thus includes only those generations during which observations were made; it does not extend beyond them. For two generations all experiments were conducted with a fairly large number of plants. Starting with the third generation it became necessary to limit the numbers because of lack of space, so that, in each of the seven experiments, only a sample of those plants of the second generation (which either bred true or varied) could be observed further. The observations were extended over four to six generations (p. 13). Of the varieties which bred true (pp. 15–18) some plants were observed for four generations. I must further mention the case of a variety which bred true for six generations, although the parental types differed in four characters. In 1859 I obtained a very fertile descendent with large, tasty, seeds from a first generation hybrid. Since, in the following year, its progeny retained the desirable characteristics and were uniform, the variety was cultivated in our vegetable garden, and many plants were raised every year up to 1865. The parental plants were $bcDg$ and $BCdG$:

B. albumen yellow	b. albumen green
C. seed-coat grayish-brown	c. seed-coat white
D. pod inflated	d. pod constricted
G. axis long	g. axis short

The hybrid just mentioned was $BcDG$.

The color of the albumen could be determined only in the plants saved for seed production, for the other pods were harvested in an immature condition. Never was green albumen observed in these plants, reddish-purple flower color (an indication of brown seed-coat), constriction of the pod, nor short axis.

This is the extent of my experience. I cannot judge whether these findings would permit a decision as to constancy of type; however, I am inclined to regard the separation of parental characteristics in the progeny of hybrids in Pisum as complete, and thus permanent. The progeny of hybrids carries one or the other of the parental characteristics, or the hybrid form of the two; I have never observed gradual transitions between the parental characters or a progressive approach toward one of them. The course of development consists simply in this; that in each generation the two parental characteristics appear, separated and unchanged, and there is nothing to indicate that one of them has either inherited or taken over anything from the other. For an example, permit me to point to the packets, numbers 1035–1088, which I sent you. All the seeds originated in the first generation of a hybrid in which brown and white seed-coats were combined. Out of the brown seed of this hybrid, some plants were obtained with seed-coats of a pure white color, without any admixture of brown. I expect those to retain the same constancy of character as found in the parental plant.

The second point, on which I wish to elaborate briefly, contains the following statement: "You should regard the numerical expressions as being only empirical, because they can not be proved rational."

My experiments with single characters all lead to the same result: that from the seeds of the hybrids, plants are obtained half of which in turn carry the hybrid character (Aa), the other half, however, receive the parental characters A and a in equal amounts. Thus, on the average, among four plants two have the hybrid character Aa, one the parental character A, and the other the parental character a. Therefore $2Aa+A+a$ or $A+2Aa+a$ is the empirical simple, developmental series for two differentiating characters. Likewise it was shown in an empirical manner that, if two or three differentiating characters are combined in the hybrid, the developmental series is a combination of two or three simple series. Up to this point I don't believe I can be accused of having left the realm of experimentation. If then I extend this combination of simple series to any number of differences between the two parental plants, I have indeed entered the rational domain. This seems permissible, however, because I have proved by previous experiments that the development of any two differentiating characteristics proceeds independently of any other differences. Finally, regarding my statements on the differences among the ovules and pollen cells of the hybrids; they also are based on experiments. These and similar experiments on the germ cells appear to be important, for I believe that their results furnish the explanation for the development of hybrids as observed in Pisum. These experiments should be repeated and verified.

I regret very much not being able to send your honor the varieties you desire. As I mentioned above, the experiments were conducted up to and including 1863; at that time they were terminated in order to obtain space and time for the growing of other experimental plants. Therefore seeds from those experiments are no longer available. Only one experiment on differences in the time of flowering was continued; and seeds are available from the 1864 harvest of this experiment. These are the last I collected, since I had to abandon the experiment in the following year because of devastation by the pea beetle, *Bruchus pisi*. In the early years of experimentation this insect was only rarely found on the plants, in 1864 it caused considerable damage, and appeared in such numbers in the following summer that hardly a 4th or 5th of the seeds was spared. In the last few years it has been necessary to discontinue cultivation of peas in the vicinity of Brünn. The seeds remaining can still be useful, among them are some varieties which I expect to remain constant; they are derived from hybrids in which two, three, and four differentiating characters are combined. All the seeds were obtained from members of the first generation, i.e., of such plants as were grown directly from the seeds of the original hybrids.

I should have scruples against complying with your honor's request to send these seeds for experimentation, were it not in such complete agreement with my own wishes. I fear that there has been partial loss of viability. Furthermore the seeds were obtained at a time when *Bruchus pisi* was already rampant, and I cannot acquit this beetle of possibly transferring pollen; also, I must mention again that the plants were destined for a study of differences in flowering time. The other differences were also taken into account at the harvest, but with less care than in the major experiment. The legend which I have added to the packet numbers on a separate sheet is a copy of the notes I made for each individual plant, with pencil, on its envelope at the time of harvest. The dominant characters are designated as A, B, C, D, E, F, G and as concerns their dual meaning please refer to p. 11. The recessive characters are designated $a, b, c, d, e, f, g;$ these should remain constant in the next generation. Therefore, from those seeds which stem from plants with recessive characters only, identical plants are expected (as regards the characters studied).

Please compare the numbers of the seed packets with those in my record, to detect any possible error in the designations—each packet contains the seeds of a single plant only.

Some of the varieties represented are suitable for experiments on the germ cells; their results can be obtained during the current summer. The round yellow seeds of packets 715, 730, 736, 741, 742, 745, 756, 757, and on the other hand, the green angular seeds of packets 712, 719, 734, 737, 749, and 750 can be recommended for this purpose. By repeated experiments it was proved that, if plants with green seeds are fertilized by those with yellow seeds, the albumen of the resulting seeds has lost the green color and has taken up the yellow color. The same is true for the shape of the seed. Plants with angular seeds, if fertilized by those with round or rounded seeds, produce round or rounded seeds. Thus, due to the changes induced in the color and shape of the seeds by fertilization with foreign pollen, it is possible to recognize the constitution of the fertilizing pollen.

Let B designate yellow color; b, green color of the albumen.

Let A designate round shape; a, angular shape of the seeds.

If flowers of such plants as produce green and angular seeds by self-fertilization are fertilized with foreign pollen, and if the seeds remain green and angular, then the pollen of the donor plant was, as regards the two characters
.... ab
If the shape of the seeds is changed, the pollen was taken from.......... Ab
If the color of the seeds is changed, the pollen was taken from.......... aB
If both shape and color is changed, the pollen was taken from.......... AB

The packets enumerated above contain round and yellow, round and green, angular and yellow, and angular and green seeds from the hybrids $ab+AB$. The round and yellow seeds would be best suited for the experiment. Among them (see experiment p. 15) the varieties AB, ABb, Aab, and $AaBb$ may occur; thus four cases are possible when plants, grown from green and angular seeds, are fertilized by the pollen of those grown from the above mentioned round and yellow seeds, i.e.

I. $ab+AB$

II. $ab+ABb$

III. $ab+AaB$

IV. $ab+AaBb$

If the hypothesis that hybrids form as many types of pollen cells as there are possible constant combination types is correct, plants of the makeup

AB	produce pollen of the type AB
ABb	" " " " " AB and Ab
AaB	" " " " " AB and aB
$AaBb$	" " " " " AB, Ab, aB, and ab

Fertilization of ovules occurs:

I. Ovules ab with pollen AB

II. " ab " " AB and Ab

III. " ab " " AB and aB

IV. " ab " " AB, Ab, aB, and ab

The following varieties may be obtained from this fertilization:

I. $AaBb$

II. $AaBb$ and Aab

III. $AaBb$ and aBb

IV. $AaBb$, Aab, aBb, and ab

If the different types of pollen are produced in equal numbers, there should be in

I. All seeds round and yellow

II. one half round and yellow
one half round and green

III. one half round and yellow
one half angular and yellow

IV. one quarter round and yellow
one quarter round and green
one quarter angular and yellow
one quarter angular and green

Furthermore, since the numerical relations between AB, ABb, AaB, $AaBb$ are $1:2:2:4$, among any nine plants grown from round yellow seed there should be found on the average $AaBb$ four times, ABb and AaB twice each, and AB

once; thus the IVth case should occur four times as frequently as the Ist and twice as frequently as the IInd or IIIrd.

If on the other hand, plants grown from the round yellow seeds mentioned are fertilized by pollen from green angular plants, the results should be exactly the same, provided that the ovules are of the same types, and formed in the same proportions, as was reported for the pollen.

I have not performed this experiment myself, but I believe, on the basis of similar experiments, that one can depend on the result indicated.

In the same fashion individual experiments may be performed for each of the two seed characters separately, all those round seeds which occurred together with angular ones, and all the yellow ones which occurred with green seeds on the same plant are suitable. If, for instance, a plant with green seeds was fertilized by one with yellow seeds, the seeds obtained should be either 1) all yellow, or 2) half yellow and half green, since the plants originating from yellow seeds are of the varieties B and Bb. Since, furthermore, B and Bb occur in the ratio of $1:2$, the 2nd fertilization will occur twice as frequently as the 1st.

Regarding the other characters, the experiments may be conducted in the same way; results, however, will not be obtained until next year....

As must be expected, the experiments proceed slowly. At first beginning, some patience is required, but later, when several experiments are progressing concurrently, matters are improved. Every day, from spring to fall, one's interest is refreshed daily, and the care which must be given to one's wards is thus amply repaid. In addition, if I should, by my experiments, succeed in hastening the solution of these problems, I should be doubly happy.

Accept, highly esteemed Sir, the expression of most sincere respect from

> Your devoted,
> G. MENDEL
> (Altbrünn, Monastery of St. Thomas)

Brünn, 18 April, 1867

THE RELATION OF GENETICS TO PHYSIOLOGY AND MEDICINE

NOBEL LECTURE, PRESENTED IN STOCKHOLM ON JUNE 4, 1934

By Dr. THOMAS HUNT MORGAN

DIRECTOR OF THE WM. G. KERCKHOFF LABORATORIES, CALIFORNIA INSTITUTE OF TECHNOLOGY

THE study of heredity, now called genetics, has undergone such an extraordinary development in the present century, both in theory and in practice, that it is not possible in a short address to review even briefly all its outstanding achievements. At most I can do no more than take up a few topics for discussion.

Since the group of men with whom I have worked for twenty years has been interested for the most part in the chromosome-mechanism of heredity, I shall first briefly describe the relation between the facts of heredity and the theory of the gene. Then I should like to discuss one of the physiological problems implied in the theory of the gene; and finally, I hope to say a few words about the applications of genetics to medicine.

The modern theory of genetics dates from the opening years of the present century, with the discovery of Mendel's long-lost paper that had been overlooked for thirty-five years. The data obtained by de Vries in Holland, Correns in Germany and Tschermak in Austria showed that Mendel's laws are not confined to garden peas, but apply to other plants. A year or two later the work of Bateson and Punnett in England and Cuénot in France made it evident that the same laws apply to animals.

In 1902 a young student, William Sutton, working in the laboratory of E. B. Wilson, pointed out clearly and completely that the known behavior of the chromosomes at the time of maturation of the germ-cells furnishes us with a mechanism that accounts for the kind of separation of the hereditary units postulated in Mendel's theory.

The discovery of a mechanism, that suffices to explain both the first and the second law of Mendel, has had far-reaching consequences for genetic theory, especially in relation to the discovery of additional laws; because the recognition of a mechanism that can be seen and followed demands that any extension of Mendel's theories must conform to such a recognized mechanism; and also because the apparent exceptions to Mendel's laws, that came to light before long, might, in the absence of a known mechanism, have called forth purely fictitious modifications of Mendel's laws or even seemed to invalidate their generality. We now know that some of these "exceptions" are due to newly discovered and demonstrable properties of the chromosome mechanism, and others to recognizable irregularities in the machine.

Mendel knew of no processes taking place in the formation of pollen and egg-

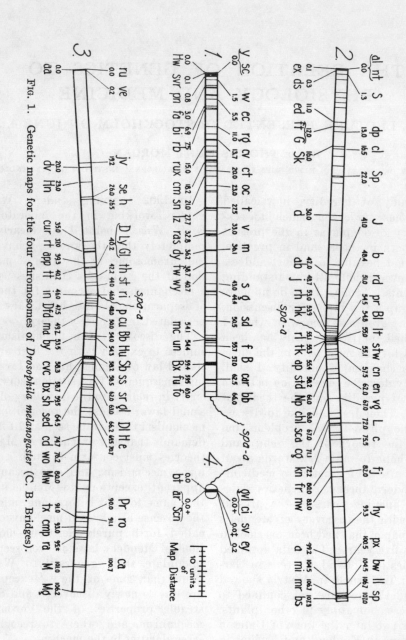

FIG. 1. Genetic maps for the four chromosomes of *Drosophila melanogaster* (C. B. Bridges).

cell that could furnish a basis for his primary assumption that the hereditary elements separate in the germ-cells in such a way that each ripe germ-cell comes to contain only one of each kind of element: but he justified the validity of this assumption by putting it to a crucial test. His analysis was a wonderful feat of reasoning. He verified his reasoning by the recognized experimental procedure of science.

As a matter of fact it would not have been possible in Mendel's time to give an objective demonstration of the basic mechanism involved in the separation of the hereditary elements in the germ-cells. The preparation for this demonstration took all the thirty-five years between Mendel's paper in 1865 and 1900. It is here that the names of the most prominent European cytologists stand out as the discoverers of the rôle of the chromosomes in the maturation of the germ-cells. It is largely a result of their work that it was possible in 1902 to relate the well-known cytological evidence to Mendel's laws. So much in retrospect.

The most significant additions that have been made to Mendel's two laws may be called linkage and crossing over. In 1906 Bateson and Punnett reported a two-factor case in sweet peas that did not give the expected ratio for two pairs of characters entering the cross at the same time.

By 1911 two genes had been found in Drosophila that gave sex-linked inheritance. It had earlier been shown that such genes lie in the X-chromosomes. Ratios were found in the second generation that did not conform to Mendel's second law when these two pairs of characters are present, and the suggestion was made that the ratios in such cases could be explained on the basis of interchange between the two X-chromosomes in the female. It was also pointed out that the further apart the genes for such characters happen to lie in the chromo-some, the greater the chance for interchange to take place. This would give the approximate location of the genes with respect to other genes. By further extension and clarification of this idea it became possible, as more evidence accumulated, to demonstrate that the genes lie in a single line in each chromosome.

Two years previously (1909) a Belgian investigator, Janssens, had described a phenomenon in the conjugating chromosomes of a salamander, Batracoseps, which he interpreted to mean that interchanges take place between homologous chromosomes. This he called chiasmatypie—a phenomenon that has occupied the attention of cytologists down to the present day. Janssens' observations were destined shortly to supply an objective support to the demonstration of genetic interchange between linked genes carried in the sex chromosomes of the female Drosophila.

To-day we arrange the genes in a chart or map, Fig. 1. The numbers attached express the distance of each gene from some arbitrary point taken as zero. These numbers make it possible to foretell how any new character that may appear will be inherited with respect to all other characters, as soon as its crossing over value with respect to any other two characters is determined. This ability to predict would in itself justify the construction of such maps, even if there were no other facts concerning the location of the genes; but there is to-day direct evidence in support of the view that genes lie in a serial order in the chromosomes.

What are the Genes?

What is the nature of the elements of heredity that Mendel postulated as purely theoretical units? What are genes? Now that we locate them in the chromosomes are we justified in regarding them as material units; as chemical bodies of a higher order than molecules?

Frankly, these are questions with which the working geneticist has not much concern himself, except now and then to speculate as to the nature of the postulated elements. There is no consensus of opinion amongst geneticists as to what the genes are—whether they are real or purely fictitious—because at the level at which the genetic experiments lie it does not make the slightest difference whether the gene is a hypothetical unit or whether the gene is a material particle. In either case the unit is associated with a specific chromosome, and can be localized there by purely genetic analysis. Hence, if the gene is a material unit, it is a piece of a chromosome; if it is a fictitious unit, it must be referred to a definite location in a chromosome—the same place as on the other hypothesis. Therefore, it makes no difference in the actual work in genetics which point of view is taken.

Between the characters that are used by the geneticist and the genes that the theory postulates lies the whole field of embryonic development, where the properties implicit in the genes become explicit in the protoplasm of the cells. Here we appear to approach a physiological problem, but one that is new and strange to the classical physiology of the schools.

We ascribe certain general properties to the genes, in part from genetic evidence and in part from microscopical observations. These properties we may next consider.

Since chromosomes divide in such a way that the line of genes is split (each daughter chromosome receiving exactly half of the original line) we can scarcely avoid the inference that the genes divide into exactly equal parts; but just how this takes place is not known. The analogy of cell-division creates a presumption that the gene divides in the same way, but we should not forget that the relatively gross process involved in cell-division may seem quite inadequate to cover the refined separation of the gene into equal halves. As we do not know of any comparable division phenomena in organic molecules, we must also be careful in ascribing a simple molecular constitution to the gene. On the other hand, the elaborate chains of molecules built up in organic material may give us, some day, a better opportunity to picture the molecular or aggregate structure of the gene and furnish a clue concerning its mode of division....

THE PRODUCTION OF MUTATIONS

IF, as Darwin maintained, the adaptiveness of living things results from natural selection, rather than from a teleological tendency in the process of variation itself, then heritable variations must, under most conditions, occur in numerous directions, so as to give a wide range of choice for the selective process. Such a state of affairs seems, however, in more or less contradiction to the commonly held idea, to which Darwin also gave some credence, that heritable variations of given kinds tend to be produced, in a fairly regular way, by given kinds of external conditions. For then we are again confronted with the difficulty, how is it that the "right kinds" of variations (*i.e.* the adaptive ones) manage to arise in response to the "right kinds" of conditions (*i.e.* those they are adapted to)? Moreover, the de Vriesian notion of mutations does not help us in this connection. On that view, there are sudden jumps, going all the way from one "elementary species" to another, and involving radical changes in numerous characters at once, and there are relatively few different jumps to choose between. This obviously would fail to explain how, through such coarse steps, the body could have come to be so remarkably streamlined in its internal and external organization, or, in other words, so thoroughly adaptive.

The older selectionists, thinking in terms of chemical reactions on a molar scale when they thought in terms of chemistry at all, did not realize sufficiently the ultramicroscopic randomness of the processes causing inherited variations. The earliest mutationists failed, in addition, to appreciate the qualitative and quantitative multiplicity of mutations. It was not long, however, before the results of Baur on *Antirrhi-num* and of Morgan on *Drosophila,* supplemented by scattered observations on other forms, gave evidence of the occurrence of numerous Mendelizing mutations, many of them small ones, in varied directions, and they showed no discoverable relation between the type of mutation and the type of environment or condition of living under which it arose. These observations, then, came closer to the statistical requirements for a process of evolution which has its basis in accidents. In what sense, however, could the events be regarded as accidental? Were they perhaps expressions of veiled forces working in a more determinate manner? It was more than ever evident that further investigation of the manner of occurrence of mutations was called for.

If the mutations were really non-teleological, with no relation between type of environment and type of change, and above all no adaptive relation, and if they were of as numerous types as the theory of natural selection would demand, then the great majority of the changes should be harmful in their effects, just as any alterations made blindly in a complicated apparatus are usually detrimental to its proper functioning, and many of the larger changes should even be totally incompatible with the functioning of the whole, or, as we say, lethal. That is, strange as it may seem at first sight, we should expect most mutations to be disadvantageous if the theory of natural selection is correct. We should also expect these mainly disadvantageous changes to be highly diversified in their genetic basis.

Frequency of Mutations

To get exact evidence on these points required the elaboration of special genetic methods, adapted to the recognition of mutations that ordinarily escape detection—(1) lethals, (2) changes with but small visible effects, and (3) changes without any externally visible effects but influencing the viability more or less unfavorably. It would take us too far afield to explain these techniques here. Suffice it to say that they made use of the principle according to which a chromosome is, as we say, "marked," by having had inserted into it to begin with one or more known mutant genes with conspicuous visible effects, to differentiate it from the homologous chromosome. An individual with two such differentiated chromosomes, when appropriately bred, will then be expected to give two groups of visibly different offspring, holding certain expected ratios to one another. If, however, a lethal mutation has occurred in one of the two chromosomes, its existence will be made evident by the absence of the corresponding expected group of offspring. Similarly, a mutated gene with invisible but somewhat detrimental action, though not fully lethal, will be recognized by the fact that the corresponding group of offspring are found in smaller numbers than expected. And a gene with a very small visible effect, that might be overlooked in a single individual, will have a greatly increased chance of being seen because the given group of offspring as a whole will tend to be distinguished in this regard from the corresponding group derived from a non-mutant.

In this way, it was possible in the first tests of this kind, which Altenburg and the writer conducted, partly in collaboration, in 1918-19, to get definite evidence in *Drosophila* that the lethal mutations greatly outnumbered those with visible effects, and that among the latter the types having an obscure manifestation were more numerous than the definite conspicuous ones used in ordinary genetic work. Visible or not, the great majority had lowered viability. Tests of their genetic basis, using the newly found facts of linkage, showed them to be most varied in their locus in the chromosomes, and it could be calcu-

lated by a simple extrapolative process that there must be at least hundreds, and probably thousands, of different kinds arising in the course of spontaneous mutation. In work done much later, employing induced mutations, it was also shown (in independent experiments both of the present writer and Kerkis, and of Timoféeff and his co-workers, done in 1934) that "invisible" mutations, which by reason of one or another physiological change lower viability without being fully lethal, form the most abundant group of any detected thus far, being at least two to three times as numerous as the complete lethals. No doubt there are in addition very many, perhaps even more, with effects too small to have been detected at all by our rather crude methods. It is among these that we should be most apt to find those rare accidents which, under given conditions or in given combinations with others, may happen to have some adaptive value. Tests of Timoféeff, however, have shown that even a few of the more conspicuous visible mutations do in certain combinations give an advantage in laboratory breeding.

Because of the nature of the test whereby it is detected—the absence of an entire group of offspring bearing certain conspicuous expected characters— a lethal is surer of being detected, and detected by any observer, than is the inconspicuous or invisible, merely detrimental, mutation. Fortunately, there are relatively few borderline cases, of nearly but not quite completely lethal genes. It was this objectivity of recognition, combined with the fact that they were so much more numerous than conspicuous visible mutations, that made it feasible for lethals to be used as an index of mutation frequency, even though they suffer from the disadvantage of requiring the breeding of an individual, rather than its mere inspection, for the recognition that it carries a lethal. In the earliest published work, we (Altenburg and the author) attempted not only to find a quantitative value for the "normal" mutation frequency, but also to determine whether a certain condition, which we considered of especial interest, affected the mutation frequency. The plan was ultimately to use the method as a general one for studying the effects of various conditions. The condition chosen for the first experiment was temperature, and the results, verified by later work of the writer's, indicated that a rise of temperature, within limits normal to the organism, produced an increase of mutation frequency of about the amount to be expected if mutations were, in essentials, orthodox chemical reactions.

Mutations as Chemical Reactions

On this view, however, single mutations correspond with individual molecular changes, and an extended series of mutations, in a great number of identical genes in a population, spread out over thousands of years, is what corresponds with the course of an ordinary chemical reaction that takes place in a whole collection of molecules in a test tube in the course of a fraction of a second or a few seconds. For the individual gene, in its biological setting, is far more stable than the ordinary chemical molecule is, when the latter is exposed to a reagent in the laboratory. Thus, mutations, when taken collectively, should be subject to the statistical laws applying to mass reactions, but the individual mutation, corresponding to a change in one molecule, should be subject to the vicissitudes of ultramicroscopic or atomic events, and the apparition of a mutant individual represents an enormous amplification of such a phenomenon. This is a principle which gives the clue to the fact, which otherwise seems opposed to a rational, scientific and molarly deterministic point of view, that differences in external conditions or conditions of living do not appear to affect the occurrence of mutations, while on the other hand, even in a normal and sensibly constant environment, mutations of varied kinds do occur. It is also in harmony with our finding, of about the same time, that when a mutation takes place in a given gene, the other gene of identical type present nearby in the same cell usually remains unaffected though it must of course have been subjected to the same macroscopic physicochemical conditions. On this conception, then, the mutations ordinarily result from submicroscopic accidents, that is, from caprices of thermal agitation, that occur on a molecular and submolecular scale. More recently Delbrück and Timoféeff, in more extended work on temperature, have shown that the amount of increase in mutation frequency with rising temperature is not merely that of an ordinary test-tube chemical reaction, but in fact corresponds closely with that larger rise to be expected of a reaction as slow in absolute time rate (*i.e.* with as small a proportion of molecular changes per unit of time) as the observed mutation frequency shows this reaction to be, and this quantitative correspondence helps to confirm the entire conception.

Now this inference concerning the non-molar nature of the individual mutation process, which sets it in so different a class from most other grossly observable chemical changes in nature, led naturally to the expectation that some of the "point effects" brought about by high-energy radiation like X-rays would also work to produce alternations in the hereditary material. For if even the relatively mild events of thermal agitation can, some of them, have such consequences, surely the energetically far more potent changes caused by powerful radiation should succeed. And, as a matter of fact, our trials of X-rays, carried out with the same kind of genetic methods as previously used for temperature, proved that such radiation is extremely effective, and inordinately more so than a mere temperature rise, since by this method it was possible to obtain, by a half hour's treatment, over a hundred times as many mutations in a group of treated cells as would have occurred in them spontaneously in the course of a whole generation. These mutations, too, were found ordinarily to occur pointwise and randomly, in one gene at a time, without affecting an identical gene that might be present nearby in a homologous chromosome.

Radiation-Effects

In addition to the individual gene changes, radiation also produced rearrangements of parts of chromosomes. As our later work (including that with co-workers, especially Raychaudhuri and Pontecorvo) has shown, these latter were caused in the first place by breakages of the chromosomes, followed afterwards by attachments occurring between the adhesive broken ends, that joined them in a different order than before. The two or more breaks involved in such a rearrangement may be far apart, caused by independent hits, and thus result in what we call a *gross* structural change. Such changes are of various kinds, depending upon just where the breaks are and just which broken ends become attached to which. But, though the effects of the individual "hits" are rather narrowly localized, it is not uncommon for two breaks to be produced at nearby points by what amounts to one local change (or at any rate one localized group of changes) whose influence becomes somewhat spread out. By the rejoining, in a new order, of broken ends resulting from two such nearby breaks, a *minute* change of sequence of the genes is brought about. More usually, the small piece between the two breaks becomes lost (a "deficiency"), but sometimes it becomes inverted, or even becomes transferred into a totally different position, made available by a separate hit.

Both earlier and later work by collaborators (Oliver, Hanson, etc.) showed definitely that the frequency of the gene mutations is directly and simply proportional to the dose of irradiation applied, and this despite the wave length used, whether X- or gamma or even beta rays, and despite the timing of the irradiation. These facts have since been established with great exactitude and detail, more especially by Timoféeff and his coworkers. In our more recent work with Raychaudhuri these principles have been extended to total doses as low as 400r, and rates as low as .01r per minute, with gamma rays. They leave, we believe, no escape from the conclusion that there is no threshold dose, and that the individual mutations result from individual "hits", producing genetic effects in their immediate neighborhood. Whether these so-called "hits" are the individual ionizations, or may even be the activations that occur at lower energy levels, or whether, at the other end of the scale, they require the clustering of ionizations that occurs at the termini of electron tracks and of their side branches (as Lea and Fano point out might be the case), is as yet undecided. But in any case they are, even when microscopically considered, what we have termed "point mutations," as they involve only disturbances on an ultramicroscopically localized scale. And whether or not they are to occur at any particular point is entirely a matter of accident, using this term in the sense in which it is employed in the mathematics of statistics.

Naturally, other agents than photons which produce effects of this kind must also produce mutations, as has been shown by students and collaborators working under Altenburg in Houston for neutrons (Nagai and Locher) and for alpha rays (Ward) and confirmed by Timoféeff and his co-workers (Zimmer, et al). Moreover, as Altenburg showed, even the smaller quantum changes induced by ultraviolet exert this effect on the genes. They cause, however, only a relatively small amount of rearrangement of chromosome parts (Muller and Mackenzie), and, in fact, they also tend to inhibit such rearrangement, as Swanson, followed by Kauffmann and Hollaender, has found. Since the effective ultraviolet hits are in the form of randomly scattered single-atom changes in the purines and pyrimidines of the chromosome, rather than in groups of atom changes, it seems likely that clusters of ionizations are not necessary for the gene mutation effects, at any rate, although we cannot be sure of this until the relation of mutation frequency to dosage is better known for this agent.

Induced and Natural Mutations

Inasmuch as the changes brought about in the genes by radiation must certainly be of an accidental nature, unpremeditated, ateleological, without reference to the value of the end result for the organism or its descendants, it is of interest to compare them with the so-called spontaneous or natural mutations. For in the radiation mutations we have a yardstick of what really random changes should be. Now it is found in *Drosophila* that the radiation-induced mutations of the genes (we exclude here the demonstrable chromosome rearrangements) are in every respect which has been investigated of the same essential nature as those arising naturally in the laboratory or field. They usually occur in one gene without affecting an identical one nearby. They are distributed similarly in the chromosomes. The effects, similarly, may be large or small and there is a similar ratio of fully lethal to so-called visible gene mutations. That is, the radiation mutations of the genes do not give evidence of being more deleterious. And when one concentrates attention upon given genes one finds that a whole series of different forms, or alleles, may be produced, of a similar and in many cases sensibly identical nature in the two cases. In fact, every natural mutation, when searched for long enough, is found to be producible also by radiation. Moreover, under any given condition of living tried, without radiation, the effects appear as scattered as when radiation is applied, even though of much lower frequency. All this surely means then, does it not, that the natural mutations have in truth no innate tendency to be adaptive, nor even to be different, as a whole group, under some natural conditions than under others? In other words, they cannot be determinate in a molar sense, but must themselves be caused by the ultramicroscopic accidents of the molecular and submolecular motions, *i.e.* by the individual quantum exchanges of thermal agitation, taking this word in a broad sense. The only escape from this would be to suppose that they are caused by the radiation present in nature, resulting from natural radioactive substances and cosmic rays, but a little calculation (by Mott-Smith and the writer, corroborated by others) has shown that this radiation is quite inadequate in amount to account for the majority of mutations occurring in most organisms.

But to say that most natural mutations are the results of the quantum exchanges of thermal agitation, and, further, that a given energy level must be reached to produce them, does not, as some authors have seemed to imply, mean that the physicochemical conditions in and around the organism, other than temperature, have no influence upon their chance of occurrence. That such circumstances may play a decided role was early evident from the studies of spontaneous mutation frequency, when it was found (1921, reported 1928) that the frequency in one experiment, with one genetic stock, might be ten times as high as in another, with another stock. And more recently we have found that, in different portions of the natural life cycle of the same individual, the mutation frequency may be very different. Finally, in the work of Auerbach and Robson, with mustard gas and related substances, it has been proved that these chemicals may induce mutations at as high a frequency as a heavy dose of X-rays. In all these cases, however, the effects are similarly scattered at random, individually uncontrolled, and similarly non-adaptive.

It should also be noted in this connection that the genes are not under all conditions equally vulnerable to the mutating effects of X-rays themselves. Genes in the condensed chromosomes of spermatozoa, for example, appear to be changed more easily than those in the more usual "resting" stages. We have mentioned that, as Swanson has shown, ultraviolet exerts besides its own mutating effect an inhibition on the process of chromosome breakage, or at any rate on that of reunion of the broken parts in a new viable order, while infrared, in Hollaender's and Kaufmann's recent experiments, has a contrary action. And Stadler, in his great work on the production of mutations in cereals, started independently of our own, has obtained evidence that in this material X-radiation in the doses used is unable to produce a sensible rise in the gene mutation frequency, though numerous chromosome breakages do arise, leading to both gross and minute rearrangements of chromosome parts. Either the genes are more resistant in this material to permanent changes by X-rays as compared with their responsiveness to thermal agitation, or a break or loss must usually be produced by X-rays along with the gene change. The milder ultraviolet quanta, on the other hand, do produce gene mutations like the natural ones in these plants.

Such variations in effectiveness are, I believe, to have been expected. They do not shake our conclusion as to the accidental, quantum character of the event which usually initiates a gene mutation. But they give rise to the hope that, through further study of them, more may be learned concerning the nature of the mutation process, as well as of the genetic material that undergoes the changes.

Controlled Mutation?

No one can answer the question whether some special means may not be found whereby, through the application of molar influences, such as specific antibodies, individual genes could be changed to order. Certainly the search for such influences, and for increasing control of things on a microscopic and submicroscopic scale as well, must be carried further. But there is as yet no good evidence that anything of the sort has been done artificially, or that it occurs naturally. Even if possible, there could be no generalized method of control of gene composition without far greater knowledge than we now have of the intimate chemical structure and the mode of working of the most complicated and diverse substances that exist, namely, nucleoproteins, proteins in general, and enzymes. The works of Sumner, North-

rup and Stanley, together with those of other protein chemists, point the way in this direction, but everyone will agree that it is a long and devious system of roads which is beginning here.

It is true that some cases are known of mutable genes which change selectively in response to special conditions. Such cases may be very informative in shedding light on gene structure, but we have as yet no indication that the alterations of these genes, which in the great majority of instances known are abnormal genes, have anything in common with ordinary natural mutations. It is also true that cases are known among bacteria and viruses of the induction of particular kinds of hereditary changes by application of particular substances, but here the substances applied are in each case the same as those whose presence is later found to have been induced, and so there is every reason to infer that they have in fact become implanted in some way, that is, that we do not really have a specifically induced mutation.

So far, then, we have no means, or prospect of means, of inducing given mutations at will in normal material; though the production of mutations in abundance at random may be regarded as a first step along such a path, if there is to be such a path. So long as we cannot direct mutations, then, selection is indispensable, and progressive change in the hereditary constitution of a living thing can be made only with the aid of a most thoroughgoing selection of the mutations that occur since, being non-adaptive except by accident, an overwhelming majority is always harmful. For a sensible advance, usually a considerable number of rare steps must be accumulated in this painful selective process. By far the most of these are individually small steps, but, as species and race crossings have shown, there may be a few large distinctive steps that have been, as Huxley terms it, "buffered", by small changes that readjust the organism to them. Not only is this accumulation of many rare, mainly tiny changes the chief means of artificial animal and plant improvement, but it is, even more, the way in which natural evolution has occurred, under the guidance of natural selection. Thus the Darwinian theory becomes implemented, and freed from the accretions of directed variation and of Lamarckism that once encumbered it.

It is probable that, in a state of nature, most species have a not very much (though somewhat) lower frequency of gene mutation than would be most advantageous for them, in consideration of the degree of rigor of the natural selection that occurs in the given species. A much higher frequency would probably lead to faster genetic degenerative processes than the existing selection could well cope with. But, under conditions of artificial breeding, where selection can be made more effective, a higher mutation frequency can for a time at least be tolerated in some cases, and larger mutations also can be nursed through to the point where they become suitably buffered. Here it may become of practical use to apply X-rays, ultraviolet, or other means of inducing mutations, as Gustafsson especially has demonstrated for X-rays. This will be especially true in species which naturally undergo much inbreeding, or in which there is a well expressed haploid phase, or a considerable haploid portion of the genotype, for under these circumstances many of the spontaneous mutations that might otherwise have accumulated in the population and that could be brought to light by inbreeding, will have become eliminated before they could be found, and the natural mutation rate itself will be lower.

We have above largely confined ourselves to considering the relation of the production of gene mutations to the problems of the general method of evolution, including that of the nature of hereditary variation, because this has been, historically, the main line of approach to the subject of artificial mutations. It was from the first evident, however, that the production of mutations would, as we once stated, provide us with tools of the greatest nicety, wherewith to dissect piece by piece the physiological, embryological, and biochemical structure of the organism and to analyze its workings. Already with natural mutations, such works as those of Bonnevie, Grueneberg, Scott-Moncrief, Ephrussi and Beadle, etc., have shown how the intensive tracing of the effects, and interrelations of effects, of just one or a few mutations, can lead to a deeper understanding of the complex processes whereby the genes operate to produce the organism. But there are thousands of genes, and it is desirable to be able to choose them for study in an orderly fashion as we proceed with our dissection process. For this purpose we have thought that it would often be advantageous to produce mutations artificially in abundance, so as then to take our pick of those more suited for successive steps in our analysis. The work of Beadle and his co-workers on *Neurospora* in recent years, followed by similar work of Malin and Fries and of others, has brilliantly shown the applicability of this method for studies of the paths of biochemical synthesis of amino-acids, vitamins, purines and pyrimidines. And yet, in a sense, the surface of the subject as a whole has barely been scratched, and we may look forward with confidence to the combination of this technique with that of tracer substances and with all the other techniques of biochemistry, physiology and experimental embryology, for the increasing unravelling of that surpassingly intricate tangle of processes of which the living organism is constituted. There is no time, however, to go further into this subject here.

Chromosome Analysis

For we cannot neglect here a brief outline of another phase of the artificial mutation work, more specifically of interest to geneticists: that is, the further analysis of the properties of the chromosomes and their parts, gained chiefly from studies in which parts have been removed, added, or rearranged. We have already spoken, in passing, of the studies of the mechanism of such structural change, in which a relatively simple general scheme lying at the basis of all such alterations has emerged: namely, breakage first, followed by adhesion of broken ends. It was early evident that by the use of such rearranged chromosomes additional proof of the physical validity of the linkage maps could be obtained, and this was done (Muller and Painter). Furthermore, it has been possible to throw light on problems of crossing over, as in the demonstration (Muller, Stone, and Offermann) that to whatever position the centromere is moved, it causes a strong inhibition of crossing over, the strenth of which gradually diminishes with distance. Moreover, the same proves to be true of any point of discontinuity in pairing, caused by heterozygosity in regard to a structural change. Such studies on crossing over, and on the pairing forces that affect segregation, are still capable of considerable extension.

We must remember, in speaking of the centromere and other apparently distinctive chromosome parts, that we have no right to infer that they are autonomous, locally determined structures, dependent on the genes of the regions in which they are seen to lie, before observations have been made that show the effects of removing or displacing those regions. Therefore, it has in the main been necessary to wait for the study of induced inversions, deletions and translocations of chromosomes, before the inference could be secure that the centromere is, in most instances, such an autonomous organelle, dependent upon a gene or genes in the immediate neighborhood (but not in all instances in the neighborhood, as Rhoades has recently shown in a special strain of maize). Similarly, it has been possible to show (despite some contrary claims, the validity or invalidity of which cannot be discussed here) that the free end of the chromosome, or telomere, constitutes in much material a locally determined distinctive structure.

By a combined genetic and cytological analysis of various cases of breakage and rearrangement of parts, it was found that there are distinctive, largely locally determined, regions of the chromosomes, usually most markedly developed near the centromeres, which we at first called "inactive" but which are now usually referred to as "heterochromatic." These were also found independently in purely cytological studies by Heitz. It would be fascinating to enter here into a discussion of the remarkable peculiarities which the cytogenetic studies have shown these regions to have—the evidence of repetition of more or less similar parts, of a tendency to conjugation between the differently placed parts, of distinctive cytological appearance correlated with whether or not such conjugation occurs, of inordinately high tendency to structural change, of strong influence of certain of their genes upon segregation, etc.,—and then to go on to discuss hypotheses of their evolutionary origin and their functions. This would unfortunately take us too far afield. We must, however, insist upon one point—as it is not yet generally enough recognized,—namely, that the evidence is very strong that what, in the *Drosophila* chromosome as seen at mitosis, is called "the heterochromatic region," is simply a large temporary body of accessory, non-genic nucleoprotein, produced under the influence of one or two particular genes from among the dozen or more that constitute the whole heterochromatic region, as detected by genetic analysis and by the chromosome as seen at the resting stage (as in the salivary gland). And it is not these conspicuous non-genic blocks which are responsible for the other known peculiarities of the heterochromatin, above mentioned—the function of the blocks is still undetermined. In other words, the so-called "heterochromatin" with which the cytologist deals in studying mitotic chromosomes is a quite different thing from, although in the neighborhood of, the heterochromatin proper having the above described complex of properties. Moreover, it has been possible to show (Sutton-Gersh in collaboration with the author, unpublished) that the conspicuous nucleoli often associated with the heterochromatin are produced under the influence of still other autonomous genes in it, that are separate from those for the mitotically visible blocks.

One of the most interesting findings which has come out of the study of *Drosophila* chromosomes that underwent rearrangement of parts as a result of irradiation has been the generalization of the existence of the phenomenon known as "position effect." This effect was first found by Sturtevant in the case of the spontaneous mutant known as Bar eye, but it was not known to what extent the effect might be a special one until numerous rearrangements could be studied. The term position effect implies that the functioning of a gene is to a certain extent at least dependent upon what other genes lie in its neighborhood. There is now adequate evidence that this is a general principle, applying to very many if not all the genes in *Drosophila,* and that their functioning can be qualitatively as well as quantitatively conditioned by the character of the genes in their vicinity, some of the genes having much more effect than others and different genes working in different ways and to different extents.

It is possible that, as Sturtevant suggested, the position effect is caused by the interaction between gene products in the vicinity of the genes producing them, assuming that such products are more concentrated there and under such circumstances tend to react more with one another than when dispersed. However, the interpretation which we favor is that the functioning of the gene is affected by its shape and that this, in turn, varies with the strength and nature of synaptic forces acting on the region of the chromosome in which it lies. These might consist of forces directly exerted on the gene by other genes, whether allelic or not (Muller), or they might be resultants of the state of spiralization, etc., of the chromosome region, circumstances which in their turn are in part dependent on synaptic forces (Ephrussi and Sutton). This interpretation, in either of its variants, would explain why position effects are so much more general in *Drosophila,* an organism in which the synaptic forces are known to operate strongly even in somatic cells, than in other organisms tested, in which such

forces are much weaker or absent in somatic cells. It would also fit in with the author's findings that the heterochromatic regions tend to have especially strong, extensive, and distinctive kinds of position effects, effects varying in degree with the total amount of heterochromatin present in a cell, as well as with vacillating embryological factors. For these genetic findings are in conformity with the cytological effects of heterochromatin, observed first by Prokofyeva, on the degree of extension, synaptic properties, etc., of euchromatin in its neighborhood, effects which she showed to be subject to similar vacillations, that are correlated with the variations in the phenotypically observed position effects. Recent observations, both by Ephrussi and by Sutton, following suggestions of the author, and by Stern, also seem to point in this direction, for they show an influence, on the position effects exhibited by given parts, of the arrangement of *homologous* chromosome parts. If this interpretation based on gene shape should hold, it would open up a new angle of attack on the structure and method of functioning of the gene, perhaps ultimately relating it to nucleoprotein composition and properties.

Another use to which the process of breakage and rearrangement of chromosome parts by irradiation has been put is for the study of the effects of adding and of subtracting small pieces of chromosomes, in order to determine the relation of gene dosage to gene expression. In this way, it has been found out (1) that most normal genes are, even in single dose, near the upper limit of their effectiveness, and (2) that most mutant genes have a final effect qualitatively similar to but quantitatively less than that of their allelic normal gene. The dominance of normal genes over their mutant alleles, then, turns out in most instances to be a special case of the principle that one dose of a normal gene usually produces nearly though not quite as much effect as two doses. This in turn is best understood as resulting from a long course of selection of the normal gene and its modifiers for stability of expression, when under the influence of environmental and genetic conditions which would affect the gene's operation quantitatively, *i.e.* in a manner similar to that of dosage changes. This does not mean that selection has specifically worked to produce dominance of the normal gene over its alleles, however, because (3) not all mutant genes behave merely like weaker normal genes, and (4) those which the dosage tests show to produce qualitatively different effects from the normal genes seem oftener to escape from the principle of being dominated over by the normals, just as would be expected on our hypothesis.

Among the further results of gene dosage studies carried out by the use of chromosome fragments produced by irradiation, attention should be especially called to the findings coming under the head of "dosage compensation." These have shown (1) that, when the dosage of virtually all genes in the X chromosome except a given one is held constant, the expression of that one is usually so very nearly the same when present in one dose as in two that no difference in the character can ordinarily be seen, and (2) that nevertheless this invisible difference has been so important for the organism that, in the course of the past natural selection, a system of modifying genes, called compensators, has been established, having the function of making the effects of the one and two doses normally present in the two respective sexes much more nearly equal still, when these dosage differences in the given genes are present simultaneously with those in all the other X-chromosomal genes. Each gene seems to have acquired a different system of compensators, the interrelations of all together being extremely complicated. This then gives evidence from a new angle of the meticulousness of natural selection, of the very precise adaptiveness of the characters existing in a species, and of the final grade of a character having ordinarily become established through the accumulation of numerous small mutations having very

complex functional relations with one another. It is in line with our previous thesis of evolution through the selection of multitudinous tiny accidental changes.

When attention is concentrated on a given very circumscribed region of a chromosome, by a comparison of various induced rearrangements all of which have a point of breakage within that region, other facts come to light, bearing on the problems of chromosome and gene divisibility. By means of special genetic methods, which cannot be detailed here, evidence has been obtained that the breaks in any such limited region tend to occur at specific points, giving indication that discrete units or segments lie between these points, and thus arguing against the idea of the chromosome being a continuum and in favor of its genes corresponding to physical entities rather than merely to concepts arbitrarily set up for the convenience of geneticists. We are also enabled in this way to make estimates of the probable number of genes in the chromosome, as well as to get maximally limiting figures for their size. These estimates agree as closely as could have been expected with those based on previous genetic work, using entirely different methods, although not with the estimates based on the "sensitive volume" hypothesis.

Duplications and Evolution

Another finding made in studies of cases having a small fragment of chromosome moved, as a result of irradiation, to another position, was that individuals are frequently able to survive and reproduce even when they have the given chromosome part present in its original position as well as in the new position. In fact, it was in work of this kind that the effect of extra doses of genes was determined. Now, in some of these cases stocks could even be obtained which were homozygous for the duplicated piece as well as for the original piece. This led to the idea that duplications of chromosome material might in this manner have become established in the previous course of evolution. When, in the analysis of a limited region of the

X chromosome, including the locus of the so-called "scute" effect, it was found that there are in fact, within the normal X chromosome, two genes of closely related effect ("achaete" and "scute") very close or adjacent to one another, it became evident that this was in all probability an example of the above postulated occurrence. This then showed the way, and apparently the main if not the only way (aside from the far rarer phenomena of polyploidy and "tetrasomy"), by which the number of genes has become increased during the course of evolution. By a curious coincidence, Bridges was at the same time making his studies of salivary chromosomes and finding direct cytological evidence for the existence of such "repeats," as he called them, in the normal chromosome, and he interpreted these in the same manner. In the twelve years since that time, various other clear cases of the same kind have been demonstrated. Thus, increase in gene number, brought about by the duplication of small parts of chromosomes, more usually in positions near their original ones, must be set down as one of the major processes in evolution, in addition to the mutations in the individual genes. By itself, this process would not be of great importance, but it becomes important because, by allowing gene mutations to come afterwards that differentiate the genes in one position from the originally identical ones in the other position, the number of different kinds of genes is increased and so the germ plasm, and with it the processes of development and the organism as a whole, are eventually enabled to grow more complex.

Rearrangements of chromosome parts which do not lead to an increase in gene number can of course also occur in evolution, although it is unlikely that their role is so fundamental. By producing such changes in the laboratory it has been possible to find out a good deal more about what types can arise, and what their properties are. Various inferences can then be drawn concerning the viability and fertility that the different types would have, under varied genetic circumstances, and whether they would tend to become eliminated or to accumulate in a population of a given type. Some of them can be shown to have, under given conditions, an evolutionary survival value, both by aiding in the process of genetic isolation and in other ways, as by affecting heterosis. In this manner, evolutionary inferences have been drawn which have later been confirmed by comparison of the chromosome differences actually existing between related races, sub-species, and species.

Probably of greater ultimate interest will be the results of studies of gene mutations occurring at individual loci. Radiation mutations are frequent enough to lend themselves to comparisons of the potentialities of different loci, although not nearly enough has yet been done along these lines. Similarly, a comparison of the different mutations which can occur at the same locus can lead to very important results, especially since it has been shown that the different alleles may have every complex relationships to one another, so as even, in some cases, to reconstitute the normal type when they are crossed together. The way in which genes may change as a result of successive mutations remains to be gone into at much greater length. So, too, does the question of changes in gene mutability, brought about by gene mutation itself.

Somatic Radiation Effects

The further the analysis of the genetic effects of irradiation has gone, particularly of the breakage and rearrangement of chromosome parts, the more does our conviction grow that a large proportion if not the great majority of the somatic effects of irradiation that have been observed by medical men and by students of embryology, regeneration, and general biology, arise secondarily as consequences of genetic effects produced in the somatic cells. The usefulness of this interpretation has been shown in recent studies of Koller, dealing with improved methods of irradiation of mammalian carcinoma. This is too large a subject to digress upon here, but it is to be noted that it has been the analyses based in the first place on genetic and cytogenetic studies of the reproductive cells, as shown by subsequent generations, which are thus helping to clear the way for an understanding of the mechanism by which radiation acts in inhibiting growth, in causing sterilization, in producing necrosis and burns, in causing recession of malignant tissue, and perhaps also, on occasion at least, in inducing the initiation of such tissue.

During the war years, a curious confirmation of the correctness of the above inference regarding the nature of the somatic effects of irradiation has come to light. While working with mustard gas in Edinburgh, J. H. Robson was struck with the remarkable similarity between the somatic effects of this agent and those produced by X-ray and radium irradiation. This led him to wonder whether perhaps mustard gas might produce genetic changes of essentially the same kind as those known to be brought about by irradiation. Comprehensive experiments were thereupon undertaken by C. Auerbach, working in collaboration with Robson, and (as mentioned on p. 263) she succeeded in showing that in fact this substance does produce mutations, both in the individual genes and by breakage and rearrangement of chromosome parts, such as X-rays and radium do, and in similar abundance. Other substances of the same general group were then found to have a similar effect. This constitutes the first decided break in the chemical attack on mutation. The fact that these findings were made as a direct result of the above inference, when so many previous attempts to produce mutations by chemical means had failed, appears to provide strong evidence that these peculiar somatic effects are in truth consequences of the more underlying ones which, when occurring in the germ cells, are analyzed by the geneticist in his breeding tests.

There are, however, some very interesting differences between the nature of the genetic effects of irradiation and of these chemicals, which we cannot go into here, but which give promise of allowing an extension of the genetic and somatic analyses.

We see then that production of mutations by radiation is a method, capable of being turned in various directions, both for the analysis of the germ plasm itself, and of the organism which is in a sense an outgrowth of that germ plasm. It is to be hoped that it may also, in certain fields, prove of increasing practical use in plant and animal improvement, in the service of man. So far as direct practical application in man himself is concerned, however, we are as yet a long way from practicing any intentional selection over our own germ plasm, although like most species we are already encumbered by countless undesirable mutations, from which no individual is immune. In this situation we can, however, draw the practical lesson, from the fact of the great majority of mutations being undesirable, that their further random production in ourselves should so far as possible be rigorously avoided. As we can infer with certainty from experiments on lower organisms that all high-energy radiation must produce such mutations in man, it becomes an obligation for radiologists — though one far too little observed as yet in most countries—to insist that the simple precautions are taken which are necessary for shielding the gonads, whenever people are exposed to such radiation, either in industry or in medical practice. And, with the coming increasing use of atomic energy, even for peacetime purposes, the problem will become very important of insuring that the human germ plasm— the all-important material of which we are the temporary custodians—is effectively protected from this additional and potent source of permanent contamination.

GENES AND CHEMICAL REACTIONS IN NEUROSPORA

by

GEORGE W. BEADLE.

Pasadena, California, California Institute of Technology.

Nobel Lecture, December 11, 1958.

On this occasion of sharing the high honor of a Nobel Award with EDWARD L. TATUM for our "... discovery that genes act by regulating chemical events", and with JOSHUA LEDERBERG for his related "... discoveries concerning the organization of the genetic material of bacteria", it seems appropriate that I sketch briefly the background events that led to the work on Neurospora that TATUM and I initiated in 1940. I shall leave to my co-recipients of the Award the task of describing in detail the developments in Neurospora that followed our first success, and the relation of this to the rise of bacterial genetics, which has depended largely on studies of genetic recombination following conjugation and transduction.

I shall make no attempt to review the entire history of biochemical genetics, for this has been done elsewhere (2, 13, 22, 23).

Anthocyanins and Alcaptonuria.

Soon after DE VRIES, CORRENS and TSCHERMAK "rediscovered" MENDEL'S 1865 paper and appreciated its full significance, investigators in the exciting new field, which was to be called genetics, naturally speculated about the physical nature of the "elements" of MENDEL and the manner of their action. Renamed genes, these units of inheritance were soon found to be carried in the chromosomes.

One line of investigation that was destined to reveal much about what genes do was started by WHELDALE (later ONSLOW) in 1903. It began with a genetic study of flower pigmentation in snapdragons. But soon the genetic observations began to be correlated with the chemistry of the anthocyanin and related pigments that were responsible. The material was favorable for both genetic and chemical studies and the work has continued to yield new information ever since and almost without interruption. Many workers and many species of plants have been involved (2, 4, 13, 22, 23).

It became clear very soon that a number of genes were involved and that they acted by somehow controlling the onset of various identifiable and specific chemical reactions. Since an understanding of the genetics helped in interpreting the chemistry and *vice versa*, the anthrocyanin work was well known to both geneticists and biochemists. It significantly influenced the thinking in both fields and thus had great importance in further developments.

A second important line of investigation was begun even earlier by the Oxford physician-biochemist Sir Archibald E. Garrod. At the turn of the century he was interested in a group of congenital metabolic diseases in man, which he later named, "inborn errors of metabolism". There are now many diseases described as such; in fact, they have come to be recognized as a category of diseases of major medical importance.

One of the first inborn errors to be studied by Garrod was alcaptonuria. Its most striking symptom is blackening of urine on exposure to air. It had been recorded medically long before Garrod became interested in it and important aspects of its biochemistry were understood. The substance responsible for blackening of the urine is alcapton or homogenetisie acid (2,5-dihydroxyphenylacetic acid). Garrod suggested early that alcaptonuria behaved in inheritance as though it were differentiated by a single recessive gene.

By 1908 a considerable body of knowledge about alcaptonuria had accumulated. This was brought together and interpreted by Garrod in his Croonian lectures and in the two editions of his book, *"Inborn Errors of Metabolism"*, which were based on them (11). It was his belief that alcaptonuria was the result of inability of affected individuals to cleave the ring of homogentisic acid as do normal individuals. He believed this to be due to absence or inactivity of the enzyme that normally catalyzes this reaction. This in turn was dependent on the absence of the normal form of a specific gene.

Thus Garrod had clearly in mind the concept of a gene-enzyme-chemical-reaction system in which all three entities were interrelated in a very specific way. In the 1923 edition of "Inborn Errors" (11) he wrote:

"We may further conceive that the splitting of the benzene ring of homogentisic acid in normal metabolism is the work of a special enzyme, that in congenital alcaptonuria this enzyme is wanting . . ."

Failure to metabolize an intermediate compound when its normal pathway is thus blocked by a gene-enzyme defect was a part of the interpretation and accounted for the accumulation and excretion of homogentisic acid. GARROD recognized this as a means of identifying an intermediate compound that might otherwise not appear in sufficient amounts to be detected.

He also clearly appreciated that alcaptonurics would be used experimentally to explore the metabolic pathways by which homogentisic acid was formed. He summarized a large body of evidence indicating that when normal precursors of homogentisic acid are fed to alcaptonurics there is an almost quantitative increase in homogentisic acid excretion. In this way evidence was accumulated that phenylalanine, tyrosine and the keto acid analog of the latter were almost certainly the direct precursors of homogentisic acid.

Despite the simplicity and elegance of GARROD's interpretation of alcaptonuria and other inborn errors of metabolism as gene defects which resulted in inactivity of specific enzymes and thus in blocked reactions, his work had relatively little influence on the thinking of the geneticists of his time. BATESON's *"Mendel's Principles of Heredity"* and a few other books of its time discuss the concept briefly. But up to the 1940's, no widely used later text book of genetics that I have examined even so much as refers to alcaptonuria. It is true that a number of other workers had seriously considered that genes might act in regulating chemical reactions by way of enzymes (2, 13, 17, 21, 23). But there was no other known instance as simple as alcaptonuria. It is interesting — and significant, I think — that it was approximately 50 years after GARROD proposed his hypothesis before it was anything like fully verified through the resolution into six enzymatically catalyzed steps of phenylalanine-tyrosine metabolism via the homogentisic acid pathway, and by the clear demonstration that homogentisate oxidase is indeed lacking in the liver of an alcaptonuric (17). Perhaps it is also well to recall that it was not until 1926 that the first enzyme was isolated in crystalline form and shown in a convincing way to consist solely of protein.

Eye Pigments of Drosophila.

I shall now shift to a consideration of an independent line of investigation that ended up with conclusions very much like those of GARROD and which led directly to the work with Neurospora that TATUM and I subsequently began.

In 1933, BORIS EPHRUSSI came to the California Institute of Technology to work on developmental aspects of genetics. During his stay he and I had many long discussions in which we deplored the lack of information about the manner in which genes act on development. This we ascribed to the fact that the classical organisms of experimental embryology did not lend themselves readily to genetic investigation. Contrariwise, those plants and animals about which most was known genetically had been little used in studies of development.

It would be worth-while, we believed, to attempt to remedy this situation by finding new ways experimentally to study Drosophila melanogaster — which, genetically, was the best understood organism of the time. Tissue culture technics seemed to offer hope. In the spring of 1935 we joined forces in EUPHRUSSI's section of l'Institut de Biologie physio-chimique in Paris, resolved to find ways of culturing tissues of the larvae of Drosophila.

After some discouraging preliminary attempts, we followed EPHRUSSI's suggestion and shifted to a transplantation technic. It was our hope that in this way we could make use of non-autonomous genetic characters as a means of investigating gene action in development.

Drosophila larvae are small. And we were told by a noted Sorbonne authority on the development of diptera that the prospects were not good. In fact, he said, they were terrible.

But we were determined to try, so returned to the laboratory, made micropipettes, dissected larvae and attempted to transfer embryonic buds from one larva to the body cavity of another. The results were discouraging. But we persisted, and finally one day discovered we had produced a fly with three eyes. Although our joy was great with this small success, we immediately began to worry about three points: First, could we do it again? Second, if we could, would we be able to characterize the diffusible substances responsible for interactions between tissues of different genetic types? And, third, how many non-autonomous characters could we find?

We first investigated the sex-linked eye-color mutant vermilion because of the earlier finding of STURTEVANT that in gynandromorphs genetically vermilion eye tissue often fails to follow the general rule of autonomy (20).

Gynandromorphs may result if in an embryo that begins development as a female from an egg with two X chromosomes, one X chromosome is lost during an early cleavage, giving rise to a sector that has one X chromosome and is male. If the original egg is heterozygous for a sex-linked gene, say vermilion, and the lost chromosome carries the normal allele, the male sector will be genetically vermilion, whereas the female parts are normal or wild type. (Other sex-linked characters like yellow body or forked bristles can be used as markers to independently reveal genetic constitution in most parts of the body.)

Yet in STURTEVANT's gynandromorphs in which only a small part of the body including eye tissue was vermilion, the appearance of that tissue was usually not vermilion but wild type — as though some substance had diffused from wild-type tissue to the eye and caused it to become normally pigmented.

It was on the basis of this observation that EPHRUSSI and I transplanted vermilion eyes into wild type larvae. The result was as expected — the transplanted eyes were indeed wild type.

At that time there were some 26 separate eye-color genes known in Drosophila. We obtained stocks of all of them and made a series of transplants of mutant eyes into wild-type hosts. We found only one other clear-cut non-autonomous eye character. This was cinnabar, a bright red eye color, like vermilion but differentiated by a second chromosome recessive gene. We had a third less clear case, claret, but this was never entirely satisfactory from an experimental point of view because it was difficult to distinguish claret from wild-type eyes in transplants.

The vermilion and cinnabar characters are alike in appearance; both lack the brown pigment of the wild-type fly but retain the bright red component. Were the diffusible substances that caused them to develop brown pigment when grown in wild-type hosts the same or different? If the same, reciprocal transplants between the two mutants should give mutant transplanted eyes in both cases. If two separate and independent substances were involved, such reciprocal transplants should give wild-type transplanted eyes in both instances.

We made the experiment and were much puzzled that neither of these results was obtained. A cinnabar eye in a vermilion host remained cinnabar, but a vermilion eye in a cinnabar host became wild type.

To explain this result we formulated the hypothesis that there must be two diffusible substances involved, one formed from the other according to the scheme: $\rightarrow$ Precursor $\rightarrow v^+$ substance $\rightarrow cn^+$ substance $\rightarrow$ Pigment ... where v^+ substance is a diffusible material capable of making a vermilion eye become wild type and cn^+ substance is capable of doing the same to a cinnabar eye (9).

The vermilion (v) mutant gene blocks the first reaction and the cinnabar (cn) mutant gene interrupts the second. A vermilion eye in a cinnabar host makes pigment because it can, in its own tissues, convert the v^+ substance into cn^+ substance and pigment. In it, the second reaction is not blocked.

This scheme involves the following concepts:

a. A sequence of two gene-regulated chemical reactions, one gene identified with each.

b. The accumulation of intermediates prior to blocked reactions.

c. The ability of the mutant blocked in the first reaction to make use of an intermediate accumulated as a result of a genetic interruption of the second reaction. The principle involved is the same as that employed in the cross-feeding technic later so much used in detecting biosynthetic intermediates in microorganisms.

What was later called the one gene-one enzyme concept was clearly in our minds at this time although as I remember, we did not so designate it.

Ours was a scheme closely similar to that proposed by GARROD for alcaptonuria, except that he did not have genes that blocked an adjacent reaction in the sequence. But at the time we were oblivious of GARROD's work, partly because geneticists were not in the habit of referring to it, and partly through failure of ourselves to explore the literature. GARROD's book was available in many libraries.

We continued the eye-color investigations at the California Institute of Technology, EPHRUSSI having returned there to spend part of 1936. Late in the year, EPHRUSSI returned to Paris and I went for a year to Harvard, both continuing to work along similar lines. We identified the source of diffusible substances — fat bodies and malpighian tubercules — and began to devise ways of determining their chemical nature. In this I collaborated to some extent with Professor KENNETH THIMANN.

In the fall of 1937 I moved to Stanford, where TATUM shortly joined me to take charge of the chemical aspects identifying the eye-color substances. Dr. YVONNE KHOUVINE worked in a similar rcle with EPHRUSSI. We made progress slowly. EPHRUSSI and KHOUVINE discovered that under certain conditions feeding tryptophane had an effect on vermilion eye color. Following this lead, TATUM found — through accidental contamination of an asceptic culture containing tryptophane and test flies — an aerobic Bacillus that converted tryptophane into a substance highly active in inducing formation of brown pigment in vermilion flies. He soon isolated and crystallized this, but its final identification was slowed down by what later proved to be a sucrose molecule esterified with the active compound.

Professor BUTENANDT and co-workers (6) in Germany who had been collaborating with Professor KÜHN on an analogous eye-color mutant in the meal moth *Ephestia*, and AMANO *et al.* (1), working at Osaka University, showed that v^+ substance was kynurinine. Later, BUTENANDT and HALLMANN (5), and BUTENANDT *et al.* (7) showed that our original cn^+ substance was 3-hydroxykynurenine.

Thus was established a reaction series of the kind we had originally conceived. Substituting the known chemical, it is as follows:

$$
\begin{array}{c}
\underset{\substack{\text{Tryptophan}}}{\text{C}-\text{C}-\text{COOH}} \\
\end{array}
$$

Tryptophan

$$\downarrow \ldots\ldots v$$

N-Formylkynurenine

NII

$$\downarrow$$

Kynurenine

$$\downarrow \ldots\ldots cn$$

3-hydroxykynurenine

$$\downarrow$$

Brown Pigment

A New Approach.

Isolating the eye-pigment precursors of Drosophila was a slow and discouraging job. TATUM and I realized this was likely to be so in most cases of attempting to identify the chemical disturbances underlying inherited abnormalities; it would be no more than good fortune if any particular example chosen for investigation should prove to be simple chemically. Alcaptonuria was such a happy choice for GARROD, for the chemistry had been largely worked out and the homogentisic acid isolated and identified many years before.

Our idea — to reverse the procedure and look for gene mutations that influence known chemical reactions — was an obvious one. It followed logically from the concept that, in general, enzymatically catalyzed reactions are gene-dependent, presumably through genic control of enzyme specificity. Although we were without doubt influenced in arriving at this approach by the anthocyanin investigations, by LWOFF's demonstrations that parasites tend to become specialized nutritionally through loss of ability to synthesize substances that they can obtain readily from their hosts (18), and by the speculations of others as to how genes might act, the concepts on which it was based developed in our minds fairly directly from the eye-color work EPHRUSSI and I had started five years earlier.

The idea was simple: Select an organism like a fungus that has simple nutritional requirements. This will mean it can carry out many reactions by which amino acids and vitamins are made. Induce mutations by radiation or other mutagenic agents. Allow meiosis to take place so as to produce spores that are genetically homogeneous. Grow these on a medium supplemented with an array of vitamins and amino acids. Test them by vegetative transfer to a medium with no supplement. Those that have lost the ability to grow on the minimal medium will have lost the ability to synthesize one or more of the substances present in the supplemented medium. The growth requirements of the deficient strain would then be readily ascertained by a systematic series of tests on partially supplemented media.

In addition to the above specifications, we wanted an organism well suited to genetic studies, preferably one on which the basic genetic work had already been done.

Neurospora.

As a graduate student at Cornell, I had heard Dr. B. O. DODGE of the New York Botanical Garden give a seminar on inheritance in the bread mold Neurospora. So-called second division segregation of mating types and of albinism were a puzzle to him. Several of us who had just been reviewing the evidence for 4-strand crossing over in Drosophila suggested that crossing over between the centromere and the segregating gene could well explain the result.

DODGE was an enthusiastic supporter of Neurospora as an organism for genetic work. "It's even better than Drosophila", he insisted to THOMAS HUNT MORGAN, whose laboratory he often visited. He finally persuaded MORGAN to take a collection of Neurospora cultures with him from Columbia to the new Biology Division of the California Institute of Technology, which he established in 1928.

Shortly thereafter when CARL C. LINDEGREN came to MORGAN's laboratory to become a graduate student, it was suggested that he should work on the genetics of Neurospora as a basis for his thesis. This was a fortunate choice, for LINDE-GREN had an abundance of imagination, enthusiasm and energy and at the same time had the advice of E. G. ANDERSON, C. B. BRIDGES, S. EMERSON, A. H. STURTEVANT and others at the Institute who at that time were actively interested in problems of crossing over as a part of the mechanism of meiosis. In this favorable setting, LINDEGREN soon worked out much of the basic genetics of Neurospora. New characters were found and a good start was made toward mapping the chromosomes.

Thus, TATUM and I realized that Neurospora was genetically an almost ideal organism for use in our new approach.

There was one important unanswered question. We did not know the mold's nutritional requirements. But we had the monograph of Dr. NILS FRIES, which told us that the nutritional requirements of a number of related filamentous fungi were simple. Thus encouraged, we obtained strains of *Neurospora crassa* from LINDEGREN and from DODGE. TATUM soon discovered that the only growth factor required, other than the usual inorganic salts and sugar, was the recently discovered vitamin, biotin. We could not have used Neurospora for our purposes as much as a year earlier, for biotin would not then have been available in the quantities we required.

It remained only to irradiate asexual spores, cross them with a strain of the opposite mating type, allow sexual spores to be produced, isolate them, grow them on a suitably supplemented medium and test them on the un-supplemented medium. We believed so thoroughly that the gene-enzyme-reaction relation was a general one that there was no doubt in our minds that we would find the mutants we wanted. The only worry we had was that their frequency might be so low that we would get discouraged and give up before finding one.

We were so concerned about the possible discouragement of a long series of negative results that we prepared more than thousand single spore cultures on supplemented medium before we tested them. The 299th spore isolated gave a mutant strain requiring vitamin B6 and the 1085th one required B1. We made a vow to keep going until we had 10 mutants. We soon had dozens.

Because of the ease of recovery of all the products of a single meiotic process n Neurospora, it was a simple matter to determine whether our newly induced nutritional deficiencies were the result of mutations in single genes. If they were, crosses with the original should yield four mutant and four non-mutant spores in each spore sac. They did (3, 21).

In this long, roundabout way, first in Drosophila and then in Neurospora, we had rediscovered what GARROD had seen so clearly so many years before. By now we knew of his work and were aware that we had added little if anything new in principle. We were working with a more favorable organism and were able to produce, almost at will, inborn errors of metabolism for almost any chemical reaction whose product we could supply through the medium. Thus we were able to demonstrate that what GARROD had shown for a few genes and a few chemical reactions in man was true for many genes and many reactions in Neurospora.

In the fall of 1941 FRANCIS J. RYAN came to Stanford as a National Research Council Fellow and was soon deeply involved in the Neurospora work. A year later DAVID M. BONNER and NORMAN H. HOROWITZ joined the group. Shortly thereafter HERSCHEL K. MITCHELL did likewise. With the collaboration of a number of capable graduate students and a group of enthusiastic and able research assistants the work moved along at a gratifying pace.

A substantial part of the financial support that enabled us thus to expand our efforts was generously made available by the Rockefeller Foundation and the Nutrition Foundation.

The directions of our subsequent investigations and their accomplishments I shall leave to Professor TATUM to summarize.

One Gene—One Enzyme.

It is sometimes thought that the Neurospora work was responsible for the one gene—one enzyme hypothesis — the concept that genes in general have single primary functions, aside from serving an essential role in their own replication, and that in many cases this function is to direct specificities of enzymatically active proteins. The fact is that it was the other way around — the hypothesis was clearly responsible for the new approach.

Although it may not have been stated explicitly, EPHRUSSI and I had some such concept in mind. A more specific form of the hypothesis was suggested by the fact that of all the 26 known eye-color mutants in Drosophila, there was only one that blocked the first of our postulated reactions and one that similarly interrupted the second. Thus it seemed reasonable to assume that the *total* specificity of a particular enzyme might somehow be derived from a single gene. The finding in Neurospora that many nutritionally deficient mutant strains can be repaired by supplying single chemical compounds was a verification of our prediction and as such reinforced our belief in the hypothesis, at least in its more general form.

As I hope Professor TATUM will point out in detail, there are now known a number of instances in which mutations of independent origin, all abolishing or reducing the activity of a specific enzyme, have been shown to involve one small segment of genetic material (8, 12, 24). To me these lend strong support to the more restricted form of the hypothesis.

Regardless of when it was first written down on paper, or in what form, I myself am convinced that the one gene-one enzyme concept was the product of gradual evolution beginning with GARROD and contributed to by many, including MOORE, GOLDSCHMIDT, TROLAND, HALDANE, WRIGHT, GRÜNEBERG and many others (2, 13, 19, 22, 23). HOROWITZ and his co-workers (15, 16) have given it, in both forms referred to above, its clearest and most explicit formulation. They have summarized and critically evaluated the evidence for and against it, with the result that they remain convinced of its continued value.

In addittition HOROWITZ has himself made an important application of the concept in arriving at a plausible hypothesis as to how sequences of biosynthetic reactions might originally have evolved (14). He points out that many biologically important compounds are known to be synthesized in a stepwise manner in which the intermediate compounds as such seem not to serve useful purposes. How could such a synthetic pathway have evolved if it serves no purpose unless complete? Simultaneous appearance of several independent enzymes would of course be exceedingly improbable.

HOROWITZ proposes that the end product of such a series of reactions was at first obtained directly from the environment, it having been produced there in the first place by non-biological reactions such as have been postulated by a number of persons, including DARWIN, HALDANE, OPARIN and UREY and demonstrated by MILLER, FOX and others (10). It is then possible reasonably to assume that the ability to synthesize such a compound biologically could arise by a series of separate single mutations, each adding successive enzymatically catalyzed steps in the synthetic sequence, starting with the one immediately responsible for the end product. In this was each mutational step could confer a selective advantage by making the organism dependent on one less exogenous precursor of a needed end product. Without some such mechanism, by which no more than a single gene mutation is required for the origin of a new enzyme, it is difficult to see how complex synthetic pathways could have evolved. I know of no alternative hypothesis that is equally simple and plausible.

The Place of Genetics in Modern Biology.

In a sense genetics grew up as an orphan. In the beginning botanists and zoologists were often indifferent and sometimes hostile toward it. "Genetics deals only with superficial characters", it was often said. Biochemists likewise paid it little heed in its early days. They, especially medical biochemists, knew of GARROD's inborn errors of metabolism and no doubt appreciated them in the biochemical sense and as diseases; but the biological world was inadequately prepared to appreciate fully the significance of his investigations and his thinking. Geneticists, it should be said, tended to be preoccupied mainly with the mechanisms by which genetic material is transmitted from one generation to the next.

Today, happily, the situation is much changed. Genetics has an established place in modern biology. Biochemists recognize the genetic material as an integral part of the systems with which they work. Our rapidly growing knowledge of the architecture of proteins and nucleic acids is making it possible — for the first time in the history of science — for geneticists, biochemists and biophysicists to discuss basic problems of biology in the common language of molecular structure. To me, this is most encouraging and significant.

REFERENCES.

1. AMANO, T., M. TORII, and H. IRITANI, Med. J. Osaka Univ., 2, 45 (1950).
2. BEADLE, G. W., Chem. Rev. 37, 15 (1945).
3. — and E. L. TATUM, Proc. Nat. Acad. Sci. (U. S. A.), 27, 499 (1941).
4. BEALE, G. H. J. Genetics, 42, 196 (1941).
5. BUTENANDT, A. and G. HALLMANN, Z. Naturforsch., 5 b, 444 (1950).
6. — W. WEIDEL, and E. BECKER, Naturwiss., 28, 63 (1940).
7. — — and H. SCHLOSSBERGER, Z. Naturforsch., 4 b, 242 (1949).
8. DEMEREC, M., Z. HARTMAN, P. E. HARTMAN, T. YURA, J. S. GOTS, H. OZEKI, and S. W. GLOVER, Publication 612, Carnegie Inst. Wash. (1956).
9. EPHRUSSI, B., Quart. Rev. Biol. 17, 327 (1942).
10. FOX, S. W., Amer. Sci. 44, 347 (1956).
11. GARROD, A. E., Inborn Errors of Metabolism, Oxford Univ. Press (1923).
12. GILES, N. H., Proc. X Int. Cong. Genetics (in Press).
13. HALDANE, J. B. S., The Biochemistry of Genetics, London, Allen & Unwin (1954).
14. HOROWITZ, N. H., Proc. Nat. Acad. Sci. (U. S. A.), 31, 153 (1945).
15. HOROWITZ, N. H., and M. FLING, In "Enzymes", p. 139 (Gaebler, O. H., Ed.), New York, Academic Press (1956).

16. HOROWITZ, N. H., and U. LEOPOLD, Cold Spring Harbor Symp. Quant. Biol., 16- 65 (1951).
17. KNOX, W. E., Am. J. Human Genetics, *10*, 95 (1958).
18. LWOFF, A., *L'évolution physiologique*, Paris, Hermann et Cie (1944).
19. MULLER, H. J., Proc. Royal Soc. (London) *B 134*, 1 (1947).
20. STURTEVANT, A. H., Proc. VI Int. Cong. Genetics, *1*, 304 (1932).
21. TATUM, E. L., and BEADLE, G. W., Proc. Nat. Acad. Sci. (U. S. A.), *28*, 234 (1942).
22. WAGNER, R. P. and H. K. MITCHELL, *Genetics and Metaboiism*, New York, Wiley (1955).
23. WRIGHT, S., Physiol. Rev., *21*, 487 (1941).
24. YANOFSKY, C., In *"Enzymes"*, p. 147 (Gaebler, O. H., Ed.), New York, Academic Press 1 (1956).

A CASE HISTORY IN BIOLOGICAL RESEARCH.

By

E. L. TATUM.

Nobel Lecture, December 11, 1958.

In casting around in search of a new approach, an important consideration was that much of biochemical genetics has been and will be covered by Professor BEADLE and Professor LEDERBERG, and in many symposia and reviews, in which many aspects have been and will be considered in greater detail and with greater competence than I can hope to do here. It occurred to me that perhaps it might be instructive, valuable, and interesting to use the approach which I have attempted to define by the title "A Case History in Biological Research". In the development of this case history I hope to point out some of the factors involved in all research, specifically the dependence of scientific progress: on knowledge and concepts provided by investigators of the past and present all over the world; on the free interchange of ideas within the international scientific community; on the hybrid vigor resulting from cross-fertilization between disciplines; and last but not least, also dependent on chance, geographical proximity, and opportunity. I would like finally to complete this case history with a brief discussion of the present status of the field, and a prognosis of its possible development.

Under the circumstances, I hope I will be forgiven if this presentation is given from a personal viewpoint. After graduating from the University of Wisconsin in chemistry, I was fortunate in having the opportunity of doing graduate work in biochemistry and microbiology at this University under the direction and leadership of W. H. PETERSON and E. B. FRED. At that time, in the early 30's, one of the exciting areas being opened concerned the so-called "growth-factors" for microorgaisms, for the most part as yet mysterious and unidentified. I became deeply involved in this field, and was fortunate to have been able, in collaboration with H. G. WOOD, then visiting at Wisconsin, to identify one of the required growth-factors for propionic acid bacteria, as the recently synthesized vitamin B_1 or thiamine (I). This was before the universality of need for the B vitamins, and the enzymatic basis of this requirement, had been clearly defined. The vision of LWOFF and KNIGHT had already indicated a correlation of the need of microorganisms for "growth-factors" with failure of synthesis, and correlated this failure with evolution, particularly in relation to the complex environment of "fastidious" pathogenic microorganisms. However, the tendency at this time was to consider "growth-factors" as highly individual requirements, peculiar to particular strains or species of microorganisms as isolated from nature, and their variation in these respects was not generally considered as related to gene mutation and variation in higher organisms. Actually my ignorance of and naïveté in genetics was probably typical of that of most biochemists and microbiologists of the time, with my only contact with genetic concepts being a course primarily on vertebrate evolution.

After completing graduate work at Wisconsin I was fortunate in being able to spend a year studying at the University of Utrecht with F. KÖGL, the discoverer of the growth factor biotin, and to work in the same laboratory with NILS FRIES, who already had contributed significantly in the field of nutrition and growth of fungi.

At this time, Professor BEADLE was just moving to Stanford University, and invited me as a biochemist to join him in the further study of the eye-color hormones of *Drosophila*, which he and EPHRUSSI in their work at the California Institute of Technology and at Paris had so brilliantly established as diffusible products of gene-controlled reactions. During this, my first contacts with modern genetic concepts, as a consequence of a number of factors — the observation of KHOUVINE, EPHRUSSI and CHEVAIS (2) in Paris that dietary tryptophane was concerned with *Drosophila* eye-color hormone production; our studies on the nutrition of *Drosophila* in aseptic culture (3); and the chance contamination of one of our cultures of *Drosophila* with a particular bacterium — we were able to isolate the v^+ hormone in crystalline state from a bacterial culture supplied with tryptophane (4), and with A. J. HAAGEN-SMIT to identify it as kynurenine (5); originally isolated by KOTAKE, and later structurally identified correctly by BUTENANDT. It might be pointed out here that kynurenine has since been recognized to occupy a central position in tryptophane metabolism in many organisms aside from insects, including mammals and fungi.

At about this time, as the result of many discussions and considerations of the general biological applicability of chemical genetic concepts, stimulated by the wealth of potentialities among the microorganisms and their variation in nature with respect to their nutritional requirements, we began our work with the mold *Neurospora crassa*.

I shall not renumerate the factors involved in our selection of this organism for the production of chemical or nutritionally deficient mutants, but must take this opportunity of reiterating our indebtedness to the previous basic findings of a number of investigators. Foremost among these, to B. O. DODGE for his establishment of this Ascomycete as a most suitable organism for genetic studies (6); and to C. C. LINDEGREN (7), who became interested in *Neurospora* through T. H. MORGAN, a close friend of DODGE.

Our use of *Neurospora* for chemical genetic studies would also have been much more difficult, if not impossible, without the availability of synthetic biotin as the result of the work of KÖGL (8) and of DU VIGNEAUD (9). In addition, the investigations of NILS FRIES on the nutrition of *Ascomycetes* (10) were most helpful, as shown by the fact that the synthetic minimal medium used with *Neurospora* for many years was that described by him and supplemented only with biotin, and has ordinarily since been referred to as "Fries medium". It should also be pointed out that the experimental feasibility of producing the desired nutritionally deficient mutant strains depended on the early pioneering work of ROENTGEN, with X-Rays, and on that of H. J. MULLER, on the mutagenic activity of X-Rays and ultraviolet light on *Drosophila*. All that was needed was to put these various facts and findings together to produce in the laboratory with irradiation, nutritionally deficient (auxotrophic) mutant strains of *Neurospora*, and to show that each single deficiency produced was associated with the mutation of a single gene (11).

Having thus successfully tested with *Neurospora* the basic premise that the biochemical processes concerned with the synthesis of essential cell constituents are gene controlled, and alterable as a consequence of gene mutation, it then seemed a desirable and natural step to carry this approach to the bacteria, in which so many and various naturally occurring growth-factor requirements were known, to see if analogous nutritional deficiencies followed their exposure to radiation. As is known to all of you, the first mutants of this type were successfully produced in *Acetobacter* and in *E. coli* (12), and the first step had been taken in bringing the bacteria into the fold of organisms suitable for genetic study.

Now to point out some of the curious coincidences or twists of fate as involved in science: One of the first series of mutants in *Neurospora* which was studied intensely from the biochemical viewpoint was that concerned with the biosynthesis of tryptophan. In connection with the role of indole as a precursor of tryptophan, we wanted also to study the reverse process, the breakdown of tryptophan to indole, a reaction typical of the bacterium *E. coli*. For this purpose we obtained, from the Bacteriology Department at Stanford, a typical *E. coli* culture, designated K-12. Naturally, this strain was later used for the mutation experiments just described so that a variety of biochemically marked mutant strains of *E. coli* K-12 were soon available. It is also of interest that Miss ESTHER ZIMMER, who later became ESTHER LEDERBERG, assisted in the production and isolation of these mutant strains.

Another interesting coincidence is that F. J. RYAN spent some time on leave from Columbia University at Stanford, working with *Neurospora*. Shortly after I moved to Yale University in 1945, RYAN encouraged LEDERBERG, then a medical student at Columbia who had worked some with RYAN on *Neurospora*, to spend some time with me at Yale University. As all of you know, LEDERBERG was successful in showing genetic recombination between mutant strains of *E. coli* K-12 (13) and never returned to medical school, but continued his brilliant work on bacterial recombination at Wisconsin. In any case, the first demonstration of a process analogous to a sexual process in bacteria was successful only because of the clear-cut nature of the genetic markers available which permitted detection of this very rare event, and because of the combination of circumstances which had provided those selective markers in one of the rare strains of *E. coli* capable of recombination. In summing up this portion of this case history, then, I wish only to emphasize again the role of coincidence and chance played in the sequence of developments, but yet more strongly to acknowledge the even greater contributions of my close friends and associates, Professor BEADLE and Professor LEDERBERG, with whom it is a rare privilege and honor to share this award.

Now for a brief and necessarily somewhat superficial mention of some of the problems and areas of biology to which these relatively simple experiments with *Nerospora* have led and contributed. First, however, let us review the basic concepts involved in this work. Essentially these are (1) that all biochemical processes in all organisms are under genic control, (2) that these overall biochemical processes are resolvable into a series of individual stepwise reactions, (3) that each single reaction is controlled in a primary fashion by a single gene, or in other terms, in every case a 1 : 1 correspondence of gene and biochemical reaction exists, such that (4) mutation of a single gene results only in an alteration in the ability of the cell to carry out a single primary chemical reaction. As has repeatedly been stated, the underlying hypothesis, which in a number of cases has been supported by direct experimental evidence, is that each gene controls the production, function and specificity of a particular enzyme. Important experimental implications of these relations are that each and every biochemical reaction in a cell of any organism, from a bacterium to man, is theoretically alterable by gene mutation, and that each such mutant cell strain differs in only one primary way from the non-mutant parental strain. It is probably unnecessary to point out that these experimental expectations have been amply supported by the production and isolation, by many investigators during the last 15 or more years, of biochemical mutant strains of microorganisms in almost every species tried, bacteria, yeasts, algae, and fungi.

It is certainly unnecessary for me to do more than point out that mutant strains such as those produced and isolated first in *Neurospora* and *E. coli* have been of primary utility as genetic markers in detecting and elucidating the details of the often exotic mechanisms of genetic recombination of microorganisms.

Similarly, it seems superfluous even to mention the proven usefulness of mutant strains of microorganisms in unraveling the detailed steps involved in the biosynthesis of vital cellular constituents. I would like to list, however, a few of the biosynthetic sequences and biochemical interrelationships which owe their discovery and elucidation largely to the use of biochemical mutants. These include: the synthesis of the aromatic amino acids via dehydroshikimic and shikimic acids (14, 15), by way of prephenic acid to phenylalanine (16), and by way of anthranilic acid, indole glycerol phosphate (17), and condensation of indole with serine to give tryptophan (18); the conversion of tryptophan via kynurenine and 3-OH anthranilic acid to niacin (19, 20); the biosynthesis of histidine (21); of isoleucine and valine via the analogous di-OH and keto acids (22); the biosynthesis of proline and ornithine from glutamic acid (23); and the synthesis of pyrimidines via orotic acid (24).

If the postulated relationship of gene to enzyme is correct, several consequences can be predicted. First, mutation should result in the production of a changed protein, which might either be enzymatically inactive, of intermediate activity, or have otherwise detectably altered physical properties. The production of such proteins changed in respect to heat stability, enzymatic activity, or other properties such as activation energy, by mutant strains has indeed been demonstrated in a number of instances (25—31). Recognition of the molecular bases of these changes must await detailed comparison of their structures with those of the normal enzyme, using techniques similar to the elegant methods of Professor Sanger. That the primary effect of gene mutation may be as simple as the substitution of a single amino acid by another and may lead to profound secondary changes in protein structure and properties has recently been strongly indicated by the work of INGRAM on hemoglobin (32). It seems inevitable that induced mutant strains of microorganisms will play a most important part in providing material for the further examination of these problems.

A second consequence of the postulated relationship stems from the concept that the genetic constitution defines the potentialities of the cell, the time and degree of expression of which are to a certain extent modifiable by the cellular environment. The analysis of this type of secondary control at the biochemical level is one of the important and exciting new areas of biochemistry. This deals with the regulation and integration of biochemical reactions by means of feed-back mechanisms restricting the synthesis or activities of enzymes (33—36) and through substrate induced biosynthesis of enzymes (37). It seems probable that some gene mutations may affect biochemical activities at this level, (modifiers, and suppressors) and that chemical mutants will prove of great value in the analysis of the details of such control mechanisms.

An equally fascinating newer area of genetics, opened by BENZER (38) with bacteriophage, is that of the detailed correlation of fine structure of the gene in terms of mutation and recombination, with its fine structure in terms of activity. Biochemical mutants of microorganisms have recently opened this area to investigation at two levels of organization of genetic material. The higher level relates to the genetic linkage of non-allelic genes concerned with sequential biosynthetic reactions. This has been shown by DEMEREC and by HARTMANN in the biosynthesis of tryptophan and histidine by SALMONELLA (39).

At a finer level of organization of genetic material, the biological versatility of *Neurospora* in forming heterocaryotic cells has permitted the demonstration (40—42) that genes damaged by mutation in different areas, within the same locus and controlling the same enzyme, complement each other in a heterocaryon in such a way that synthesis of enzymatically active protein is restored, perhaps, in a manner analogous to the reconstitution of ribonuclease from its a and b constituents, by the production in the cytoplasm of an active protein from two gene products defective in different areas. This phenomenon of complementation, which appears also to take place in *Aspergillus* (43), permits the mapping of genetic fine structure in terms of function, and should lead to further information on the mechanism of enzyme production and clarification of the role of the gene in enzyme synthesis.

The concepts of biochemical genetics have already been, and will undoubtedly continue to be, significant in broader areas of biology. Let me cite a few examples in microbiology and medicine.

In microbiology the roles of mutation and selection in evolution are coming to be better understood through the use of bacterial cultures of mutant strains. In more immediately practical ways, mutation has proven of primary importance in the improvement of yields of important antibiotics — such as in the classic example of penicillin, the yield of which has gone up from around 40 units per ml. of culture shortly after its discovery by FLEMING to approximately 4 000, as the result of a long series of successive experimentally produced mutational steps. On the other side of the coin, the mutational origin of antibiotic resistant microorganisms is of definite medical significance. The therapeutic use of massive doses of antibiotics to reduce the numbers of bacteria which by mutation could develop resistance, is a direct consequence of the application of genetic concepts. Similarly, so is the increasing use of combined antibiotic therapy, resistance to both of which would require the simultaneous mutation of two independent characters.

As an important example of the application of these same concepts of microbial genetics to mammalian cells, we may cite the probable mutational origin of resistance to chemotherapeutic agents in leukemic cells (44), and the increasing and effective simultaneous use of two or more chemotherapeutic agents in the treatment of this disease. In this connection it should be pointed out that the most effective cancer chemotherapeutic agents so far found are those which interfere with DNA synthesis, and that more detailed information on the biochemical steps involved in this synthesis is making possible a more rational design of such agents. Parenthetically, I want to emphasize the analogy between the situation in a bacterial culture consisting of two or more cell types, and that involved in the competition and survival of a malignant cell, regardless of its origin, in a population of normal cells. Changes in the cellular environment, such as involved in chemotherapy, would be expected to affect the metabolic efficiency of an altered cell, and hence its growth characteristics. However, as in the operation of selection pressures in bacterial populations, based on the interaction between cell types, it would seem that the effects of chemotherapeutic agents on the efficiency of selective pressures among mammalian cell populations can be examined most effectively only in controlled mixed populations of the cell types concerned.

In other areas in cancer, the concepts of genetics are becoming increasingly important, both theoretically and practically. It seems probable that neoplastic changes are directly correlated with changes in the biochemistry of the cell. The relationships between DNA, RNA, and enzymes which have evolved during the last few decades, lead one to look for the basic neoplastic change in one of these intimately interrelated hierarchies of cellular materials.

In relation to DNA hereditary changes are now known to take place as a consequence of mutation, or of the introduction of new genetic material through virus infection (as in transduction) or directly (as in transformation). Although each of these related hereditary changes may theoretically be involved in cancer, definite evidence is available only for the role of viruses, stemming from the classic investigations of ROUS on fowl sarcoma (45). At the RNA level of genetic determination, any one of these classes of change might take place, as in the RNA containing viruses, and result in an heritable change, perhaps of the cytoplasmic type, semi-autonomous with respect to the gene. At the protein level, regulatory mechanisms determining gene activity and enzyme synthesis as mentioned earlier, likewise provide promising areas for exploration.

Among the many exciting applications of microbial-genetic concepts and techniques to the problems of cancer, may I mention in addition the exploration by KLEIN (46) of the genetic basis of the immunological changes which distinguish the cancer cell from the normal, and the studies on the culture, nutrition, morphology and mutation of isolated normal and malignant mammalian cells of PUCK (47) and of EAGLE (48). Such studies are basic to our exploration and to our eventual understanding of the origin and nature of the change to malignancy.

Regardless of the origin of a cancer cell, however, and of the precise genetic level at which the primary change takes place, it is not too much to hope and expect eventually to be able to correct or alleviate the consequences of the metabolic defect, just as a closer understanding of a heritable metabolic defect in man permits its correction or alleviation. In terms of biochemical genetics, the consequences of a metabolic block may be rectified by dietary limitation of the precursor of an injurious accumulation product, aromatic amino acids in phenylketonuria; or by supplying the essential end-product from without the cell, the specific blood protein in hemophilia, or a specific essential nutrient molecule such as a vitamin.

Time does not permit the continuation of these examples. Perhaps, however, I will be pardoned if I venture briefly on a few more predictions and hopes for the future.

It does not seem unrealistic to expect that as more is learned about control of cell machinery and heredity, we will see the complete conquering of many of man's ills, including hereditary defects in metabolism, and the momentarily more obscure conditions such as cancer and the degenerative diseases, just as disease of bacterial and viral etiology are now being conquered.

With a more complete understandig of the functioning and regulation of gene activity in development and differentiation these processes may be more efficiently controlled and regulated, not only to avoid structural or metabolic errors in the developing organism, but also to produce better organisms.

Perhaps within the lifetime of some of us here, the code of life processes tied up in the molecular structure of proteins and nucleic acids will be broken. This may permit the improvement of all living organisms by processes which we might call biological engineering.

This might proceed in stages from the *in vitro* biosynthesis of better and more efficient enzymes, to the biosynthesis of the corresponding nucleic acid molecules, and to the introduction of these molecules into the genome of organisms, whether via injection, viral introduction into germ cells, or via a process analogous to transformation. Alternatively, it may be possible to reach the same goal by a process involving directed mutation.

As a biologist, and more particularly as a geneticist, I have great faith in the versatility of the gene and of living organisms in providing the material with which to meet the challenges of life at any level. Selection, survival and evolution take place in response to environmental pressures of all kinds, including sociological and intellectual. In the larger view, the dangerous and often poorly understood and controlled forces of modern civilization, including atomic energy and its attendant hazards, are but more complex and sophisticated environmental challenges of life. If man cannot meet those challenges, in a biological sense he is not fit to survive.

However, it may confidently be hoped that with real understanding of the roles of heredity and environment, together with the consequent improvement in man's physical capacities and greater freedom from physical disease, will come an improvement in his approach to, and understanding of, sociological and economic problems. As in any scientific research, a problem clearly seen is already half solved. Hence, a renaissance may be foreseen, in which the major sociological problems will be solved, and mankind will take a big stride towards the state of world brotherhood and mutual trust and well-being envisaged by that great humanitarian and philanthropist Alfred Nobel.

BIBLIOGRAPHY.

1. E. L. TATUM, H. G. WOOD and W. H. PETERSON, Biochem. J., *30*, 1898, 1936.
2. Y. KHOUVINE, B. EPHRUSSI and S. CHEVAIS, Biol. Bull., *75*, 425, 1938.
3. E. L. TATUM, Proc. Nat. Acad. Sci., U. S., *27*, 193, 1941.
4. — and G. W. BEADLE, Science, *91*, 458, 1940.
5. — and A. J. HAAGEN-SMIT, J. Biol. Chem., *140*, 575, 1941.
6. B. O. DODGE, J. Agric. Res., *35*, 289, 1927.
7. C. C. LINDEGREN, Bull. Torrey Bot. Club., *59*, 85, 1932.
8. F. KÖGL, Ber., *68*, 16, 1935.
9. V. DU VIGNEAUD, Science, *96*, 455, 1942.
10. N. FRIES, Symbolae Bot. Upsalienses, *3*, 1—188, 1938.
11. G. W. BEADLE and E. L. TATUM, Proc. Nat. Acad. Sci. U. S., *27*, 499, 1941.
12. E. L. TATUM, Cold Spring Harbor Symposia Quant. Biol., *11*, 278, 1946.
13. J. LEDERBERG and E. L. TATUM, Nature, *158*, 558, 1946.
14. B. D. DAVIS, in Amino Acid Metabolism, Baltimore, 799, 1955.
15. E. L. TATUM, S. R. GROSS, G. EHRENSVÄRD and L. GARNJOBST, Proc. Nat. Acad. Sci. U. S., *40*, 271, 1954.
16. R. L. METZENBERG and H. K. MITCHELL, Biochem. J., *68*, 168, 1958.
17. C. YANOFSKY, J. Biol. Chem., *224*, 783, 1957.
18. E. L. TATUM and D. M. BONNER, Proc. Nat. Acad. Sci. U. S., *30*, 30, 1944.
19. D. BONNER, Proc. Nat. Acad. Sci. U. S., *34*, 5, 1948.
20. H. K. MITCHELL and J. F. NYE, Proc. Nat. Acad. Sci. U. S., *34*, 1, 1948.
21. B. N. AMES, in Amino Acid Metabolism, Baltimore, 1955.
22. E. A. ADELBERG, J. Bact., *61*, 365, 1951.
23. H. J. VOGEL, in Amino Acid Metabolism, Baltimore, 1955.
24. H. K. MITCHELL, M. B. HONLAHAN and J. F. NYE, J. Biol. Chem., *172*, 525, 1948.
25. W. K. MAAS and B. D. DAVIS, Proc. Nat. Acad. Sci. U. S., *38*, 785, 1952.
26. N. H. HOROWITZ and M. FLING, Genetics, *38*, 360, 1953.
27. T. YURA and H. J. VOGEL, Biochim. Biophys. Acta, *17*, 582, 1955.
28. J. R. S. FINCHAM, Biochem. J., *65*, 721, 1957.
29. D. R. SUSKIND and L. I. KUREK, Science, *126*, 1068, 1957.
30. N. H. GILES, C. W. H. PARTRIDGE, and N. J. NELSON, Proc. Nat. Acad. Sci. U. S., *43*, 305, 1957.
31. T. YURA, Proc. Nat. Acad. Sci., U. S., (In press).
32. V. M. INGRAM, Nature, *180*, 326, 1957.
33. H. J. VOGEL, in Symposium on the Genetic Basis of Heredity, Baltimore, 1957.
34. L. GORINI and W. K. MAAS, Biochim. Biophys. Acta, *25*, 208, 1957.
35. R. A. YATES and A. B. PARDEE, J. Biol. Chem., *221*, 757, 1956.
36. H. E. UMBARGER and B. BROWN, J. Biol. Chem., *233*, 415, 1958.
37. M. COHN and J. MONOD, Symposium Soc. Gen. Microbiol., *3*, 132, 1953.
38. S. BENZER, in Symposium on the Chemical Basis of Heredity, Baltimore, 1957.
39. P. E. HARTMAN, in Symposium on the Chemical Basis of Heredity, Baltimore, 1957.
40. N. H. GILES, C. W. H. PARTRIDGE and N. J. NELSON, Proc. Nat. Acad. Sci., U. S., *43*, 305, 1957.
41. M. E. CASE and N. H. GILES, Proc. Nat. Acad. Sci., U. S., *44*, 378, 1958.
42. J. A. PATEMAN and J. R. S. FINCHAM, Heredity, *12*, 317, 1958.
43. E. CALEF, Heredity, *10*, 83, 1956.
44. L. W. LAW, Nature, *169*, 628, 1952.
45. P. ROUS, J. Exp. Med., *12*, 696, 1910.
46. G. KLEIN, E. KLEIN and L. RÉVÉSZ, Nature, *178*, 1389, 1956.
47. T. T. PUCK, in Symposium on Growth and Development, Princeton, 1957.
48. H. EAGLE, V. I. OYAMA, M. LEVY and A. E. FREIMAN, Science, *123*, 845, 1956.

THE BIOLOGIC SYNTHESIS OF DEOXYRIBONUCLEIC ACID

by

ARTHUR KORNBERG.

Nobel Lecture, December 11, 1959.

The knowledge drawn in recent years from studies of bacterial transformation (1) and viral infection of bacterial cells (2, 3) combined with other evidence (3), has just about convinced most of us that deoxyribonucleic acid (DNA) is the genetic substance. We shall assume then that it is DNA which not only directs the synthesis of the proteins and the development of the cell but that it must also be the substance which is copied so as to provide for a similar development of the progeny of that cell for many generations. DNA, like a tape recording, carries a message in which there are specific instructions for a job to be done. Also like a tape recording, exact copies can be made from it so that this information can be used again and elsewhere in time and space.

Are these two functions, the expression of the code (protein synthesis) and the copying of the code (preservation of the race) closely integrated or are they separable? What we have learned from our studies over the past five years and what I shall present is that the replication of DNA can be examined and at least partially understood at the enzymatic level even though the secret of how DNA directs protein synthesis is still locked in the cell.

DNA structure.

First I should like to review very briefly some aspects of DNA structure which are essential for this discussion. Analysis of the composition of samples of DNA from a great variety of sources and by many investigators (4) revealed the remarkable fact that the purine content always equals the pyrimidine content. Among the purines, the adenine content may differ considerably from the guanine, and among the pyrimidines, the thymine from the cytosine.

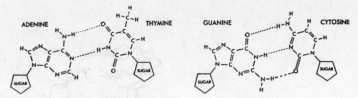

Fig. 1. Hydrogen Bonding of Bases.

However, there is an equivalence of the bases with an amino group in the 6-position of the ring, to the bases with a keto group in the 6-position. These facts were interpreted by WATSON and CRICK (5) in their masterful hypothesis on the structure of DNA. As shown in Fig. 1, they proposed in connection with their double-stranded model for DNA, to be discussed presently, that the 6-amino group of adenine is linked by hydrogen bonds to the 6-keto group of thymine and in a like manner guanine is hydrogen-bonded to cytosine, thus accounting for the equivalence of the purines to the pyrimidines. On the basis of these considerations and the results of X-ray crystallographic measurements by WILKINS and associates (6), WATSON and CRICK proposed a structure for DNA in which two long strands are wound about each other in a helical manner. Fig. 2 is diagrammatic representation of a fragment of a DNA chain about ten nucleotide units long. According to physical measurements, DNA chains are on the average 10 000 units long. We see here the deoxypentose rings linked by phosphate residues to form the backbone of the chain; the purine and pyrimidine rings are the planar structures emerging at right angles from the main axis of the chain. Fig. 3 is a more detailed molecular model (7) and gives a better idea of the packing of the atoms in the structure. The purine and pyrimidine bases of one chain are bonded to the pyrimidine and purine bases of the complementary chain by the hydrogen bonds described in Fig. 1. The X-ray measurements have indicated that the space between the opposing chains in the model agrees with the calculated value for the hydrogen-bond linkage of a purine to a pyrimidine; it is too small for two purines and too large for two pyrimidines. Most rewarding from the biological point of view, the structure provides a useful model to explain how cellular replication of DNA may come about. For, if you imagine that these two chains separate and that a new chain is formed complementary to each of them, the result will be two pairs of strands, each pair identical to the original parent duplex and identical to each other.

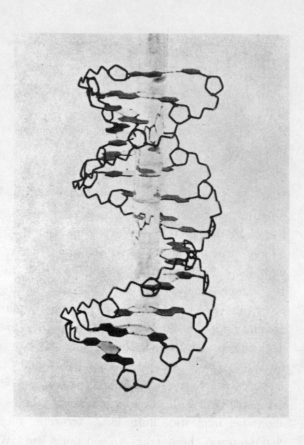

Fig. 2. Double Helical Structure
of DNA (Watson and Crick Model).

Enzymatic approach to the problem of DNA replication.

Although we have in the WATSON and CRICK proposal a mechanical model
of replication, we may at this point pose the question: "What is the chemical
mechanism by which this super molecule is built up in the cell?" Some sixty
years ago the alcoholic fermentation of sugar by a yeast cell was a "vital"
process inseparable from the living cell, but through the Buchner discovery
of fermentation in extracts and the march of enzymology during the first half
of this century we understand fermentation by yeast as a, now familiar,
sequence of integrated chemical reactions. Five years ago the synthesis of
DNA was also regarded as a "vital" process. Some people considered it useful
for biochemists to examine the combustion chambers of the cell, but tampering
with the very genetic apparatus itself would surely produce nothing but disorder. These gloomy predictions were not justified then nor are similar pessi-
mistic attitudes justified now with regard to the problems of cellular structure

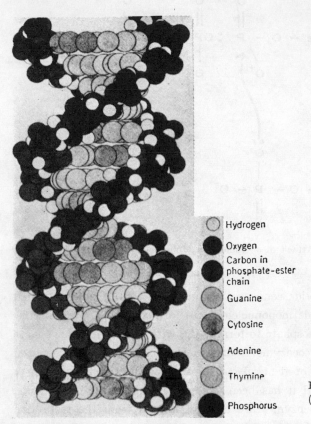

Hydrogen

Oxygen

Carbon in phosphate-ester chain

Guanine

Cytosine

Adenine

Thymine

Phosphorus

Fig. 3. Molecular Model of DNA (After M. FEUGHELMAN, *et al.* (7)).

and specialized function which face us. High adventures in enzymology lie ahead and many of the explorers will come from the training fields of carbohydrate, fat, amino acid and nucleic acid enzymology.

I feel now, as we did then, that for an effective approach to the problem of nucleic acid biosynthesis it was essential to understand the biosynthesis of the simple nucleotides and the coenzymes and to have these concepts and methodology well in hand. It was from these studies that we developed the conviction that an activated nucleoside 5′-phosphate is the basic biosynthetic building block of the nucleic acids (8). You will recall that the main pathways of purine and pyrimidine biosynthesis all lead to the nucleoside 5′-phosphate (8); they do not, except as salvage mechanisms, usually include the free bases or nucleosides. While the 2′ and 3′ isomers of the nucleotides are known, they probably arise mainly from certain types of enzymatic degradation of the nucleic acids. You will also recall from the biosynthesis of coenzymes (9),

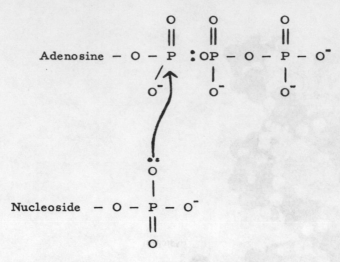

Fig. 4. Nucleophilic Attack of a Nucleoside Monophosphate on ATP.

the simplest of the nucleotide condensation products, that it is ATP which condenses with nicotinamide mononucleotide to form diphosphopyridine nucleotide, with riboflavin phosphate to form FAD, with pantetheine phosphate to form the precursor of coenzyme A and so forth. This pattern has been amplified by the discovery of identical mechanisms for the activation of fatty acids and amino acids and it has been demonstrated further that uridine, cytidine and guanosine coenzymes are likewise formed from the respective triphosphates of these nucleosides.

This mechanism (Fig. 4), in which a nucleophilic attack (10) on the pyrophosphate-activated adenyl group by a nucleoside monophosphate leads to the formation of a coenzyme, was adopted as a working hypothesis for studying the synthesis of a DNA chain. As illustrated in Fig. 5, it was postulated that the basic building block is a deoxynucleoside 5′-triphosphate which is attacked by the 3′-hydroxyl group at the growing end of a polydeoxynucleotide chain; inorganic pyrophosphate is eliminated and the chain is lengthened by one unit. The results of our studies on DNA synthesis, as will be mentioned presently, are in keeping with this type of reaction.

Properties of the DNA-synthesizing enzyme.

First let us consider the enzyme and comment on its discovery (8, 11, 12). Mixing the triphosphates of the four deoxynucleosides which commonly occur in DNA with an extract of thymus or bone-marrow or of *Escherichia coli*

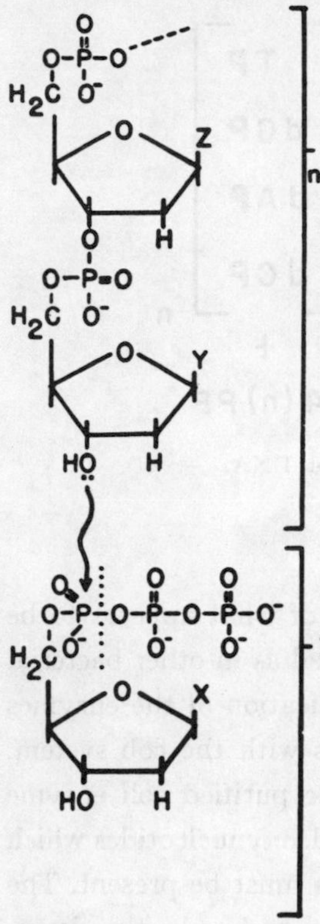

Fig. 5. Postulated Mechanism for Extending a DNA
Chain.

would not be expected to lead to the net synthesis of DNA. Instead, as might
be expected, the destruction of DNA by the extracts of such cells and tissues
was by far the predominant process and one had to resort to the use of more
subtle devices for detection of such a biosynthetic reaction. We used a C^{14}-
labeled substrate of high specific radioactivity and incubated it with ATP
and extracts of *Escherichia coli*, an organism which reproduces itself every
20 minutes. The first positive results represented the conversion of only a
very small fraction of the acid-soluble substrate into an acid-insoluble fraction
(50 or so counts out of a million added). While this represented only a few
$\mu\mu$moles of reaction, it was something. Through this tiny crack we tried to
drive a wedge and the hammer was enzyme purification (13). This has been
and still is a major preoccupation. Our best preparations are several thousand-
fold enriched with respect to protein over the crude extracts, but there are
still contaminating quantities of one or more of the many varieties of nuclease

$$
\begin{array}{l}
n \quad \text{TP PP} \\
n \quad \text{dGP PP} \\
n \quad \text{dAP PP} \quad + \text{DNA} \rightleftharpoons \text{DNA} - \begin{bmatrix} \text{TP} \\ \text{dGP} \\ \text{dAP} \\ \text{dCP} \end{bmatrix}_n \\
n \quad \text{dCP PP} \\
\end{array}
\qquad
\begin{array}{c}
+ \\
4(n)\,\text{PP}
\end{array}
$$

Fig. 6. Equation for Enzymatic Synthesis of DNA.

and diesterase present in the coli cell. The occurrence of what appears to be a similar DNA synthesizing system in animal cells as well as in other bacterial species has been observed (14). We must wait for purification of the enzymes from these sources in order to make valid comparisons with the coli system.

The requirements for net synthesis of DNA with the purified coli enzyme (15) are shown in the equation in Fig. 6. All four of the deoxynucleotides which form the adenine-thymine and guanine-cytosine couples must be present. The substrates must be the tri- and not the diphosphates and only the deoxy sugar compounds are active. DNA which must be present may be obtained from animal, plant, bacterial or viral sources and the best indications are that all these DNA samples serve equally well in DNA synthesis provided their molecular weight is high. The product, which we will discuss in further detail, accumulates until one of the substrates is exhausted and may be 20 or more times greater in amount than the DNA added and thus is composed to the extent of 95 % or more of the substrates added to the reaction mixture. Inorganic pyrophosphate is released in quantities equimolar to the deoxynucleotides converted to DNA.

Should one of these substrates be omitted, the extent of reaction is diminished by a factor of greater than 10^4 and special methods are now required for its detection. It turns out that when one of the deoxynucleotide substrates is lacking, an extremely small but yet significant quantity of nucleotide is linked to the DNA primer. We have described this so-called "limited reaction" (16), and have shown that under these circumstances a few deoxynucleotides are added to the nucleoside ends of some of the DNA chains but

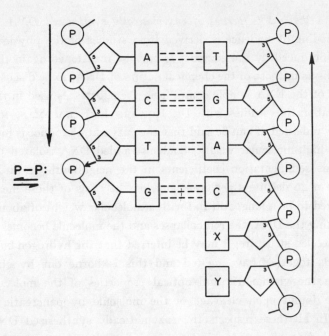

Fig. 7. Mechanism for Enzymatic DNA Replication.

that further synthesis is blocked for lack of the missing nucleotide. Current studies suggest to us that this limited reaction represents the repair of the shorter strand of a double helix in which the strands are of unequal length, and that the reaction is governed by the hydrogen bonding of adenine to thymine and of guanine to cytosine.

When all four triphosphates are present, but when DNA is omitted, no reaction at all takes place. What is the basis for this requirement? Does the DNA function as a primer in the manner of glycogen or does it function as a template in directing the synthesis of exact copies of itself? We have good reason to believe that it is the latter and as the central and restricted theme of this lecture I would like to emphasize that it is the capacity for base pairing by hydrogen bonding between the preexisting DNA and the nucleotides added as substrates that accounts for the requirement for DNA.

The enzyme we are studying is thus unique in present experience in taking directions from a template — it adds the particular purine or pyrimidine substrate which will form a hydrogen-bonded pair with a base on the template (Fig. 7). There are five major lines of evidence that I would like to present to support this thesis.

Physical properties of enzymatically synthesized DNA.

The first line of evidence is derived from studies of the physical nature of the DNA produced by the enzyme. It may be mentioned again that in these descriptions as in those of the chemical nature of DNA, to be discussed shortly, 90—95 % of the DNA sample comes from the substrates used in the reaction. From collaborative studies with Dr. HOWARD K. SCHACHMAN, to whom we are greatly indebted, it can be said that the enzymatic product is indistinguishable from high-molecular weight, double-stranded DNA isolated from nature (17). It has sedimentation coefficients in the neighbourhood of 25, reduced viscosities of 40 deciliters per gram and, on the basis of these measurements, it is believed to be a long, stiff rod with a molecular weight of about 6 million. Upon heating the DNA, the rod collapses and the molecule becomes a compact, randomly coiled structure; it may be inferred that the hydrogen bonds holding the strands together have melted and this is borne out by characteristic changes in the viscometric and optical properties of the molecule. Similar results are found upon cleavage of the molecule by pancreatic deoxyribonuclease. In all these respects the enzymatically synthesized DNA is indistinguishable from the material isolated from nature, and may thus be presumed to have a hydrogen-bonded structure similar to that possessed by natural DNA.

Would one imagine that the collapsed jumbled strands of heated DNA would serve as a primer for DNA synthesis? Very likely one would think not. Guided by intuition derived from everyday experience with a jumbled strand of twine one might regard this as a hopeless template for replication. It turns out that the collapsed DNA is an excellent primer and the nonviscous, randomly coiled, single-stranded DNA leads to the synthesis of highly viscous, double-stranded DNA (18). SINSHEIMER has isolated from the tiny ØX 174 virus a DNA which appears to be single-stranded (19). Like heated DNA it has proved to be an excellent primer (18) and a favorable material in current studies (20) for demonstrating in density gradient sedimentations that it is progressively converted to a double-stranded condition during the course of enzymatic synthesis.

While a detailed discussion of the physical aspects of replication is not feasible in this lecture, it should be mentioned that the DNA in the single-stranded condition is not only a suitable primer but is the only active form when the most purified enzyme preparations are used. With such coli preparations, the native, double-stranded DNA is inert unless it is heated or pretreated very slightly with deoxyribonuclease. BOLLUM has made similar observations with the enzyme that he has purified from calf thymus (21).

Substitution of analogues in DNA synthesis.

The second line of evidence is derived from studies of the activity of the substrates when substitutions are made in the purine and pyrimidine bases. From the many interesting reports on the incorporation of bromouracil (22), azaguanine (23) and other analogues into bacterial and viral DNA, it might be surmised that some latitude in the structure of the bases can be tolerated provided there is no interference with their hydrogen bondings. When experiments were carried out with deoxyuridine triphosphate or 5-bromodeoxyuridine triphosphate, it was found that they supported DNA synthesis when used in place of thymidine triphosphate but not when substituted for the triphosphates of deoxyadenosine, deoxyguanosine or deoxycytidine. As already described (24), 5-methyl- and 5-bromocytosine specifically replaced cytosine; hypoxanthine substituted only for guanine; and, as just mentioned, uracil and 5-bromouracil specifically replaced thymine. These findings are best interpreted on the basis of hydrogen bonding of the adenine-thymine and guanine-cytosine type.

Along these lines it is relevant to mention the existence of a naturally occurring "analogue" of cytosine, hydroxymethyl cytosine (HMC), which is found in place of cytosine in the DNA of the coli bacteriophages of the T-even series (25). In this case the DNA contains equivalent amounts of HMC and guanine and, as usual, equivalent amounts of adenine and thymine. Of additional interest is the fact that the DNA's of T2, T4 and T6 contain glucose linked to the hydroxymethyl groups of the HMC in characteristic ratios (26, 27, 28) although it is clear that in T2 and T6 some of the HMC groups contain no glucose (27). These characteristics have posed two problems regarding the synthesis of these DNA's which might appear to be incompatible with the simple base-pairing hypothesis. First, what mechanism is there for preventing the inclusion of cytosine in a cell which under normal conditions has deoxycytidine triphosphate and incorporates it into its DNA? Secondly, how does one conceive of the origin of the constant ratios of glucose to HMC in DNA if the incorporation were to occur via glucosylated and non-glucosylated HMC nucleotides? Our recent experiments have shown that the polymerase reaction in the virus-infected cell is governed by the usual hydrogen-bonding restrictions but with the auxiliary action of several new enzymes developed specifically in response to infection with a given virus (29, 30). Among the new enzymes is one which splits deoxycytidine triphosphate and thus removes it from the sites of polymerase action (30). Another is a type of glucosylating

DNA			A	T	G	C	$\dfrac{A+G}{T+C}$	$\dfrac{A+T}{G+C}$
M, phle	primer		0.65	0.66	1.35	1.34	1.01	0.49
	product		0.66	0.65	1.34	1.37	0.99	0.48
E, coli	primer		1.00	0.97	0.98	1.05	0.98	0.97
	product		1.04	1.00	0.97	0.98	1.01	1.02
Calf thymus	primer		1.14	1.05	0.90	0.85	1.05	1.25
	product		1.12	1.08	0.85	0.85	1.02	1.29
Becteriophage T2	primer		1.31	1.32	0.67	0.70	0.98	1.92
	product		1.33	1.29	0.69	0.70	1.02	1.90
A-T Copolymer			1.99	1.93	<0.05	<0.05	1.03	>40

Fig. 8. Chemical Composition of Enzymatically Synthesized DNA with Different Primers.

enzyme which transfers glucose from uridine diphosphate glucose directly and specifically to certain HMC residues in the DNA (30).

Chemical composition of enzymatically synthesized DNA.

The third line of evidence is supplied by an analysis of the purine and pyrimidine base composition of the enzymatically synthesized DNA. We may ask two questions. First, will the product have the equivalence of adenine to thymine and of guanine to cytosine that characterize natural DNA? Secondly, will the composition of the natural DNA used as primer influence and determine the composition of the product? In Fig. 8 are the results which answer these two questions (31). The experiments are identical except that in each case a different DNA primer was used: *Mycobacterium phlei*, *Escherichia coli*, calf thymus and phage T2 DNA. In answer to the first question it is clear that in the enzymatically synthesized DNA, adenine equals thymine and guanine equals cytosine so that the purine content is in every case identical to the pyrimidine. In answer to the second question it is again apparent that the characteristic ratio of adenine-thymine pairs to guanine-cytosine pairs of a given DNA primer is imposed rather faithfully on the product that is synthesized. Whether these measurements are made with isotopic tracers when the net DNA increase is only 1 % or if it is 1 000 % the results are the same. It can be said further that it has not been possible to distort these base ratios by using widely differing molar concentrations of substrates or by any other means. In the last line of Fig. 8 is a rather novel "DNA" which is synthesized under conditions that I will not describe here (18, 32). Suffice it to say that after very long lag periods a copolymer of deoxyadenylate and thymidylate

(A-T) develops which has the physical size and properties of natural DNA and in which the adenine and thymine are in a perfectly alternating sequence. When this rare form of DNA-like polymer is used as a primer, new A-T polymer synthesis starts immediately and even though all four triphosphates be present, no trace of guanine or cytosine can be detected in the product. The conclusion from these several experiments thus seems inescapable that the base composition is replicated in the enzymatic synthesis and that hydrogen-bonding of adenine to thymine and guanine to cytosine is the guiding mechanism.

Enzymatic replication of nucleotide sequences.

The fourth line of evidence which I would like to cite is drawn from current studies of base sequences in DNA and their replication. As I have suggested already, we believe that DNA is the genetic code; the four kinds of nucleotides make up a four-letter alphabet and their sequence spells out the message. At present we do not know the sequence; what SANGER has done for peptide sequence in protein remains to be done for nucleic acids. The problem is more difficult, but not insoluble.

Our present attempts at determining the nucleotide sequences (33) will be described in detail elsewhere and I will only summarize them here. DNA is enzymatically synthesized using P^{32} as label in one of the deoxynucleoside triphosphates; the other three substrates are unlabeled. This radioactive phosphate, attached to the 5-carbon of the deoxyribose, now becomes the bridge between that substrate molecule and the nucleotide at the growing end of the chain with which it has reacted (Fig. 9). At the end of the synthetic reaction (after some 10^{16} diester bonds have been formed), the DNA is isolated and digested enzymatically to yield the 3' deoxynucleotides quantitatively. It is apparent (Fig. 9) that the P atom formerly attached to the 5-carbon of the deoxynucleoside triphosphate substrate is now attached to the 3-carbon of the nucleotide with which it reacted during the course of synthesis of the DNA chains. The P^{32} content of each of the 3' deoxynucleotides, isolated by paper electrophoresis, is a measure of the relative frequency with which a particular substrate reacted with each of the four available nucleotides in the course of synthesis of the DNA chains. This procedure carried out four times, using in turn a different labeled substrate, yields the relative frequencies of all the sixteen possible kinds of dinucleotide (nearest neighbor) sequences.

Such studies have to date been carried out using DNA primer samples from six different natural sources. The conclusions are:

1) All 16 possible dinucleotide sequences are found in each case.

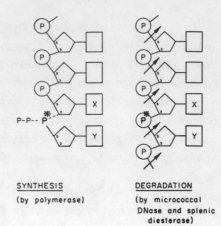

Fig. 9. Method for Determining Sequences in
　　　DNA.

SYNTHESIS
(by polymerase)

DEGRADATION
(by micrococcal
DNase and splenic
diesterase)

2) The pattern of relative frequencies of the sequences is unique and re-producible in each case and is not readily predicted from the base composition of the DNA.

3) Enzymatic replication involves base pairing of adenine to thymine and guanine to cytosine and, most significantly:

4) The frequencies also indicate clearly that the enzymatic replication produces two strands of opposite direction, as predicted by the WATSON and CRICK model.

These studies and anticipated extensions of them should yield the dinucleotide frequencies of any DNA sample which can serve as an effective primer for enzymatic replication and thus provide some clues for deciphering the DNA code. Unfortunately this method does not provide information about trinucleotide frequencies but we are hopeful that with the improvement of enzymatic tools for analysis and chromatographic techniques for isolation some start can be made in this direction.

Requirement for four triphosphates and DNA for DNA synthesis.

Returning to the earlier-stated requirement for all four deoxynucleoside triphosphates and DNA in order to obtain DNA synthesis, we can now regard and understand these requirements as another and final line of evidence for hydrogen bonding. Without added DNA there is no template for hydrogen bonding and without all four triphosphates synthesis stops early and abruptly for lack of a hydrogen bonding mate for one of the bases in the template.

Summary.

The enzymatic approaches to the problem of DNA replication and the properties of the DNA-synthesizing enzyme purified from *Escherichia coli* have been sketched. The unifying and basic generalization about the action of this enzyme is that it catalyzes the synthesis of a new DNA chain in response to directions from a DNA template; these directions are dictated by the hydrogen bonding relationship of adenine to thymine and guanine to cytosine. The experimental basis for this conclusion is derived from the observations of: (1) The double-stranded character of the enzymatically synthesized DNA and its origin from a single stranded molecule, (2) the pattern of substitution of analogues for the naturally-occurring bases, (3) the replication of the chemical composition, (4) the replication of the nucleotide (nearest neighbor) sequences and the antiparallel direction of the strands, and (5) the requirement for all four deoxynucleoside triphosphates (adenine, thymine, guanine and cytosine) and DNA for DNA synthesis.

In closing may I repeat what was said at the banquet last night: Any credit for the work cited here is shared by my colleagues in New York, Bethesda, Saint Louis and Stanford, and by the whole international community of chemists, geneticists and physiologists, which is truly responsible for the progress in nucleic acid biochemistry.

REFERENCES.

1. O. T. AVERY, C. M. MacLEOD and M. McCARTY, J. Exptl. Med. *79*, 137 (1944); R. D. HOTCHKISS, in "The Chemical Basis of Heredity" (W. D. McElroy and B. Glass, editors), p. 321 (1957), Johns Hopkins Press, Baltimore.
2. A. D. HERSHEY, Cold Spring Harbor Symposia Quant. Biol. *18*, 135 (1953).
3. G. W. BEADLE, in "Chemical Basis of Heredity" (W. D. McElroy and B. Glass, editors), p. 3 (1957), Johns Hopkins Press, Baltimore.
4. E. CHARGAFF, in "Nucleic Acids" (E. Chargaff and J. N. Davidson, editors), Vol. I, p. 307—371 (1955), Academic Press, New York.
5. J. D. WATSON and F. H. C. CRICK, Nature *171*, 737 (1953); Cold Spring Harbor Symposia Quant. Biol. *18*, 123 (1953).
6. M. H. F. WILKINS, Biochem. Soc. Symposia (Cambridge, England) *14*, 13 (1957).
7. M. FEUGHELMAN, R. LANGRIDGE, W. E. SEEDS, A. R. STOKES, H. R. WILSON, C. W. HOOPER, M. H. F. WILKINS, R. K. BARCLAY, and L. D. HAMILTON, Nature *175*, 834 (1955).
8. A. KORNBERG, in "The Chemical Basis of Heredity" (W. D. McElroy and B. Glass, editors), p. 579 (1957), Johns Hopkins Press, Baltimore; Rev. Mod. Physics *31*, 200 (1959).

9. A. Kornberg, in "Phosphorus Metabolism" (W. D. McElroy and B. Glass, editor)' p. 392 (1951), Johns Hopkins Press, Baltimore; Advances in Enzymol. *18*, 191 (1957).

10. D. E. Koshland, Jr., in "The Mechanism of Enzyme Action" (W. D. McElroy and B. Glass, editors), p. 608 (1954), Johns Hopkins Press, Baltimore.

11. A. Kornberg, I. R. Lehman and E. S. Simms, Federation Proc. *15*, 291 (1956).

12. A. Kornberg, Harvey Lectures *53*, 83 (1957—1958).

13. I. R. Lehman, M. J. Bessman, E. S. Simms and A. Kornberg, J. Biol. Chem. *233*, 163 (1958).

14. F. J. Bollum and V. R. Potter, J. Am. Chem. Soc. *79*, 3603 (1957); C. G. Harford and A. Kornberg, Federation Proc. *17*, 515 (1958); F. J. Bollum, Federation Proc. *17*, 193 (1958); *18*, 194 (1959).

15. M. J. Bessman, I. R. Lehman, E. S. Simms and A. Kornberg, J. Biol. Chem. *233*, 171 (1958).

16. J. Adler, I. R. Lehman, M. J. Bessman, E. S. Simms and A. Kornberg, Proc. Nat. Acad. Sci. (U. S. A.) *44*, 641 (1958).

17. H. K. Schachman, I. R. Lehman, M. J. Bessman, J. Adler, E. S. Simms and A. Kornberg, Federation Proc. *17*, 304 (1958).

18. I. R. Lehman, Ann. N. Y. Acad. Sci. *81*, 745 (1959).

19. R. L. Sinsheimer, J. Mol. Biol. *1*, 43 (1959).

20. I. R. Lehman, R. L. Sinsheimer and A. Kornberg (Unpublished observations).

21. F. J. Bollum, J. Biol. Chem. *234*, 2733 (1959).

22. F. Weygand, A. Wacker and Z. Dellweg, Z. Naturforsch. *7 b*, 19 (1952); D. B. Dunn and J. D. Smith, Nature *174*, 305 (1954); S. Zamenhof and G. Griboff, Nature *174*, 306 (1954).

23. M. R. Heinrich, V. C. Dewey, R. E. Parks, Jr., and G. W. Kidder, J. Biol. Chem. *197*, 199 (1952).

24. M. J. Bessman, I. R. Lehman, J. Adler, S. B. Zimmerman, E. S. Simms and A. Kornberg, Proc. Nat. Acad. Sci. (U. S. A.) *44*, 633 (1958).

25. G. R. Wyatt and S. S. Cohen, Biochem. J. *55*, 774 (1953).

26. R. L. Sinsheimer, Science *120*, 551 (1954); E. Volkin, J. Am. Chem. Soc. *76*, 5892 (1954).

27. R. L. Sinsheimer, Proc. Nat. Acad. Sci. (U. S. A.) *42*, 502 (1956); M. A. Jesaitis, J. Exp. Med. *106*, 233 (1957); Federation Proc. *17*, 250 (1958).

28. G. Streisinger and J. Weigle, Proc. Nat. Acad. Sci. (U. S. A.) *42*, 504 (1956).

29. J. G. Flaks and S. S. Cohen, J. Biol. Chem. *234*, 1501 (1959); J. G. Flaks, J. Lichtenstein and S. S. Cohen, J. Biol. Chem. *234*, 1507 (1959).

30. A. Kornberg, S. B. Zimmerman, S. R. Kornberg and J. Josse, Proc. Nat. Acad. Sci. (U. S. A.) *45*, 772 (1959).

31. I. R. Lehman, S. B. Zimmerman, J. Adler, M. J. Bessman, E. S. Simms and A. Kornberg, Proc. Nat. Acad. Sci. (U. S. A.) *44*, 1191 (1958).

32. C. M. Radding, J. Adler and H. K. Schachman, Federation Proc., *19*, 307 (1960).

33. J. Josse and A. Kornberg, Federation Proc., *19*, 305 (1960).

A VIEW OF GENETICS*

JOSHUA LEDERBERG

Department of Genetics, Stanford University School of Medicine

The Nobel Statutes of 1900 charge each prize-winner to give a public lecture in Stockholm within six months of Commemoration Day. That I have fully used this margin is not altogether ingenuous, since it furnishes a pleasant occasion to revisit my many friends and colleagues in your beautiful city during its best season.

The charge might call for a historical account of past "studies on genetic recombination and organization of the genetic material in bacteria," studies in which I have enjoyed the companionship of many colleagues, above all my wife. However, this subject has been reviewed regularly (36, 37, 38, 41, 42, 45, 49, 54, 55, 58) and I hope you will share my own inclination to assume a more speculative task, to look at the context of contemporary science in which bacterial genetics can be better understood, and to scrutinize the future prospects of experimental genetics.

The dispersion of a Nobel award in the field of genetics symbolizes the convergent efforts of a world-wide community of investigators. That genetics should now be recognized is also timely—for its axial role in the conceptual structure of biology, and for its ripening yield for the theory and practice of medicine. However, experimental genetics is reaching its full powers in coalescence with biochemistry: in principle, each phenotype should eventually be denoted as an exact sequence of amino acids in protein (79) and the genotype as a corresponding sequence of nucleotides in DNA (a, 63). The precise demarcation of genetics from biochemistry is already futile: but when genetics has been fully reduced to its molecular foundations, it may continue to serve in the same relation as thermodynamics to mechanics (69). The coordination of so many adja-

cent sciences will be a cogent challenge to the intellectual powers of our successors.

That bacteria and their genetics should now be so relevant to general biology is already a fresh cycle in our scientific outlook. When thought of at all, they have often been relegated to some obscure byway of evolution, their complexity and their homology with other organisms grossly underrated. "Since Pasteur's startling discoveries of the important role played by microbes in human affairs, microbiology as a science has always suffered from its eminent practical applications. By far the majority of the microbiological studies were undertaken to answer questions connected with the well-being of mankind" (30). The pedagogic cleavage of academic biology from medical education has helped sustain this distortion. Happily, the repatriation of bacteria and viruses is only the first measure of the repayment of medicine's debt to biology (6, 7, 8).

Comparative biochemistry has consummated the unification of biology revitalized by Darwin one hundred years ago. Throughout the living world we see a common set of structural units—amino acids, coenzymes, nucleins, carbohydrates and so forth—from which every organism builds itself. The same holds for the fundamental process of biosynthesis and of energy metabolism. The exceptions to this rule thus command special interest as meaningful tokens of biological individuality, e.g., the replacement of cytosine by hydroxymethyl cytosine in the DNA of T2 phage (12).

Nutrition has been a special triumph. Bacteria which required no vitamins had seemed simpler than man. But deeper insights (32, 61) interpret nutritional simplicity as a greater power of synthesis. The requirements of more exacting organisms comprise just those metabolites they cannot synthesize with their own enzymatic machinery.

Species differ in their nutrition: if species are delimited by their genes, then genes must control the biosynthetic steps which are reflected

* Received for publication May 14, 1959. Nobel Prize lecture given at the Royal Caroline Medico-Surgical Institute, Stockholm, May 29, 1959. The Nobel Prize in Physiology or Medicine was awarded December 10, 1958, jointly to G. W. Beadle, E. L. Tatum, and J. Lederberg.

in nutritional patterns. This syllogism, so evident once told, has been amplified by Beadle and Tatum from this podium. Its implications for experimental biology and medicine are well known: among these, the methodology of bacterial genetics. Tatum has related how his early experience with bacterial nutrition reinforced the foundations of the biochemical genetics of Neurospora. Then, disregarding the common knowledge that bacteria were too simple to have genes, Tatum took courage to look for the genes that would indeed control bacterial nutrition. This conjunction marked the start of my own happy association with him, and with the fascinating challenges of bacterial genetics.

Contemporary genetic research is predicated on the role of DNA as the genetic material, of enzyme proteins as the cell's working tools, and of RNA as the communication channel between them (63). Three lines of evidence substantiate the genetic function of DNA. Two are related to bacterial genetics; the third and most general is the cytochemical observation of DNA in the chromosomes, which are undeniably strings of genes. But chromosomes also contain other constituents besides DNA: we want a technique to isolate a chromosome or a fragment of one, to analyze it, and to retransplant it to verify its functional capacity. The impressive achievements of nuclear transplantation (29) should encourage the audacity needed to try such experiments. The constructive equivalent to chromosome transplantation was discovered by a bacteriologist thirty years ago (20). The genetic implications of the "pneumococcus transformation" in the minds of some of Griffith's successors were clouded by its involvement with the gummy outer capsule of the bacteria. However, by 1943, Avery and his colleagues had shown that this inherited trait was transmitted from one pneumococcal strain to another by DNA. The general transmission of other traits by the same mechanism (25) can only mean that DNA comprises the genes (b).

To reinforce this conclusion, Hershey and Chase (23) proved that the genetic element of a bacterial virus is also DNA. Infection of a host cell requires the injection of just the DNA content of the adsorbed particle. This DNA controls not only its own replication in the production of new phage but also the specificity of the protein coat, which governs the serological and host range specificity of the intact phage.

At least in some small viruses, RNA also displays genetic functions. However, the hereditary autonomy of gene-initiated RNA of the cytoplasm is now very doubtful—at least some of the plasmagenes that have been proposed as fulfilling this function are now better understood as feedback-regulated systems of substrate-transport (81, 65, 72).

The work of the past decade thus strongly supports the simple doctrine that genetic information is nucleic, i.e., is coded in a linear sequence of nucleotides. This simplification of life may appear too facile, and has furnished a tempting target for agnostic criticism (37, 41, 44, 74). But, while no scientific theory would decry continual refinement and amplification, such criticism has little value if it detracts from the evident fruitfulness of the doctrine in experimental design.

The cell may, of course, carry information other than nucleic either in the cytoplasm or, accessory to the polynucleotide sequence, in the chromosomes. Epinucleic information has been invoked, without being more precisely defined, in many recent speculations on cytodifferentiation and on such models of this as antigenic phase variation in *Salmonella* (71, 52, 56, 47). Alternative schemes have so much less information capacity than the nucleic cycle that they are more likely to concern the regulation of genic functions than to mimic their specificities.

DNA AS A SUBSTANCE

The chemistry of DNA deserves to be exposed by apter craftsmen (86, 31, 13) and I shall merely recapitulate before addressing its biological implications. A segment of DNA is illustrated in Fig. 1. This shows a linear polymer whose backbone contains the repeating unit:

$$-O-PO_2^- -O-CH_2-\overset{|}{C}H-\overset{|}{C}H-$$
$$\text{diester phosphate} \quad C_5' \quad C_4' \quad C_3'$$

The carbon atoms are conventionally numbered according to their position in the furan-

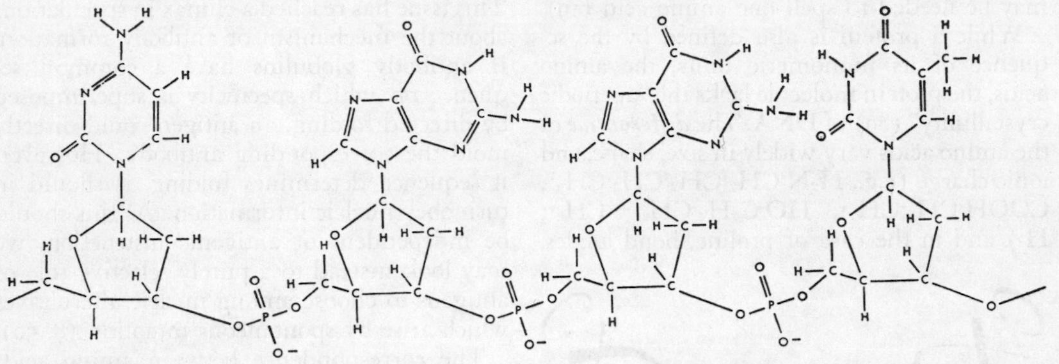

Fig. 1.—Primary structure of DNA—a segment of a polynucleotide sequence CGGT. From (13).

ose ring of deoxyribose, which is coupled as an N-glycoside to one of the nuclein bases: adenine, guanine, cytosine, or thymine, symbolized A, G, C, or T, the now well-known alphabet in which genetic instructions are composed. With a chain length of about 10,000 residues, one molecule of DNA contains 20,000 "bits of information," comparable to the text of this article, or in a page of newsprint.

Pyrophosphate - activated monomer units (e.g., thymidine triphosphate) have been identified as the metabolic precursors of DNA (31). For genetic replication, the monomer units must be assembled in a sequence that reflects that of the parent molecule. A plausible mechanism has been forwarded by Watson and Crick (87) as a corollary to their structural model whereby DNA occurs as a two-stranded helix, the bases being centrally oriented. When their relative positions are fixed by the deoxyribose-phosphate backbones, just two pairs of bases are able to form hydrogen bonds between their respective NH and CO groups; these are A : T and G : C. This pairing of bases would tie the two strands together for the length of the helix. In conformity with this model, extensive analytical evidence shows a remarkable equality of A with T and of G with C in DNA from various sources. The two strands of any DNA are then mutually complementary, the A, T, G, and C of one strand being represented by T, A, C, and G, respectively, of the other. The information of one strand is therefore equivalent to, because fully determined by, the other. The determination occurs at the replication of one parent

strand by the controlled stepwise accretion of monomers to form a complementary strand. At each step, only the monomer which is complementary to the template would fit for a chain-lengthening esterification with the adjacent nucleotide. The model requires the unraveling of the intertwined helices to allow each of them to serve as a template. This might, however, occur gradually, with the growth of the daughter chain—a concept embedded in Fig. 2 which symbolizes the new Cabala. The discovery of a single-stranded configuration of DNA (85) makes complete unraveling more tenable as an alternative model.

For the vehicle of life's continuity, DNA may seem a remarkably undistinguished molecule. Its over-all shape is controlled by the uniform deoxyribose-phosphate backbone whose monotony then gives X-ray diffraction patterns of high crystallinity. The nucleins themselves are relatively unreactive, hardly different from one to the other, and in DNA introverted and mutually saturated. Nor are any of the hydroxyls of deoxyribose left unsubstituted in the polymer. The structure of DNA befits the solipsism of its function.

The most plausible function of DNA is ultimately to specify the amino acid sequence in proteins. However, as there are twenty amino acids to choose among, there cannot be a one:one correspondence of nucleotide to amino acid. Taking account of the code duplication in complementary structures and the need to indicate spacing of the words in the code sequence, from three to four nucleins may be needed to spell one amino acid (19).

While a protein is also defined by the sequence of its monomeric units, the amino acids, the protein molecule lacks the "aperiodic crystallinity" (80) of DNA. The *differentiae* of the amino acids vary widely in size, shape, and ionic charge (e.g., $H_2N \cdot CH_2 \cdot CH_2 \cdot CH_2 \cdot CH_2 \cdot$; $COOH \cdot CH_2 \cdot CH_2 \cdot$; $HO \cdot C_6H_4 \cdot CH_2 \cdot$; $CH_3 \cdot$; $H \cdot$) and in the case of proline, bond angles.

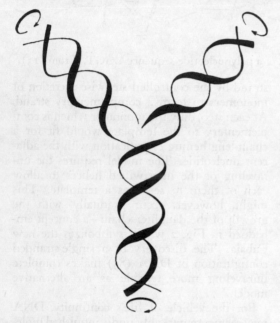

FIG. 2.—The scheme of Watson and Crick for DNA replication. "Unwinding and replication proceed *pari passu*. All three arms of the Y rotate as indicated" (14).

The biological action of a protein is, therefore, attributable to the shape of the critical surface into which the polypeptide chain folds (73). The one-dimensional specificity of the DNA must therefore be translated into the three-dimensional specificity of an enzyme or antibody surface. The simplest assumption would be that the amino acid sequence of the extended polypeptide, as it is released from the protein-building template in the cytoplasm, fully determines the folding pattern of the complete protein, which may, of course, be stabilized by nonpeptide linkages. If not, we should have to interpose some accessory mechanism to govern the folding of the protein.

This issue has reached a climax in speculations about the mechanism of antibody formation. If antibody globulins have a common sequence on which specificity is superimposed by directed folding, an antigen could directly mold the corresponding antibody. However, if sequence determines folding, it should in turn obey nucleic information. As this should be independent of antigenic instruction, we may look instead to a purely selective role of antigens to choose among nucleic alternatives which arise by spontaneous mutation (8, 50).

The correspondence between amino acids and clusters of nucleotides has no evident basis in their inherent chemical make-up and it now appears more probable that this *code* has evolved secondarily and arbitrarily to be translated by some biological intermediary. The coding relationship would then be analogous to, say, Morse-English (binary linear) to Chinese (pictographic). Encouragingly, several workers have reported the enzymatic reaction of amino acids with RNA fragments (22, 75). Apparently each amino acid has a different RNA receptor and an enzyme whose twofold specificity thus obviates any direct recognition of amino acid by polynucleotides. The alignment of amino-acyl residues for protein synthesis could then follow controlled assembly of their nucleotidates on an RNA template, by analogy with the model for DNA replication. We then visualize the following modes of information transfer:

(1) DNA replication — assembly of complementary deoxyribonucleotides on a DNA template.

(2) Transfer to RNA by some comparable mechanism of assembling ribonucleotides. Our understanding of this is limited by uncertainties of the structure of RNA (16).

(3) Protein synthesis:
   (*a*) Aminoacylation of polynucleotide fragments;
   (*b*) Assembly of the nucleotidates on an RNA template by analogy with step (1);
   (*c*) Peptide condensation of the amino acid residues.

Some workers have suggested that RNA is

replicated in step (3) concurrently with protein synthesis, in addition to its initiation from DNA.

The chief difference in primary structure between DNA and RNA is the hydroxylation of C_2' in the ribose, so that a reactive sugar hydroxyl is available in RNA. This may prove to be important in the less ordered secondary structure of RNA, and in its function as an intermediary to protein. It remains to be determined whether the aminoacyl nucleotidates are esterified at C_2' or at C_3' which is also available in the terminal residue. From this résumé we may observe that the DNA backbone constitutes an inert but rigid framework on which the differential nucleins are strung. Their spatial constraint lends specificity to the pattern of hydrogen bonding exposed at each level. This extended pattern is a plausible basis for replication; it is difficult to visualize any reagents besides other nucleotides to which this pattern would be relevant. These conditions are quite apt for a memory device—rubber and guncotton are poor choices for a computing tape.

DNA AND BACTERIAL MUTATION

The *ignis fatuus* of genetics has been the specific mutagen, the reagent that would penetrate to a given gene, recognize and modify it in a specific way. Directed mutation has long been discredited for higher organisms and the "molar indeterminacy" of mutation established both for its spontaneous occurrence and for its enhancement by X-rays (68). However, the development of resistance apparently induced by drugs revived illusions that bacterial genes might be alterable, an inference that would inevitably undermine the conception of "gene" for these organisms. No wonder that the mechanism of drug resistance has excited so much controversy (89)!

What sort of molecule could function as a specific mutagen, a reagent for a particular one of the bacterium's complement of genes, which can hardly number less than a thousand targets? On the nucleic hypothesis, the smallest segment capable of this variety would be a *hexa*nucleotide, all possible configurations of which must be discriminated by the specific mutagen. How could this be generally accom-plished except by another molecule of conforming length and periodicity, that is, an analogous polynucleotide? Certainly there is nothing in the chemistry of penicillin or streptomycin to support their direct intervention in nucleic instructions.

In addition, we recognize no chemical reagent capable of substituting one nuclein for another in the structure of existent DNA. However, as the modification of a nuclein, even to give an unnatural base, could have mutagenic effect, the chief limitation for specific mutagenesis is the recognition of the appropriate target.

Of course the origin of drug resistance, for all its theoretical implications, poses an experimental challenge of its own. Concededly, experiments cannot decide untried situations. Nevertheless, the mechanism whereby resistant mutants arise spontaneously and are then selected by the drug can account for every well-studied case of inherited resistance (10, 5). Furthermore, in favorable instances the spontaneous origin of drug-resistant mutants can be verified unambiguously by contriving to isolate them without their ever being exposed to the drug. One method entails indirect selection. To illustrate its application, consider a culture of *Escherichia coli* containing 10^9 bacteria per ml. By plating samples on agar containing streptomycin, we infer that one bacterium per million or 10^3 per ml produce resistant clones. But to count these clones they were selected in the presence of streptomycin which hypothetically might have induced the resistance. We may however dilute the original bacteria in plain broth to give samples containing 10^5 per ml. Since 10^{-6} of the bacteria are resistant, each sample has a mathematical expectation of 0.1 of including a resistant bacterium. The individual bacterium being indivisible by dilution, nine samples in ten will include no resistants; the tenth will have one, but now augmented to 10^{-5}. Which one this is can be readily determined by retrospective assay on the incubated samples. The procedure can be reiterated to enrich for the resistant organisms until they are obtained in pure culture (11). The same result is reached more conveniently if we spread the original culture out on a nutrient agar plate rather than distribute samples into separate test tubes. Replica plating, transposing a pattern of surface growth from plate to plate with a sheet of velvet, takes the place of assaying inocula distributed in tubes (53). Dilution sampling and replica plating are, then, alternative methods of indirect selection whereby the test line is spared direct contact with the drug. Selection is accomplished by saving sublines whose *sibling* clones show the resistant reaction. This proof merely reinforces the incisive arguments that had already been forwarded by many other authors.

If mutations are not specific responses to the cellular environment, how do they arise? We still have very little information on the proximate causes of spontaneous, even of radiation and chemically induced, mutation. Most mutagenic chemicals are potent alkylating agents, e.g., formaldehyde or nitrogen mustard, which attack a variety of reactive groups in the cell. Similar compounds may occur in normal metabolism and account for part of the spontaneous mutation rate; they may also play a role as chemical intermediates in radiation effects. For the most part, then, studies on mutagenesis, especially by the more vigorous reagents, have told us little about the chemistry of the gene. Probably any agent that can penetrate to the chromosomes and have a localized chemical effect is capable of introducing random errors into the genetic information. If the cell were not first killed by other mechanisms most toxic agents would then probably be mutagenic.

Another class of mutagenic chemicals promises more information: analogues of the natural nucleins which are incorporated into DNA. For example, bromouracil specifically replaces thymine in phage DNA when furnished as bromodeoxyuridine to infected bacteria. Freese has shown, by genetic analyses of the utmost refinement, that the loci of resulting mutations in T4 phage are distributed differently from the mutants of spontaneous origin or those induced by other chemicals (18). This method presumably maps the locations of thymine in the original DNA. In order to account for wide variations in mutation rate for different loci, further interactions among the nucleotides must be supposed. So far, these studies represent the closest approach to a rational basis for chemical mutagenesis. However, every gene must present many targets to any nuclein analogue and the specificity of their mutagenesis can be detected only in systems where the resolution of genetic loci approximates the spacing of single nucleotides (4). At present this is feasible only in microorganisms; similar studies with bacteria and fungi would be of the greatest interest.

More specific effects might result from the insertion of oligo- and polynucleotides, a program which, however, faces a number of technical difficulties: even if the requisite polymers were to be synthesized, there are obstacles to their penetration into cells. The use of DNA extracted from mutant bacteria to transfer the corresponding genetic qualities is discussed as "genetic transduction."

RNA is the one other reagent that may be expected to recognize particular genes. As yet we have no direct evidence that the transfer of information from DNA to RNA is reversible. However, the anti-mutagenic effect of nuclein ribosides (21, 71) may implicate RNA in mutation. The reversibility of DNA $\rightleftharpoons$ RNA information is also implicit in Stent's closely reasoned scheme for DNA replication (82). The needed experiment is the transfer of DNA information by some isolated RNA. Although not reported, this has probably not been fairly tried.

One motivation for this approach is the difficult problem of finding sources of homogeneous nucleic acids. DNA occurs biologically as sets of different molecules presumably in equimolar proportions. (A useful exception may be a remarkably small phage which seems to be unimolecular [85]). The species of RNA, however, may vary with the predominant metabolic activity of the cells. If so, some molecular species may be sufficiently exaggerated in specialized cells to facilitate their isolation. A purified RNA would have many potential applications, among others as a vehicle for the recognition of the corresponding DNA implied by our theory of information transfer. Pending such advances, *specific* mutagenesis is an implausible expectation.

Adaptive mutations, of which drug resistance is a familiar example, are crucial to the methodology of microbial genetics. Once having connected adaptive variation with gene mutation (78), we could proceed to exploit these systems for the detection of specific genotypes in very large test populations. The genotypes of interest may arise, as in the previous examples, by mutation: the most extensive studies of the physiology of mutation now use these methods for precise assay. For, in order to count the number of mutants of a given kind, it suffices to plate large numbers of bacteria into selective media and count the surviving colonies which appear after incubation. In this way, mutation rates as low as one per 10^9 divisions can be treated in routine fashion.

GENETIC RECOMBINATION IN BACTERIA

The selective isolation of designed genotypes is also the most efficient way to detect genetic recombination. For example, the sexual mechanism of *Escherichia coli* was first exposed when prototrophic (nutritionally self-sufficient) recombinants arose in mixed cultures of two auxotrophic (nutritionally dependent) mutants (35, 57, 84). At first only one recombinant appeared per million parental bacteria and the selective procedure was quite obligatory. Later, more fertile strains were discovered which have been most helpful to further analysis (45, 51). This has shown that typical multinucleate vegetative bacteria unite by a conjugation bridge through which part or all of a male genome migrates into the female cell (43). The gametic cells then separate. The exconjugant male forms an unaltered clone, surviving by virtue of its remaining nuclei. The exconjugant female generates a mixed clone including recombinants (46, 1). Wollman, Jacob, and Hayes (88) have since demonstrated that the paternal chromosome migrates during fertilization in an orderly, progressive way. When fertilization is prematurely interrupted, the chromosome may be broken so that only anterior markers appear among the recombinants. All of the genetic markers are arranged in a single linkage group and their order can be established either by timing their passage during fertilization or by their statistical association with one another among the recombinants. Finally, the transfer of genetic markers can be correlated with the transfer of DNA as inferred from the lethal effect of the radioactive decay of incorporated P^{32} (27).

Sexual recombination is one of the methods for analyzing the gene-enzyme relationship. The studies so far are fragmentary but they support the conception that the gene is a string of nucleotides which must function as a coherent unit in order to produce an active enzyme (4, 33, 67, 15, 90). However, metabolic blocks may originate through interference with accessory regulatory mechanisms instead of the fundamental capacity to produce the enzyme. For example, many "lactase-negative" mutants have an altered pattern of enzyme induction or a defective permease system for substrate transport (55, 65). Several laboratories are now working to correlate the relative sequence of genetic defects with the sequence of corresponding alterations in enzyme proteins; this may be the next best approach to the coding problem short of a system where a pure DNA can be matched with its protein phenotype.

At first these recombination experiments were confined to a single strain of *E. coli*, K-12. For many purposes this is a favorable choice of material—perhaps the main advantage is the accumulation of a library of many thousands of substrains carrying the various markers called for by the design of genetic tests. However, strain K-12 is rather unsuitable for serological studies, having lost the characteristic surface antigens which are the basis of serological typing. In any event it would be important to know the breeding structure of the group of enteric bacteria. Systematic studies have therefore been made of the interfertility of different strains of bacteria, principally with a convenient tester of the K-12 strain (39, 93). About one-fourth of the serotype strains of *E. coli* are fertile with strain K-12, and in at least some instances with one another. Whether the remaining three-fourths of strains are completely sterile, or whether they include different, closed, breeding groups (i.e., different genetic species) has not been systematically tested, partly because of the preliminary work needed to establish suitable strains.

E. coli K-12 is also interfertile with a number of strains of *Shigella* spp. (59). Finally although attempted crosses of *E. coli* with many

Salmonella types and of *Salmonellas* with one another have usually failed, Baron has demonstrated crosses of *E. coli* with a unique strain of *Salmonella typhimurium* (3). This may be especially useful as a means of developing hybrids which can be used to bridge the studies of sexuality in *E. coli* and transduction in *Salmonella*.

GENES AND VIRUSES

Bacteria furnish a unique opportunity to study the genetic relationships with their host cells. Another treasure of strain K-12 was for a time hidden: it carries the temperate bacteriophage, λ, which is technically quite favorable for genetic work. In accord with Burnet's early predictions, we had anticipated that the provirus for λ would behave as a genetic unit, but Dr. Esther Lederberg's first crosses were quite startling in their implication that the prophage segregated as a typical chromosomal marker (34). This was shown quite unambiguously by the segregation of lysogenicity versus sensitivity from persistent heterozygous cells, a test that bypassed the then controversial details of fertilization. The viability of such heterozygous cells supports the hypothesis that lysogenicity depends in part on the development of a cytoplasmic immunity to the cytopathic effects of infecting phage as a secondary result of the establishment of the prophage in a bacterial chromosome. This picture is also brought out by *zygotic induction* (26) whereby the fertilization of a sensitive cell by a prophage-bearing chromosome may provoke the maturation and progressive growth of the phage and the lysis of the complex. On the other hand, the introduction of a sensitive chromosome into a lysogenic bacterium does not result in this induction. The mode of attachment of prophage to its chromosomal site is as unsettled as the general picture of the higher organization of DNA, but most students favor a lateral rather than an axial relationship for the prophage. The isolation of intact chromosomes of bacteria would give a new approach to this question but has so far been inconclusive.

Another infectious particle that has jumped out of our Pandora's box determines the very capacity of *E. coli* to function as a male partner in fertilization (51). For lack of a better inspiration, we call this particle "F." Two kinds of male strains are now recognized according to whether the F particle has a chromosomal or a cytoplasmic location. F+ strains, like the original K-12, are highly contagious for F and will rapidly convert populations of female, F— strains in which they are introduced. Hfr males, on the other hand, have a chromosomal localization of the F factor resulting from occasional transpositions in F+ strains. The different localization of the F particle in the two cases is diagnosed primarily by the behavior of the particle in crosses. In addition, Hirota and Iijima (24) found that the F particle could be eliminated from F+ strains by treatment with acridine dyes. Hfr clones are unaffected by acridine orange, but when they revert to the F+ state, as occasionally happens, the F particle again becomes vulnerable to the dye. The accessibility of extrachromosomal F is paralleled by several other examples of plasmid disinfection (reviewed in 40); perhaps the most notable is the bleaching of green plant cells by streptomycin (17, 76). No reagent is known to inactivate F or prophage while bound to the chromosome.

The virus λ and the plasmagene F are analogous in many features (28, 48). Their main differences are:

(1) Cytopathogenicity. A bacterium cannot long tolerate λ in its cytoplasmic state and remain viable. The vegetative λ must promptly reduce itself to a chromosomal state or multiply aggressively and lyse the host bacterium. F has no known cytopathic effect.

(2) Maturation. Vegetative λ organizes a protein coat and matures into an infective phage particle. F is known only as an intracellular vegetative element; however, the coat of the F+ cell may be analogous to that of the phage.

(3) Transmission. λ is infective, i.e., forms a free particle which can penetrate susceptible cells. F is transmitted only by cell-to-cell conjugation.

(4) Fixation. λ has a foreordained site of fixation on the bacterial chromosome; F has been identified at a variety of sites. How-

ever, this difference may be illusory. In special situations, F does have preferential sites of fixation (77), and generally, translocations of F to different sites are more readily discovered than those of λ would be.

(5) Induction. Exposure of lysogenic bacteria to small doses of ultraviolet light causes the prophage to initiate a lytic cycle with the appearance first of vegetative, then of mature phage (62). Hfr bacteria make no analogous response. However, the kinetics of the reversion, Hfr → F+, has not been carefully studied.

The genetic function of bacteriophages is further exemplified by *transduction* whereby genes are transferred from cell to cell by the intervention of phage particles (42, 91). In our first studies we concluded that the bacterial genes were adventitiously carried in normal phage particles (92, 66, 83). Further studies favor the view that the transducing particle has a normal phage coat but a defective phage nucleus. This correlation has suggested that a gene becomes transducible when a prophage segment is translocated to its vicinity (2, 9, 60).

Transduction focuses special attention on the phenomenon of specific pairing of homologous chromosome segments. Howsoever a transduced gene is finally integrated into the bacterial genome, at some stage it must locate the homologous gene in the recipient chromosome. For in transduction, as in sexual recombination, new information is not merely added to the complement; it must also replace the old. This must involve the confrontation of the two homologues prior to the decision which one is to be retained. Synapsis is even more puzzling as between chromosomes whose DNA is in the stabilized double helix and then further contracted by supercoiling. Conceivably gene products rather than DNA are the agency of synaptic pairing.

The integration of a transduced fragment raises further issues (41). The competing hypotheses are the physical incorporation of the fragment in the recipient chromosome, or the use of its information when new DNA is replicated. The same issues still confound models of crossing over at meiosis in higher forms;

once again the fundamentals of chromosome structure are needed for a resolution.

VIRUS VERSUS GENE

The homology of gene and virus in their fundamental aspects makes their overt differences even more puzzling. According to the simplest nucleic doctrine, DNA plays no active role in its own replication other than furnishing a useful pattern. Various nucleotide sequences should then be equally replicable. What then distinguishes virus DNA, which replicates itself at the expense of the other pathways of cellular anabolism? For the T-even phages, the presence of the unique glucosylated hydroxymethylcytosine furnishes a partial answer (12). However, other viruses such as λ display no unique constituents; furthermore, as prophage they replicate coordinately with bacterial DNA. Does the virus have a unique element of structure, either chemical or physical, so far undetected? Or does it instruct its own preferential synthesis by a code for supporting enzymes?

THE CREATION OF LIFE

The mutualism of DNA, RNA, and proteins as just reviewed is fundamental to all contemporary life. Viruses are simpler as infective particles but must, of course, parasitize the metabolic machinery of the host cell. What would be the least requirements of a primeval organism, the simplest starting point for progressive replication of DNA in terms of presently known or conjectured mechanisms? They include at least:

(1) DNA.

(2) The four deoxyribotide pyrophosphates in abundance.

(3) One molecule of the protein, DNA polymerase.

(4) Ribotide phosphates as precursors for RNA.

(5) One molecule of the protein RNA polymerase.

(6) A supply of the twenty amino acyl nucleotidates.

(a) Failing these, each of the twenty enzymes which catalyze the condensation of an amino acid and corresponding RNA fragments together with sources of these components.

(7) One molecule of the protein aminoacyl-RNA polymerase.

In principle, this formidable list might be reduced to a single polynucleotide polymerized by a single enzyme. However, any scheme for the enzymatic synthesis of nucleic acid calls for the coincidence of a particular nucleic acid and of a particular protein. This is a far more stringent improbability than the sudden emergence of an isolated DNA such as many authors have suggested, so much more so that we must look for alternative solutions to the problem of the origin of life. These are of two kinds. The primeval organism could still be a nucleic cycle if nucleic replication occurs, however imperfectly, without the intervention of protein. The polymerase enzyme, and the transfer of information from nucleic acid to protein, would then be evolved refinements. Alternatively, DNA has evolved from a simpler, spontaneously condensing polymer. The exquisite perfection of DNA makes the second suggestion all the more plausible.

The nucleoprotein cycle is the climax of biochemical evolution. Its antiquity is shown by its adoption by all phyla. Having persisted for $\sim 10^9$ years, nucleoprotein may be the most durable feature of the geochemistry of this planet.

At the present time, no other self-replicating polymers are known or understood. Nevertheless, the nucleic system illustrates the basic requirements for such a polymer. It must have a rigid periodic structure in which two or more alternative units can be readily substituted. It must allow for the reversible sorption of specific monomers to the units in its own sequence. Adjacent, sorbed monomers must then condense to form the replica polymer, which must be able to desorb from the template. Primitively, the condensation must be spontaneous but reliable. In DNA, the sorption depends on the hydrogen bonding of nuclein molecules constrained on a rigid helical backbone. This highly specific but subtle design would be difficult to imitate. For the more primitive stages, both of biological evolution and of our own experimental insight, we may prefer to invoke somewhat cruder techniques of complementary attachment. The simplest of these is perhaps the attraction between ionic groups of opposite charge, for example, NH_3^+ and COO^- which are so prevalent in simple organic compounds. If the ingenuity and craftsmanship so successfully directed at the fabrication of organic polymers for the practical needs of mankind were to be concentrated on the problem of constructing a self-replicating assembly along these lines I predict that the construction of an artificial molecule having the essential function of primitive life would fall within the grasp of our current knowledge of organic chemistry.

CONCLUSIONS

The experimental control of cellular genotype is one of the measures of the scope of genetic science. However, nucleic genes will not be readily approached for experimental manipulation except by reagents that mimic them in periodic structure. Specifically induced mutation, if ever accomplished, will then consist of an act of genetic recombination between the target DNA and the controlled information specified by the reagent. Methods for the step-wise analysis and reassembly of nucleic acids are likely to be perfected in the near future in pace with the accessibility of nucleic acid preparations which are homogeneous enough to make their use worth while. For the immediate future, it is likely that the greatest success will attend the use of biological reagents to furnish the selectivity needed to discriminate one among innumerable classes of polynucleotides. Synthetic chemistry is, however, challenged to produce model polymers that can emulate the essential features of genetic systems.

REFERENCES

1. Anderson, T. F., "Recombination and Segregation in *Escherichia coli*," *Cold Spring Harbor Symposia Quant. Biol.*, **23** : 47, 1958.

2. Arber, W., "Transduction des caractéres Gal par le bactériophage Lambda," *Archives des Sciences, Soc. Phys. Hist. Nat. Genève,* **11** : 259, 1958.

3. Baron, L. S., Carey, W. F., and Spilman, W. M., "Hybridization of *Salmonella* Species by Mating with *Escherichia coli*," *Abst. 7th Int.*

Cong. Microbiol. (Stockholm), pp. 50–51, 1958.

4. Benzer, S., "The Elementary Units of Heredity," in *The Chemical Basis of Heredity*, W. D. McElroy and B. Glass (eds.), Baltimore: The Johns Hopkins Press, 1957, pp. 70–93.

5. Bryson, V., and Szybalski, W., "Microbial Drug Resistance," *Adv. Genetics,* 7: 1, 1955.

6. Burnet, F. M., *Biological Aspects of Infectious Disease*, Cambridge: Cambridge University Press, 1940.

7. Burnet, F. M., *Virus as Organism*, Cambridge, Mass.: Harvard University Press, 1945.

8. Burnet, Sir MacFarlane, *The Clonal Selection Theory of Immunity* (Abraham Flexner Lectures, 1958), Nashville: Vanderbilt University Press, 1959.

9. Campbell, A., "Transduction and Segregation in *Escherichia coli* K-12," *Virology,* 4: 366, 1957.

10. Cavalli-Sforza, L. L., and Lederberg, J., "Genetics of Resistance to Bacterial Inhibitors," in *Symposium on Growth Inhibition and Chemotherapy*, Int. Cong. Microbiol. (Rome), 1953, pp. 108–42.

11. ———, "Isolation of Preadaptive Mutants in Bacteria by Sib Selection," *Genetics,* 41: 367, 1956.

12. Cohen, S. S., "Molecular Bases of Parasitism of Some Bacterial Viruses," *Science,* 123: 653, 1956.

13. Crick, F. H. C., "The Structure of the Hereditary Material," *Scient. Am.,* 151: 54, 1954.

14. Delbrück, M., and Stent, G. S., "On the Mechanism of DNA Replication," in *The Chemical Basis of Heredity*, W. D. McElroy and B. Glass (eds.), Baltimore: The Johns Hopkins Press, 1957, pp. 699–736.

15. Demerec, M., Hartman, Z., Hartman, P. E., Yura, T., Gots, J. S., Ozeki, H., and Glover, S. W., *Genetic Studies with Bacteria*, Washington, D.C.: Carnegie Inst. Publ. 612, 1956.

16. Doty, P., Boedtker, H., Fresco, J. R., Haselkorn, R., and Litt, M., "Secondary Structure in Ribonucleic Acids," *Proc. Nat. Acad. Sc.,* 45: 482, 1959.

17. von Euler, H., "Einfluss des Streptomycins auf die Chlorophyllbildung," *Kem. Arb.,* 9: 1, 1947.

18. Freese, E., "The Difference Between Spontaneous and Base-Analogue Induced Mutations of Phage T4," *Pros. Nat. Acad. Sc.,* 45: 622, 1959.

19. Golomb, S. W., Welch, L. R., and Delbrück, M., "Construction and Properties of Comma-Free Codes," *Biol. Medd. Can. Vid. Selsk.,* 23: 1, 1958.

20. Griffith, F., "The Significance of Pneumococcal Types," *J. Hyg.,* 27: 113, 1928.

21. Haas, F. L., and Doudney, C. O., "A Relation of Nucleic Acid Synthesis to Radiation-Induced Mutation Frequency in Bacteria," *Proc. Nat. Acad. Sc.,* 43: 871, 1957.

22. Hecht, L. I., Stephenson, M. L., and Zamecnik, P. C., "Binding of Amino Acids to the End Group of a Soluble Ribonucleic Acid," *Proc. Nat. Acad. Sc.,* 45: 505, 1959.

23. Hershey, A. D., and Chase, M., "Independent Function of Viral Protein and Nucleic Acid in Growth of Bacteriophage," *J. Gen. Physiol.,* 36: 39, 1951.

24. Hirota, Y., and Iijima, T., "Acriflavine as an Effective Agent for Eliminating F-Factor in *Escherichia coli* K-12," *Nature,* 180: 655, 1957.

25. Hotchkiss, R. D., "The Genetic Chemistry of the Pneumococcal Transformations," *Harvey Lect.,* 49: 124, 1955.

26. Jacob, F., and Wollman, E. L., "Sur les processus de conjugaison et de recombinaison chez *Escherichia coli*: I. L'induction par conjugaison ou induction zygotique," *Ann Inst. Pasteur,* 91: 486, 1956.

27. ———, "Genetic and Physical Determination of Chromosomal Segments in *Escherichia coli*," *Symp. Soc. Exper. Biol.,* 7: 75, 1958.

28. ———, "Les épisomes, éléments génétiques ajoutés," *C. R. Acad. Sc., Paris,* 247: 154, 1958.

29. King, T. J., and Briggs, R., "Serial Transplantation of Embryonic Nuclei," *Cold Spring Harbor Symposia Quant. Biol.,* 21: 271, 1956.

30. Kluyver, A. J., and van Niel, C. B., *The Microbe's Contribution to Biology*, Cambridge, Mass.: Harvard University Press, 1956.

31. Kornberg, A., "Enzymatic Synthesis of Deoxyribonucleic Acid," *Harvey Lect.,* 53: 83, 1959.

32. Knight, B. C. J. G., "Bacterial Nutrition," *Med. Res. Council* (Brit.), Spec. Rep. Ser. No. 210, 1936.

33. Lederberg, E. M., "Allelic Relationships and Reverse Mutation in *Escherichia coli*," *Genetics,* 37: 469, 1952.

34. Lederberg, E. M., and Lederberg, J., "Genetic Studies of Lysogenicity in *Escherichia coli*," *Genetics,* 38: 51, 1953.

35. Lederberg, J., "Gene Recombination and Linked Segregations in *Escherichia coli*," *Genetics,* 32: 505, 1947.

36. ———, "Problems in Microbial Genetics," *Heredity,* 2: 145, 1948.

37. ———, "Bacterial Variation," *Ann. Rev. Microbiol.,* 3 : 1, 1949.

38. ———, "Genetic Studies with Bacteria," in *Genetics in the 20th Century,* L. C. Dunn (ed.), New York: The Macmillan Company, 1951, pp. 263–89.

39. ———, "Prevalence of *Escherichia coli* Strains Exhibiting Genetic Recombination," *Science,* 114 : 68, 1951.

40. ———, "Cell Genetics and Hereditary Symbiosis," *Physiol. Rev.,* 32 : 403, 1952.

41. ———, "Recombination Mechanisms in Bacteria," *J. Cell & Comp. Physiol.,* 45 (Suppl. 2): 75, 1955.

42. ———, "Genetic Transduction," *Am. Scientist,* 44 : 264, 1956.

43. ———, "Conjugal Pairing in *Escherichia coli,*" *J. Bact.,* 71 : 497, 1956.

44. ———, "Comments on Gene-Enzyme Relationship," in *Enzymes: Units of Biological Structure and Function,* O. H. Gaebler (ed.), New York: Academic Press Inc., 1956, pp. 161–69.

45. ———, "Viruses, Genes and Cells," *Bact. Rev.,* 21 : 133, 1957.

46. ———, "Sibling Recombinants in Zygote Pedigrees of Escherichia coli," *Proc. Nat. Acad. Sc.,* 43 : 1060, 1957.

47. ———, "Genetic Approaches to Somatic Cell Variation: Summary Comment," *J. Cell. & Comp. Physiol.,* 52 (Suppl. 1): 383, 1958.

48. ———, "Extranuclear Transmission of the F Compatibility Factor in *Escherichia coli,*" *Abstr. 7th Int. Cong. Microbiol.* (Stockholm), pp. 58–60, 1958.

49. ———, "Bacterial Reproduction," *Harvey Lect.,* 53 : 69, 1959.

50. ———, "Genes and Antibodies," *Science,* 129 : 1649, 1959.

51. Lederberg, J., Cavalli, L. L., and Lederberg, E. M., "Sex Compatibility in *Escherichia coli,*" *Genetics,* 37 : 720, 1952.

52. Lederberg, J., and Edwards, P. R., "Serotypic Recombination in *Salmonella,*" *J. Immunol.,* 71 : 232, 1953.

53. Lederberg, J., and Lederberg, E. M., "Replica Plating and Indirect Selection of Bacterial Mutants," *J. Bact.,* 63 : 399, 1952.

54. ———, "Infection and Heredity," *Symp. Soc. Growth and Develop.,* 14 : 101, 1956.

55. Lederberg, J., Lederberg, E. M., Zinder, N.D., and Lively, E. R., "Recombination Analysis of Bacterial Heredity," *Cold Spring Harbor Symposia Quant. Biol.,* 16 : 413, 1951.

56. Lederberg, J., and Iino, T., "Phase Variation in *Salmonella,*" *Genetics,* 41 : 743, 1956.

57. Lederberg, J., and Tatum, E. L., "Gene Recombination in *Escherichia coli,*" *Nature,* 158 : 558, 1946.

58. ———, "Sex in Bacteria: Genetic Studies, 1945–1952," *Science,* 118 : 169, 1954.

59. Luria, S. E., and Burrous, J. W., "Hybridization Between *Escherichia coli* and *Shigella,*" *J. Bact.,* 74 : 461, 1957.

60. Luria, S. E., Fraser, D. K., Adams, J. N., and Burrous, J. W., "Lysogenization, Transduction, and Genetic Recombination in Bacteria," *Cold Spring Harbor Symposia Quant. Biol.,* 23 : 71, 1958.

61. Lwoff, A., "Les facteurs de croissance pour les microorganismes," *Ann. Inst. Pasteur,* 61 : 580, 1938.

62. Lwoff, A., Siminovitch, L., and Kjeldgaard, N., "Induction de la production de bactériophages chez une bactérie lysogène," *Ann. Inst. Pasteur,* 79 : 815, 1950.

63. McElroy, W. D., and Glass, B. (eds.), *The Chemical Basis of Heredity,* Baltimore: The Johns Hopkins Press, 1957.

64. Meselson, M., and Stahl, F. W., "The Replication of DNA in *Escherichia coli,*" *Proc. Nat. Acad. Sc.,* 44 : 671, 1958.

65. Monod, J., "Remarks on the Mechanism of Enzyme Induction," in *Enzymes: Units of Biological Structure and Function,* O. H. Gaebler (ed.), New York: Academic Press Inc., 1956, pp. 7–28.

66. Morse, M. L., Lederberg, E. M., and Lederberg, J., "Transduction in *Escherichia coli* K-12," *Genetics,* 41 : 142, 1956.

67. ———, "Transductional Heterogenotes in *Escherichia coli,*" *Genetics,* 41 : 758, 1956.

68. Muller, H. J., "The Production of Mutations," *Les Prix Nobel en 1946,* Stockholm, 1948, pp. 257–74.

69. Nagel, E., "The Meaning of Reduction in the Natural Sciences," in *Science and Civilization,* R. C. Stauffer (ed.), Madison: University of Wisconsin Press, 1949, pp. 99–138.

70. Nanney, D. L., "Epigenetic Control Systems," *Proc. Nat. Acad. Sc.,* 44 : 712, 1958.

71. Novick, A., "Mutagens and Antimutagens," *Brookhaven Symposia in Biology,* 8 (Mutation): 201–15, Washington, D.C.: Office of Tech. Serv., U.S. Dept. Commerce, 1956.

72. Novick, A., and McCoy, A., "Quasi-Genetic Regulation of Enzyme Level," in *Physiological Adaptation,* Washington, D.C.: Amer. Physiol. Soc., 1958, pp. 140–50.

73. Pauling, L., "Molecular Structure and Intermolecular Forces," in *The Specificity of Serological Reactions,* K. Landsteiner, Cambridge,

Mass.: Harvard University Press, 1945, pp. 275–93.

74. Pirie, N. W., "Some Aspects of the Origins of Life Considered in the Light of the Moscow International Symposium," *ICSU Rev.,* 1: 40, 1959.

75. Preiss, J., Berg, P., Ofengand, E. J., Bergmann, F. H., and Dieckmann, M., "The Chemical Nature of the RNA–Amino Acid Compound Formed by Amino Acid-Activating Enzymes," *Proc. Nat. Acad. Sc.,* 45: 319, 1959.

76. Provasoli, L., Hutner, S. H., and Pintner, I. J., "Destruction of Chloroplasts by Streptomycin," *Cold Spring Harbor Symposia Quant. Biol.,* 16: 113, 1951.

77. Richter, A. A., "Determinants of Mating Type in Escherichia coli," Ph.D. Dissertation, University of Wisconsin (University Microfilm, Ann Arbor, Mich.), 1959.

78. Ryan, F. J., and Lederberg, J., "Reverse-Mutation in Leucineless *Neurospora,*" *Proc. Nat. Acad. Sc.,* 32: 163, 1946.

79. Sanger, F., *Les Prix Nobel en 1958,* Stockholm, 1959.

80. Schrödinger, E., *What Is Life?* Cambridge: Cambridge University Press, 1944.

81. Spiegelman, S., Lindegren, C. C., and Lindegren, G., "Maintenance and Increase of a Genetic Character by a Substrate-Cytoplasmic Interaction in the Absence of the Specific Gene," *Proc. Nat. Acad. Sc.,* 31: 95, 1945.

82. Stent, G. S., "Mating in the Reproduction of Bacterial Viruses," *Adv. Virus Research,* 5: 95, 1958.

83. Stocker, B. A. D. S., Zinder, N. D., and Lederberg, J., "Transduction of Flagellar Characters in *Salmonella,*" *J. Gen. Micróbiol.,* 9: 410, 1593.

84. Tatum, E. L., and Lederberg, J., "Gene Recombination in the Bacterium *Escherichia coli,*" *J. Bact.,* 53: 673, 1947.

85. Tessman, I., "Some Unusual Properties of the Nucleic Acid in Bacteriophages S13 and ΦX174," *Virology,* 7: 263, 1959.

86. Todd, Sir Alexander, "Synthesis in the Study of Nucleotides," *Les Prix Nobel en 1957,* Stockholm, pp. 119–33, 1958.

87. Watson, J. D., and Crick, F. H. C., "The Structure of DNA," *Cold Spring Harbor Symposia Quant. Biol.,* 23: 123, 1953.

88. Wollman, E. L., Jacob, F., and Hayes, W., "Conjugation and Genetic Recombination in *Escherichia coli* K-12," *Cold Spring Harbor Symposia Quant. Biol.,* 21: 141, 1956.

89. Wolstenholme, G. E. W., and O'Connor, C. M. (eds.), *Ciba Foundation Symposium on Drug Resistance in Microorganisms,* London: J. and A. Churchill, Ltd., 1957.

90. Yanofsky, C., and Crawford, I. P., "Effects of Deletions, Point Mutations, Suppressor Mutations and Reversions on the Two Components of Tryptophane Synthetase of *Escherichia coli,*" *Proc. Nat. Acad. Sc.,* 45 (in press), 1959.

91. Zinder, N. D., "Bacterial Transduction," *J. Cell. & Comp. Physiol.,* 45 (Suppl. 2): 23, 1955.

92. Zinder, N. D., and Lederberg, J., "Genetic Exchange in *Salmonella,*" *J. Bact.,* 64: 679, 1952.

93. Ørskov, F., and Ørskov, I., unpublished observations.

NOTES

a. No reader who recognizes *deoxyribonucleic acid* will need to be reminded what DNA stands for.

b. One might be tempted to write: "One DNA molecule = one gene." However, the quanta of factorial genetics, based on mutation, recombination, and enzymatic function are all smaller than the DNA unit of molecular weight $\sim 6 \times 10^6$ (4). There is increasing evidence that such a molecule is a natural unit rather than an artefact of fragmentation.

c. The experimental work from my laboratory summarized in this paper has been generously supported by research grants from the National Institutes of Health, U.S. Public Health Service, the National Science Foundation, the Rockefeller Foundation, the Wisconsin Alumni Research Foundation, the University of Wisconsin, and, most recently, Stanford University. It is also a pleasure to record my thanks to the Jane Coffin Childs Fund for Medical Research for a research fellowship which supported my first association with Professor E. L. Tatum.